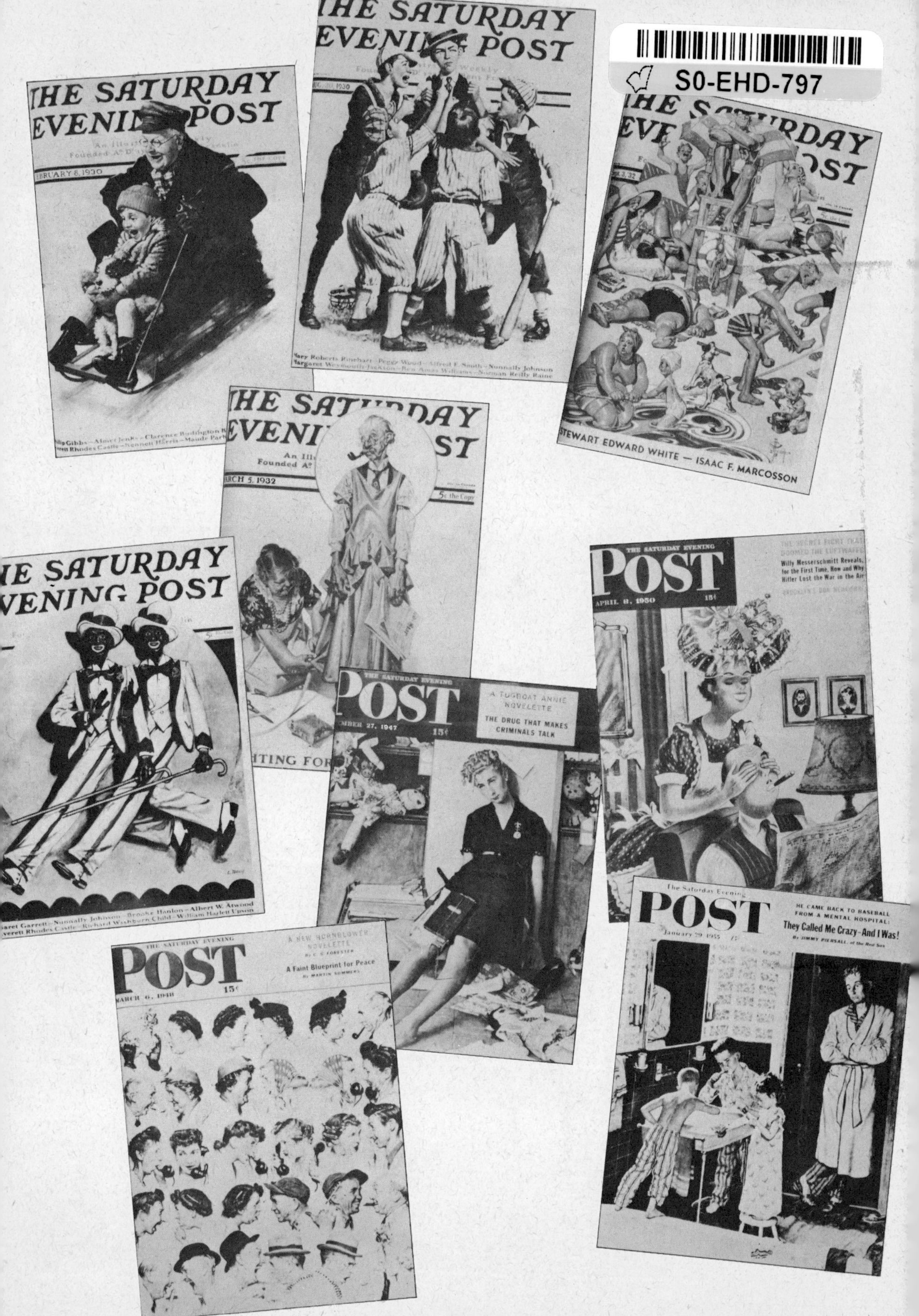
THE SATURDAY EVENING POST
THE SATURDAY EVENING POST
Mary Roberts Rinehart—Peggy Wood—Alfred E. Smith—Nunnally Johnson
Margaret Weymouth Jackson—Ben Ames Williams—Norman Reilly Raine
THE SATURDAY EVENING POST
STEWART EDWARD WHITE — ISAAC F. MARCOSSON
THE SATURDAY EVENING POST
MARCH 5, 1932
5c the Copy
THE SATURDAY EVENING POST
Albert W. Atwood
Richard Washburn Child—William Hazlett Upson
THE SATURDAY EVENING
POST
APRIL 8, 1950
15¢
Willy Messerschmitt Reveals, for the First Time, How and Why Hitler Lost the War in the Air
THE SATURDAY EVENING
POST
15¢
A TUGBOAT ANNIE NOVELETTE
THE DRUG THAT MAKES CRIMINALS TALK
THE SATURDAY EVENING
POST
A NEW HORNBLOWER NOVELETTE
A Faint Blueprint for Peace
15¢
The Saturday Evening
POST
HE CAME BACK TO BASEBALL FROM A MENTAL HOSPITAL:
They Called Me Crazy—And I Was!

The Saturday Evening Post
CARNIVAL OF HUMOR

Edited by Robert M. Yoder

From a half century of good reading in *The Saturday Evening Post* comes this distillation of funny and nostalgic stories, articles, epigrams, cartoons and verse by America's greatest humorists. (See partial listing on the back flap.)

There's a Carnival variety, embracing every humor from hearty to sprightly, from whimsy to farce . . . tailored to fit your mood and change it for the merrier.

Enjoy, once more, "The Pig-Bristle Slugger," one of the most popular stories ever to appear in the *Post*.

Read a typical adventure of Booth Tarkington's immortal Penrod . . . and Alexander Botts' first epical encounter with the Earthworm Tractor.

Turn to Irvin S. Cobb's wry discourse on man and culture.

Join Tugboat Annie in a tale that echoes to pounding seas and Annie's salty wit.

Remember Damon Runyon's "A Call On The President"?—one of his best. It's yours to savor again.

Here they are—classics of their kind—the happiest, best-remembered selections from fifty years of *The Saturday Evening Post*.

The Saturday Evening Post

CARNIVAL OF HUMOR

THE SATURDAY EVENING POST CARNIVAL OF HUMOR

Edited by Robert M. Yoder

PRENTICE-HALL, INC.
ENGLEWOOD CLIFFS, N. J.

 Library of Congress Catalog Card Number 58-12728. Printed in the United States of America.

79127

ACKNOWLEDGMENTS

Thanks are due the following authors, publishers, representatives and agents for permission to use the material indicated. All copyrights are by The Curtis Publishing Company and, where applicable, have been renewed.

Dick Ashbaugh for "The Case of the Missing Sources," © 1946; Baker and Daniels for "Talleyrand Penrod," by Booth Tarkington, © 1913; Samuel Becker for "A Call on the President," by Damon Runyon, © 1937; Brandt & Brandt, Inc., for "Mr. Pope Rides Again," by Walter Brooks, © 1942, "The Last of the Flatfeet," by Richard Connell, © 1923, "Tugboat Annie Quotes the Law," by Norman Reilly Raine, © 1946, "The Ugly Mollusk," by Frank Sullivan, © 1938, "I'm a Natural-Born Salesman," by William Hazlett Upson, © 1927, and "Mr Digby and the Talking Dog," by Douglass Welch, © 1946; Laura Baker Cobb, % Buhler, King & Buhler, 247 Madison Avenue, New York, N.Y., for "Literature," "Music," "Art," by Irvin S. Cobb, © 1912; Kathleen O'Malley Clark for "Shipping the Claret to Port," by Frank Ward O'Malley, © 1922; Curtis Brown, Ltd., for "Or In and Bear Left," by Ogden Nash, © 1947; Octavus Roy Cohen for "Nuts and Reasons," © 1930; Doubleday & Company, Inc., for "O'Meara at Troy," by Don Marquis, © 1930; John T. Foote for "A Wedding Gift," by John Taintor Foote, © 1923; May S. Gilpatric for "The Artful Mr. Glencannon," by Guy Gilpatric, © 1937; Ruth Dayton Greenwood for "Gypsies, Nobles, Peasants, Etc.," by Katharine Dayton, © 1923; Nunnally Johnson for "The Laughing Death," © 1925; Ralph Knight for "I Just Don't Understand Women," ©1952, and "I Love Crab Grass," © 1950; Ellis A. Lardner for "Some Like Them Cold," by Ring Lardner, © 1921; Harry G. Nickles for "F.Y.L., I.L.Y.," © 1948; Harold Ober Associates, Inc., for "Mascot," by Ellis Parker Butler, © 1925, "Your Wife Is Like That," by Corey Ford, © 1952, "The Eternal Duffer," by Willard H. Temple, © 1946, and "My Own True Love Story," by Horatio Winslow, © 1927; Dorothy Parker for "An Apartment House Anthology," © 1921, and "Men I'm Not Married To," © 1922; Joseph H. Peck for "How I Put Down the Redskins," © 1948; Will Rogers, Jr., for "There Is Life in the Old Gal Yet, Al," by Will Rogers, © 1929; H. Allen Smith for "Why Pay for Advice?" © 1953; James Thurber for "You Could Look It Up," © 1941; P. G. Wodehouse and the author's agent, Scott Meredith Literary Agency, Inc., for "The Aunt and the Sluggard," © 1916; Robert M. Yoder for "Let's Not Worry," © 1949.

Also to the Curtis Publishing Company for "The Cynic's Dictionary," Lester Berrey, © 1952; "Who Is Kilroy?" William F. French, © 1945; "A Child's Garden of Curses," S. J. Perelman, © 1942; "On Speaking Russian," J. M. Kucera, © 1948; "Cinderella Hassenpfeffer," Dave Morrah, © 1946; "Who Killed Cock Robin?" Katharine Dayton, © 1928; "A Glossary for Innocents," Martin Levin and Selene Holzman, © 1951; "Little Ride Hooding Red," Colonel Stoopnagel, © 1945; "The Octopus," Will Cuppy, © 1943; "Office News," W. F. Miksch, © 1948; "You Pays Your Money," Robert Fontaine, © 1946; Fables for All Ages, "How Hamilcar Wilts Prepared for Everything," "How Hard Work Got an Eager Beaver Just What You'd Expect," "To the Stars and Back with Launcelot Briggle," Robert M. Yoder, © 1948, and "Why Lester Laches Quit Finishing People's Sentences," Robert M. Yoder, © 1949; "Squaw Trouble," Dick Ashbaugh, © 1952; "Here's the Pitch," Peg Bracken, © 1951; "The Fittest Don't Always Survive," Caskie Stinnett, © 1946, and "Truth Crushed to Earth Shall Rise Again," © 1946; "Sleepy Head," Robert Fontaine, © 1950; "It had to Upcome," Scott Corbett, © 1955; "Toll Bridge," Sam Hellman, © 1930; "Sure, You're a Nice Girl . . . ," Rufus H. Jones, © 1937; "The Greek Double Cross," George Fitch, © 1911; "The Pig-Bristle Slugger," Louis Graves, © 1911; "Wanna Buy a Duck?" Joe Penner, © 1934; "How to Be a Baseball Expert Although Ignorant," John Keasler © 1952; *Post* War Anecdotes: "The Tactful Admiral," Louis H. Brendel, © 1951, "One Way Left to Go," R. H. Crot, © 1946, "Money Came in Thick and Fast," Glenn P. Holman, © 1946, "Crisis for a Coxswain," Tom McKelvie, © 1946, "As the German Prisoner Said," James Sawyer, © 1945, "The Colonel Who Had Who-Dat Trouble," Irving Uttal, © 1946; The Perfect Squelch: M. Gordon Beverley, © 1949, Ed Hutchinson, © 1951, C. E. Mann, © 1951, John P. McKnight, © 1951, Edward C. Morgan, © 1954, Frances Rodman, © 1949, A. D. Schoenleber, © 1954, Virginia S. Stroemel, © 1952, Harold Winerip, © 1951, Roger M. Wood, © 1948.

Also to the following cartoonists for permission to use copyrighted cartoons: S. Aagaard, © 1949; Alain, © 1941; Fred Balk, © 1937; Berenstain, © 1948, 1949; Henry Boltinoff, © 1941; Bob Brown, © 1952; Irwin Caplan, © 1945, 1946, 1950, 1951, 1952. 1954; Gene Carr, © 1950; Charles Cartwright, © 1946; Chon Day, © 1946, 1952; Robert Day, © 1952; John Dempsey, © 1951; Eric Ericson, © 1945; Vincent Faletti, © 1952; Joseph Farris, © 1953; Lew Follette, © 1951; Larry Frick, © 1950; John Gallagher, © 1951, 1953; Leo Garel, © 1953; Herbert Goldberg, © 1952; Walter Goldstein, © 1951; George Hamilton Green, © 1939; Larry Harris, © 1952; Gene Hazelton, © 1945; Ray Helle, © 1953; Ned Hilton, © 1946; David Huffine, © 1942, 1945; Stan Hunt, © 1946; Ralston Jones, © 1954; A. John Kaunus, © 1939; Jeff Keate, © 1936, 1945, 1953; Redmer Keller © 1952; Hank Ketcham, © 1950; Al Kaelin, © 1945; Bill King, © 1945, 1949; Lawrence Lariar, © 1945; Lafe Locke, © 1951; Martin Lowenstein, © 1950; Gustav Lundberg, © 1952; Harry Mace, © 1951; Jerry Marcus, © 1953; Charles E. Martin, © 1946; Herb Middlecamp, © 1941; Franklyn B. Modell, © 1946; Ed Nofziger, © 1945, 1953; John Norment, © 1950; Gardner Rea, © 1946, 1949, 1951, 1953; Frank Ridgeway, © 1953; Frank Owen, © 1946; George Reckas, © 1953; Salo Roth, © 1946; Charles D. Saxon, © 1945, 1946; Bob Schroeter, © 1954; Burr Shafer, © 1945, 1946, 1949; Vahan Shirvanian, © 1952, 1953; John Art Sibley, © 1945; George Sixta, © 1948; Henry Syverson, © 1949, 1952; Mort Temes, © 1953; Barney Tobey, © 1945, 1946; Don Tobin, © 1945, 1952, 1953; James Whiting, © 1954; George Wolfe, © 1950; Joseph Zeis, © 1951.

CONTENTS

CONTENTS

INTRODUCTION

By ROBERT M. YODER

AT THIS POINT, if someone will kindly get the squawk out of the public address system and if the Mayor will take the folding-chair of honor, we will have a ribbon-snipping or cornerstone laying or something of the ceremonious sort. But not, please, the usual introduction. If this book fulfills its simple intentions, an introduction is superfluous and superfluous in a distinctive way.

It would be something like getting a four-page booklet when you order pie, a manual entitled *Suggested Uses.* Or something like putting up with a hammy bugler who plays the Bunny Berrigan chorus of "Can't Get Started" before blowing chow call. Come to think of it, that would be a struggle worth hearing, a bugle having no valves. So let's say something like getting a bottle of the admirable bourbon in favor at the National Press Club, and known as The Breakfast of Champions—but getting with it a long-winded brochure entitled "Directions for Taking."

Not that there haven't been some fine introductions. Many wise and witty things are said in introductions, though it might be smarter to put them in a bottle and toss them into the Baltic. It is in a preface that E. B. White declines to analyze humor—"Humor can be dissected, as a frog can, but the thing dies in the process and the innards are discouraging to any but the pure scientific mind"—and then goes on to write with great candlepower on the subject. So that no one else need ever struggle to say that humorous writing has "an extra content" because "it plays close to the big hot fire which is Truth." That of course is one reason why humor, to clean up an old story referring to another of the great pleasures, is too good for the common people; only the best, to which company you are hereby welcomed, deserve it.

Introductions often are functional. Often they are used to thank those who contributed, maybe by helping in research. That's mannerly, but it doesn't apply to a collection like this. Nor is anyone involved who merits the kind of carbolic thanks Ring Lardner extended to a real estate man in one of his introductions. "The contents of *The Big Town*," Lardner said, "were written in a furnished house in Greenwich, Connecticut, and the author wishes to thank the rats for staying out of the room while he worked. It was winter time and the furnished house was a summer cottage but we didn't realize that when we rented it. Nor apparently did the rats."

Another useful purpose sometimes served by introductions is to describe the plan on which the author or editor proceeded, now that he looks back on it. Maybe the book in question extends some classic study of life in the hen-yard to cover the peck-order in a modern business office. Maybe it is a study of love's bliss as demonstrated in the idyllic relationship of William Saroyan to William Saroyan. Maybe the book traces the evolution of husbands as Darwin traced the evolution of flightless birds, if he did.

In works of that scholarly nature, it may be useful to describe the operation, and better still, impressive. The procedure used here, however, doesn't lend itself to much explaining. It doesn't follow the system by which Palgrave assembled *The Golden Treasury*, it isn't exactly the plan used by Mahan in his study of seapower. It is more the plan used by John Dillinger and Willie Sutton in robbing the First National Bank. You take out all you can carry and regret that you can't carry more. This book takes out as much as we could tote of the funnier stories, articles and cartoons printed by *The Saturday Evening Post*. In twenty trips you couldn't even make a dent in the riches heaped in those vaults; still, we think this is a pretty good score, as they say in larceny circles.

The idea was to assemble a bountiful book like one of those fancy tubs of foodstuffs well-heeled friends send you for Christmas. You don't know what-all is inside, but you unpack it with pleasant anticipation because everything from which you shuck the tissue, whether it turns out to be duck and wild rice or sweet pickled watermelon rind, is going to be Our Very Best Old Superior, and there's a lot of it.

There's no immodesty on the part of those who packed this hamper (hence the title, *A Carnival of Humor*) in saying that there is some purely wonderful stuff herein. It's been like putting together a program of jazz (hence the title, metaphors mixed while you wait) with all the stars available. Look who's here: Lardner, Thurber, Frank Sullivan, Dorothy Parker, Don Marquis, Runyon, Frank Ward O'Malley, Nunnally Johnson, P. G. Wodehouse—and it goes on like that.

Look at the cast. William Hazlett Upson's unsinkable salesman, Alexander Botts, a pure delight to all who long to tell their own boss what a meathead he is. Jeeves. Tugboat Annie. Penrod, though without Herman and Verman, and in an anxious moment, too. The one and only, the veritable Colin Glencannon. And Happy Digby; do you remember when he had a big legend on his car reading "Andrew's Super Service Sold Me This Lemon, Nine Miles to the Gallon and Low Geer on All Hills"? And many another boon companion, in every conceivable setting from the 9th hole of Heaven's golf course, where Willard Temple's Barnaby Jessup almost gives up the game, to Rudolph Speckeldonner's invasion of the Polo Grounds in Louis Graves' delightful "The Pig-Bristle Slugger."

We're at the opera, with Katherine Dayton telling us about the chorus and the two duties of a contralto, we're at the White House, with Joe's (and Damon Runyon's) Ethel making snoots at that hick cop, we even get to Old Siwash, long the most famous college, real or fictional, in the land. In that one, the word "frat" and the parody names of Greek letter societies may grate a little on present day ears but it's a high-spirited costume piece and first-rate Americana.

You'll note that the men of Siwash were not intense about fraternities but rather were devoted to a rousing underhanded sport, that of truly imaginative rushing. In my more sophisticated day we were intensely casual about fraternities and we didn't compete so blatantly. We went in more for stagecraft than for abduction and it was a Cheese Scion rather than a Pickle Heir on whom we wasted our talents one beautiful fall. Then, as at Siwash, we could rely on bum steers from the alumni and doubtless the lads in the active chapter still get them. Shows there are some things a man can tie to.

Editors of collections like this often use the introduction to explain how some items got in and others got overlooked or omitted. How that appeases the reader with a beef isn't very clear. He thinks the editor is a knucklehead and now you're giving him additional evidence. But if anyone is interested, the system used here was a variation of Christmas shopping. You see something Joe would like very much, something Ann would like, something that would please Uncle Ted, you see something that's got to be included or a certain faction of readers will get testy, and pretty soon there you are, overset by twenty-seven yards.

The joint looks like the paper-packed mansion of the Collier boys, and will be condemned next week as a fire hazard. You hardly dare light a cigaret in this shambles so a further selection must be made. That's when things get tough. The situation calls for some way of preferring one story out of say sixty-five, all fine, and obviously if you thought you had a test which solved that you would be psychiatry's delusional darling, the patient who must be tucked in a drawer every night because he thinks he is a green-handled sieve.

So the fact is, what you find here was chosen sort of as Dagwood of the comic strip chooses the various items which go into his five-inch sandwiches. Chicken because there's chicken, cold beans because they look good, cheese because it'll go good with the pickled green tomato, and so on. Other articles, stories, cartoons and merry conceits very probably are here in accordance with the Sneem Principle, which is invaluable in cases like this. Laid down by Corey Ford, the Sneem Principle—as you know or will learn with much pleasure—states that you keep the hat because if you didn't you would be throwing away the hat you keep fish in.

If that sounds as if whimsy had been given its mad, mad head, it's wrong. For the use of any single item there are reasons, though they vary greatly. This particular piece of Will Rogers, for example, is chosen because it goes to show what Rogers was all about, and the stuff usually quoted certainly doesn't do much in that line. This may help dispel the ridiculous theory that sweetness and light were Sunny Will's favorite tools. Note with pleasure his conclusion that only a desperate political emergency could have kept Charles Evans Hughes up after 9 P.M. and his account of a Cabinet meeting. Only optimists think that times change. The Secretary of Agriculture still is reporting progress.

If you ask on the other hand why this particular excerpt is taken from the works of Octavus Roy Cohen, who used to seem vastly entertaining when dealing with the Over The River Burial Society, it's probably because Guffy's case shows the power of positive thinking, especially when that thinking is cockeyed. If you like humor (a miserable word, but all there is) you suspect that there are two trolls under every bridge, and this will give you faith. You'll observe that Guffy never does get run over by a locomotive on Main Street.

Similar considerations have prevailed throughout, but the stories themselves are a darned sight better reading, and about the only reason for writing an introduction is to say thanks to the *Post.* This is not intended as a sample of *Post* humor, and certainly not as a study of *Post* humor or a study of anything else, God forbid. It is not intended as a tribute to the *Post,* either, though it is, in a way. Something like the tribute you pay to a good hotel when you take home its towels. You don't bother unless they are very good towels.

The sole consideration has been to create a book for enjoyment. We had a purpose: to assemble a lot of rare spirits, who hear life's harmonics a little more clearly and sing them out for us. The book even has an ideal. The hope has been to put together a collection that would create a feeling thousands of *Post* readers know very well.

That's the feeling devoted followers of Mr. Colin Glencannon had when they opened the *Post* and found a Glencannon story awaiting them. We're tied up on a broad but loutish river in northern Africa, perhaps, and the Inchiffe Castle is loading peanuts, practically by the peanut. Recreation is limited to catching malaria. Mr. Glencannon is killing time with The Scots Presbyterian Churchman and a bottle of Dugan's Dew of Kirkintilloch, and Mr. Glencannon is bored. From that happy point on—from the first word, for that matter—we knew we were in for a very good time. That was the time Mr. Glencannon took up alligator-stuffing and with reasonably honest intentions, but they subsided quickly.

That pleasant feeling, that you are in for a good time, is exactly and entirely what this book shoots for. If it makes it there's no function an introduction can perform except to impede. It's my duty to write one because I didn't do much of the real toil connected with getting together a collection like this. Shortly after making a start I was chosen as the skimpy stage for a whole little pageant of ailments, all of the kind other people regard as trifles so that you don't get a nickle's worth of sympathy. It took me out of play, however, long enough for others to do the spade work and the least I can do, unless I missed a goldbricking trick or two along the way, is to write an introduction. I got to get een, as Nunnally Johnson's crossword-puzzle champion would say, in spite of a conviction that a standard introduction in this case is strictly for the emu's. All that really needs to be done is to borrow a phrase from Octavus Roy Cohen's girl Toy and say that here is our Potpurri of Melody and Health Building and all hands hope you get as much pleasure out of it as they have.

The Saturday Evening Post

CARNIVAL OF HUMOR

THE UGLY MOLLUSK

By FRANK SULLIVAN

§ *Even as a young oyster, Adrian was ungainly. But he knew that it is the lot of genius to be misunderstood. Despite the fact that his efforts to produce a pearl go awry, he is neither discouraged nor dismayed. It was Adrian's first pearl, too, and everyone knows that a young oyster's first pearl is a big event in his life.*

APRIL 9, 1938

ONE quiet summer afternoon a large oyster sat on a rock, in an estuary off Cape Cod, thoughtfully surveying the world about him. He was not exactly a handsome oyster, yet he had an air of distinction. There was a gravity in his mien, a kind of dignity amounting almost to melancholy, that set him apart.

Indeed, he was apart. The rest of the oysters lived in the oyster bed, down the estuary a bit. The big oyster lived, a solitary exile, on the rock. His name was Adrian, but the other oysters referred to him sneeringly as the Ugly Mollusk.

Adrian was not like other oysters, and because he was not like other oysters, because he did not play the game as his fellow oysters thought it should be played, he was paying the price.

Many people seem to feel that an oyster leads a sheltered life. Far from it. Aside from the raids which decimate and redecimate, and sometimes re-redecimate an oyster colony during months containing an *R*, there are other dangers with which an oyster must cope. He is subject to constant attack from his natural enemy, the sponge, and from a series of other ferocious creatures with such names as sea anemone, whelk, whelk tingle and sea squirt. He is also subject to periodical and unpredictable changes in sex. This is the factor which, more than any other, militates against dullness and precludes boredom in an oyster's life. He never knows, from day to day, and this gives a fillip to oyster courtships which must make even such classic romances, in our species, as that of Romeo and Juliet, or Abélard and Héloïse, seem rather routine. If an oyster leads a dull life, then so does a parachute jumper with a hole in his parachute.

From the beginning Adrian had been—well, different. As a very young oyster, he had been so much larger than the others that he was the object of many gibes directed at his ungainliness, but his size would not have been a major disability, had there been nothing else wrong. Such was not the case. Shortly after Adrian, with the other apprentice oysters, had started work on his first pearl, sinister rumors began to circulate.

At first the older oysters paid them no

heed. A young oyster's first pearl is a big event in his life, and such pearls often go wrong because of overenthusiasm or nervousness on the part of the novice. But it soon became apparent that Adrian presented a problem which could no longer be ignored. After due allowance for false starts, every other novice had some kind of pearl started, for better or for worse. Adrian also had got something started, but not by the widest stretch of the imagination could it be called a pearl. It was an ugly, nondescript, greenish-black atrocity. Nothing like it had ever been seen in the oyster colony, not by the oldest inhabitant.

Nobody was more bewildered by the turn events had taken than poor Adrian. He had followed all the directions and had taken exactly the same measures as his fellow apprentices. It was farthest from his thoughts to turn out a greenish-black monstrosity instead of a pearl. He did not want to be different. More than anything else, he wanted to be like other oysters—like Sheldon, for instance.

Sheldon, an oyster somewhat older than Adrian, had only recently graduated from the novice class, yet he had already turned out several pearls of a fineness that had won the acclaim of veteran oysters. A brilliant future was predicted for him. He was clever, ambitious, resourceful, and industrious almost to the point of stuffiness. His every waking thought was devoted to planning schemes whereby he could produce a larger quantity of pearls without impairing the quality. And he was formally betrothed to Flora, the fairest of the twenty-two hundred living daughters of old Dean Cotuit, the head oyster of the bed. No doubt of it, Sheldon was going places.

Naturally, a successful oyster like Sheldon could have little but contempt for a blunderer like Adrian. This contempt he made no effort to conceal. Often he would twit Adrian, saying, "Well, how is your so-called pearl getting on?" for he had a sharp wit.

Public opinion in the bed was dead against Adrian. The general feeling was that there was no excuse for him. If an oyster wanted to turn out a pearl, he could do so, if he had a mind to. It always had been done. All felt that Adrian was a disgrace to the community and that sympathy for him was wasted.

Every morning Adrian awoke, hoping against hope that the situation might have remedied itself overnight. It never did. The "pearl" grew odder and more misshapen, until it reached the proportions of a public scandal. Between the jeers of the young oysters, for youth can be cruel to youth, and the cold disapproval of the elders, his lot grew steadily more unhappy. More than once he thought of ending it all.

Matters came to a head quite unexpectedly one day. It was during the inspection of pearls. Dean Cotuit arrived at Adrian's place in the ranks and, nerving himself to the ordeal with a visible effort, took a peek inside Adrian's shell. The dean drew back with a shudder.

"Ugh!" he said. "Worse than ever."

"If that's a pearl," young Sheldon observed, "I'm your grandmother."

This sally drew a laugh from the coterie of sycophants which surrounded him.

"This can't go on any longer," said the dean, with decision.

"If you'd give me just a little more time," Adrian ventured.

"Time? You've had all the time in the world. We can't afford to have a situation like this continue. If this thing got noised abroad, we'd be the laughing-stock of every oyster bed along the Atlantic coast."

"If you'll only be patient," Adrian pleaded, "I'm sure I can make good."

"A likely story," sneered Sheldon.

"He ought to be thrown out of the oyster bed," said a second oyster indignantly.

Others contributed similar comments.

"This colony certainly ought to be proud of you—I don't think," Sheldon hurled at Adrian.

For some time past, into Adrian's admiration for Sheldon there had been creeping, insidiously but surely, another emotion, of which, due to the disturbed state of his affairs, he had not been quite conscious. Now it suddenly jelled.

"You keep out of this," he heard himself hissing at Sheldon.

The oysters were petrified. This was the first sign of anything like defiance that had come from Adrian. Cotuit was the first to recover from the general astonishment.

"It ill behooves you, sir," he told Adrian sharply, "to take a tone like that to a member of this bed of Sheldon's standing. You ought to thank your lucky stars that you are tolerated here, without vilifying your betters."

"Oh, pay no attention to him," said Sheldon. "I consider the source."

"Apologize to Sheldon," the dean commanded.

Something snapped inside Adrian. "I'll be damned if I will," he barked.

The oysters reeled under the impact of this defi. A strange intoxication seized Adrian now, and he plunged on recklessly.

"Apologize to that prig!" he shouted. "Ha! I should say not!"

Then he had a sudden impulse. Crazed by success, he obeyed it. He tripped Sheldon and sent him sprawling.

"There," he said, with a mocking laugh. "There's your apology."

Again the dean was first to find his voice. "I think," he said, with forced calm, "you had better go."

"You bet I'm going," said Adrian, "but before I go, I have something to say to you. I don't know why I haven't said it before. I don't know why I've taken any nonsense from the likes of you. But something snapped in me just now and I see you all in your true colors. I see you for what you are —a pack of mean, smug, insufferable, self-seeking, pearl-worshiping, mean——"

"Oh, come now, you said 'mean' before. Fair play, you know," protested one aggrieved oyster.

"Mean," repeated Adrian, glaring at him, "low-down, grubby little stuffed shirts."

The oysters winced. They had never before been called all those names at once.

"You had better go now," the dean said, "before you say something you'll be sorry for."

"That—for you!" Adrian snapped.

Feeling better than he had in months, he turned and stalked down the estuary, looked about him for a likely Elba, and finally chose the rock.

"Look where the sap anchored," Sheldon said to Dean Cotuit. "A bunch of the toughest anemones along the Atlantic coast hang out around that rock. He won't last a week."

That was what Sheldon thought. It was what the tough anemones thought too. All were disillusioned. The first anemone that attacked Adrian with a view to making a meal of him barely escaped with its life. The second didn't. The third, and successive anemones, stayed away. Adrian became known up and down the estuary as one oyster who would brook no nonsense from any anemone. Sponges, whelks, tingles, starfish and sea squirts also learned to give him a wide berth.

Somehow, from the crucible of sorrow, Adrian emerged a better, a finer oyster. Suffering ennobled him and adversity stamped him with a certain tragic glamour. His exile had its compensations. At least he no longer had to worry about the "pearl." This was just as well, for it did not grow any better—just kept getting larger and more queer looking, and less like a pearl all the time. Adrian seldom bothered to look at it. On the whole, he was not unhappy in his exile, and the days slipped by until the afternoon arrived on which we found him sitting pensively on the rock. He was thinking of the turbulent life that had been his and reflecting that, if he had not achieved happiness, he had at least won a measure of serenity.

Suddenly he was aroused by a cry. He looked. There, some distance from the rock, was a beautiful young oyster in the grip of a burly sponge.

Flora Cotuit, lovely daughter of the dean, and betrothed of Sheldon, had felt that afternoon that she would scream if she did not get away from her twenty-one hundred and ninety-nine sisters with their silly chatter, and her eligible, but sometimes wearisome, fiancé with his eternal shop talk about pearls. She had slipped out of the oyster bed and down the estuary to get a little peace and quiet. Suddenly the sponge had confronted her, leering, menacing and ravenous.

Adrian took in the situation at a glance. There was not a moment to lose. In a week at the outside, Flora Cotuit would have met a slow death by absorption. He unhitched himself from his mooring and, by bending every effort, reached her side late in the afternoon of the same day.

The sponge, absorbed in his preparations for the kill, did not notice Adrian's approach until the latter squeezed him. Accustomed to dealing with oysters who rarely put up a fight, the sponge was taken off guard. Before he had time to collect his wits, Adrian nipped him again, nipped off a segment fully large enough to make one of those little sponges used for cleaning white shoes. It floated off. The sponge looked after it in astonishment. While he was looking, Adrian pinched off another hunk. It floated off. Adrian nipped another. And another. Pieces of sponge were floating down the current like toy balloons escaped from tots at a county fair. It demoralized the sponge. Like all bullies, he was a coward at heart. Releasing Flora from his grip, he beat an ignominous rereat, frantically gathering up as many portions of his anatomy as he could, with a view to reassembling himself when he had reached a place of safety.

"How can I ever thank you?" said Flora.

"It was nothing," said Adrian.

"Nothing? You call saving a life nothing?"

"Life," echoed Adrian cynically.

"You are—bitter."

"I have good reason to be."

"I know."

"You know that I am the Ugly Mollusk, eh?" Adrian laughed, and there was something in his laugh that was not pleasant to hear.

"How they must have hurt you to make you laugh like that," said Flora gently.

Kind words from an oyster were something Adrian was not prepared to cope with. In self-defense, he resorted to gruffness:

"You had a close call. You have no business down here. This neighborhood is filled with unscrupulous sponges who would stop at nothing."

"I had to get away from it all—up there," sighed Flora. "Well——"

She turned to go. Then she paused and turned.

"I do not think that you are—ugly," she said.

Then she turned and went. As she went she upset Adrian's life.

Next afternoon Adrian sat on his rock, his life upset, thinking of Flora. Suddenly a cry! Her voice!

This time it was not a sponge that had her in its fell clutch, but a particularly ferocious sea squirt. It took some time to rescue her.

"You," said Adrian, facing her after the rescue. "You—here?"

"I had to come," said Flora simply.

After that she came every day. Each afternoon at the same time Adrian would hear the same cry for help, and there would be Flora, in the clutch of some new enemy. The rescues grew to be fun. They both looked forward to them.

Love is a peculiar emotion and it has peculiar effects. It makes some creatures want to go out and knock down fellow creatures and trample on them. It makes others dye their hair, or commence to wear fancy neckties. Others write sonnets. Love affected Flora's pearl.

She had never been much of a hand at pearls. Her attempts were the despair of her father, the cause of much hilarity among her sisters and a source of grave concern to her ambitious fiancé. No matter how she tried, Flora could never seem to get the knack of turning out a first-class pearl. The one she had been working on at the time of her first meeting with Adrian had been a dull, lusterless pellicle.

Now, under the impact of love, it bloomed. Almost overnight, and with scarcely any attention from Flora, it became a lovely, shimmering globule, with overtones of pink suggestive of rosy-fingered dawn in one of her less flamboyant moods.

Adrian became a new oyster. Hitherto careless of his personal appearance, he now spent half the morning scraping himself against the rock, so that by the time Flora appeared on the scene for her daily rescue, all the tiny barnacles which attach themselves to an oyster and make it so difficult for him to keep himself neat and clean had been scrubbed off, leaving Adrian quite the Beau Brummell.

They were very happy in their newfound love, but it could not last. The course of true love never does run smooth. If it did, the movie theaters would be empty. It was not long until news of the liaison reached the oyster bed.

One day Sheldon went to old Cotuit in a state of great agitation.

"Mr. Cotuit," he said, "Flora has been seeing that cad."

"Which cad?"

"The Ugly Mollusk."

"No!"

"Every day. Every single day."

Sheldon told the dean the story. Flora was sent for. She admitted everything readily.

"I cannot understand you, Flora," Sheldon complained. "Here you are, the affianced bride of the most brilliant pearl producer in the estuary——"

Flora turned on him.

"Pearls!" she cried. "That's all you think of—pearls. Doesn't it ever occur to you that there is something more to life than pearls? Don't you ever think of romance, beauty, love?"

"There is also duty," said old Cotuit sternly.

"Duty," sniffed Flora, as though she were saying "Nerts!"

"Silence!" thundered her father. "I have heard enough. You marry Sheldon immediately."

"Never," said Flora.

"Flora," Sheldon warned her, "any oyster in her right mind would jump at this chance."

"I am not here to argue," Cotuit said. "You marry Sheldon or you leave this oyster bed, never to return. You have until tomorrow to decide."

That night Flora slipped out, made her way to the rock and told Adrian what had happened. He heard her in silence. He seemed troubled. He sighed and dropped occasional comments such as "I knew there would have to be a showdown," and "Doesn't it beat all?" When Flora finished, he was lost in thought for quite some time.

"No," he said finally. "There is no other way out."

Somehow, Flora did not like his tone. "Adrian, what is it?"

"Flora, you must go with Sheldon," said Adrian.

"Are you mad, Adrian?"

"Please try to understand."

"Don't ask me to understand. When a girl is in love she never understands. I love you, Adrian."

"I have thought it all out. It—it cannot be."

"Cannot be?"

"Cannot be. What have I to offer you? Hardship, penury, exile, social ostracism. He offers you security, wealth, social position."

"Do you think I care for those baubles?"

"You don't now. Later you would miss them. You would hate me."

"Adrian, you are cruel."

"I am cruel only in order to be kind. I cannot let you sacrifice yourself for me."

"Why not?"

"Because I love you too much."

"This is your final decision?"

"It is better so, Flora."

"Then it is good-by."

"I shall always think of you, Flora."

"With what?" said Flora, in a sudden burst of hurt pride and baffled love, and with that she swept out. The next morning she told her father she was ready to marry Sheldon.

"Good for you, Flora," said Cotuit. "I knew you would see things in the right light."

They sought Sheldon to tell him, and found him sitting pensively on an abandoned chambered-nautilus shell.

"Sheldon, great news!" said Cotuit. "Flora has changed her mind."

Sheldon sat silent, looking rather embarrassed.

"Well, aren't you tickled?"

"The truth is, sir, a rather awkward situation has developed."

Cotuit paled. Flora looked sharply at Sheldon.

"You mean?" asked Cotuit.

"Yes," said Sheldon demurely.

Cotuit took no pains to conceal his irritation.

"I must say you picked a fine time to change your sex," he barked.

"I had nothing to do with it," Sheldon returned with spirit. "You know that as well as I do. It could happen to any oyster. It could happen to Flora."

There was a thought. The dean eyed Flora.

"Flora," he began ingratiatingly.

"No, thanks, father," said Flora, hastily but decisively.

"But, Flora, it would solve everything."

"Not for me. I'm quite comfortable as I am."

"That's right. Be stubborn. Well, we might postpone the wedding." The dean was in no mood for not grasping at straws. "If Sheldon can give us any idea when he'll be—uh—back——"

"Haven't the faintest idea; sorry," said Sheldon. "You know how these things are with us oysters."

"This is a fine mess," stormed old Cotuit. "We oysters boast that we have the ideal solution of the sex problem. Sometimes I wonder."

"Well, at least we don't get in a rut," said Sheldon philosophically.

"Oh, shut up," said the dean.

"Never mind, Sheldon," said Flora. "I'll be a sister to you."

"And I'll be one to you," said Sheldon cordially.

Quite a crowd had collected by this time, and suddenly on its outskirts there was a commotion. In another moment a form had elbowed its way through the crowd.

It was Adrian.

"Adrian!" cried Flora. "You—here?"

"Flora! What a fool I was to think I could give you up. Can you ever forgive me for being so noble?"

"I knew that you would come," she said simply.

"Flora," cried Adrian in a glad, ringing voice, "you and I against the world. Who dares say us nay?"

He glanced about belligerently in search of possible nay sayers. He caught sight of Sheldon. He paled.

"Flora," he cried, "don't–is it–am I–too late?"

Sheldon answered. "Adrian," he said, "I will be brief and to the point. No."

Adrian took in the situation at a glance. It would scarcely have been cricket to crow over a defeated rival. He started to offer Sheldon his sympathy, but Sheldon would have none of it.

"Quite all right," said Sheldon. " 'What can't be cured must be endured,' you know. Matter of fact, I'm beginning to be reconciled. It's not such a bad system. You get every point of view."

Something strange was happening. The crowd, to an oyster, was staring at Adrian.

Around him there hung a curious aura of shimmering green light. The oysters had never seen anything like it. They murmured, wondering. Cotuit stood transfixed.

Then Adrian opened his shell. As he did so, the light became a blaze as a green radiance poured out and was caught by a thousand sunbeams flickering down through the water. Cotuit, blinded by the radiance, fell back. Adrian blinked a little himself.

There, in place of the ugly, greenish-black mass that had brought contumely, scorn and exile on Adrian, was–a Gem of Purest Ray Serene!

"A square-cut emerald!" cried Cotuit, in a voice hoarse with awe.

A square-cut emerald. The dream and ambition of every oyster in the world.

Any oyster can whip up a pearl, but from time immemorial every oyster with a spark of ambition had cherished the secret hope that he might be the genius who would pass on to greater triumphs and give to oysterdom its first emerald. Now the dream had been achieved–by an oyster whom his fellow oysters had scorned; whom they had considered unworthy the very name of oyster.

"Adrian," Flora reproached, "you never told me."

"I didn't know about it," Adrian whispered, for he also was momentarily nonplused. "Hadn't looked at it in months."

"Can you ever forgive us, Adrian?" said Dean Cotuit.

"Why, you didn't know any better," Adrian forgave.

"To think," said Cotuit, "that we had in our midst the greatest oyster of his time, and we failed to recognize him."

"It is the lot of genius to be misunderstood," Adrian comforted.

The oysters were crowding around Adrian to view the wonder. Exclamations of awe and admiration were heard on all sides.

"I always knew Adrian had it in him," said the oyster who had been the first to suggest that he be thrown out of the bed.

"I always liked him," enthused another–the one who had first called Adrian a disgrace to the community–"but you couldn't tell some people anything." The oyster glared at Dean Cotuit.

"One matter I'd like to settle immediately," said Adrian. "May I have the honor of your daughter's hand in marriage, Dean Cotuit?"

"Pardon me," said Cotuit. "I am not Dean Cotuit."

Flora started. She looked uneasily at her father. So many odd things had been happening.

"Do you think," Cotuit continued, "that I would presume to continue in that office when this colony is honored by having in its midst the greatest oyster in the world today?"

Adrian looked behind him, modestly pretending he thought the dean meant someone else.

"Ah, I mean you, Adrian," smiled Cotuit. "You are the head man here from now on."

"But really––" Adrian felt he ought to

protest a little for the sake of appearances.

"Nonsense," said Cotuit. "After you, if you please."

A cheer went up from the oysters.

Adrian made a short speech in which he thanked the dean and promising the oysters that he would endeavor to the best of his ability to fulfill the sacred trust that they had reposed in him, and declaring that he owed everything to Flora.

Another cheer went up from the oysters.

Flora looked happily at Adrian.

"My—Ugly Mollusk," she murmured tenderly.

The Perfect Squelch

A RATHER scatterbrained young lady recently visited the home of her fiancé's wealthy spinster aunt for the week end. While unpacking her bag, she discovered to her dismay that she had brought a worn and badly faded pair of pajamas. Eager to make a perfect impression, and a bit awed by the elderly Victorian-looking maid who attended her, the young lady hid the pajamas under her mattress after she arose on the first morning.

Waking late the second morning after her arrival, she dressed hurriedly and completely forgot about hiding the pajamas until after breakfast.

Then, giving her fiancé and her hostess a hasty excuse, she rushed upstairs, only to find her bed already made and the stern-looking maid dusting the room. She stooped quickly and peered under the mattress.

"If you're looking for the pajamas, miss, you needn't worry," the maid said calmly. "I put them back in the young gentleman's room."

—FRANCES RODMAN.

The Colonel Had Who-Dat Trouble

A *POST* WAR ANECDOTE

THE Flying Fortresses were winging high over France, heading for the Channel and their bases in Britain. They had successfully bombed a certain bridge in the Vosges Mountains and it had been a milk run—sporadic flak and no fighter opposition. Now that they were out of enemy territory, it was time for the pilots to engage in a little banter over the radio to break the monotony and lighten the fatigue of the long run home. But all they expected to hear this trip was the monotonous droning of their engines and an occasional crisp command from the old man in the lead plane, because that morning, at briefing, the order had come down that there would be stricter radio discipline in the future and that violators would be punished.

Finally, however, one bored pilot could stand the silence no longer. Depressing his mike button, he whispered softly into his mask, "Who dat?"

Almost immediately another pilot inquired in a muffled voice, "Who dat say who dat?"

Then a third cut in, "Who dat say who dat say who dat?"

And a fourth came back with, "Who dat say who dat say who dat say who dat?"

Undoubtedly this would have gone on until all thirty-six planes had checked in, if the command pilot had not barked exasperatedly into his microphone, "The next man who speaks extraneously will be court-martialed!"

The colonel's warning was followed by a moment of dutiful silence. But then a low and obviously disguised voice firmly demanded, "Who dat say dat?"

—IRVING L. UTTAL, 1ST LT., AC (INACTIVE) AUS.

I'M A NATURAL-BORN SALESMAN

By WILLIAM HAZLETT UPSON

§ *Did you ever wonder how Alexander Botts got into that business? The irrepressible salesman of Earthworm tractors has had many a scrape since the initial adventure described here. But, as you'll see, Botts has remained the same resourceful character from the very beginning.*

APRIL 16, 1927

STONEWALL JACKSON HOTEL,
MEMPHIS, TENNESSEE.
MARCH 11, 1920.
THE FARMERS' FRIEND TRACTOR COMPANY,
EARTHWORM CITY, ILLINOIS.

GENTLEMEN: I have decided you are the best tractor company in the country, and consequently I am giving you first chance to hire me as your salesman to sell tractors in this region.

I'm a natural-born salesman, have a very quick mind, am twenty-eight years old, am honest and reliable, and can give references if required. I have already had considerable experience as a machinery salesman, and I became familiar with your Earthworm tractors as a member of the motorized field artillery in France. I can demonstrate tractors as well as sell them.

When do I start work?

Very truly yours,
ALEXANDER BOTTS.

FARMERS' FRIEND TRACTOR COMPANY
MAKERS OF EARTHWORM TRACTORS
EARTHWORM CITY, ILLINOIS
March 13, 1920.

MR. ALEXANDER BOTTS,
STONEWALL JACKSON HOTEL,
MEMPHIS, TENNESSEE.

Dear Mr. Botts: Your letter is received. We have no opening for a salesman at present, but we are badly in need of a service mechanic. As you say you are familiar with our tractors, we will try you out on this job at $100 per month plus traveling expenses.

You will report at once to our Mr. George Healy, salesman for Tennessee and Mississippi, who is now at the Dartmouth Hotel, Memphis. You will go with him to Cyprus City, Mississippi, to demonstrate a ten-ton Earthworm tractor for Mr. Jackson, a lumber operator of that place. Mr. Healy will tell you just what you are to do.

We inclose check for $100 advance expense money.

Very truly,
GILBERT HENDERSON.
Sales Manager.

STONEWALL JACKSON HOTEL,
MEMPHIS, TENNESSEE.
MARCH 16, 1920.

THE FARMERS' FRIEND TRACTOR COMPANY,
EARTHWORM CITY, ILLINOIS.

Gentlemen: As soon as your letter came I went around to see Mr. Healy, and it is lucky for you that you hired me, because Mr. Healy has just been taken sick with appendicitis. They were getting ready to take him to the hospital, and he was pretty weak, but he managed to tell me that the tractor for the demonstration had already arrived at the freight station in Cyprus City.

He also explained that this Mr. Jackson down there owns about a million feet of cyprus timber which he wants to get out and sell right away before the present high price of lumber goes down. It seems the ground is so swampy and soft from the winter rains that with his present equipment of mules and wagons he won't be able to move any of his timber until summer.

But Mr. Healy was down there a couple of weeks ago, and he arranged to put on a demonstration to show Mr. Jackson that an Earthworm tractor can go into those swamps and drag out the timber right away. Mr. Jackson said he would buy the tractor if it did the work, and Mr. Healy was feeling very low because he was sick and couldn't go down to hold the demonstration.

"You can rest easy, Mr. Healy," I said. "When you look at me you're gazing on a natural-born salesman. I will go down there and do your work, as well as mine. I will put on a swell demonstration, and then I will sell the goods."

As Mr. Healy did not seem to know just what to say to this, I gathered up all his order blanks, selling literature, price lists, and so on, and also the bill of lading and the check to pay the freight on the tractor. Then I wished him good luck, and left.

From this you can see that I am quick to grasp an opportunity, and that you made no mistake in hiring me. I am leaving for Cyprus City tonight.

Cordially yours,
ALEXANDER BOTTS.

FARMERS' FRIEND TRACTOR COMPANY
SALESMAN'S DAILY REPORT

Date: March 17, 1920.
Written from: Delta Hotel, Cyprus City, Mississippi.
Written by: Alexander Botts, Service Mechanic and Pinch-Hitter Salesman.

I found this pad of salesman's report blanks among the stuff I got from Mr. Healy. I see by the instructions on the cover that each salesman is supposed to send in a full and complete report of everything he does, so I will give you all particulars of a very busy day.

I arrived at 7:51 this morning at Cyprus City—which turns out to be pretty much of a hick town in what they call the Yazoo Delta. The whole country here is nothing but a swamp, and the main street of the town ends in a high bank that they call a levee, on the other side of which is the Mississippi River flowing along about twenty feet higher than the town.

After alighting from the train, and after noting that it was a cloudy day and looked like rain, I engaged a room at the Delta Hotel. I then hurried over to the freight station, where I found the big ten-ton Earthworm tractor on the unloading platform. They had dragged it off the car with a block and tackle. And when I saw that beautiful machine standing there so big and powerful, with its fine wide tracks like an army tank, with its elegant new shiny paint and with its stylish cab for the driver, I will admit that I felt a glow of pride to think that I was the salesman and service mechanic for such a splendid piece of machinery.

Note: Of course, as I said in my letter, I am an old machinery salesman. But the largest thing I ever sold before was the Excelsior Peerless Self-Adjusting Automatic Safety-Razor-Blade Sharpener. I did very well with this machine, but I could not take the pride in it that I feel I am going to have in this wonderful ten-ton Earthworm tractor.

After paying the freight I hired several guys from the town garage to put gas and oil in the tractor, and then I started them bolting the little cleats onto the tracks. You see I am right up on my toes all the time. I think of everything. And I figured that if we were going through the mud we would need these cleats to prevent slipping. While they were being put on I stepped over to the office of Mr. Johnson, the lumberman.

Note: This bird's name is Johnson—not Jackson, as you and Mr. Healy told me. Also it strikes me that Mr. Healy may have been fairly sick even as long as two weeks ago, when he was down here. In addition to getting the name wrong he did very poor work in preparing this prospect. He did not seem to be in a buying mood at all.

As soon as I had explained my errand to this Mr. Johnson—who is a very large, hard-boiled bozo—he gave me what you might call a horse laugh.

"You are wasting your time," he said. "I told that fool salesman who was here before that tractors would be no good to me. All my timber is four miles away on the other side of the Great Gumbo Swamp, which means that it would have to be brought through mud that is deeper and stickier than anything you ever seen, young feller."

"You would like to get it out, wouldn't you?" I asked.

"I sure would," he said, "but it's impossible. You don't understand conditions down here. Right on the roads the mules and horses sink in up to their bellies; and when you get off the roads, even ducks and turtles can hardly navigate."

"The Earthworm tractor," I said, "has more power than any duck or turtle. And if you'll come out with me I'll show you that I can pull your logs through that swamp."

"I can't afford to waste my time with such crazy ideas," he said. "I've tried motor equipment. I have a motor truck now that is stuck three feet deep right on the main road at the edge of town."

"All right," I said, always quick to grasp an opportunity, "how about coming along with me while I pull out your truck?"

"Well," said Mr. Johnson, "I can spare about an hour this morning. If you'll go right now, I'll go with you, although I doubt if you can even pull out the truck. And even if you do, I won't buy your tractor."

"How about going this afternoon?" I asked.

"I'll be busy every minute of this afternoon. It's now or never."

"Come on!" I said.

We walked over together to the freight platform, and as the cleats were now all bolted on we both climbed into the cab.

Note: I will explain that I was sorry that Mr. Johnson had been unable to wait until afternoon, as I had intended to use the morning in practicing up on driving the machine. It is true, as I said in my letter, that I became familiar with Earthworm tractors when I was a member of a motorized-artillery outfit in France, but as my job in the artillery was that of cook, and as I had never before sat in the seat of one of these tractors, I was not as familiar with the details of driving as I might have wished. However, I was pleased to see that the tractor seemed to have a clutch and gear shift like the automobiles I have often driven.

I sat down on the driver's seat with reasonable confidence; Mr. Johnson sat down beside me; and one of the garage men cranked up the motor. It started at once, and when I heard the splendid roar of the powerful exhaust, and saw that thirty or forty of the inhabitants, both white and otherwise, were standing around with wondering and admiring faces, I can tell you I felt proud of myself. I put the gear in low, opened the throttle and let in the clutch.

Note: I would suggest that you tell your chief engineer, or whoever it is that designs your tractors, that he ought to put in a standard gear shift. You can understand that it is very annoying, after you have pulled the gear-shift lever to the left and then back, to find that instead of being in low you are really in reverse.

As I said, I opened the throttle, let in the clutch, and started forward. But I found that when I started forward, I was really—on account of the funny gear shift—moving backward. And instead of going down the gentle slope of the ramp in front, the whole works backed off the rear edge of the platform, dropping at least four feet into a pile of crates with such a sickening crash that I thought the machine was wrecked and both of us killed.

But it soon appeared that, although we were both very much shaken up, we were still alive—especially Mr. Johnson, who began talking so loud and vigorously that I saw I need have no worry about his health. After I had got Mr. Johnson quieted down a bit, I inspected the machine and found that it was not hurt at all. As I am always alert to seize an opportunity, I told Mr. Johnson that I had run off the platform on purpose to show him how strongly built the tractor was. Then, after I had promised I would not make any more of these jumps, he consented to remain in the tractor, and we started off again.

Note: Kindly tell your chief engineer that Alexander Botts congratulates him on producing a practically unbreakable tractor. But tell him that I wish he would design some thicker and softer seat cushions. If the base of the chief engineer's spine was as sore as mine still is, he would realize that there are times when good thick seat cushions are highly desirable.

As we drove up the main street of Cyprus City, with a large crowd of admiring natives following after, I seemed to smell something burning. At once I stopped, opened up the hood and discovered that the paint on the cylinders was crackling and smoking like bacon in a frying pan.

"Perhaps," suggested Mr. Johnson, "there is no water in the radiator."

I promptly inspected the radiator, and, sure enough, that was the trouble.

Note: I would suggest that if your chief engineer would design an air-cooled motor for the tractor, such incidents as the above would be avoided.

I borrowed a pail from a store and filled the radiator. Apparently, owing to my alertness in this emergency, no damage had been done.

When we started up again we had not gone more than a few yards before I felt the tractor give a little lurch. After we had got a little farther along I looked back, and right at the side of the street I saw one of the biggest fountains I have ever seen in all my life. A solid column of water about eight inches thick was spouting high in the air, spreading out at the top like a mushroom, and raining down all around like Niagara Falls.

I heard somebody yell something about a fire plug; and as I have a quick mind, I saw right away what had happened. The hood of the tractor is so big that it had prevented me from seeing a fire plug right in front of me. I had unfortunately run into it, and as it was of very cheap, inferior construction, it had broken right off.

For a while there was great excitement, with people running here and there, hollering and yelling. The sheriff came up and took my name, as he seemed to think I was to blame—in spite of the fact that the fire plug was in such an exposed position. I was a bit worried at the way the water was accumulating in the street, and consequently I was much relieved when they finally got hold of the water-works authorities and got the fountain turned off. You see the fire mains here are connected to the Mississippi River, and if they had not turned the water off the whole river would have flowed into the business district of Cyprus City.

Note: I would suggest that your chief engineer design these tractor hoods a little lower, so as to avoid such accidents in the future.

After the water had been turned off we got under way again, clanking along the main street in high gear, and then driving out of town to the eastward over one of the muddiest roads I ever saw. The tractor, on account of its wide tracks, stayed right up on top of the mud, and rolled along as easy and smooth as a Pullman car. Behind us a large crowd of local sightseers floundered along as best they could; some of them wading through the mud and slop, and others riding in buggies pulled by horses or mules.

Mr. Johnson acted as if he was pretty sore, and I did not blame him. Although the various mishaps and accidents we had been through were unavoidable and not my fault at all, I could understand that they might have been very annoying to my passenger. Perhaps that is one reason I am such a good salesman; I can always get the other feller's point of view. I livened up the journey a bit by telling Mr. Johnson a number of Irish jokes, but I did not seem to get any laughs, possibly because the motor made so much noise Mr. Johnson couldn't hear me.

By this time I had got the hang of driving the machine very well, and I was going along like a veteran. When we reached Mr. Johnson's truck—which was deep in the mud at the side of the road about half a mile from town—I swung around and backed up in front of it in great style.

The road, as I have said, was soft and muddy enough; but off to the right was a low flat stretch of swamp land that looked much muddier and a whole lot softer. There were patches of standing water here and there, and most of it was covered with canebrake—which is a growth of tall canes that look like bamboo fishing poles.

Mr. Johnson pointed out over this mass of canebrake and mud. "That is an arm of the Great Gumbo Swamp," he yelled very loud, so I could hear him above the noise of the motor. "Your machine may be able to navigate these roads, but it would never pull a load through a slough like that."

I rather doubted it myself, but I didn't admit it. "First of all," I said, "we'll pull out this truck."

We both got out of the tractor, and right away we sank up to our knees in the soft, sticky mud. The truck was a big one, loaded with lumber, and it was mired down so deep that the wheels were practically out of sight, and the body seemed to be resting on the ground. Mr. Johnson didn't think the tractor could budge it, but I told him to get into the driver's seat of the truck so he could steer it when it got going.

By this time a gentle rain had started up, and Mr. Johnson told me to hurry up, as the truck had no cab and he was getting wet. I grabbed a big chain out of the truck tool box, and told Mr. Johnson to get out his watch. He did so.

"In just thirty seconds," I said, "things are going to start moving around here."

I then rapidly hooked one end of the chain to the back of the tractor, fastened the other end to the truck, sprang into the tractor seat and started the splendid machine moving forward. As the tractor rolled steadily and powerfully down the road, I could hear the shouting of the crowd even above the noise of the motor. Looking around, however, I saw that something was wrong. The truck—or rather, the major portion of it—was still in the same place, and I was pulling only the radiator. As I have a quick mind I saw at once what had happened. Quite naturally I had slung the chain around the handiest thing on the front of the truck—which happened to be the radiator cap. And as the truck was of a cheap make, with the radiator not properly anchored, it had come off.

I stopped at once, and then I had to spend about ten minutes calming down Mr. Johnson by assuring him that the Farmers' Friend Tractor Company would pay for a new radiator. I backed up to the truck again, and Mr. Johnson took the chain himself, and by burrowing down in the mud managed to get it fastened around the front axle. Then he climbed back into the seat of the truck and scowled at me very disagreeably. By this time the rain was falling fairly briskly, and this may have had something to do with his ill-humor.

When I started up again everything went well. The motor roared, the cleats on the tracks dug into the mud, and slowly and majestically the tractor moved down the road, dragging the heavy truck through the mud behind it.

At this point I stuck my head out of the tractor cab to acknowledge the cheers of the bystanders, and in so doing I unfortunately knocked off my hat, which was caught by the wind and blown some distance away. At once I jumped out and began chasing it through the mud. The crowd began to shout and yell, but I paid no attention to this noise until I had reached my hat and picked it up—which took me some time, as the hat had blown a good ways, and I could not make any speed through the mud. When at last I looked around I saw that a curious thing had happened.

In getting out of the tractor I had accidentally pulled on one of the handlebars enough to turn the tractor sidewise. And in my natural excitement—the hat having cost me $8.98 last week in Memphis—I had forgotten to pull out the clutch. So when I looked up I saw that the tractor, with Mr. Johnson and his truck in tow, was headed right out into the Great Gumbo Swamp. It had already got a good start and it was going strong. As Mr. Johnson seemed to be waving and yelling for help, I ran after him.

But as soon as I got off the road the mud was so deep and soft that I could make no headway at all. Several of the bystanders also attempted to follow, but had to give it up as a bad job. There was nothing to do but let poor Mr. Johnson go dragging off through the swamp.

Although I was really sorry to see Mr. Johnson going off all by himself this way, with no protection from the pouring rain, I could not help feeling a thrill of pride when I saw how the great ten-ton Earthworm tractor was eating up that terrible soft mud.

The wide tracks kept it from sinking in more than a few inches; the cleats gave it good traction; and the motor was so powerful that it pulled that big truck like it was a mere match box, and this in spite of the fact that the truck sank in so deep that it plowed a regular ditch as it went along.

As I am a natural-born salesman and quick to grasp every opportunity, I yelled a little sales talk after Mr. Johnson. "It's all right!" I hollered. "I'm doing this on purpose to show you that the Earthworm can go through any swamp you got!" But I doubt if he heard me; the roar of the tractor motor was too loud. And a moment later the tractor, the truck and Mr. Johnson had disappeared in the canebrake.

"I was afraid he might turn out this way—all those cheap tubes and wirings."

RIVETS

RUSH HOUR.

"Arthur, you rascal! . . . You didn't tell me you were bringing a friend home to dinner!"

"He's just a big, clumsy, good-natured country boy. That thing behind the barn is an oil well."

"I never saw a man who was so fussy about his eggs!"

"Dineen covered the fights for his paper before they made him drama critic, you know."

FAMOUS LAST WORDS

"I'm sick and tired of working in an office all day. I'm going to quit work and get married."

While I was considering what to do next, a nice-looking man in a corduroy suit came over to me from one of the groups of bystanders. "This is only an arm of the Great Gumbo Swamp," he said. "If that tractor doesn't mire down, and if it goes straight, it will come out on the levee on the other side, about a mile from here."

"An Earthworm tractor never mires down," I said. "And as long as there is nobody there to pull on the handlebars, it can't help going straight."

"All right," said the man, "if you want to hop in my buggy, I'll drive you back to town and out the levee so we can meet it when it gets there."

"Fine!" I said. "Let's go." I have always been noted for my quick decisions, being similar to Napoleon in this particular. I at once climbed in the buggy with the man in the corduroy suit, and he drove the horse as fast as possible into town and then out the levee, with all the sight-seers plowing along behind, both on foot and in buggies.

When we reached the place where the tractor ought to come out, we stopped and listened. Far out in the swamp we could hear the roar of the tractor motor. It got gradually louder and louder. We waited. It was still raining hard. Suddenly there was a shout from the crowd. The tractor came nosing out of the canebrake, and a moment later it had reached the bottom of the levee, with the big truck and Mr. Johnson dragging along behind. As the tractor was in low gear, I had no trouble in jumping aboard and stopping it; and it is just as well I was there to do this. If I had not stopped it, it would have shot right on over the levee and into the Mississippi River, probably drowning poor Mr. Johnson.

As it was, Mr. Johnson was as wet as a sponge, on account of the heavy rain, and because he had been too cheap to get himself a truck with a cab on it. But he was a long way from being drowned. In fact, he seemed very lively; and as I got down from the tractor he jumped out of the truck and came running at me, waving his arms around, and shouting and yelling, and with a very dirty look on his face. What he had to say to me would fill a small book; in fact, he said so much that I'm afraid I will have to put off telling you about it until my report tomorrow.

It is now midnight and I am very tired, so I will merely inclose my expense account for the day and wish you a pleasant good night. Kindly send check to cover expenses as soon as possible. As you will see, my $100 advance is already gone, and I have had to pay money out of my own pocket.

Cordially yours,

ALEXANDER BOTTS.

EXPENSE ACCOUNT

Railroad fare (Memphis to Cyprus City)	$ 6.10
Pullman ticket	3.20
Gas and oil for tractor	8.50
Labor (putting on cleats, and so on)	9.00
36 doz. eggs @ 50c per doz.	18.00
NOTE: It seems the crates we landed on when we dropped off the freight platform were full of eggs.	
1 Plate-glass window	80.00
NOTE: I forgot to say in my report that in the confusion following the break of the fire plug I accidentally sideswiped a drug store with the tractor.	
Radiator for truck, and labor to install	46.75
Cleaning hat and pressing trousers	3.50
Total	$175.05

NOTE: I will list the hotel bill, the bill for the fire plug and other expenses when I pay them.

FARMERS' FRIEND TRACTOR COMPANY
SALESMAN'S DAILY REPORT

Date: March 18, 1920.

Written from: Delta Hotel, Cyprus City, Miss.

Written by: Alexander Botts.

I will take up the report of my activities at the point where I stopped yesterday when Mr. Johnson had just gotten out of the truck and was coming in my direction. As I stated, he had a good deal to say. Instead of being grateful to me for having given him such a splendid demonstration of the ability of the Earthworm tractor to go through a swamp, and instead of thanking me for saving his life by stopping him just as he was about to shoot over the levee into the Mississippi River, he began using very abusive language, which I will not repeat, except to say that he told me he would not buy my tractor, and that he never wanted to see me or my damn machinery again. He also said he was going to slam me down in the mud and jump on my face, and it took six of the bystanders to hold him and prevent him from doing this. And, although there were six of them, they had a lot of trouble holding him, owing to the fact that he was so wet and slippery from the rain.

As I am a natural-born salesman I saw right away that this was not an auspicious time to give Mr. Johnson any sales talk about tractors. I decided to wait until later, and I walked back to the tractor in a dignified manner, looking back over my shoulder, however, to make sure Mr. Johnson was not getting away from the guys that were holding him.

After they had led Mr. Johnson back to town I made up my mind to be a good sport, and I hauled his truck into town and left it at the garage to be repaired. The rest of the day I spent settling up various expense items—which appeared on my yesterday's expense account—and in writing up my report. When I finally went to bed at midnight, it was with a glow of pride that I thought of the splendid work I had done on the first day of my employment with the great Farmers' Friend Tractor Company, Makers of Earthworm Tractors. Although I had not as yet made any sales, I could congratulate myself on having put on the best tractor demonstration ever seen in Cyprus City, Mississippi.

This morning, after breakfast, I had a visit from the nice-looking man in the corduroy suit who gave me the buggy ride yesterday.

"I am a lumber operator," he said, "and I have a lot of cyprus back in the swamps that I have been wanting to get out. I haven't been able to move it because the ground has been so soft. However, since I saw your tractor drag that big heavy truck through the swamp yesterday, I know that it is just what I want. I understand the price is $6000, and if you will let me have the machine right away I will take you over to the bank and give you a certified check for that amount."

"Well," I said, "I was supposed to sell this machine to Mr. Johnson, but as he has had a chance at it and hasn't taken it, I suppose I might as well let you have it."

"I don't see why you gave him first chance," said the man in the corduroy suit. "When your other salesman, Mr. Healy, was down here, I gave him more encouragement than anybody else he talked to. And he said he would ship a tractor down here and put on a demonstration for me."

"What is your name," I asked.

"William Jackson," he said.

As I have a quick mind I saw at once what had happened. This was the guy I had been supposed to give the demonstration for in the first place, but I had very naturally confused his name with that of Mr. Johnson. There ought to be a law against two men with similar names being in the same business in the same town.

However, it had come out all right. And as I am a natural-born salesman, I decided that the thing to do was to take Mr. Jackson over to the bank right away—which I did. And now the tractor is his.

I inclose the certified check. And I have decided to remain in town several days more on the chance of selling some more machines.

Cordially yours,

Alexander Botts.

TELEGRAM

EARTHWORM CITY ILL 1015A MAR 19 1920
ALEXANDER BOTTS
DELTA HOTEL
CYPRUS CITY MISS

YOUR FIRST REPORT AND EXPENSE ACCOUNT RECEIVED STOP YOU ARE FIRED STOP WILL DISCUSS THAT EXPENSE ACCOUNT BY LETTER STOP IF YOU SO MUCH AS TOUCH THAT TRACTOR AGAIN WE WILL PROSECUTE YOU TO THE FULLEST EXTENT OF THE LAW

FARMERS FRIEND TRACTOR COMPANY
GILBERT HENDERSON SALES MANAGER

NIGHT LETTER

CYPRUS CITY MISS 510P MAR 19 1920
FARMERS FRIEND TRACTOR CO
EARTHWORM CITY ILL

YOUR TELEGRAM HERE STOP WAIT TILL YOU GET MY SECOND REPORT STOP AND THAT IS NOT ALL STOP THE WHOLE TOWN IS TALKING ABOUT MY WONDERFUL TRACTOR DEMONSTRATION STOP JOHNSON HAS COME AROUND AND ORDERED TWO TRACTORS STOP THE LEVEE CONSTRUCTION COMPANY OF THIS PLACE HAS ORDERED ONE STOP NEXT WEEK IS TO BE QUOTE USE MORE TRACTORS WEEK UNQUOTE IN CYPRUS CITY STOP MASS MEETING MONDAY TO DECIDE HOW MANY EARTHWORMS THE CITY WILL BUY FOR GRADING ROADS STOP LUMBERMENS MASS MEETING TUESDAY AT WHICH I WILL URGE THEM TO BUY TRACTORS AND JACKSON AND JOHNSON WILL BACK ME UP STOP WEDNESDAY THURSDAY FRIDAY AND SATURDAY RESERVED FOR WRITING UP ORDERS FROM LUMBERMEN CONTRACTORS AND OTHERS STOP TELL YOUR CHIEF ENGINEER TO GET READY TO INCREASE PRODUCTION STOP YOU BETTER RECONSIDER YOUR WIRE OF THIS MORNING

ALEXANDER BOTTS

TELEGRAM

EARTHWORM CITY ILL 945A MAR 20 1920
ALEXANDER BOTTS
DELTA HOTEL
CYPRUS CITY MISS

OUR WIRE OF YESTERDAY STANDS STOP YOUR JOB AS SERVICE MECHANIC WITH THIS COMPANY IS GONE FOREVER STOP WE ARE PUTTING YOU ON PAY ROLL AS SALESMAN STOP TWO HUNDRED PER MONTH PLUS EXPENSES PLUS FIVE PER CENT COMMISSION ON ALL SALES

FARMERS FRIEND TRACTOR COMPANY
GILBERT HENDERSON SALES MANAGER

The Cynic's Dictionary

- Reticence: Knowing what you're talking about, but keeping your mouth shut.
- Proposal: A girl listening faster than a man can talk.
- Nostalgia: A long, lingering regret that things were never what they used to be.
- Wife: An ingenious device for detecting lies.
- Advice: The approval sought for doing something one has decided to do.

—LESTER V. BERREY.

YOUR WIFE IS LIKE THAT

By COREY FORD

§ *Any man who recognizes a familiar situation here should be sued for divorce; any man who sees truth in the title may be sued for libel; any man who agrees with the author will be wise to keep his silence. Ladies may complain, if they wish, to the editor.*

JANUARY 12, 1952

FELLOW on the train last night was saying that his wife keeps string. "I'll bet my wife has over a hundred miles of string," this fellow said. "I'll bet she never threw away a piece of string in her life. She saves little pieces and ties them together. Every time she opens a package, she'll spend an hour undoing each knot, and then she'll wind the string around and around her fingers into a neat ball, and tuck the loose end inside the loop, and put it away in a bureau drawer to keep. And when I ask her why she keeps it, she says you never can tell when you'll need a piece of string."

"A lot of women are like that," a fellow across the aisle said. "My wife keeps boxes. Candy boxes, jewelry boxes, hatboxes, cigar boxes—all kinds of boxes. She even keeps big boxes to keep the little boxes in. She says she can't bear to get rid of a perfectly good box, because you never know when you might want a box."

"My wife keeps the paper that things are wrapped up in," said the conductor, a fellow named Smeed or Sneed. "She takes it off very carefully so she won't tear it, and flattens it to smooth out the wrinkles, and folds it once lengthwise and once across, and puts it where she'll know where it is." He picked up a pin from the aisle, and stuck it absently in his lapel. "She says you never can tell when you'll have to wrap up something else."

"Tell me, Sneem," I asked him, "why are you sticking that pin in your lapel?"

"You never can tell when you'll need a pin," said Smee.

The trouble with all these fellows, I told them frankly, is that they are married to thing-keepers. Every woman is a thing-keeper at heart. Men are thing-keepers, too, but they keep only sensible things like last year's license plates, or burned-out fuses, or the hands of an old clock, or the key that used to fit the garage door before the lock was changed. The difference is that men keep things in their pockets, whereas women keep things in the top of the closet. Statistics reveal that if all the things a woman keeps in a closet were taken out one by one, and placed in the center of the floor, there'd be enough room in the closet for all the other things she'd like to keep if she had any place to put them.

As far as I can tell, the reason women keep things is that they hate to throw them away. My wife has a collection of things she keeps in the icebox, for instance, which is the envy of thing-collectors everywhere. The last time I looked, there was a plate with seven string beans on it, one spoonful of mashed potato wrapped up in waxed paper, the salad I didn't eat the other night, and some giblet gravy left over from two weeks ago Sunday. She also has a pretty good collection of things she keeps in the medicine cabinet, consisting of several empty tubes (we might want to renew them sometime), a jar without a label (isn't that the poison-ivy ointment that Doctor Gurry gave you last summer?), a box containing some white pills (they ought to be for something), and an assortment of small bottles with brown stuff caked in the bottom. On the other hand, she can never understand the things I keep, such as my fishing hat.

"I can't understand why you keep that filthy hat, George. It's a disgrace, the lining's gone, and there's a hole in the brim, and the band is all frayed where you've stuck trout flies in it, and it smells of fish."

"I keep the fish in my hat," I told her.

"And this old pair of boots with the soles gone, and this checkered shirt you've had for a thousand years, and all these pipes with the stems broken, they just clutter up the attic, George, and besides I need the space, the new washing machine came today."

"Are you going to keep the washing machine in the attic?"

"I'm saving the crate," my wife explained, "in case I ever have to send it back."

I have just taken a complete inventory of our house from top to bottom, which is the only way I can get into it these days, and I have made a list of the things that people keep. They may be grouped roughly as follows:

1. *Things that go on things,* like the tops of jelly glasses, covers of peanut-butter jars, caps of bottles, lids of pots, and saucers to put upside down over other saucers with things in them.

2. *Things that come off things,* such as buttons, buckles, suitcase straps, hinges, a bolt from Junior's bicycle, the nozzle of the garden hose, some screws that fell out of the vacuum cleaner, dear, and this nut I found lying under the car when I tried to start it this morning.

3. *Things that other things came in,* such as paper bags, egg cartons, wicker baskets, round tin boxes that contained preserved fruits—no real thing-keeper can ever resist a round tin box—and any kind of empty jar at all.

4. *Things that seem a shame to throw away,* such as a deck of playing cards with only three or four missing, the top of a pair of silk pajamas that could be used for cleaning rags or something, this vest that's still as good as ever even if the suit is all gone, and a left-hand fur mitten if we could ever find the right-hand one.

5. *Things in the cellar,* such as between thirty and forty flowerpots which I knock over every time I go downstairs, the handle of an ice-cream freezer, a stack of tomato flats from last spring with the dirt still in them, and several empty barrels in case we ever have to move again.

6. *Things to keep things from going in and out,* such as old vacuum-bottle corks to plug up mouse holes, some short pieces of felt weather stripping, and a triangular section of wire mesh left over from the new porch screens which might come in handy to patch them sometime if they ever wear out.

7. *Things that have a certain sentimental value*, like the snapshots of that summer in the Adirondacks, wedding announcements, high-school diplomas, that derby hat you wore in college, and all last year's Christmas cards.

8. *Things that are too nice to use*, such as the crocheted bedspread that Great-Aunt Effie made with her own two hands, that set of hand-painted demi-tasse cups that were a wedding present from the Alvords, and a bottle of Napoleon brandy we've been saving for ten years for some special occasion.

Thing-keepers have their own devices for storing the things they keep. The system of classification employed by wives in arranging the contents of shelves and bureau drawers has been baffling their husbands for years, and there is no sense in my trying to explain it here. When a man misses something, his wife may ask him, "Where did you lose it?" But when a woman misses something, her husband asks her, "Where did you put it?" (If he's smart, that is.) I have been looking into the matter very carefully, and I have yet to discover a woman who doesn't know right where everything is, if she could only find it.

Take the keys to the car. (Only be sure to bring them back, because I might have to leave in a hurry if my wife reads this article.) A man keeps the car keys in the pocket of his pants where he can always find them, provided he is wearing the same pair of pants. A woman, on the other hand, puts them where she knows right where they are. "They're in the upper left-hand drawer of my dresser," she tells her husband, just as he is rushing to make the 8:19, "under my sewing things."

The husband climbs out of the car, dashes upstairs and paws hastily through a tangle of stockings, brassières, gloves, empty perfume bottles (women always keep empty perfume bottles), several yards of ribbon (they also keep ribbon), evening slippers, hairnets and unpaid bills. Next he goes through the contents of the upper right-hand drawer. He then goes in rapid succession through the lower left-hand drawer, the lower right-hand drawer, the cedar chest and his wife's pocketbook.

As a last resort, he dumps all the contents of the bureau onto the bed, sorts them over carefully one by one, and finally staggers back downstairs and asks his wife, "Where did you say you put them, dear?" Whereupon his wife goes upstairs, reaches into the upper left-hand drawer under her sewing things and hands him the car keys. This is why so many husbands have that resigned look.

When it comes to putting things away in closets, women follow a plan which is a cross between a squirrel storing nuts for the winter, the binomial theorem, a street map of Boston and canasta. Objects which are used only once a year, such as Christmas-tree ornaments, are kept on the bottom shelf, right in front; whereas an item that is used every day, like the vacuum cleaner, is invariably located at the rear of the top shelf behind some hat boxes, where the wife can reach it only by means of a tall stepladder surmounted by her husband. All woolen articles are wrapped up carefully in newspapers, on which are written abbreviations like "Thwg." or "Fkl., 9/17/51." A woman can always solve the meaning of these code words by poking a hole in the paper and seeing what's inside.

The favorite storage place for a woman's things is her husband's closet. The reason for this, according to his wife, is that she never has enough closet space. My own house is practically one big closet, with a small corridor down the center through which I can make my way with the aid of a pocket flashlight, but still my wife complains that she hasn't any place to keep anything. As a result, the top of my closet contains a complete collection of my wife's wardrobe, skillfully arranged with the larger items balanced on top of the smaller items, so that whenever the closet door is opened the entire contents cascade out onto the floor, where they may be picked up readily as soon as I regain consciousness.

It is in the kitchen, however, that the art of thing-keeping reaches its height. We got to talking about it last night on the train, and the conductor, Sneep, said that last year his wife went to visit his mother-in-law for a few days, and he decided to do his own cooking while she was gone. "She told me I could find everything I needed in the kitchen," he remarked with a bitter smile. That night, when he started dinner, he reached for the tin marked "Salt," and discovered it was full of sugar. The "Sugar" tin contained coffee, and the "Coffee" tin had eggs in it. Moreover, the flour bin held potatoes, the potato bin was full of floor wax, and the bread box was crammed to the lid with old recipes. After several hours, he said, he put on his hat and went out to a restaurant and had dinner, and when he came home he rolled up his sleeves and spent the rest of the evening rearranging the kitchen. He put the sugar in the tin marked "Sugar." He put coffee in "Coffee." He filled the potato bin with potatoes and the flour bin with flour. He even took the pans off the stove and hung them up on hooks where they belonged, and arranged the icebox. Well, it seems his wife came home a couple of days later, and she took one look around the kitchen and smiled patiently.

"You men are all alike," she sighed. "Now it'll take me a week to get this mess straightened out again."

We all agree that men are not like that, of course. Their method of storing things is a model of precision. Everything is put right in its place, and there is never any problem of finding anything. For example, I have my own system, which

---

Editors' Note: The last page of Mr. Ford's manuscript is missing. Unfortunately, he can't remember where he put it.

The Perfect Squelch

THE cub reporter of a Midwestern daily was sweating over the annual "circus-comes-to-town" feature story. He had already turned in one version, which had been profanely rejected by the crusty city editor, a veteran of thirty years in this same newsroom.

And now, having submitted his second effort, the cub stood shivering while the city editor read it—and groaned aloud.

"Awful!" the editor rasped. "Terrible! You don't put any life or color in your writing. Where's your imagination? Take it away! Try again!"

Desperate, and embarrassed because fellow workers had been listening, the harried cub retreated to a far corner of the city room in search of inspiration. Presently, back at his desk, he was again pounding at his typewriter. Once more he handed in his copy.

The city editor read the latest effort and slammed the copy down on his desk in disgust. "Worse and worse!" he roared. "Why, this lead alone would've got a man fired in my time."

"I can't agree with you, sir," the cub said with surprising assurance.

"Oh, you can't, can't you?" the editor roared. "And may I ask what in hell makes you so sure?"

Turning, the cub pointed over to his desk, on which stood a faded bound file of many years earlier.

"Because I copied that lead, word for word, from the 1920 files," he said, "and the story has your by-line on it."

—ED HUTCHINSON.

Who Is Kilroy?

REPORT TO THE EDITORS

WHEN an Army Air Forces lieutenant entered the bedroom of a furnished house in Long Beach, California, which the Army's 6th Ferrying Group had rented for him, he saw a baby's crib. On the crib hung a hand-lettered sign which asserted: KILROY SLEPT HERE. "Well," said the lieutenant softly, "I'll be damned."

With this comment about the Army Air Forces' celebrated man of mystery, the flier was repeating himself. He had made a similar comment after landing in Accra, Africa, after hopping the Atlantic from Natal, and again at Karachi, India, and still again when he arrived in China on his first flight over the Hump from the Mohanbari airfield in Assam.

In those faraway places messages from Kilroy had greeted him, not on a baby's crib but from the walls of rooms and the doors of hangars and from all manner of other strange places where a communication could be written or hung. In Australia, New Guinea, the Philippines, on islands all over the Pacific, he had read the record of the man who had been everywhere and, apparently, invariably been there first. Wherever he was, Kilroy had been there and left his mark behind: KILROY WAS HERE, or KILROY PASSED THROUGH, or YOU'RE IN THE FOOTSTEPS OF KILROY.

The lieutenant might have thought it was a gag aimed at him personally, if his fellow pilots—hundreds of them—weren't reporting that they were finding cryptic taunts from Kilroy all over the world. Everywhere that great traveler was kidding the ferry pilots about their lateness in getting around, needling the lads who circle the globe as nonchalantly as a taxi driver cruises around the block.

The Pilots Resent It, But What's the Use?

At last the pilots began to fight back against this everlasting insult to their globe-trotting reputation. On the wall of a room on the airfield of Canton Island, far out in the Pacific, broke out one day a ferry pilot's triumphant entry, I WAS HERE BEFORE KILROY! But the triumph was short-lived. Soon a notation appeared underneath: LIKE HELL YOU WERE. I WAS HERE WHEN THIS WAS ONLY A GLEAM IN THE C.O.'S EYE. KILROY.

On Kwajalein Atoll in the Marshall Islands other pilots tried to fight back, and they, too, failed. On Kwajalein there was a large sign that read: NO GRASS ATOLL, NO TREES ATOLL, NO WATER ATOLL, NO WOMEN ATOLL, NO LIQUOR ATOLL, NO FUN ATOLL.

At the bottom of the sign, somebody presently added the proud legend, AND NO KILROY ATOLL! Then underneath that there mysteriously appeared, I JUST DIDN'T PAUSE ATOLL. KILROY.

The war is over now, but the pilots still have a little man-hunting to do. They want to find out who the legendary wonder man of the Air Forces is, what his rank is, and to what outfit he is attached.

The search has been going on throughout the war without the slightest scrap of success. One of the first questions pilots asked the Wac rescued from the valley of Shangri-La in New Guinea was, "Any sign of Kilroy in there?" When Diebolds, the most famous jungle man of the Search and Rescue Group of the Air Force, reached Dibrugarh, India, as the only man who ever got out of the White Lolo country alive, he reported sadly, "No trace of Kilroy up there."

But the search goes stubbornly on. And as the pilots comb the skyways and byways of the world they leave messages for one another regarding the object of their concern. Written on anything that comes to hand, these messages aren't always decorative. So, on the door of a building at the John Rogers Field in the Hawaiian Islands, there is affixed a slotted box, a pad of notepaper and a pencil. On a bulletin board beside the box is lettered: KILROY HAS BEEN HERE. DON'T COMMENT ON THE WALLS. WRITE WHAT YOU HAVE TO SAY ON THE TAB AND DROP IT IN THE BOX.

—WILLIAM F. FRENCH.

A Child's Garden of Curses;

or, The Bitter Tea of Mr. P.

IF YOU can spare the gasoline to drive sixty miles into the backwoods of Eastern Pennsylvania, crouch down in a bed of poison ivy, and peer through the sumacs, you will be rewarded by an interesting sight. What you will see is a middle-aged city dweller, as lean and bronzed as a shad's belly (I keep a shad's belly hanging up in the barn for purposes of comparison), gnawing his fingernails and wondering how to abandon a farm. Outside of burning down the buildings, I have tried every known method to dispose of it. I have raffled it off, let the taxes lapse, staked it on the turn of a card, and had it condemned by the board of health. I have cut it up into building lots which proved unsalable, turned it over to picnic parties who promptly turned it back. I have sidled up to strangers and whispered hoarsely, "Psst, brother, want to buy a hot farm?" only to have them call a policeman. One rainy day, in desperation, I even tried desertion. Lowering a dory, I shouted, "Stern all for your lives!" and began sculling away rapidly. Unfortunately, I had forgotten to remove the flowers that grew in the boat, and nightfall found me still on the lawn with a backache and a fearful head cold.

I began my career as a country squire with nothing but a high heart, a flask of citronella, and a fork for toasting marshmallows in case supplies ran low. In a scant ten years I have acquired a superb library of mortgages, mostly first editions, and the finest case of sacroiliac known to science. In that period I made several important discoveries. The first was that there are no chiggers in an air-cooled movie and that a corner delicatessen at dusk is more exciting than any rainbow. On a fine night, no matter how fragrant the scent of the lilacs, I can smell the sharp pungency of a hot corned-beef sandwich all the way from New York. I also learned that to lock horns with Nature, the only equipment you really need is the constitution of Paul Bunyan and the basic training of a commando. Most of the handbooks on country living are written by flabby men at the Waldorf-Astoria, who lie in bed and dictate them to secretaries. The greatest naturalist I know lives in a penthouse overlooking Central Park. He hasn't raised his window shades in fifteen years.

Actually I never would have found myself in the middle of eighty-three unimproved acres had I been a bit less courteous. One day back in 1932, I was riding a crosstown trolley in Manhattan when I noticed a little old lady swaying before me, arms laden with bundles. Though almost thirty, she was very well preserved; her hair was ash-blond, her carmine lips wore a mocking pout, and there was such helpless innocence in her eyes that I sprang to her rescue. Dislodging the passenger next to me, I offered her the seat and we fell into conversation. It soon transpired that we had both been reared in the country and shared a mutual love for wildflowers and jam. At the next stop, I persuaded her to accompany me to a wildflower-and-jam store where we could continue our chat. It was only after our fifth glass of jam that my new friend confided her desperate plight. Her aged parents were about to be evicted from their farm unless she could raise five hundred dollars immediately. Through sheer coincidence, I happened to have drawn that amount from the bank to buy my wife a fur coat. Knowing she would have done likewise, I pressed it on the fair stranger and signed some sort of document, the exact nature of which escaped me. After a final round of jam, she presented me with her card and left, vowing eternal gratitude. On examining it, I noticed a curious inscription in fine print. It read, Licensed Real-Estate Agent.

I still have the card in my upper bureau drawer. Right next to it, in a holster, is a .38 I'm holding in escrow for the lady the next time we meet. And we will—don't you worry. I've got plenty of patience. That's one thing you develop in the country.

—S. J. PERELMAN.

WHY PAY FOR ADVICE?

By H. ALLEN SMITH

§ One thing doctors and plumbers have in common—when people meet them socially they always try to sponge a free diagnosis of an aching back or a leaky faucet. This naturally irritates the doctors and plumbers—it makes them refrain from sponging opinions off lawyers and dentists.

JANUARY 10, 1953

THERE were about thirty guests at the Sunday-afternoon cocktail party, and as the host I was under instruction to circulate, to keep moving from cluster to cluster, to make certain that no one was suffering for want of sustenance. I was performing my assignment to the best of my ability and trying, at the same time, to keep an eye on Dr. Ferdinand Wake. He's one of the best doctors in our area and I wanted to draw him aside and ask him something. Nothing real important. Just that ache in my left shoulder. Normally it didn't bother me, except when my arm was elevated at a certain angle. It wasn't really worth going to a doctor about. I figured Doctor Wake would be able to tell me in one sentence whether it was neuralgia or bursitis or just a strained muscle. A question that could be answered in one second; it would be ridiculous to go all the way down to the village and sit in a doctor's anteroom for thirty minutes just to get that small opinion.

I saw him once, standing off in a corner with Mrs. Clackett, and she was bending his ear assiduously while he was staring vacantly into his glass. I noticed that at one point she stepped back and used her index finger to describe a small circle on her own body just above the hip bone. And at that moment Rube Anders, the lawyer, called out across the room to Doctor Wake, and the doctor moved briskly over to the group where Anders was standing.

A few minutes later the doctor came bustling up to me. He glanced at his watch and said he had an important call to make at the hospital, and before I could say a word about my shoulder, he was gone.

Five minutes later, Bob Wingate, the architect, took his departure. Three minutes after that, lawyer Rube Anders left.

I didn't think much about it at the time; there are always people who drop in at cocktail parties for courtesy's sake and then go on to other appointments. The rest of the crowd had settled down to the droning buzz that is characteristic of all such functions, and as the clock moved along, that buzz grew, by slow degrees, louder and louder. Finally I got a signal from the girl who was working in the kitchen. I had misjudged on gin.

I hurried out and got into the car and

drove downtown to Hobe Renner's tavern. The moment I walked through the tavern door I saw them—Doctor Wake, Bob Wingate and Rube Anders, sitting at a table in the back corner of the room.

"What's the matter?" I asked. "Afraid you'll get poisoned up at my place?"

They were a little sheepish at first, and then Bob Wingate spoke up. "I'm sorry," he said, "but I couldn't take it any more. That dame who lives down the road from you was trying to drag me away from the party. Wanted me to run over to her house and look at her attic—tell her what I thought about partitioning off one end of it for a guest room. And then your wife—— No, I'd better not say it."

Rube Anders stared at the architect for a moment, then turned to me. "Sit down a minute," he said, and then to Wingate, "Go ahead and tell him. We've got to explain why we ran out on him."

"Your wife," said Wingate, "was trying to pull me away from the attic woman. Your wife wanted me to tell her the correct position for a picture window there in your living room."

Dr. Ferdinand Wake cleared his throat. "I don't mind telling you," he said, "that I hate cocktail parties. I never stay more than ten or fifteen minutes, and even then I always get stuck. That Clackett woman was trying to get a complete diagnosis of a pain that comes and goes in her side. And that writer friend of yours, Mabry, was pestering me about his cousin's sciatica. He stood there with a straight face and told me that his cousin had sciatica so bad that he couldn't sleep nights, and what would I recommend to ease it. Now tell me the truth. Does Mabry have sciatica?"

"Yes," I said. "I don't understand why he'd tell you it was his cousin."

"It's almost always somebody's cousin," said Rube Anders, "except in the case of your neighbor Forwood. He dragged me clear out to the front stoop to ask me if servants can be used as witnesses to a will. He said he was just curious about it; that his sister-in-law was involved in a will contest in New York."

"That's funny," I said. "I know Forwood pretty well. I never heard that he had a sister-in-law."

"Of course he doesn't have a sister-in-law," said Anders.

Doctor Wake had been sitting quietly, nursing his drink. Now he spoke again. "I've been thinking," he said, "that we professional men ought to have more courage. Like Doctor Crothers. There's a man I admire. For years he's been going to dinner regularly at Sam Miller's house over back of McLain Street. You know Sam Miller—I imagine he's got more money than anybody else around here. He has three grown children living on the place and half a dozen grandchildren. Doctor Crothers goes to dinner there every other Saturday night. And one by one, every member of that family, at some point during the evening, starts talking symptoms and wheedling advice out of Crothers. He got fed up with it. A couple of months ago he arrived as usual at Miller's house, but this time he walked in with his bag in his hand. He called the whole family together. 'Now,' he says, 'everybody line up.' Eleven Millers lined up in front of him and he went down the line, saying, 'Now, what's wrong with you?' He insisted that they recite all their ailments, and he advised and prescribed, and then, when it was over, he says, 'Examination's over. Let's not hear any more about aches and pains for the rest of the evening.' It was one of the most sensible things a doctor ever did."

"Do you mean," I put in, "that all three of you are subjected to this sort of thing whenever you go out socially?"

"Always," said Rube Anders.

"And forever," said Wingate.

"I can't go to a party," said Anders, "or even to someone's house for a quiet dinner, without somebody asking me for a legal opinion of one kind or another. Let me tell you a little story."

"Go ahead," I said, pulling out the scratch pad I usually carry in my coat pocket. "I think this whole thing is outrageous. I think I'll try to write something about it—maybe put all these people to shame."

Anders said he was sitting on the terrace over at the country club one afternoon when Jamie Bascom sat down beside him. Jamie's got one of the big automobile agencies up here. Jamie started telling Rube Anders about a snarl he was in over a lease on the building where he runs his business. He wanted to know, in a casual sort of way, what he ought to do. Rube Anders told him what he thought he ought to do. A few weeks later the two men met on the street.

"Anders," said Jamie Bascom, with more than a touch of asperity, "I just want you to know that I did what you told me to do about that lease, and everything turned out wrong. You couldn't have suggested a worse course."

"Well, Jamie," said Anders, "the advice I gave you was worth exactly what you paid for it."

Both Doctor Wake and Bob Wingate roared with laughter, and I made a note about the Jamie Bascom matter.

"I can beat that one," said Wingate. "There's a Mrs. Coningsby lives on an estate up near Katonah. She's a great bridge player and one day she drew what she considered to be a remarkable bridge hand. She thought she played it perfectly, but she wasn't sure. So she sat down and wrote a letter to Fenwick, the big bridge expert in New York. She described the hand and told how she had played it, and asked him if she had played it correctly—if he could detect any flaw in her strategy. A few days later she got a letter back from him. He said it was truly a remarkable hand and that she had played it exactly right; he couldn't improve on what she had done with it. And he enclosed a bill for a hundred dollars."

"Good for him!" said Doctor Wake.

"Well, sir," Wingate continued, "she was pretty indignant about it. She decided she simply would refuse to pay it. She'd let him sue her before she'd pay it. But she was quite disturbed about it. A week or so later she got on an afternoon train for New York and found herself sitting alongside Ev Greer. You know Ev Greer—big New York lawyer, has a place at Katonah. Well, Mrs. Coningsby knew Ev Greer and they talked a while about the parkway extension, and then she told him about that bill she got from Fenwick. She said she thought it was highway robbery. After all, he hadn't given her any advice; he only told her that she had played the hand correctly. She wanted to know what Ev Greer thought of such an outrage. Ev said, 'You knew he was an expert. You knew that he makes his living as a bridge expert. I don't see that you've got an out. I think you'd better pay him.' And the following day she got a bill for a hundred dollars from Ev Greer."

Doctor Wake laughed so hard at this one that I thought he was going to have a stroke. When he finally regained his composure, he addressed himself to me.

"You can't appreciate," he said, "how rough it can really be on doctors. Dentists too. Did you ever have a dentist at a party at your house? Well, invite one someday. Keep an eye on him. I'll make you a bet that before the party's over someone will get him aside, open his mouth wide and start pointing to teeth."

"It's brutal," said Rube Anders. "The whole world is populated by brain pickers."

"And you," said Doctor Wake, leveling a finger at me, "are a professional brain picker. What are you doing now? You're picking our brains. You go around picking everybody's brains. So don't pretend you're sympathetic."

I hadn't thought of it that way, but it was true. I remembered several occasions when I had asked both Doctor Wake and Rube Anders for technical information on some subject I was writing about. I was thinking about it, a little sheepishly, when Doctor Wake stood up and walked from the table to the bar.

"Good Lord," I said, "he's not sore at me, is he?"

"Of course not," said Rube Anders, glancing toward the doctor. "He's just gone over there to talk to Henry Caffey."

"Who's Henry Caffey?"

"Plumber."

"Well," I said, "I've got to get on my way." I went to the bar to ask Hobe Renner if he could let me take two or three bottles of gin. Hobe said he couldn't sell them to me, but he'd make me a present of them if my birthday was anywhere near. He was putting them in a bag when I overheard part of the conversation down the bar. Henry Caffey was talking to Doctor Wake.

"Tell you, doc," he said, "it's usually the little wire that hooks onto the ball plunger. That wire gets bent and throws the plunger out of line. Just fool around with that wire —keep bending it till the plunger drops straight. Then you won't have to jiggle 'er any more."

"Fine," said Doctor Wake. "I'll try that. Much obliged to you, Henry."

I took my bag and got into the car and started home, feeling a little better about things in general.

On Speaking Russian

ENTIRELY too many Americans say, "I just can't figure out Russia," and let the matter drop right there.

That's all wrong, since there's not an American living who couldn't get along famously with the inhabitants of the land behind the Iron Curtain if only he would take the trouble to learn a little bit of the Muscovite tongue. With this in mind, I submit the following simplified Russian-English conversation guide which anyone can clip out and carry with him, in case he has to go to Russia.

RUSSIAN	ENGLISH
АНа́	Caught you, didn't I?
БАЛойеч	I find your story difficult to believe, sir (madam).
неч шас!	May I have a word with you, sir?
ЧЗАН?	Certainly. What can I do for you?
ОЖАЧ	I find that perfectly agreeable.
ОБбЧбБбЧ!	My, what a charming girl!
ЗСЯАМ, БЦБ!	I'm growing weary of your company.

—J. M. KUCERA.

TUGBOAT ANNIE QUOTES THE LAW

By NORMAN REILLY RAINE

§ Bullwinkle was infuriating; furthermore, he was not to be trusted. Their rivalry made as much trouble for him as it did for Annie. The ensuing tale proves that there's no friend like an ancient enemy.

OCTOBER 19, 1946

GIANT seas, roaring out of the night under the thrust of a heavy southeast gale, slashed with white tusks at Tatoosh Island and the grim cliffs of Cape Flattery, as the deepwater tug Narcissus, inbound from the Columbia River bar for Puget Sound and her home port of Secoma, rolled rails under as she changed course and entered the comparatively sheltered reaches of Juan de Fuca Strait. In twisted davits and splintered wood where her small boat had been carried away, in a badly dented ventilator, two smashed deadlights and the thick salt rime on her funnel and house, she showed evidence of the beating she had taken; but the extent of her punishment could still better be gauged in the weary mastiff face and eyes red-rimmed with sleeplessness of her tough seafaring master, Tugboat Annie Brennan, as she wrestled open the wheelhouse door and stepped inside, yellow oilskins gleaming, skin red and numb from the beat of wind and icy rain.

"Okay, Peter," she told the paunchy, phlegmatic, tobacco-chewing mate, "I'll take the wheel."

"Look, Annie," replied Peter, concerned, as he saw her tired face, "you ain't slept since we left Portland night afore last. Why don't ye——"

"Sleep?" said Annie, with an effort at humor. "Oh, yeah; that's what folks does when they lies down wid their eyes shut. Reminds me," she went on with the loquacity of utter weariness, "o' my Terry, God rest the old rumpot!" At thought of her defunct and rascally but lovable spouse, her grin widened. "You'd a' thunk his pa an' ma was a bear an' he was born in a cave durin' a twelve-month winter!" She shook with massive laughter. "Now don't git me started tellin' ye antidotes about Terry. Better git up forrard and see kin ye make out Waadah Island light."

"Waadah Island?" Peter gaped in bovine astonishment. "Ain't we goin' home?"

"Unh-uh! Neah Bay. I'll phone the Secoma office from there. No tellin', there might be another job fer us this end o' the sound."

Peter shook his head. "You're sure a glutton for punishment, Annie!"

But Annie, her tired eyes trying to peer ahead through the rain-lashed window, no longer was listening.

During the five-mile run east along the

strait she had to fight to keep awake, and it was with a "whoosh" of relief that she swung the big tug into the sheltered expanse of Neah Bay and made fast alongside the fish wharf. The wind still screamed through the primeval evergreens on top of the precipitous crags of the western shore; the rain still beat down, but, with daylight an hour or two away, the village tranquilly slept, with only an occasional light marking the abode of an early riser or a fretful baby. And Tugboat Annie, as she stumbled ashore and up toward the telephone in the watchman's shack at the head of the wharf, paused to look around her. How wonderful it would be, she thought, to spend every night ashore in a warm, snug bed, at her age, instead of enduring the buffetings of a seafaring life in a harsh male world. Then, her mind resting on the sturdy tug that had been her home for so many years, she gazed back to where the Narcissus' lights glowed alongside her berth, steadfast and strong, and a feeling of warm and tranquil contentment flooded her heart. She'd make the phone call to the home office; then, if there were no further orders, back to her Narcissus for a hearty meal and twelve hours of blissful oblivion in her bunk.

As she turned to continue up the wharf, however, these soothing prospects suffered a rude jolt; for even in the rain and the darkness she could make out the shape of a vessel alongside, so familiar that automatically her choler rose. No need for Annie to see her name and port of registry on her counter. It was the tug Salamander, owned and commanded by her ancient rival, Capt. Horatio Bullwinkle.

"Wonder what that bowlegged scut's doin' here?" she mumbled uneasily to herself. "Whenever he shows up, it usually means I'm only one jump ahead of a conundrum!"

She put the question to the frowsy watchman while waiting in his hut for her telephone connection to Secoma.

"Who—Bullwinkle? He drug up a coupla scows for the pulpwood company yesterday afternoon," he told her. "Why, Annie?"

"Why?" Annie snorted. "That's like axin' is there any kick in this here pneumatic bomb what everybody's talkin' about! Well, just leave him sleep till I git outta here, that's all I ax. . . . Hello"—the telephone was demanding her attention—"is this Fred?"

The voice of the dispatcher in her home office assured her that it was, and inquired, with profane emphasis, why she had not communicated sooner with the office by means of the ship-shore radiophone, with which, he ironically pointed out, she must surely by now know that the Narcissus was equipped.

"Keep yer pants on!" Annie adjured equably. "Somethin's went wrong wid one o' the widgets. Clem's been workin' on it standin' on his head, off Flattery there. He kin send, but he can't hear nothin' back. Anyways, what's all the hellabaloo about?"

"It's a steamer—the Harrowgate—Annie!" Fred told her excitedly. "She's a British ship out of Melbourne for sound ports, and she's had an engine-room breakdown offshore there, between Hoh Head and The Giants' Graveyard, and her master's radioed for a tug to stand by. So——"

"Does"—Annie groaned inwardly as a thought struck her—"does Bullwinkle know anythin' about——"

"Bullwinkle?" The dispatcher's voice took on an added tautness. "Is he there?"

"Right alongside the same dock, as peaceful as a sleepin' rattlesnake. But no, he wouldn't be snoozin' if he knowed. Well, okay, Fred! I'll sashay right back out there!" She replaced the receiver, wrong end up, then rapidly thumbed through the telephone directory. "Gotta git some fuel and stores aboard fast," she told the watchman, "an' boom outta here!"

"Vessel in distress, Annie?"

"Yeah, but don't breathe a verb to Bullwinkle. Mebbe we kin clear port afore he sees us!"

Such optimism, however, was misplaced; for by the time the Narcissus was refueled and the stores aboard, it was almost full daylight. Meanwhile, Mr. Horatio Bullwinkle, always an early riser, had come on deck seeking a whiff of weather to blow the effect of the previous convivial evening ashore from his brain. And when his bandy, powerful legs had propelled him to the rail of the Salamander for a casual glance along the wharf, his small, shoebutton black eyes glittered suddenly with a malicious interest not unmixed with humor.

"Jake!" he called softly to his fat, ill-visaged mate, who was passing along the deck below. "Jake, isn't that Annie and her Narcissus along there?"

"Why ask me?" replied Jake grumpily. "You know her as well as I do. And listen. You still owe me five beers from——"

"Yeah . . . but"—Mr. Bullwinkle's tone was pleasantly speculative—"she'd took a tow down to Portland. And now——"

"And now she's on her way home. What's so strange about that?"

"There wouldn't be, stupid," returned Mr. Bullwinkle, "except that she's takin' fresh stores aboard. Looks like she might be goin' out to sea again. I wonder why?"

"Whyn't ye go ask her?" suggested Jake, whose expression now also showed a glimmer of interest.

"I'll just do that," Mr. Bullwinkle agreed.

He clumped down the ladder and along the rainswept wharf, and a few seconds later, completely unaware that his progress had been watched with deep misgiving by Tugboat Annie from the window of her cabin, was standing beside the Narcissus, watching with acute attention a procession of fresh edibles being taken aboard.

"How come you're loadin' fresh stores?" he asked Shiftless, the Narcissus' gangling deck hand, who was assisting a crateful of vegetables over the rail.

"Because," said Shiftless with a scowl and unexpected wit, "we might get hungry along about mealtimes."

"And where," pursued Mr. Bullwinkle artlessly, "might them mealtimes occur?"

But the irascible voice of Tugboat Annie interrupted further banter. "What's that smell down there?" she demanded loudly from above. "Don't them canneries ever clean that rotten fish offa the—— Oh!" She broke off suddenly as she appeared from behind the wheelhouse and gazed into the blandly innocent countenance of Mr. Bullwinkle. Then, with specious surprise, "It's you, is it?"

"H'llo, Annie, ol' pal, ol' pal!" cried Mr. Bullwinkle, grinning up at her. "How's tricks?"

"Kin I read yer dirty mind?" asked Annie. "What do you want around here, 'sides makin' a nuisance o' yerself?"

"I'm just bein' neighborly, Annie," he informed her. "And mebbe doin' a little wonderin'."

"Such as?" prompted Annie suspiciously.

"Such as why ye're layin' stores aboard that ye could get anywheres between here and Secoma. Goin' someplace, perhaps?"

"A pusson's gotta eat, don't they? Ain't no law again it, is they?" Annie rasped, defensively indignant.

"N-no-o-o, Annie. But"—he pointed to a basket of loaves that was being handed over the rail—"where was you plannin' to guzzle them?" He gestured vaguely in the direction of the cape, added archly, "Out there, mebbe?"

"Curiosity," replied Annie heavily, her tired brain for once unequal to him, "has killed wuss than a cat!" and she cut off the interview by entering the wheelhouse and pretending to be extremely busy.

Mr. Bullwinkle remained for a further

"Say—wasn't that your boss that just drove by?"

"Will you guys stop climbing—we've reached the top."

"I'm afraid, Pamela darling, this isn't much of a honeymoon."

"Dad, were you ever in love?"

DRAWN BY BURR SHAFER

"What I want to know is am I a boy or a girl?"

"I sort of miss old Johnston's talk about yachts, girls, horses . . ."

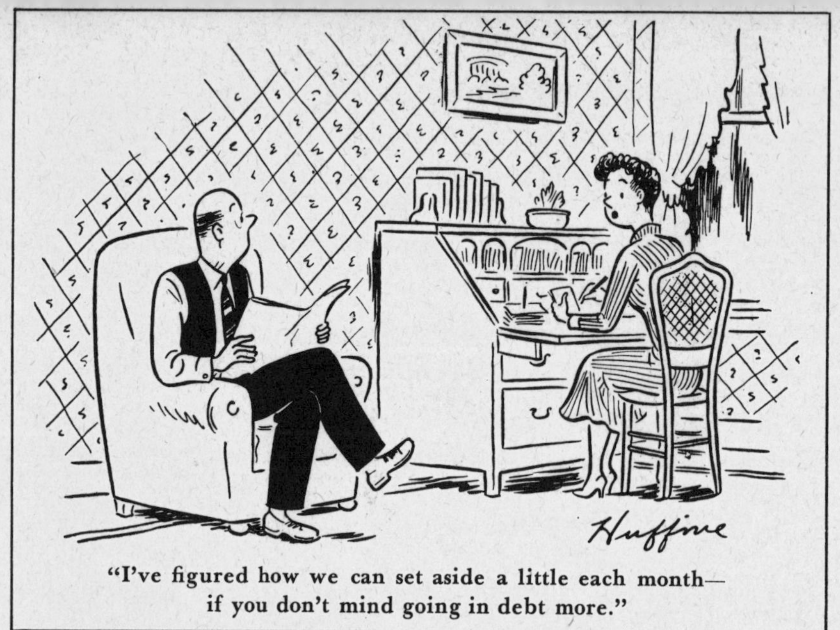

"I've figured how we can set aside a little each month—
if you don't mind going in debt more."

"The problem, as I see it, Mrs. Van Grooton, is that you've let yourself become as fat as a pig."

FAMOUS LAST WORDS

"If we drive all night tonight and tomorrow we can enjoy a full extra day at the shore."

few minutes; and Annie, from the corner of her eye, noted with growing uneasiness and a sinking heart that not only were his eyes brightly speculative but he was whistling a gay little off-key tune. And there was something in the confident set of his back when finally he returned along the wharf to the Salamander which added to her foreboding.

A half hour later the Narcissus was punching her way seaward again with Peter at the wheel, and Annie and Big Sam, the engineer, who had come up for a breather, standing on the tug's broad fantail. The rain had cleared somewhat, but ahead at the entrance to the strait was a welter of white spouting seas, while to the north of the entrance, masking Bonilla Point and the shore of Vancouver Island, was a dense and sharply defined wall of thick white fog, piled up and held there by the gale, while the prospect southward was fairly clear. But of these details Annie, for the moment, was oblivious, her gaze fixed upon the mouth of Neah Bay astern.

Suddenly she thrust out a thick, indignant finger.

"There he is, the dirty scrapegoat! I knowed he'd foller us!" she rasped, and did a commendable fandango of temper on the lifting fantail. "He's got near a knot more speed than us, and if ever he sights that steamer fust, good-by, job! . . . Sa-ay! Wait a minute!" She moved to the starboard rail and stared ahead at the wall of fog. "Maybe I got a idear!"

Hastily she waddled to the radio cabin, where Clem, the capable young operator, was working industriously amid a confusion of wires and parts.

"Got the radio phone workin' yet, Clem?" she asked as he looked up.

"Not yet, Annie. I can still send all right. But I can't receive. I guess what's wrong is——"

"Ye can send? Great!" she exclaimed. "Now listen; git on the wave length to Secoma like you'd been talkin' to our office —ye can bet Bullwinkle'll be listenin' in!— and say—now pay attention!—say: 'The steamer's forty mile nor'west o' Flattery? Okay!' Then sign off. Just that and nothin' more! Got it?"

"But, Annie, I don't understand. If I'm not talking to anybody——"

"Can't ye do what I tell ye?" Annie demanded, suddenly wrathful. "Now get talkin' and say what I telled ye, afore I tear yer scalp off an' use it fer a bow fender!"

"Okay, okay, Annie," said Clem placatingly. "I was only——"

"What a world it would be widout no men in it!" sighed Annie impatiently as she went back out on deck.

Rejoining Big Sam on the stern, and noting that the Salamander appreciably had decreased the distance between them, she briefly outlined her plan. "Instead o' goin' south where the steamer is, we're goin' to duck north into that fog bank. Bullwinkle'll foller us in"—her good humor restored at thought of fooling her rival, she tittered delightedly—"then we'll come about and head south an' leave him chasin' around in the fog like a whirlin' derby!"

There was no time to say more, for the first of the outside seas was thundering toward them. The stout tug shuddered under the vicious impact and momentarily her way was stopped. Slowly, doggedly, she threw off the tons of cascading water and her big propeller bit deep, thrusting her ahead again. Then the fog enveloped them—a thick, dank wall that cut their visibility to zero, and through which the white-lipped combers rushed at them with terrifying violence and speed.

Annie, who had returned to the wheelhouse, automatically set her hand to the whistle cord while she regaled Peter with the details of her trick on Bullwinkle.

Then, "Well, I guess I made him look silly enough be this time," Annie grinned, and thereafter neglected the fog signal while she spun the big wheel hard over.

The Narcissus came about in a smother of foam and flying spume, and headed south once more, full into the teeth of the gale.

Presently, clear of the fog bank, she was bucketing laboriously to give Flattery plenty of clearance, while Annie's eyes scanned the wild sea miles ahead and to the south. Suddenly she tensed; then hastily, almost frantically, she grabbed for her binoculars.

But Peter needed no such aids. "It's him all right, Annie," he said morosely. "Ye didn't fool him after all."

"Hold yer gawp!" Annie told him testily, while she fumblingly adjusted the lenses, but Peter and her first glimpse were correct, for far ahead and to the west and south of Cape Flattery was a wildly tossing black speck which, as the glasses assisted her vision, resolved itself into the distressingly clear image of Mr. Bullwinkle's Salamander.

"And whiles I was scullin' around in that fog, like a big conceited dope, he'd smelled a rats' nest an' was headin' south!" railed Annie in vast self-disgust. "Git below, Peter, and tell Big Sam to drive them coffee grinders o' his offa their bedplates! If Bullwinkle reaches that steamer fust——"

But the utmost engineering skill of Big Sam was unable to overcome the handicap of the Salamander's start and superior speed, and when, in late afternoon, the Harrowgate was sighted, wallowing like an ocean leviathan in the confused seas, the Salamander was already dancing, corklike, beside her.

The Harrowgate, a rusty, untidy-looking three-thousand-ton tramp, her scaly hull streaked with red lead, her dingy boot-topping hung with long sea grass, had somewhere within her unimpressive build the elements of sound design, for, although she was without headway, she bore the assaults of the seas well and buoyantly and with a certain raffish gallantry. And when Annie brought the Narcissus within hailing distance, after a bad half hour in which, momentarily, she expected to see the Salamander place a line aboard and begin to tow the prize triumphantly home, she was overjoyed to find, instead, that the redoubtable Mr. Bullwinkle, spun out to the end of a very frayed temper, was in spirited altercation with the Harrowgate's master. In fact, the latter, a portly, florid man with an apparently inexhaustible optimism and good humor, not only was refusing a line but was denying that he was in any peril whatsoever, while below him, lining the well-deck rail, were his singularly morose and dispirited-looking crew.

"But ye just got through telling me," roared Mr. Bullwinkle, with pardonable acerbity, as the Narcissus came within earshot, "that ye did send a message ashore for help!"

"Not help, chum!" the shipmaster bellowed genially back. "All I requested was for a tug to stand by! Just in case, you know! And I think it's uncommon obliging of you to do so!" Then, suddenly noticing Annie as she stood outside the Narcissus' wheelhouse lending an interested ear, he became even more jocose. "What's that," he gallantly inquired, "the Ladies' Auxiliary?"

Mr. Bullwinkle, glaring about for someone upon whom to discharge his injured feelings, skidded the Salamander down the side of a snarling comber and came as nearly alongside the Narcissus as safety would allow.

"Did ye ever see such a fool, Annie?" he yelled, conveniently ignoring his earlier duplicity. "He's blew a cylinder head and he's tryin' to fix it with a stokehold plate! And meantime the wind and current's settin' him shoreward at near three knots! And he says he don't need any help!"

"Mebbe after lookin' at that puss o' yours

he figgered there was worse things than pilin' up on the beach, ye dishonest ape!" Annie yelled back. "Ye knowed this was my job, and ye prob'ly scared him off it be axin' fer his back teeth complete wid gold fillin's!"

"No, I didn't, Annie! Honest!" protested Mr. Bullwinkle virtuously. "That dirty sculpin's a hard case! He owns the vessel and he ain't puttin' out one cent he don't have to! Hey"—his quick eye had caught a movement on the Harrowgate's deck—"there's somebody on board wants to talk to us!"

Annie looked across. Among the group of dejected-looking seamen, oilers and stokers clinging to the tramp's wildly rising and falling rail was one who, with accompanying cautious glances toward the bridge, was beckoning them to approach. Annie signaled to Peter, and he jockeyed the Narcissus a few yards closer.

The man cupped his hands to his mouth. " 'Hoy, the tug!" he called, a note of desperation in his voice, and again his eyes nervously flicked the steamer's bridge. "Take us off this bucket, will yer? Or slip forrard—watch out Captain Higgins don't see yer!—and we'll take yer line!"

"Can't do it!" Annie shouted back. "Not without your captain's say-so!"

"Well, do somethink, won't yer?" the man pleaded desperately. "We can't stand this hellhole no longer, an' he'll risk the ship an' all hands to save five quid!"

"Why, what's the matter? He said——"

"He said!" The man's voice dripped the vitriol of hatred. "She's so old the plates is hangin' together by red lead an' rust! We've had no fresh stores since we was five days out o' Melbourne; nothin' but weevily biscuit hash an' pickled beef that'd make a pig throw up!" He turned to his fellows. "Ain't that right, mates?"

There was a chorus of agreement. "Not on'y that!" said another. " 'e's logged us so many days' pay, and we've 'ad to buy so much gear from 'is slop chest—at 'is prices!—that there ain't a payday left atween us! Carn't yer 'elp us some'ow to get orf this bucket o' blood an' back ashore?"

"What can we do?" replied Annie, her big heart going out in instant response to the genuineness of the man's appeal. "He's the captain, and ye say he's the owner too! So——"

"Let the old bilge trap pile up, then!" the man replied, with the savageness of desperation. "I'd rather take me chances o' swimmin' ashore than stop aboard 'ere another night!"

"Now then, now then!" said a gruffly humorous voice from the bridge above them, and they stared hostilely up into the genial, cherubic face of Captain Higgins. "This isn't earning your pound and pint, you know!" He chuckled deeply. "Blurry lot o' scrimshankers! Get back from that rail or I'll have to log you a day's pay apiece for shirkin' your jobs!"

Silently the little group melted away and as Tugboat Annie watched them go her fatigue-lined face was grim indeed. She stuck her blowsy head inside the wheelhouse door and spoke a few terse words, and with superb seamanship Peter edged the Narcissus closer to the Salamander.

"Sa-ay, Bullwinkle!" she hailed, and in her voice there was toward him now neither bitterness nor resentment. "Did ye hear what them fellers just said?"

"I heard it!" said Mr. Bullwinkle heavily. "Looks to me he'd rather risk his crew's lives an' his own pilin' up on The Giants' Graveyard than put out the few dollars it'd cost him fer us to tow him in!" He shook his bristle head. "We'd better stick around, Annie! There's no tellin'——"

"That's what I was thinkin'!" she agreed. "Time dark falls, she's gonna be mighty close inshore if he don't git them repairs fixed up in a hurry! Look, Horatio! Whatever happens, what do ye say if me an' you smokes the hatchet and works together? Till that steamer's safe, anyways! Huh?"

"Suits me!" replied Mr. Bullwinkle huskily.

"Okay! An' no more tricks now!"

"Sa-ay!" Mr. Bullwinkle was righteously indignant. "What do ye think I am?"

Annie's eyes brightened; then, gulping, she let the opportunity pass. "That," she conceded magnanimously, "is for posteriority to decide!"

By late afternoon the Harrowgate, with her black gang working furiously below, was but two or three miles from the scattered group of jagged, surf-battered pinnacles, disastrous dead ends of many a voyage, known as The Giants' Graveyard. But the stubbornness of Captain Higgins was as unabated as his apparent good-humored optimism, and it became evident that, cupidity overcoming caution, he was willing, with two stout deep-water tugs standing by for a possible last-minute tow, to take appalling chances. And finally, unable to stand the strain as darkness closed in, Tugboat Annie bellowed up at him, her deep, hard-weather voice scarcely audible against the thunder of the seas that were breaking in murderous fury against the evil-gleaming rocks beyond the steamer.

"Listen!" she roared. "If ye'll take a line aboard now, I'll tow ye seaward for nothin'! Ye can't risk all them men——"

"Very clever, missus!" he bawled back. "And have you slap a lien on me for a salvage claim when we get into port? Thank you just the same!"

"Okay, ye horse's tail!" she boomed back. "But ye got rocks to leeward o' ye, not a quarter of a mile away, right now!"

Annie ran the Narcissus as close to the Salamander as the hissing seas would allow and again hailed Mr. Bullwinkle. "Mebbe if we bluffed that we was leavin'," she bellowed, "he'd come to his senses! Spose we run out a ways and see what happens?"

Mr. Bullwinkle made loud noises of assent, and presently the two tugs, their squat powerful hulls buried in the trough of the deep seas, threshed about and headed seaward. They had gone no more than a half mile or so, with a driving rain squall blotting out the steamer and the coast, when there came to them over the scream of the wind the frenzied hooting of the Harrowgate's whistle.

"Oh-oh!" groaned Annie. "I knowed it!"

Her big face pasty with fatigue and apprehension, she wrestled the wheel, and the Narcissus, taking a vicious beating as she came about, swung shoreward again, followed by the wildly swinging running lights of the Salamander.

When they had regained their former position, the tugs' brilliant and powerful searchlights were switched on and the Harrowgate again suddenly came into view. It was completely dark now, but in the searchlights' lurid glare Annie saw that the steamer had dropped her anchor, which, for the moment, was holding firmly on the rocky bottom. This brought her bows on to the racing seas, but her stern swung no farther than fifty yards from a maelstrom of spouting fury where the combers battered and retched over an irregular shelf of sloping rock down which the white water momentarily was sucked, baring it in all its glistening, naked menace.

Cautiously Annie allowed the Narcissus to drift down toward the steamer, keeping just enough way to be able to beat out of danger if necessary. Captain Higgins was up in the bows, his face a shining blur in the searchlight's beam. But although it was impossible to make out his expression, his voice had lost none of its jovial confidence.

"Now that I think of it," he bawled, "you'd better send a line aboard, just in case that anchor cable parts! You can hold her steady till our repairs are complete! But don't suppose, ma'am," he added humorously, "I'll pay through the nose for it!"

Annie jumped inside the wheelhouse. "Peter," she rasped, "git down on deck there! We're goin' to put a line aboard! There ain't much time! If that anchor cable ever parts——"

But even as her big, capable hands grasped the wheel, a giant comber reared its smoking crest high above the Narcissus' stern, and her sturdy frame shook and quivered in every bolt and timber as it struck—a wall of solid water that engulfed her, washed over her, then roared astern, to burst, with all its colossal might, against the steamer's flaring bows. In a welter of flying spume the Harrowgate disappeared, and when, minutes later, vision cleared, Annie, stunned and breathless, saw that, with anchor cable parted, she was drifting rapidly shoreward. A moment later she struck.

In utter defiance of safety, Annie allowed the Narcissus to drop down upon her; and presently, in the white glare of the searchlight, they saw that she hung with her stern jammed hard and fast on the broad, sloping, surf-battered ledge.

"It's gonna be a hit-an'-run affair takin' them off!" Annie grated to Peter, who had fought his way back to the wheelhouse for further instructions. "And how in the purple-starred hell——"

"They're gettin' their lifeboats swung out," Peter told her. "And if they can launch 'em, there's clear water back to us, barrin' them seas."

"Git hold o' Shif'less an' the rest o' the boys then," Annie ordered promptly, "and stand by to take 'em aboard!"

It was long after dark when the job was completed and the last of the Harrowgate's men tumbled exhausted over the Narcissus' low rail and onto her streaming deck, while the boats were made fast to long painters astern. At daybreak, although the seas were still high, most of the gale's force had spent itself; and Annie, rousing herself from druglike sleep, staggered, bleary-eyed, on deck. Shoreward, through the rain that pitted the sullen water, the land still was shrouded in early-morning gloom, but as the Narcissus pushed closer, Annie could see the black length of the Harrowgate, still afloat, still held fast by the stern to the ledge upon which she had stranded.

The fragrant odor of coffee wafted from the galley in the damp salt air, and Annie sniffed appreciatively, then turned at a hail from close aboard. It was Bullwinkle, standing outside the wheelhouse of the Salamander.

"Hi, Annie!" he called. "I've got the skipper aboard, and a few o' the men!"

"Oh, is Higgins wid you?" she hailed back, regardless of the fact that the shipmaster was standing at Bullwinkle's elbow. "I was hopin' he'd—— Well, no matter!"

"What'll I do with him?"

"Ye ain't that hard up fer ideas!" she returned.

There ensued a muttered colloquy between Higgins and Mr. Bullwinkle and the latter again addressed Annie. "He wants to come aboard you!"

"I'm all out o' clothespins fer me nose, but I guess I kin stand it!" Annie replied grudgingly. "Fetch him over!"

The Salamander's small boat was swung out, and shortly thereafter, accompanied by Mr. Bullwinkle, Captain Higgins and four of his men climbed over the Narcissus' rail.

"Good morning," said Captain Higgins, smiling affably.

"It was good till you showed up!" Annie told him bluntly. "What kind o' murders are ye plannin' today?"

"You're quite a wag, missus," he answered, his good humor apparently unimpaired; then he gestured toward the Harrowgate, now only a few hundred yards away. "Don't look too bad, does she?" he commented, and his round face suddenly was wreathed in a jolly grin. "Wouldn't be surprised if she'd float off without much trouble. I'll get some steam to the windlass forrard, and put over a kedge anchor, and away she'll come!"

Annie and Mr. Bullwinkle exchanged glances. "And what," asked Annie with heavy irony, "do we git out of it?"

"Come now!" The shipmaster was mildly reproachful. "You saved a lot of lives, didn't you? Though there's no need to tell you, I suppose, that salvage is not collectible when only lives and no property are saved."

"Only lives!" Annie said disgustedly. "Ye got a queer way o' lookin' at things, ye fat little curdudgeon!"

"Now then, missus, no need for personalities!" he expostulated mildly, then chuckled. "I will admit, however"—he fished in his pocket for his pipe and continued between puffs—"that there was a moment or two last night, before I ordered 'Abandon ship'——"

"Afore ye what?" Annie interrupted.

"I said," he repeated good-naturedly, "there was a moment or two before I ordered 'Abandon ship' when I might have wished I'd let you put a line aboard before we got in so close. However, she might have piled up anyway, and I'd ha' been that much more out of pocket. And now, if you'll allow me——" He walked to the rail and addressed his crew, who cluttered the deck below. "All right, men!" he ordered briskly. "Haul the boats alongside and we'll get back aboard!"

There was an abrupt stillness, and Annie and Bullwinkle joined him at the rail, to see a mass of sullen, pinched faces glaring up at them.

Then a lean, wide-shouldered, hard-featured Liverpool Irish stoker stepped forward. "No, sorr!" he said harshly. "We bin talkin' it over, me and me mates, and we're not goin' back on board."

"You mean," the shipmaster's voice registered gentle reproof, "you refuse?"

There was a roar of angry assent.

Looking infinitely regretful, Captain Higgins shook his head. "In that case, men," he said sorrowfully, "when we do get ashore, I shall have to charge you with desertion and mutiny, and under the rules of the British Board of Trade you all know what that means! Don't you?"

Uneasily the beaten and bedraggled crew stared at one another; then their spokesman, shaken but determined, shook his head. "I don't give a damn what it means! I'd do a ten-year stretch an' welcome before I'd set foot on that rattrap o' yours again! No," his voice rose in uncontrollable rage, "not for you and the whole blasted Admiralty, I wouldn't!" He turned to the others. "Eh, chaps?"

There was a deep, savage growl of approval.

"In that case"—and Captain Higgins turned to Annie, his round face losing nothing of its blandness—"I'll have to ask you, missus, to send a message to the authorities for help. . . . Mutiny," he again addressed his crew, but there was no mistaking now the threat beneath his smooth voice, "is a serious offense, even in American waters! And——"

"I dare say," replied Annie, whose mind, paying him bare attention, had been busy elsewhere. "Seems to me, captain, your men don't like ye, and there's somethin' "—she wagged her shaggy head—"call it woman's ignition, if ye like—that tells me I don't like ye either. Still, I wouldn't want them to cut off their nose to spite yer face. So mebbe if I was to talk to 'em——"

She was interrupted by a violent jogging of her elbow, and Mr. Bullwinkle's voice grated in her ear, "Are you nuts, Annie? C'mere," and with a quick, deft shove he propelled her away from the rail. "What's the matter wi' you?" he demanded hoarsely when they were out of earshot. "That steamer's as sweet an' easy a job o' salvage as ever I've seen, if we can keep them fellows from goin' back on board! It'll mean a hundred thousand between us, easy! And——"

"Did ye happen to take a look at them fellers' faces?" replied Annie quietly. "They been starved an' kicked around an' their pay logged by that grinnin' little squit, ever since they cleared Melbourne! And if they don't go back on board, what do they get? Their pay—what's left of it—forefooted an' five to ten years in the freezer!"

"Nobody forced 'em to ship in her!" Mr. Bullwinkle replied furiously. "And here we got a chance——"

"I don't want that kind o' chance," said Annie soberly, " 'less I can split it, tit for tat, wid them. Besides, I got a idea."

"Nuts to your idea!" said Mr. Bullwinkle rudely.

"Listen! Will you listen?"

"No!"

"I got a scheme, I tell ye."

"To hell with your schemes!" roared Mr. Bullwinkle, empurpled with disappointed fury. "Whenever you got a scheme, I come out the short end. What I want to know is: are ye goin' to string along with me an' grab that steamer for salvage?"

"No, I am not!" Annie told him. "But you promised ye'd corroborate wid me."

"That deal's all off now!" he rasped. "I don't want to associate with no lunatics!"

"Ye should ha' thought o' that afore ye was born a Bullwinkle," she told him coldly, and turning on her heel, waddled purposefully back to Captain Higgins at the rail.

"I know what you two were talking about, missus," he said roguishly before she could speak. "But no fear!" He jerked his thumb at the Harrowgate. "I'm taking repossession of her meself!"

Annie indicated the ring of sullen faces still glaring up at him. "They don't think so," she said grimly.

"They will!" he assured her with a grin. "Soon as they've had time to think what'll happen to 'em if they don't."

"It'd be cheap at double the price, ye stinkin' bilge rat!" one of the men roared.

"Mind if I talk to 'em?" said Annie, mildly now. "Mebbe they'll go back aboard for me."

"For you?" The shipmaster manifestly was astonished. "You mean you want 'em to——" He interrupted himself, shaking his head. Then, "Talk to 'em if you want to. But if they do go, don't you expect me to pay you for it!"

Disregarding him, Annie clumped down the ladder. "Come along aft," she told the Liverpool Irishman, "and fetch yer mates wid ye."

Puzzled and suspicious, the men complied, but when, after a few minutes of explanation as they grouped around her on the stern, they grasped her purpose, the hostility faded out of their hard eyes, hopelessness relaxed and there were expressions which, here and there, could almost be taken for grins.

"Now, will ye do what I ax ye?" she demanded at length; and their spokesman, after a swift glance around for approval, nodded his head.

Returning to the wheelhouse, Annie saw Bullwinkle being rowed rapidly back over the swells to the Salamander, and guessing his intention, she jingled Big Sam in the engine room. Twenty minutes later the Narcissus was rising and falling under the dangling boatfalls of the stranded steamer, while, too late, the Salamander appeared off the Harrowgate's bows and was forced to remain, impotently floating there, while the re-embarkation took place.

One of the crew members, swarming up the falls, let down a sea ladder, up which the others rapidly climbed, while Tugboat Annie, at the bottom, kept the impatient shipmaster in speciously friendly conversation until the last of his officers and crew were aboard. Then he, too, mounted triumphantly to the deck.

Allowing the Narcissus to slip astern along the steamer's hull, Annie rapidly surveyed the damage to the Harrowgate. Then in her cabin she busied herself with a long sheet of foolscap and a pen, folded the paper, stuffed it in her massive bosom, and a few minutes later was standing on the Harrowgate's after well deck, where she was met by Captain Higgins, who was emerging from the engine-room housing.

"She ain't damaged too bad," Annie began. "She——"

"I know that," Captain Higgins told her affably. "I've already been down the after-hold and along the shaft tunnel. I'll transfer some of the cargo forrard and fill the forrard tanks, and that'll lift her stern up and she'll probably float free. So you needn't," he concluded with a chuckle, "try to charge me for advice I don't need."

Annie regarded him for a somber second or two. "There's one thing I'd like to give ye that ye wouldn't need to pay for," she said at length.

"And what," asked the captain, amused, "is that?"

"I'd like to make ye a free present," she told him, "of a good kick in the teeth!"

In the ensuing couple of hours, during which the Harrowgate's boats were drawn up to the davits and secured, the forward ballast tanks were filled, and the hands, with apparent willingness, worked at transferring some of the cargo from the after-hold, Annie moved quietly from man to man. And it was after the last of these small conferences, and while she was climbing the fiddley ladder from the stokehold to the well deck, that she felt first a small, then a violent lurch, followed by the heavy grinding of metal on rock, while a tremor ran through the vessel's plates. Lumbering quickly onto the deck, she felt the Harrowgate's stern lift, then suddenly descend, and it did not need her quick, expert glance over the side and astern to tell her that the steamer was once more afloat.

As rapidly as her bulk would allow, she made her way to the bridge, pausing on the way to look out over the bows, where she saw a long steel towing wire leading out from the Harrowgate's bitts on the forecastlehead, and made fast at the other end, not to the towing drum of her Narcissus, but to that of the straining, panting Salamander, which, slowly but steadily, was drawing the freighter off into deep water. Then, she continued on to the bridge.

"Excuse me if I'm overpulchritudinous," she said to Captain Higgins, with unaccustomed meekness, "but would ye mind tellin' me just who gave Bullwinkle the job o' towin' ye?"

"I did, of course," he replied, with the utmost good nature. "We've got a smashed propeller and a bent shaft and twisted rudder post. So, when he came on board while you were below, missus, and made a reasonable offer to tow me to port, I accepted. If you object," he added humorously, "you can fight it out with him when you get ashore." He waggled a playful forefinger. "But don't forget: 'When two dogs strive for a bone, the third runs away with it.' "

"I see," said Annie quietly. "But it didn't occur to ye, no doubt, that ye no longer had the right to give either orders or jobs on board this ship?"

Taken aback, he lost something of his aplomb. Then, smiling again, "Do you mind," he said, "telling me what you're talking about?"

"I'll be glad to. In fack"—her voice took on a small enthusiasm—"I been achin' to! Because, ye see, ye're no longer master o' this vessel. The givin' of orders an' jobs is now strictly the derogative o' the salvors."

"The salvors?" Captain Higgins stiffened.

Annie nodded. "The salvors. By them, I mean yer crew. O' course," she added modestly, "I git my whack, too, what I don't even have to split wid Bullwinkle. He had his chance, but he wouldn't even listen. So all he gits is the pleasure o' towin' ye to port for nothin', since ye had no authority to give him the job. Now there's a bone," she added generously, "that you and him can reelly quarrel about when we get in."

"Look, missus," Captain Higgins returned slowly, "are you sure you're quite right in the brain?"

"Ain't had no complaints so far," said Annie complacently. "Ye still don't see it, huh? Tck-tck-tck! Well, look." And reaching into her shirt, she drew forth the sheet of lengthy foolscap upon which she had penned the single clause to which she had secured the signature or mark of each of the Harrowgate's crew. "This here's a agreement, wrote up by meself and signed by all hands, givin' my company, the Deep-Sea Towin' and Salvage Company, o' Secoma, a half interest in the salvage o' this steamer. In consideration," she added hastily, "o' sarvices and advice rendered."

"You're insane!" the shipmaster snapped. "This is no salvage case! The Harrowgate's my ship, and those men are my officers and crew, performing the duties I pay them for, and for which they signed on! Now get off my bridge! And––"

"Don't git yer bearin's so hot," Annie advised him calmly. "Leastways, not wid me." And there was a rugged something in her tired face that rang a small bell of caution in his brain. She waited a moment, then continued, "You gave the order 'Abandon ship' last night, didn't ye? . . . Oh, ye needn't to answer! Ye telled me this mornin' ye did, and I had ye repeat it afore witnesses! Now then, Admiralty law says –– Oh, my! Now ye know what I'm gettin' at! Yer face is red as a oyster! Well, Admiralty law says that when a ship is wrecked an' abandoned, the crew's contract under the ship's articles automatically terminates––"

"You can't prove that!"

"Ye'll find it on Page One Eighty-three o' The Law o' the Sea," Annie told him comfortably. "So the minute you and yer men abandoned this ship last night they was no longer yer crew. And when they come back on board again today, they done so as free agents and salvors! Ye may have noticed," she went on roguishly, "that I made sure they got aboard afore you did! And their salvage claim will hold good in any Admiralty court in the world. So ye can paste that in yer hat an' smoke it! But ye got one satisfaction left. Ye won't have to pay through the nose."

"What do you mean?" he asked, his voice shaking.

"I mean," said Annie with a grin, "ye can pay through the hole in yer head. Well"–she lumbered heavily toward the ladder, stifling a yawn as she went–"I better git back to my Narcissus. I'll be sittin' on pins and noodles till I give Bullwinkle the good news!"

COMMENT ON LIFE

Bon Vivants *are good livers—something they seldom possess.*

—SHANNON FIFE.

LONG, LONG AGO

Remember when Uncle Sam could live within his income . . . and without most of yours.

—PEGGY CAROLINE FEARS.

LITERATURE

By IRVIN S. COBB

§ Mr. Cobb felt that Fiction should stick to reliable lines (all westerns to be by eastern writers). He enjoyed all Music as long as it was band music, "Those Endearing Young Charms" or "My Old Kentucky Home." As for Art, when somebody stole the Mona Lisa, Cobb grinned, and not inscrutably.

AUGUST 31, 1912

WHEN you start to consider it from all sides literature turns out to be considerable of a proposition, what with first one thing and then another; and a presidential year is an excellent time for taking up the subject. In a presidential year Nature as well as man becomes literary. There is always the peculiar spotted spider mentioned in the special dispatch from North Colebrook, Connecticut, which weaves into its web the name of the Republican candidate, all written out so plainly that it can be readily read by anybody except a confirmed and unpleasant Democrat. And there is, belonging to an old Southern family in Alabama, the common but patriotic Dominique hen, that lays a double-yolk egg with the initials of the Democratic nominee on the lower end of it. Likewise the customary output of light fiction is greatly enhanced and enriched by the statements of the opposing campaign managers. Within the last couple of years, also, a newer note has crept into our periodical literature.

Every few minutes—seems like—you pick up a magazine and find in it a short story entitled, let us say, Everybody's Doin' It, and beginning substantially as follows:

Speaking of Leander naturally suggests Hellespont—and speaking of either one or both naturally suggests the hero of this tale. His first name was Leander and he came from Hellespont, South Carolina.

Oh, reader, seek not for Hellespont in the list of American municipalities large enough to have a Carnegie library and a graft investigation. The Postal Guide mentions it with ill-feigned reluctance, in small type; and in the railroad timetable it is indicated by a cipher—meaning stops on signal only. Approaching it, the locomotive of the Through Limited utters a loud and apprehensive shriek as though fearing it might break down and have to spend an hour there. Yet several bright people have come from Hellespont—the brighter they were the quicker they came; and our hero, Leander, was one of the first.

Our hero, I say; but on first blush there was nothing about his appearance to suggest the hero—absolutely nothing! His face consisted of the customary number of comparatively unimportant features arranged in the conventional manner, and he spoke in a way of speaking. His hair was cut like a retail shoedealer's from the central part of Ohio; but, on the other hand, he wore the necktie of a collector for an installment house, while his hat was similar to that of a traveling canvasser selling the Life of Lincoln in nine volumes. His name was such as you would hear paged in a hotel lobby at Wilkes Barre, Pennsylvania, or Little Rock, Arkansas. It was L. A. Blipp—the L. standing for Leander and the A. standing for Absalom, and Blipp standing for both of them.

The Many Shades of One O. Henry

Such, in short, is my hero—a man with a plain eye and an ear such as no stranger would pick in a crowd; and up until a few minutes ago, when I started this story, nothing had ever happened to him except being born, et cetera. He was a composite photograph of Jack Robinson, John Doe and the late Solomon Grundy. He was one in a thousand—the last one. His life, from A to Z, was an open book—only you would not have opened it. I started to say from Alpha to Omega instead of A to Z, as sounding classier and classical, but desisted from so doing for fear the editor might accuse me of trying to slip in a free reading notice for family foodstuffs and household urgents.

N. B.—If the preceding paragraph is omitted upon publication the reader may know that I was accused anyhow!

Enter now the other or female half of the sketch. She is of the elect of the universe. She has done things. She is the sole author of two successful problem novels and a salad dressing, and collaborator in a popular divorce. Suit yourself—she is either a ravishing blonde or a soulful brunette with sloe eyes—s-l-o-e, not s-l-o-w. Tastes differ in these matters, and last year's blonde is this year's brunette. Speaking calmly and dispassionately, I will merely state that she is a strong combination of Desdemona, the original smothered chicken, Helen of Troy—New York or Greece—and the kind of girl drawn by Mr. C. D. Gibson, author of the noted shirtwaist.

She, too, came from elsewhere. She came from Dowagiac—if you cannot pronounce Dowagiac make it Ypsilanti, or any of those other Michigan towns that have fishing tackle named for them. But when the action of this story starts she is seated in a Broadway restaurant at 6:15 P.M. of a summer day, just as the well-known sun is sinking, according to custom and the almanac, in the esteemed West. And she is engaged in consuming a light repast of the fruits of the season, consisting of one olive out of a Bronx and one cherry out of a dry Manhattan. Students of civic conditions may draw a lesson from the fact that Chicago has a fire named after it, while the provinces of New York are perpetuated in cocktails. Making two sips of the cherry, she raises her light or dark eyes, as the case may be; and approaching her she sees——

But why should I continue to quote further along this strain? If you are a regular reader of the fiction of the hour you must know, ere you have got this far, that you have encountered the latest brainchild of some one or another of the forty thousand bright, observant young men—and women—in this country upon whom the mantle of O. Henry descended. As mantles go, this is one of the roomiest and most commodious mantles we have. There are forty thousand of them under it now and there is room for forty thousand more. Ever since O. Henry died the crop of O.-Henryized stories is the one crop that has never failed us. Were I a critic of literature, I would say O. Henry himself was a solitary leviathan of the vasty deeps, while the subsequent sharers of the mantle run in schools and spawn close to shore. And before changing the subject I might also say that it seemed to me that too strong an admixture of the O. H. essence was likely to result in a decided preponderance of H_2O which, as any chemist will tell you, means something decidedly thin and waterish.

But who am I that I should say these things? I am no critic of literature. That is a vocation for other and weightier intellects than mine. There are several things that I know about, but literature is not one of them. I know, for example, that the Civil War was partly brought on by slavery, and partly by secession and partly by a Yankee who came South in the julep season of 1860 and insisted on crushing the mint. I know why a hen lays one egg and cackles an hour, and a shad lays a couple of hundred thousand and never says a word about it! I know why the robins go South in the fall and the ballplayers in the spring, and why it used to be that a boy with a John Henry face and a Plain Bub figure was always christened a fancy name and condemned to wear those Little Short Pantsleroy clothes. These are—all of them—puzzles of natural and profane history, to the solving of which I have given years of study; but I am not so well up on literature.

I judge this is the result of my early training—or the lack of it. Yet in the days of my youth every effort was made to give me a correct taste in reading and to ballast my mind with the right kind of books. I guess, though, the foundations were too heavy for the top structure—they were beginning to pull it out of plumb and make it sag down at one end, like a fireman's hat. As soon as I had outgrown the Sunday-school style of books, kind adult friends took me in hand and undertook to start me upon the proper course in these matters. They recommended to me a course of reading that not one of them would have waded through himself—not if you paid him day wages, he wouldn't! But they were willing that I, who had never done them any harm, should sweat and suffer over Gibbon's Rome, while in my secret soul I fairly ached to know whether Long John Silver got the treasure and what became of Ben Gunn, and how the fight at the stockade turned out. There are some books that are meant to be read and others that are meant to be recommended to others to read; I had a long line of the last-named goods wished on me. I reckon nearly every growing boy passes through this heartrending experience.

I recall distinctly how it was in my own case. As I was saying just now, I had outgrown the Sunday-school style of juvenile reading. There was a Sunday-school superintendent—a tall, pale, willowy, earnest young man, with a voice that was about three fathoms too deep for a person of his dimensions, and an infuriated Adam's apple that was forever trying to beat his brains out; and this Sunday-school superintendent had a way of patting you on the head and then conferring upon you little books of a dark blue and dismal aspect—books that had woodcut illustrations in them, which were apparently put there to divert attention from the other contents and keep people from saying the story was the worst thing in the book.

He likewise was much given to conversation. When he started talking he didn't know when to stop and nobody else knew when he would either. He had one of those mouths that you could start running and go away for an hour or two hours and come back and find it still going. I always considered the story of David and Goliath a middling good, exciting story until once when he told it to my class with interpolations of his own, which took him—and us—all over Asia Minor on a hot day. The Roman augurs, we are told, used to laugh in each other's face when they met in the forum, but this Sunday-school superintendent of ours never laughed—thus, I take it, illustrating one of the main differences between an augur and a bore. He was serious until it was painful. It was an open question with me which I hated most—his pats upon the head or his little blue books or his Sunday morning talks to the young, all of them being cursed with a sameness which was maddening.

I View the Remains of the Classics

Finally, though, I emancipated myself from these afflictions; and then, just about the time I began whitewashing fences with Tom Sawyer and being cast away on desert islands with R. Crusoe, a flinty-hearted grown person came along and saddened my young life with a list of the books I ought to read right off, unless I wanted to be a literary ignoramus and have the finger of scorn pointed at me.

I believed it too. Probably you believed it when the same thing happened to you. You were callow and trusting; and you took the list he gave you and you went to the public library, and the librarian unlocked the morgue department and toted out a lot of moldering remains, and you tottered homeward under a load of classical corpses that no really humane man would have asked a mule to haul. And then, full of enthusiasm and the ardor of youth, you tackled them; but you weren't equal to the strain—or, anyhow, I wasn't. I had been told that Chaucer and Spenser would sharpen my literary palate, but they only seemed to affect my spelling adversely. I had on hand a large number of volumes, any one of which was excellently adapted for pressing wild flowers or holding a balky door open; but to me they did not seem to be meant for reading purposes. Here I was loading myself to the gunwales with Lord Bacon, when what I really desired to ascertain was whether Huck and Jim got back to the raft that time.

The proverbs of Uncle Remus seemed to appeal to me where the moralizings of an old gentleman named Epictetus fell upon barren soil. Take Sir Izaak Walton now: I was interested in fishing; and I thought maybe, in addition to helping my literary taste, Sir Izaak might give me a few ideas touching on bait; but I never got very far beyond his preface. Right at the outset of his preface I found this remark: "As no man is born an artist, so no man is born an angler"; and I remarked to myself that this seemed to be pretty good doctrine. But only a little farther along—mind you, in the very first chapter—I struck this one: "Angling is something like poetry—men are to be born so." And to myself I said: "This is no proper authority for me to follow—this person changes his mind too often. He's liable to tell me in one line that chicken liver is the correct thing for channel cats, and in the next line say that a catfish wouldn't take liver if you threw in trading stamps! I will now slip Sir Izaak into the discard." And I did it and fell back on Old Cap Collier, and in the very first chapter I ran into a situation that thrilled me clear down to the taproot of my being.

Oh, gosh!—those Sunday afternoons in the summertime, when the dusty street drowsed in the heat and the only sounds that came in at the window were the remarks of a katydid correcting gossip in regard to herself, and the creak-creak-cre-e-e-ak of warped hickory as my little sister sat in a wooden swing letting the cat die. Swinging in a swing was the only form of play permitted to the children of a strict Presbyterian household on a Sunday afternoon in those times; but if you swung too hard it became sinful and somebody made you stop it.

On our street the families were mainly of Scotch descent; not the Highland Scotch—those fascinating persons who dressed up like plaid pen-wipers with their knees outdoors, and played The Campbells are Coming on a hot-water bag with fishing canes stuck in it, and followed the fortune of Bonnie Prince Charley until he ran out of that commodity—but the genuine blue-stockinged Lowlander type; and we were reared to believe that The Other Place was located due south and was a red-hot place full of flames and smells like somebody cooking ham, where the first deputy devil came in at breakfast-time wearing hoofs and horns and a napkin over his arm and leaned upon the chair of Old Nick and remarked pleasantly: "Good morning, boss; how're you going to have your lost souls this morning—fried on one side or turned over?" And it was impressed upon us that if we were bad we were going there, and more especially if we were bad on a Sunday, which made it look like a mighty slim chance, because no matter what you did on a Sunday it was wrong and you should stop it right away. Even now, every time I hear one of those old-fashioned swings creaking I think of those dear, peaceful Sunday afternoons that were each from two to three weeks long.

I see myself lying on a haircloth sofa that was specially designed for the purpose of stabbing a small boy through a pair of linen pants in four thousand separate and distinct places at once; and I have Locke on the Human Understanding, in one volume, balanced upon my stomach; and I am trying to keep awake and am being assisted in doing so by an argus-eyed female relative who believed the young of the race should remain quiet of a Sunday afternoon and improve the mind by substantial reading. She was more than argus-eyed merely—when it came to having that kind of an eye she had old Argus the First looking like a cross between a mine mule and a Mammoth Cave fish. And just about the time the lines upon the printed page began to run together and the horsehairs in the sofa began to lose their edge she would come and stir me up briskly before I had quite forgotten my troubles.

Prescriptions for Popular Authors

It was then and there I made up my mind that no person should be required to read the works of the great master minds of the English-speaking races until he was full grown and his own boss, by which time he would know better—and personally I wish to say that I am still adhering to that resolution.

Perhaps that is why I am not qualified to be a critic of literature, but I know what I want in reading matter. I merely ask that the authors shall stick to the original prescriptions; and in justice to them I would state that thus far very few of them have disappointed me. There is the Southern wartime novel now—a pronounced favorite of mine when done according to the regular formula. There must be an old plantation, preferably located in Virginia and now laid waste by the iron hands and feet of war; and the divisional arrangement of heroes and villains must be as follows:

Heroes	Southern—1 Northern—1
Villains	Northern—1 Southern—1

With this ground plan to start on, the working out of the plot is comparatively easy to the point where peace descends upon a distracted country, and a Southern girl, whose last name is generally Byrd, though sometimes Peyton or Calvert, is married to a Northern hero. Frequently also a Northern girl is married to a Southern hero—though this last is not demanded absolutely, but may be regarded as optional with the author. Also, there must be an old family servant, called Uncle Claiborne, who declines to accept his freedom and run away with the rest of the slaves, but continues to stick to the old place and furnish a touch of comedy relief for the sad chapters.

To round out the work properly and give it the correct historical finish, there should be an eccentric old maiden aunt specializing in family trees; and an Irish sergeant of the Union forces who is a diamond in the rough; and, as a foil to him, a Confederate corporal who refers to everybody as "you-all" and has a sallow complexion; and of course there must be a distant cousin of the family named Lieutenant Cary Somebody, who has black hair and eyes and seems to be sort of low in his mind; and it is customary for him to be wounded about the middle of the book and die after lingering painfully for about two chapters and a half.

If, instead of Virginia, the scene is laid in Kentucky, at least two Breckinridges and one Clay, or two Clays and one Breckinridge, are required to provide the right local color; and if it is South Carolina a few Huguenot names should be sprinkled in here and there, while if it is Louisiana there must be some Creole types.

To afford me the greatest amount of satisfaction, a typical Western story should be written by a young gentleman who has resided all his life in Brooklyn, New York. I have noticed that the Western fiction writers of the Brooklyn school seem to endow their cowboy heroes with a more fascinating gift of persiflage, and make them quicker at drawing their forty-fours, and cause them to show a much deeper contempt for Eastern people and Eastern things than is the case when a Western-born or

Western-reared author is writing the story.

Similarly I prefer that my stories of New York newspaper life should be written by invalid maiden ladies residing in small towns in Northern Vermont, as indeed I judge most of them are; and I insist that they shall follow the correct and orthodox lines—to wit: That there shall be a crab of a city editor, nasty and mean, who hates all the rest of the world and lives only for the paper; and a supercilious, highly superior star reporter who rolls his own cigarettes and puts his legs up on his desk and despises beginners in the business; and finally a scared, shrinking, green but brilliant young cub reporter who goes forth at eventide and, single-handed, turns up the biggest scoop of the year—and then he comes staggering in, barely half an hour before press-time, when the city room is in an uproar and the star has fallen down on his talented face and the old bear of a city editor is storming in despair because the paper is about to be beaten, and the cub flings himself down at a typewriter and turns out the greatest story that ever was printed.

Experience in such matters and study of the prevalent customs have taught me, also, that an English novel should start off with a young and timid curate eating strawberries on a lawn with somebody; and at an early stage there should be introduced a maidservant answering to the name of Dawson or Meadows, and an elderly housekeeper in a rustling black silk gown. If the gown is not of black silk, and if it fails to rustle, this person is an impostor. However, to date, it always has rustled in the desired manner.

These old favorites have never failed me yet; but if they ever do I can always turn to a story by one of the forty thousand bright young people upon whom the mantle of O. Henry has smotheringly descended.

MUSIC

JULY 13, 1912

IF YOU, the reader, are anything like me, the writer, it happens to you about every once in so long that some well-meaning but semi-witted friend rigs a deadfall for you, and traps you and carries you off, a helpless captive, for an evening among the real music-lovers.

Catching you, so to speak, with your defense leveled and your breastworks unmanned, he speaks to you substantially as follows: "Old man, we're going to have a few people up to the house tonight—just a little informal affair, you understand, with a song or two and some music—and the missus and I would appreciate it mightily if you'd put on your Young Prince Charmings and drop in on us along toward eight. How about it—can we count on you to be among those prominently present?"

Forewarned is forearmed, and you know all about this person already. You know him to be one of the elect in the most exclusive musical coterie of your fair city, wherever your fair city may be. You know him to be on terms of the utmost intimacy with the works of all the great composers. Bill Opus and Jeremiah Fugue have no secrets from him—none whatever—and in conversation he creates the impression that Issy Sonata was his first cousin. He can tell you offhand which one of the Shuberts—Lee or Jake—wrote that Serenade. He speaks of Mozart and Beethoven in such a way a stranger would probably get the idea that Mote and Bate used to work for his folks. He can go to a musical show, and while the performance is going on he can tell everybody in his section just which composer each song number was stolen from, humming the original air aloud to show the points of resemblance. He can do this, I say, and, what is more, he does do it. At the table d'hôte place, when the Neapolitan troubadours come out in their little green jackets and their wide red sashes he is right there at the middle table, poised and waiting; and when they put their heads together and lean in toward the center and sing their national air, Come Into the Garlic, Maud, it is he who beats time for them with his handy lead-pencil, only pausing occasionally to point out errors in technic and execution on the part of the performers. He is that kind of a pest, and you know it.

What you should do under these circumstances, after he has invited you to come up to his house, would be to look him straight in the eye and say to him: "Well, old chap, that's awfully kind of you to include me in your little musical party, and just to show you how much I appreciate it and how I feel about it here's something for you." And then hit him right where his hair parts with a cut-glass paperweight or a bronze clock or a fire-ax or something, after which you should leap madly upon his prostrate form and dance on his cozy corner with both feet and cave in his inglenook for him. That is what you should do, but, being a vacillating person—I am still assuming, you see, that you are constituted as I am—you weakly surrender and accept the invitation and promise to be there promptly on time, and he goes away to snare more victims in order to have enough to make a mess.

Can Music be the Food of Love?

And so it befalls at the appointed time that you deck your form in your after-six-P.M. clothes and go up. On the way you get full and fuller of dark forebodings at every step; and your worst expectations are realized as soon as you enter and are relieved of your hat by a colored person in white gloves, and behold spread before you a great horde of those ladies and gentlemen whose rapt expressions and general air of eager expectancy stamp them as true devotees of whatever is most classical in the realm of music. You realize that in such a company as this you are no better than a rank outsider, and that it behooves you to attract as little attention as possible. There is nobody else here who will be interested in discussing with you whether the Giants or the Cubs will finish first this season; nobody except you who cares a whoop how Indiana goes for president—in fact, most of them probably haven't heard that Indiana was thinking of going. Their souls are soaring among the stars in a rarefied atmosphere of culture, and even if you could you wouldn't dare venture up that far with yours, for fear of being seized by an uncontrollable impulse to leap off and end all, the same as some persons are affected when on the roof of a tall building. So you back into the nearest corner and try to look like a part of the furniture—and wait in dumb misery.

Usually you don't have to wait very long. These people are beggars for punishment and like to start early. It is customary to lead off the program with a selection on the piano by a distinguished lady graduate of somebody-with-an-Italian-name's school of piano expression. Under no circumstances is it to be expected that this lady will play anything that you can understand or that I could understand. It would be contrary to the ethics of her calling and deeply repugnant to her artistic temperament to play a tune that would sound well on a phonograph record. This would never do. She comes forward, stripped for battle, and bows and peels off her gloves and fiddles with the piano-stool until she gets it adjusted to suit her, and then she sits down, prepared to render an immortal work composed by one of the old masters, who was probably intoxicated at the time.

She starts gently. She throws her head far back and closes her eyes dreamily, and hits the keys a soft, dainty little lick—tippy-tap! Then leaving a call with the night clerk for eight o'clock in the morning, she seems to drift off into a peaceful slumber, but awakens on the moment and hurrying all the way up to the other end of Main Street she slams the bass keys a couple of hard blows—bumetty-bum! And so it goes for quite a long spell after that: Tippy-tap! —off to the country for a week-end party, Friday to Monday; bumetty-bum!—six months elapse between the third and fourth acts; tippetty-tip!—two years later; dear me, how the old place has changed! Biffetty-biff! Gracious, how time flies, for here it is summer again and the flowers are all in bloom! You sink farther and farther into your chair and debate with yourself whether you ought to run like a coward or stay and die like a hero. One of your legs goes to sleep and the rest of you envies the leg. You can feel your whiskers growing, and you begin to itch in two hundred separate places, but you can't scratch.

The strangest thing about it is that those round you appear to be enjoying it. Incredible though it seems, they are apparently finding pleasure in this. You can tell that they are enjoying themselves because they begin to act as real music-lovers always act under such circumstances—some put their heads on one side and wall up their eyes in a kind of a dying-calf attitude and listen so hard you can hear them listening, and some bend over toward their nearest neighbors and murmur their rapture. It is all right for them to murmur, but if you so much as scrooge your feet, or utter a low, despairing moan or anything, they all turn and glare at you reproachfully and go "Sh!" like a collection of steam-heating fixtures. Depend on them to keep you in your place!

All of a sudden the lady operator comes out of her trance. She comes out of it with a violent start, as though she had just been bee-stung. She now cuts loose, regardless of the cost of the piano and its associations to its owners. She skitters her flying fingers up and down the instrument from one end to the other, producing a sound like hailstones falling on a tin roof. She grabs the helpless thing by its upper lip and tries to tear all its front teeth out with her bare hands. She fails in this, and then she goes mad from disappointment and in a frenzy resorts to her fists.

As nearly as you are able to gather, a terrific fire has broken out in one of the most congested tenement districts. You can hear the engines coming and the hook-and-ladder trucks clattering over the cobbles. Ambulances come, too, clanging their gongs, and one of them runs over a dog; and a wall falls, burying several victims in the ruin. At this juncture persons begin jumping out of the top-floor windows, holding cooking stoves in their arms, and a team runs away and plunges through a plate-glass window into a tinware and crockery store. People are all running round and shrieking, and the dog that was run over is still yelping—he wasn't killed outright evidently, but only crippled—and several tons of dynamite explode in a basement.

As the crashing reverberations die away the lady arises, wan but game, and bows low in response to the applause and backs away, leaving the wreck of the piano pushed back on its haunches and trembling like a leaf in every limb.

All to yourself, off in your little corner, you are thinking that surely this has been suffering and disaster enough for one evening and everybody will be willing to go away and seek a place of quiet. But no. In its demand for fresh horrors this crowd is as insatiate as the ancient Romans used to be when Nero was giving one of those benefits at the Colosseum for the fire sufferers of his home city. There now advances to the platform a somber person of a bass aspect, he having a double-yolk face and a three-ply chin and a chest like two or three chests.

Harking Back to the Ark

You know in advance what the big-mouthed black bass is going to sing—there is only one regular song for a bass singer to sing. From time to time insidious efforts have been made to work in songs for basses dealing with the love affairs of Bedouins and the joys of life down in a coal mine; but after all, to a bass singer who really values his gift of song and wishes to make the most of it, there is but one suitable selection, beginning as follows:

Ro-hocked in the cra-hadle of the da-heep,
I la-hay me down in pe-heace to sa-leep!
Collum and pa-heaceful be my sa-leep
Ro-hocked in the cra-hadle of the da-heep!

That is the orthodox offering for a bass. The basses of the world have always used it, I believe, and generally to advantage. From what I have been able to ascertain I judge that it was first written for use on the Ark. Shem sang it probably. If there is anything in this doctrine of heredity Ham specialized in banjo solos and soft-shoe dancing, and Japhet, I take it, was the tenor—he certainly had a tenor-sounding kind of a name. So it must have been Shem, and undoubtedly he sang it when the animals were hungry, so as to drown out the sounds of their roaring.

So this, his descendant—this chip off the old cheese, as it were—stands up on the platform facing you, with his chest well extended to show his red suspender straps peeping coyly out from the arm openings of his vest, and he inserts one hand into his bosom, and over and over again he tells you that he is contemplating laying himself down in peace to sleep—which is more than anybody else on the block will be able to do; and he rocks you in the cradle of the deep until you are as seasick as a cow. You could stand that, maybe, if only he wouldn't make faces at you while he sings. Some day I am going to take the time off to make scientific research and ascertain why all bass singers make faces when they are singing. Surely there is some psychological reason for this, and if there isn't it should be stopped by legislative enactment.

When Sing-Bad the Sailor has quit rocking the boat and come ashore, a female singer generally obliges and comes off the nest after a merry lay, cackling her triumph. Then there is something more of a difficult and painful nature on the piano; and nearly always, too, there is a large lady wearing a low-vamp gown on a high-arch form, who in flutelike notes renders one of those French ballads that's full of la-las and is supposed to be devilish and naughty because nobody can understand it. For the finish, some person addicted to elocution usually recites a poem to piano accompaniment. The poem Robert of Sicily is much used for these purposes, and whenever I hear it Robert invariably has my deepest sympathy and so has Sicily. Toward midnight a cold collation is served, and you recapture your hat and escape forth into the starry night, swearing to yourself that never again will you permit yourself to be lured into an orgy of the true believers.

But the next time an invitation comes along you will fall again. Anyhow that's what I always do, meanwhile raging inwardly and cursing myself for a weak and spineless creature who doesn't know when he's well off. Yet I would not be regarded as one who is insensible to the charms of music. In its place I like music, if it's the kind of music I like. These times, when so much of our music is punched out for us by machinery like buttonholes and the air vents in Swiss cheese, and then is put up in cans for the trade like Boston beans and baking-powder, nothing gives me more pleasure than to drop a nickel in the slot and hear an inspiring selection by the author of Alexander's Ragtime Band.

I am also partial to band music. When John Philip Sousa comes to town you can find me down in the very front row.

I appreciate John Philip Sousa when he faces me and shows me that breast full of medals extending from the whiskerline to the beltline, and I appreciate him still more when he turns round and gives me a look at that back of his. Since Colonel W. F. Cody practically retired and Miss Mary Garden went away to Europe, I know of no public back which for inherent grace and poetry of spinal motion can quite compare with Mr. Sousa's.

I am in my element then. I do not care so very much for Home, Sweet Home, as rendered with so many variations that it's almost impossible to recognize the old place any more; but when they switch to a march, a regular Sousa march full of umpahs, then I begin to spread myself. A little tingle of anticipatory joy runs through me as Mr. Sousa advances to the footlights and first waves his baton at the great big German who plays the little shiny thing that looks like a hypodermic and sounds like stepping on the cat, and then turns the other way and waves it at the little bit of a German who plays the big thing that looks like a ventilator off an ocean liner and sounds like feeding-time at the zoo. And then he makes the invitation general and calls up the brasses and the drums and the woods and the woodwinds, and also the thunders and the lightnings and the cyclones and the earthquakes. And three or four of the trombonists pull the slides away out and let go full steam right in my face, with a blast that blows my hair out by the roots, and all hands join in and make so much noise that you can't hear the music. And I enjoy it more than words can tell!

The Best Part of Elektra

On the other hand, grand opera does not appeal to me. I can enthuse over the robin's song in the spring, and the sound of the summer wind rippling through the ripened wheat is not without its attractions for me; but when I hear people going into convulsions of joy over Signor Massacre's immortal opera of Medulla Oblongata I feel that I am out of my element and I start back-pedaling. Lucy D. Lammermore may have been a lovely person, but to hear a lot of foreigners singing about her for three hours on a stretch does not appeal to me. I have a better use for my little two dollars. For that amount I can go to a good minstrel show and sit in a box.

You may recall when Strauss' Elektra was creating such a furor in this country a couple of years ago. All the people you met were talking about it whether they knew anything about it or not, and generally they didn't. I caught the disease myself; I went to hear it sung.

I only lasted a little while. I confess it unabashedly—if there is such a word as unabashedly—and if there isn't then I confess it unashamedly. As well as a mere layman could gather from the opening proceedings, this opera of Elektra was what the life story of the Borgia family of Italy would be if set to music by Fire-Chief Croker. In the quieter moments of the action, when nobody was being put out of the way, half of the chorus assembled on one side of the stage and imitated the last ravings of John McCullough, and the other half went over on the other side of the stage and clubbed in and imitated Wallace, the Untamable Lion, while the orchestra, to show its impartiality, imitated something else—Old Home Week in a boiler factory, I think. It moved me strangely—strangely and also rapidly.

Taking advantage of one of these periods of comparative calm I arose and softly stole away. I put a dummy in my place to deceive the turnkeys and I found a door providentially unlocked and I escaped out into the night. Three or four thousand automobiles were charging up and down Broadway, and there was a fire going on a couple of blocks up the street, and I think a suffragette procession was passing too; but after what I'd just been through the quiet was very soothing to my eardrums. I don't know when I've enjoyed anything more than the last part of Elektra, that I didn't hear.

Yet my reader should not argue from this admission that I am deaf to the charms of the human voice when raised in song. Unnaturalized aliens of a beefy aspect vocalizing in a strange tongue while an orchestra of two hundred pieces performs—that, I admit, is not for me. But just let a pretty girl in a white dress with a flower in her hair come out on a stage, and let her have nice clear eyes and a big wholesome-looking mouth, and let her open that mouth and show a double row of white teeth that'd remind you of the first roasting ear of the season—just let her be all that and do all that, and then let her look right at me and sing The Last Rose of Summer or Annie Laurie or Believe Me, If All Those Endearing Young Charms—and I am hers to command, world without end, forever and ever, amen! My eyes cloud up for a rainy spell, and in my throat there comes a lump so big I feel like a coach-whip snake that has inadvertently swallowed a china darning-egg. And when she is through I am the person sitting in the second row down front who applauds until the flooring gives way and the plastering is jarred loose on the next floor. She can sing for me by the hour and I'll sit there by the hour and listen to her, and forget that there ever was such a person in the world as the late Vogner! That's the kind of a music-lover I am, and I suspect, if the truth were known, there are a whole lot more just like me.

If I may be excused for getting sort of personal and reminiscent at this point I should like to make brief mention here of the finest music I ever heard. As it happened this was instrumental music. I had come to New York with a view to revolutionizing metropolitan journalism, and journalism had shown a reluctance amounting to positive diffidence about coming forward and being revolutionized. Pending the time when it should see fit to do so, I was stopping at a boarding house on West Fifty-Seventh Street. It has been my observation that practically everybody who comes to New York stops for a while in a boarding house on West Fifty-Seventh Street.

West Fifty-Seventh Street was where I was established in a hall bedroom on the top floor—a hall bedroom so form-fitting and cozy that when I went to bed I always opened the transom to prevent a feeling of closeness across the chest. If I had as many as three callers in my room of an evening and one of them got up to go first, the others had to sit quietly while he was picking out his own legs. But up to the time I speak of I hadn't had any callers. I hadn't been there very long and I hadn't met any of the other boarders socially, except at the table. I had only what you might call a feeding acquaintance with them.

Christmas Eve came round. I was a thousand miles from home and felt a million. I shouldn't be surprised if I was a little bit homesick. Anyhow it was Christmas Eve, and it was snowing outside according to the orthodox Christmas Eve formula, and upward of five million other people in New York were getting ready for Christmas without my company, coöperation or assistance. You'd be surprised to know how lonesome you can feel in the midst of five million people—until you try it on a Christmas Eve.

After dinner I went up to my room and sat down with my back against the door and my feet on the window-ledge, and I rested one elbow in the washpitcher and put one knee on the mantel and tried to read the newspapers. The first article I struck was a Christmas poem, a sentimental Christmas poem full of allusions to the family circle, and the old homestead, and the stockings hanging by the fireplace, and all that sort of thing.

That was enough. I put on my hat and overcoat and went down into the street. The snow was coming down in long, slanting lines and the sidewalks were all white, and where the lamplight shone on them they looked like the frosting on birthday cakes. People laden with bundles were diving in and out of all the shops. Every other shop window had a holly wreath hung in it, and when the doors were opened those spicy Christmassy smells of green hemlock and pine came gushing out in my face.

Away From My Old Kentucky Home

So far as I could tell, everybody in New York—except me—was buying something for his or her or some other body's Christmas. It was a tolerably lonesome sensation. I walked two blocks, loitering sometimes in front of a store. Nobody spoke to me except a policeman. He told me to keep moving. Finally I went into a little family liquor store. Strangely enough, considering the season, there was nobody there except the proprietor. He was reading a German newspaper behind the bar. I spoke with him concerning the advisability of an egg-nog. He had never heard of such a thing as an egg-nog. I mentioned two old friends of mine, named Tom and Jerry, respectively, and he didn't know them either. So I compromised on a hot lemon toddy. The lemon was one that had grown up with him in the liquor business, I think, and it wasn't what you would call a spectacular success as a hot toddy; but it was warming, anyhow, and that helped. I expanded a trifle. I asked him whether he wouldn't take something on me.

He took a small glass of beer! He was a foreigner and he probably knew no better, so I suppose I shouldn't have judged him too harshly. But it was Christmas Eve and snowing outside—and he took a small beer!

I paid him and came away. I went back to my hall bedroom up on the top floor and sat down at the window with my face against the pane, like Little Maggie in the poem.

It continued to snow. I reckon I must have sat there an hour or more.

Down in the street four stories below I heard something—music. I raised the sash and looked out. An Italian had halted in front of the boarding house with a grind organ and he was turning the crank and the thing was playing. It wasn't much of a grind organ as grind organs go. I judge it must have been the original grind organ that played with Booth and Barrett. It had lost a lot of its most important works, and it had the asthma and the heaves and had one thing and another the matter with it.

But the tune it was playing was My Old Kentucky Home—and Kentucky was where I'd come from. The Italian played it through twice, once on his own hook and once because I went downstairs and divided my money with him.

I regard that as the finest music I ever heard.

As I was saying before, the classical stuff may do for those who like it well enough to stand it, but the domestic article suits me.

I like the kind of beer that this man Bach turned out in the spring of the year, but I don't seem to be able to care much for his music. And so far as Chopin is concerned, I hope you'll all do your Christmas Chopin early.

ART

AUGUST 10, 1912

IN ART as in music I am one who is very easily satisfied. All I ask of a picture is that it shall look like something, and all I ask of music is that it shall sound like something.

In this attitude I feel confident that I am one of a group of about seventy million people in this country, more or less, but only a few of us, a very heroic few of us, have the nerve to come right out and take a firm position and publicly express our true sentiments on these important subjects. Some are under the dominion of strong-minded wives. Some hesitate to reveal their true artistic leanings for fear of being called low-browed vulgarians. Some are plastic posers and so pretend to be something they are not to win the approval of the ultra-intellectuals. There are only a handful of us who are ready and willing to go on record as saying where we stand.

It is because of this cowardice on the part of the great silent majority that every year sees us backed farther and farther into a corner. We walk through miles and miles of galleries, or else we are led through them by our wives and our friends, and we look in vain for the kind of pictures that mother used to make and father used to buy. What do we find? Once in a while we behold a picture of something that we can recognize without a chart, and it looms before our gladdened vision like a rock-and-rye in a weary land. But that it not apt to happen often—not in a 1912-model gallery. In such an establishment one is likely to meet only Old Masters and Young Messers. If it's an Old Master we probably behold a Flemish saint or a German saint or an Italian saint—depending on whether the artist was Flemish or German or Italian—depicted as being shot full of arrows and enjoying same to the uttermost. If it is a Young Messer the canvas probably presents to us a view of a poached egg apparently bursting into a Welsh rarebit. At least that is what it looks like to us—golden buck, forty cents at any good restaurant—in the act of undergoing spontaneous combustion. But we are informed that this is an impressionistic interpretation of a sunset at sea, and we are expected to stand before it.

The Age of the Gilded Shovel

But I for one must positively decline to carry on. This sort of thing does not appeal to me. I don't want to have to consult the official catalogue in order to ascertain for sure whether this year's prize picture is a quick lunch or an Italian gloaming. I'm very peculiar that way. I like to be able to tell what a picture aims to represent just by looking at it. I presume this is the result of my early training. I was reared in the Rutherford B. Hayes School of Interior Decorating. In a considerable degree I am still wedded to my early ideals. I distinctly recall the time when upon the walls of every wealthy home of America there hung, among other things, two staple oil paintings —a still-life for the dining room, showing a dead fish on a plate, and a pastoral for the parlor, showing a collection of cows drinking out of a purling brook. A dead fish with a glazed eye and a cold, clammy fin was not a thing you would care to have round the house for any considerable period of time, except in a picture, and the same was true of cows. People who could not abide the idea of a cow in the kitchen gladly welcomed one into the parlor when painted in connection with the above purling brook and several shade trees.

Those who could not afford oil paintings went in for steel engravings and chromos—good reliable brands, such as the steel engraving of Henry Clay's Farewell to the American Senate and the Teaching Baby to Waltz art chromo. War pictures were also very popular back in that period. If it were a Northern household you could be pretty sure of seeing a work entitled Gettysburg, showing three Union soldiers, two plain and one colored, in the act of repulsing Pickett's charge. If it were a Southern household there would be one that had been sold on subscription by a strictly nonpartisan publishing house in Charleston, South Carolina, and guaranteed to be historically correct in all particulars, representing Robert E. Lee chasing U. S. Grant up a palmetto tree, while in the background were a large number of deceased Northern invaders neatly racked up like cordwood.

Such things as these were a part of the art education of our early youth. Along with them we learned to value the family photograph album, which fastened with a latch like a henhouse door, and contained, among other treasures, the photograph of our Uncle Hiram wearing his annual collar. And there were also enlarged crayon portraits in heavy gold frames with red plush insertions, the agent having thrown in the portraits in consideration of our taking the frames; and souvenirs of the Philadelphia Centennial; and wooden scoop shovels heavily gilded by hand with moss roses painted on the scoop part and blue ribbon bows to hang them up by; and on the what-not in the corner you were reasonably certain of finding a conch shell with the Lord's Prayer engraved on it; and if you held the shell up to your young ear you could hear the murmur of the sea just as plain as anything. Of course you could secure the same murmuring effect by holding an old-fashioned tin cuspidor up to your ear, too, but in this case the poetic effect would have been lacking. And, besides, there were other uses for the cuspidor.

Almost the only Old Masters with whose works we were well acquainted were John L. Sullivan and Nonpareil Jack Dempsey. But Rosa Bonheur's Horse Fair suited us clear down to the ground—her horses looked like real horses, even if they were the kind that haul brewery wagons; and in the matter of sculpture Powers' Greek Slave seemed to fill the bill to the satisfaction of all. Anthony Comstock and the Boston Purity League had not taken charge of our art as yet, and nobody seemed to find any fault because the Greek lady looked as though she'd slipped on the top step and come down just as she was, wearing nothing to speak of except a pair of handcuffs. Nobody did speak of it either—not in a mixed company anyhow.

Furniture was preferred when it was new—the newer the better. We went in for golden oak and for bird's-eye maple, depending on whether we liked our furniture to look tanned or freckled; and when the careful housekeeper threw open her parlor for a social occasion, the furniture gave off a splendid new sticky smell, similar to a paint and varnish store on a hot day. The vogue for antiques hadn't got started yet; that was to descend upon us later on. We rather liked the dining-room table to have all its legs still, and the bureau to have drawers that could be opened without blasting. In short, that was the period of our national life when only the very poor had to put up with decrepit second-hand furniture, as opposed to these times when only the very rich can afford to own it. If you have any doubts regarding this last assertion of mine I should advise you to drop into any reliable antique shop and inquire the price of a mahogany sideboard suffering from tetter and other skin diseases, or a black-walnut cupboard with doors that froze up solid about the time of the last Seminole War. I suppose these things go in cycles—in fact, I'm sure they do. Some day the bare sight of the kind of furniture which most people favor nowadays will cause a person of artistic sensibilities to burst into tears, just as the memory of the things that everybody liked twenty-five or thirty years ago gives such poignant pain to so many at present.

Even up to the time of the World's Fair quite a lot of people still favored the simpler and more understandable forms of art expression. We went to Chicago and religiously visited the Art Building, and in our nice new creaky shoes we walked past miles and miles of brought-on paintings by foreign artists, whose names we could not pronounce, in order to find some sentimental domestic subject. After we had found it we would stand in front of it for hours on a stretch with the tears rolling down our cheeks. Some of us wept because the spirit of the picture moved us, and some because our poor tired feet hurt us and the picture gave us a good excuse for crying in public, and so we did so—freely and copiously. Grant if you will that our taste was crude and raw and provincial, yet we knew what we liked and the bulk of us weren't ashamed to say so either. What we liked was a picture or a statue which remotely at least resembled the thing that it was presumed to represent. Likewise we preferred pictures of things that we ourselves knew about and could understand.

Maybe it was because of that early training that a good many of us have never yet been able to work up any intense enthusiasm over the Old Masters. Mind you, we have no quarrel with those who become incoherent and babbling with joy in the presence of an Old Master, but—doggone 'em! —they insist on quarreling with us because we think differently. We fail to see anything ravishingly beautiful in a faded, blistered, cracked, crumbling painting of an early Christian martyr on a grill, happily frying on one side like an egg—a picture that looks as though the Old Master had painted it some morning before breakfast, when he wasn't feeling the best in the world, and then worn it as a liver pad for forty or fifty years. We cannot understand why they love the Old Masters so, and they cannot understand why we prefer the picture of Custer's Last Stand that the harvesting company used to give away to advertise its mowing machines.

The Amateur Smiler of the Louvre

Once you get away from the early settlers among the Old Masters the situation becomes different. Rembrandt and Hals painted some portraits that appeal deeply to the imagination of nearly all of my set. The portraits which they painted not only looked like regular persons, but so far as my limited powers of observation go, they were among the few painters of Dutch subjects who didn't always paint a windmill or two into the background. It probably took great resolution and self-restraint, but they did it and I respect them for it.

I may say that I am also drawn to the kind of ladies that Gainsborough and Sir Joshua Reynolds painted. They certainly turned out some mighty good-looking ladies in those days, and they were tasty dressers, too, and I enjoy looking at their pictures. Coming down the line a little farther, I want to state that there is also something very fascinating in those soft-boiled pink ladies, sixteen hands high, with sorrel manes, that Bouguereau did; and the soldier pictures of Meissonier and Detaille appeal to me mightily. Their soldiers are always such nice neat soldiers, and they never have their uniforms mussed up or their accouterments disarranged, even when they are being shot up or cut down or something. Corot and Rousseau did some landscapes that seem to approximate the real thing, and there are several others whose names escape me; but, speaking for myself alone, I wish to say that this is about as far as I can go at this writing. I must admit that I have never been held spellbound and enthralled for hours on a stretch by a contemplation of the inscrutable smile on Mona Lisa. To me she seems merely a lady smiling about something—simply that and nothing more. Any woman can smile inscrutably; that is one of the specialties of her sex. The inscrutable smile of a saleslady in an exclusive Fifth Avenue shop when a customer asks to look at something a little cheaper would make Mona Lisa seem a mere amateur as an inscrutable smiler. Quite a number of us remained perfectly calm when some gentlemen stole Miss Lisa out of the Louvre, and we expect to remain equally calm if she is never restored.

As I said before, though, our little band is shrinking in numbers day by day. The population as a whole are being educated up to higher ideals in art. On the wings of symbolism and idealism they are soaring ever higher and higher, until a whole lot of them must be getting dizzy in the head by now.

First, there was the impressionistic school, which started it; and then there was the post-impressionistic school, suffering from the same disease but in a more violent form; and here just recently there have come along the Cubists and the Futurists.

You know about the Cubists? A Cubist is a person who for reasons best known to the police has not been locked up yet, who asserts that all things in Nature, living and inanimate, properly resolve themselves into cubes. What is more, he goes and paints pictures to prove it—pictures of cubic waterfalls pouring down cubic precipices, and cubic ships sailing on cubic oceans, and cubic cows being milked by cubic milkmaids. He makes portraits too—portraits of persons with cubic hands and cubic feet, who are smoking cubeb cigarettes and have solid cubiform heads. On that last proposition we are with them unanimously; we will concede that there are people in this world with cube-shaped heads, they being the people who profess to enjoy this style of picture.

The Futurists haven't reached this country yet; but from what can be gathered from newspaper reading, we judge that a Futurist begins right where a Cubist leaves off, and gets worse. The Futurists have already had exhibitions in Paris and London and they are fixing to invade New York. They call themselves art anarchists. Their doctrine is a simple and a cheerful one—they merely preach that whatever is normal is wrong. They not only preach it, they practice it.

Here are some of their teachings:

We teach the plunge into shadowy death under the white set eyes of the ideal!

The mind must launch the flaming body, like a fireship, against the enemy, the eternal enemy that, if he do not exist must be invented!

The victory is ours—I am sure of it, for the maniacs are already hurling their hearts to heaven like bombs! Attention! Fire! Our blood? Yes! All our blood in torrents to redye the sickly auroras of the earth! Yes, and we shall also be able to warm thee within our smoking arms, O wretched, decrepit, chilly Sun, shivering upon the summit of the Gorisankor!

Works of Art That Make Us Wonder

There you have the whole thing, you see, simply, dispassionately and quietly presented. We have seen newspaper reproductions of some of the best examples of the Futurists' school. As well as a body can judge from these reproductions, a Futurist's method of execution must be comparatively simple. After looking at his picture, you would say that he first put on a woolly overcoat and a pair of overshoes; that he then poured a mixture of hearth paint, tomato catsup, liquid bluing, burnt cork, English mustard, Easter dyes and the yolks of a dozen eggs over himself, seasoning to taste with red peppers. Then he spread a large square of canvas on the floor and lay down on it and had an epileptic fit, the result being a picture which he labeled Revolt, or Collision Between Two Heavenly Bodies, or Premature Explosion of a Custard Pie, or something else equally appropriate. The Futurists ought to make quite a number of converts in this country, especially among those advanced lovers of art who are beginning to realize that the old impressionistic school lacked emphasis and individuality in its work. But I expect to stand firm, and when everybody else nearly is a Futurist and is tearing down Sargent's pictures and Abbey's and Whistler's to make room for immortal Young Messers, I and a few others will still be holding out resolutely to the end.

At such times as these I fain would send my thoughts back longingly to an artist who flourished in the town where I was born and brought up. He was practically the only artist we had, but he was versatile in the extreme. He was several kinds of a painter rolled into one—house, sign, portrait, landscape, marine and wagon. In his lighter hours, when building operations were dull, he specialized in oil paintings of life and motion—mainly pictures of horse races and steamboat races. When he painted a horse race, the horses were always shown running neck and neck with their mouths wide open and their eyes gleaming; and their nostrils were widely extended and painted a deep crimson, and their legs were neatly arranged just so, and not scrambled together in any old fashion, as seems to be the case with the legs of the horses that are being painted nowadays. And when he painted a steamboat race it would always be the *Natchez* and the *Robert E. Lee* coming down the river abreast in the middle of the night, with the darkies dancing on the lower decks and heavy black smoke rolling out of the smokestacks in four distinct columns—one column to each smokestack—and showers of sparks belching up into the vault of night. There was action for you—action and attention to detail. With this man's paintings you could tell a horse from a steamboat at a glance. He was nothing of an impressionist; he never put smokestacks on the horse or legs on the steamboat. And his work gave general satisfaction throughout that community.

Frederic Remington wasn't any impressionist either; and so far as I can learn he didn't have a cubiform idea in stock. When Remington painted an Indian on a pony it was a regular Indian and a regular pony—not one of those cotton-batting things with fat legs that an impressionist slaps on to a canvas and labels a horse. You could smell the lathered sweat on the pony's hide and feel the dust of the dry prairie tickling your nostrils. You could see the slide of the horse's withers and watch the play of the naked Indian's arm muscles. I should like to enroll as a charter member of a league of Americans who believe that Frederic Remington and Howard Pyle were greater painters than any Old Master that ever turned out blistered saints and fly-blown cherubim. And if every one who secretly thinks the same way about it would only join in—of course they wouldn't, but if they would—we'd be strong enough to elect a president on a platform calling for a prohibitive tariff against the foreign-pauper-labor Old Masters of Europe.

While we were about it our league could probably do something in the interests of sculpture. It is apparent to any fair-minded person that sculpture has been very much overdone in this country. It seems to us there should be a law against perpetuating any of our great men in marble or bronze or stone or amalgam fillings until after he has been dead a couple of hundred years, and by that time a fresh crop ought to be coming on and probably we shall have lost the desire to create such statues.

A great man who cannot live in the affectionate and grateful memories of his fellow countrymen isn't liable to live if you put up statues of him; that, however, is not the main point.

The artistic aspect is the thing to consider. So few of our great men have been really pretty to look at. Andrew Jackson made a considerable dent in the history of his period, but when it comes to beauty, there isn't a floorwalker in a department store anywhere that hasn't got him backed clear off the pedestal. In addition to that, the sort of clothes we've been wearing for the last century or so do not show up especially well in marble. Putting classical draperies on our departed solons has been tried, but carving a statesman with only a towel draped over him, like a Roman senator coming out of a Turkish bath, is a departure from the real facts and must be embarrassing to his shade. The greatest celebrities were modest.

I'll bet the spirit of the Father of His Country blushes every time he flits over that statue of himself alongside the Capitol at Washington—the one showing him sitting in a bath cabinet with nothing on but a sheet.

Sticking to the actual conditions doesn't seem to help much either. Future generations will come and stand in front of the statue of a leader of thought who flourished back about 1840, say, and wonder how anybody ever had feet like those and lived. Horace Greeley's chin whiskers no doubt looked all right on Horace when he was alive, but when done in bronze they invariably present a droopy not to say dropsical appearance; and the kind of a bone-handled umbrella that Daniel Webster habitually carried has never yet been successfully worked out in marble. When you contemplate the average statue of Abraham Lincoln—and most of them, as you may have noticed, are very average—you do not see there the majesty and the grandeur and the abiding sorrow of the man and the tragedy of his life. At least I know I do not see those things. I see a pair of massive square-toed boots, such as I'm sure Old Abe Lincoln never wore—he couldn't have worn 'em and walked a step—and I see a beegum hat weighing a ton and a half, and I say to myself: "This is not the Abraham Lincoln who freed the slaves and wrote the Gettysburg address. No sir! A man with those legs would never have been president—he'd have been in a dime museum exhibiting his legs for ten cents a look—and they'd have been worth the money too."

Nobody seems to have noticed it, but we undoubtedly had the cube form of expression in our native sculpture long before it came out in painting.

To get a better idea of what I'm trying to drive at, just take a trip up through Central Park the next time you are in New York and pause a while before those bronzes of Sir Walter Scott and Robert Burns which stand on the Mall. They are called bronzes, but to me they always looked more like castings. I don't care if you are as Scotch as a haggis, I know in advance what your feelings will be. If you decide that these two men ever looked in life like those two bronzes you are going to lose some of your love and veneration for them right there on the spot; or else you are going to be filled with an intense hate for the persons who have libeled them thus, after they were dead and gone and not in position to protect themselves legally. But you don't necessarily have to come to New York—you've probably got some decoration in your home town that is equally sad. There've been a lot of good stonemasons spoiled in this country to make enough sculptors to go round.

But while we are thinking these things about art and not daring to express them, I take note that new schools may come and new schools may go, but there is one class of pictures that always gets the money and continues to give general satisfaction among the masses.

I refer, of course, to the moving pictures.

A Glossary for Innocents

WHAT THEY SAY:	WHAT THEY MEAN:
To tell you the truth, I——	To skirt around the truth.
Don't misunderstand me, but——	Don't let it reflect on me, but here's the truth.
Incidentally——	This is what I've been leading up to and what is foremost in my mind.
Have you heard this joke?	If you've heard it before, let me finish anyhow.
A package? For me? You really shouldn't have——	I wonder what you brought me, and I'm glad you brought it.
It's a long story.	Coax me to tell it.

—MARTIN LEVIN AND SELENE HOLZMAN.

Who Killed Cock Robin?

(As It Might Have Been Written If the Modern Newspaper Had Handled It)

Motive Sought in Robin Murder

VICTIM DESPONDENT, SAYS MATE OF SLAIN BIRD. ARRESTS NEAR

"Mr. Robin had been acting queer for some time," according to Mrs. Jenny Robin, widow of Cock Robin, whose alleged body was discovered early yesterday morning on the edge of an abandoned bird bath owned by the Mayor's Committee of Plants and Structures of Hoboken, N. J. Mrs. Robin, who was formerly a Miss Wren, of Jersey City, was seen by a reporter for the Bazoo at the Robins' pretty home on Pine Street. "Yes, my husband never seemed the same since the children were born," declared the sad-eyed little woman. "You see, there were five this time. I remember Cock saying that two was company and three was a crowd, but that five was too much of a good thing. Sunday morning he was terribly discouraged. 'What's the use?' he said to me. 'I might just as well go out in the garden and eat worms!' And that was the last I saw of him."

Prosecutor Boob predicts an arrest within twenty-four hours.

Robin Had Love Nest!

DOVE ADMITS SHE WAS CUCKOO OVER CRIME VICTIM

(Special Article, With Pictures, by Effie Irene Sobb)

Cherchez la femme! One of the most pathetic angles of the Robin murder mystery is Bertha Dove, the plump, pretty little bird who was in love with the slaughtered victim. "Who'll be chief mourner?" we asked her. "I," said Miss Dove, "I mourn for my love. I'll be chief mourner." And as we left her we murmured again, "*Cherchez la femme!*"

Fish Grilled in Robin Slaying

AUTOPSY SHOWS MURDERED BIRD BLED TO DEATH

Dr. A. Poore Fish, of Bound Brook, who performed the autopsy on the alleged body of Cock Robin, issued the following statement from the prosecutor's office, in response to the Bazoo reporter's query: "Who caught his blood?" "I," said Doctor Fish, "with my little dish. I caught his blood."

Eyewitness Quizzed in Robin Killing

LADY BIRD AT SCENE OF CRIME SOUGHT

The mystery of the Robin slaying is on the eve of solution with the appearance in the case today of an eyewitness in the person of Mr. Philip Fly, who has for many years been connected with the Street Cleaning Department of this city. When asked point-blank if he had seen him—the murdered bird—die, "Yes," replied Mr. Fly, "with my little eye. I saw him die!" When questioned further by the Bazoo reporter as to what he—Mr. Fly—was doing at the abandoned bird bath at such a time, Mr. Fly became confused. "Can't you boys lemme alone?" he pleaded with the reporters. "I wasn't doin' nothin'! Just buzzin' round!" Arrests are expected at least three times a day after meals.

Gangster Confesses Robin Slaying

MEMBER OF UNDERWORLD FLAYED BY PROSECUTOR. ARROW WAS WEAPON

With the arrest and confession today of "The Sparrow," as he is known to the police of two continents—names furnished on request—the celebrated Robin mystery has been solved. The alleged slayer's confession is as follows: "Who killed Cock Robin? I," said The Sparrow, "with my bow and arrow. I killed Cock Robin."

—KATHARINE DAYTON.

Tales Mein Grossfader Told
Cinderella Hassenpfeffer

GRETCHEN und Bertha und Cinderella Hassenpfeffer ben geliven mit der steppen-mudder. Der steppen-mudder ben outfitten Gretchen und Bertha mit ein wunderbar warden-roben mit frillers und rufflers. Gretchen und Bertha ben haben also curlenwavers und lippen-sticken.

Cinderella ben gesitten der stover besiden mit raggen-tatters und smutten-facen.

Ein Princer ben residen der towner insiden. Das Princer vas getossen ein grosser Dancein mit musickers und costumen. Der inviters ben gecomen und Cinderella vas out-leften.

Cinderella ben gesitten der stover besiden mit sobben und snifflen und grosser weepen. Ach! Ein brighten-flashen ben gecomen und der gooten witcher vas gestanden mit ein pumpkiner und micers. Sooner ein coacher mit horsen iss. Der witcher ben getappen Cinderella und der raggen-tatters iss gebloomen mit silken und lacen mit sparklers. On der footsers iss glassen slippers. Cinderella ben upjumpen mit clappen der handsers und squeelen mit delighters.

Der gooten witcher ben gewarnen Cinderella das magicker iss gebroken midden-nighten.

Cinderella ben off-tooten mit der coacher und arriven mit grosser pompen. Der Dancer ben proceeden mit reelers und flingen. Das Princer ben gecorten Cinderella mit dancen und winken mit sweeten-talken. Gretchen und Bertha ben wallenposies mit fussen und nailenbiten.

Suddener das clocker ben upsneaken mit gestriken der midden-nighten! Cinderella iss out-gerunnen mit muchen hasten und ben losen ein glassen slipper.

Das Princer ben gesearchen mit hunten der smallen footster das slipper iss gefitten. Gretchen und Bertha ben outsticken der footsers mit hopen. Ach! Der slipper iss fitten Bertha!

Mit grosser glee das Princer ben proposen! Bertha Hassenpfeffer iss becomen der Princesser. Cinderella ben gesitten der stover besiden mit raggen-tatters und smutten-facen.

—DAVE MORRAH.

THE AUNT AND THE SLUGGARD

By PELHAM GRENVILLE WODEHOUSE

§ *"I rely on my man Jeeves at every turn." So says Bertie Wooster, young master of the most famous butler in fiction. Proving as usual that he's a mighty handy man to have around, the ingenious Jeeves comes to the rescue again when Rocky Todd, a sedentary crony of Bertie's, finds himself hard put to fulfill the eccentric wish of a wealthy aunt. Jeeves himself nearly admits defeat in trying to solve this one.*

APRIL 22, 1916

NOW that it's all over, I may as well admit that there was a time during the rather rummy affair of Rockmetteller Todd when I thought that Jeeves was going to let me down. The man had the appearance of being baffled.

Jeeves is my man, you know. Officially he pulls in his weekly wage for pressing my clothes, and all that sort of thing; but actually he's more like what the poet Johnny called some fellow of his acquaintance who was apt to rally round him in times of need—a guide, don't you know; philosopher, if I remember rightly, and—I rather fancy—friend.

I rely on my man Jeeves at every turn.

So naturally, when Rocky Todd told me about his aunt, Jeeves was in on the thing from the start.

The affair of Rocky Todd broke loose early one morning in spring. I was in bed, restoring the good old tissues with about nine hours of the dreamless, when the door flew open and somebody prodded me in the lower ribs and began to shake the bedclothes. After blinking a bit and generally pulling myself together, I located Rocky—and my first impression was that it was a dream.

Rocky, you see, lived down on Long Island somewhere, miles away from New York; and not only that, but he had told me himself more than once that he never got up before twelve, and seldom earlier than one. Constitutionally the laziest young devil in America, his walk in life enabled him to go the limit in that direction. He was a poet. At least, he wrote poems when he did anything; but most of his time, as far as I could make out, he spent in a sort of trance. He told me once that he could sit on a fence, watching a worm and wondering what on earth it was up to, for hours at a stretch.

He had his scheme of life worked out to a fine point. About once a month he would take three days writing a few poems; the other three hundred and twenty-nine days of the year he rested. I didn't know there was enough money in poetry to support a man, even in the way in which Rocky lived; but it seems that if you stick to exhortations to young men to lead the strenuous life and don't shove in any rimes, editors fight for the stuff. Rocky showed me one of his things once. It began:

Be!
Be!
The past is dead.
To-morrow is not born.
Be to-day!
To-day!
Be with every nerve,
With every muscle,
With every drop of your red blood!
Be!

It was printed opposite the frontispiece of a magazine, with a sort of scroll round it, and a picture in the middle of a fairly nude chappie with bulging muscles, giving the rising sun the once-over. Rocky said they gave him a hundred dollars for it, and he stayed in bed till four in the afternoon for over a month.

As regarded the future, he had a moneyed aunt tucked away somewhere in Illinois; and, as he had been named Rockmetteller after her and was her only nephew, his position was pretty sound. He told me that when he did come into the money he meant to do no work at all, except perhaps an occasional poem recommending the young man with life opening out before him, with all its splendid possibilities, to light a pipe and shove his feet up on the mantelpiece.

And this was the man who was prodding me in the ribs in the gray dawn.

"Read this, Bertie!" I could just see that he was waving a letter or something equally foul in my face. "Wake up and read this!"

I can't read before I've had my morning tea and a cigarette. I groped for the bell.

Jeeves came in, looking as fresh as a dewy violet. It's a mystery to me how he does it.

"Tea, Jeeves."

"Very good, sir."

He flowed silently out of the room—he always gives you the impression of being some liquid substance when he moves; and I found that Rocky was surging round with his beastly letter again.

"What is it?" I said. "What on earth's the matter?"

"Read it!"

"I can't. I haven't had my tea."

"Well, listen, then."

"Who's it from?"

"My aunt."

At this point I fell asleep again. I woke to hear him saying: "So what on earth am I to do?"

Jeeves trickled in with the tray, like some silent stream meandering over its mossy bed.

"Read it again, Rocky, old top," I said. "I want Jeeves to hear it. Mr. Todd's aunt has written him a rather rummy letter, Jeeves, and we want your advice."

"Very good, sir."

He stood in the middle of the room, registering devotion to the cause, and Rocky started again:

" '*My dear Rockmetteller:* I have been thinking things over for a long while, and I have come to the conclusion that I have been very thoughtless to wait so long before doing what I have made up my mind to do now.' "

"What do you make of that, Jeeves?"

"It seems a little obscure at present, sir; but no doubt the lady's intention becomes clearer at a later point in the communication."

"Proceed, old scout," I said, champing my bread and butter.

" 'You know how all my life I have longed to visit New York and see for myself the wonderful gay life of which I have read so much. I fear that now it will be impossible for me to fulfill my dream. I am old and worn out. I seem to have no strength left in me.' "

"It's from us."

"Another crack like that and I'll pull your beautiful blond hair out by its ugly dark roots!"

"I could probably cure you of these periods of depression—but as you say, everything seems so futile."

"Just *read* the first line; never mind pronouncing it."

"John! . . . You got the raise!"

"How about Zoo Parade?"

FARRIS

"You rang, sir?"

"Wanna chase a few?"

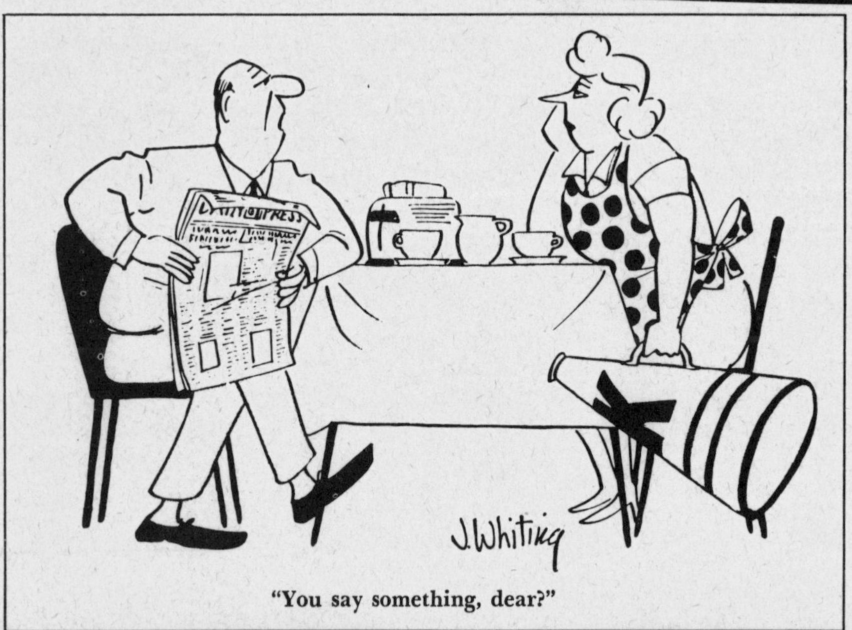

"You say something, dear?"

"Sad, Jeeves, what?"

"Extremely, sir."

"Sad nothing!" said Rocky. "It's sheer laziness. I went to see her last Christmas and she was bursting with health. Her doctor told me himself that there was nothing wrong with her whatever, and that if she would walk occasionally instead of driving, and cut her meals down to three a day, she could sign articles with Jess Willard in a couple of weeks. But she will insist that she's a hopeless invalid; so he has to agree with her. She's got a fixed idea that the trip to New York would kill her; so, though it's been her ambition all her life to come here, she stays where she is."

"Rather like the chappie whose heart was 'in the Highlands a-chasing of the deer,' Jeeves?"

"The cases are in some respects parallel, sir."

"Carry on, Rocky, dear boy."

" 'So I have decided that, if I cannot enjoy all the marvels of the city myself, I can at least enjoy them through you. I suddenly thought of this yesterday after reading a beautiful poem in the Sunday paper, by Luella Delia Philpotts, about a young man who had longed all his life for a certain thing and won it in the end only when he was too old to enjoy it. It was very sad; and it touched me.' "

"A thing," interpolated Rocky bitterly, "that I've not been able to do in ten years."

" 'As you know, you will have my money when I am gone; but until now I have never been able to see my way to giving you an allowance. I have now decided to do so—on one condition. I have written to a firm of lawyers in New York, giving them instructions to pay you quite a substantial sum each month. My one condition is that you live in New York and enjoy yourself as I have always wished to do. I want you to be my representative, to spend this money for me as I should do myself. I want you to plunge into the gay, prismatic life of New York. I want you to be the life and soul of brilliant supper parties.

" 'Above all, I want you—indeed, I insist on this—to write me letters at least once a week giving me a full description of all you are doing and all that is going on in the city, so that I may enjoy at secondhand what my wretched health prevents my enjoying for myself. Remember that I shall expect full details, and that no detail is too trivial to interest

Your affectionate aunt,

ISABEL ROCKMETTELLER.' "

"What about it?" said Rocky.

"What about it?" I said.

"Yes. What on earth am I going to do?"

It was only then that I really got on to the extremely rummy attitude of the chappie, in view of the fact that a quite unexpected mess of the right stuff had suddenly descended on him from a blue sky.

"Aren't you bucked?" I said.

"Bucked!"

"If I were in your place I should be frightfully braced. I consider this pretty soft for you."

He gave a kind of yelp, goggled at me for a moment, and then began to talk of New York in a way that reminded me of Jimmy Mundy, the evangelist chappie. Jimmy had just come to New York on a hit-the-trail campaign, and I had popped in at the Garden a couple of days before, for half an hour or so, to hear him. He had certainly handed New York some pretty hot stuff about itself, having apparently taken a dislike to the place; but, by Jove, you know, dear old Rocky made him look like a publicity agent for the old metrop!

"Pretty soft!" he yowled. "To have to come and live in New York! To have to leave my little cottage and take a damned, stuffy, smelly, overheated hole of an apartment in this heaven-forsaken, festering Gehenna! To have to mix night after night with a mob of blanked paranoiacs, who think that life is a sort of St. Vitus' dance, and imagine that they're having a good time because they're making enough noise for six and drinking too much for ten! I loathe New York, Bertie. I wouldn't come near the place if I hadn't got to see editors occasionally. There's a blight on it!

"It's got moral delirium tremens. It's the city of Dreadful Dippiness. It's the limit! It's the extreme edge. The very thought of staying more than a day in it gives me the willies clear down my spine. And you call this thing pretty soft for me!"

I felt rather like Lot's friends must have done when they dropped in for a quiet chat and their genial host began to criticize the Cities of the Plain. I had no idea old Rocky could be so eloquent.

"It would kill me to have to live in New York," he went on. "To have to share the air with six million people! To have to wear stiff collars and decent clothes all the time! To——"

He started.

"Good Lord! I suppose I should have to dress for dinner in the evenings. What a ghastly notion!"

I was shocked, absolutely shocked.

"My dear chap!" I said reproachfully.

"Do you dress for dinner every night, Bertie?"

"Jeeves," I said coldly. The man was still standing like a statue by the door. "How many suits of evening clothes have I?"

"We have three suits of full evening dress, sir, and three dinner jackets. We have also seven white waistcoats."

"And shirts?"

"Four dozen, sir."

"And white ties?"

"The first two shallow shelves in the chest of drawers are completely filled with our white ties, sir."

I turned the Rocky.

"You see?"

The chappie writhed like an electric fan.

"I won't do it! I can't do it! I'll be hanged if I'll do it! How on earth can I dress up like that? Do you realize that most days I don't get out of my pyjamas till five in the afternoon, and then I just put on an old sweater?"

I saw Jeeves wince, poor chap. This sort of revelation shocked his finest feelings.

"Then what are you going to do about it?" I said.

"That's what I want to know."

"You might write and explain to your aunt."

"I might—if I wanted her to get round to her lawyer's in two rapid leaps and cut me out of her will."

I saw his point.

"What do you suggest, Jeeves?" I said.

Jeeves cleared his throat respectfully.

"The crux of the matter would appear to be, sir, that Mr. Todd is obliged, by the conditions under which the money is delivered into his possession, to write Miss Rockmetteller long and detailed letters relating to his movements; and the only method by which this can be accomplished, if Mr. Todd adheres to his expressed intention of remaining in the country, is for Mr. Todd to induce some second party to gather the actual experiences which Miss Rockmetteller wishes reported to her, and to convey these to him in the shape of a careful report, on which it would be possible for him, with the aid of his imagination, to base the suggested correspondence."

Having got which off the old diaphragm, Jeeves was silent. Rocky looked at me in a helpless sort of way. He hasn't been brought up on Jeeves, as I have, and he isn't onto his curves.

"Could he put it a little clearer, Bertie," he said. "I thought at the start it was going to make sense, but it kind of flickered. What's the idea?"

"My dear old man, perfectly simple. I knew we could stand on Jeeves. All you've got to do is to get somebody to go round the town for you and take a few notes, and then you work the notes up into letters. That's it, isn't it, Jeeves?"

"Precisely, sir."

The light of hope gleamed in Rocky's eyes. He looked at Jeeves in a startled way, dazed by the man's vast intellect.

"But who would do it?" he said. "It would have to be a pretty smart sort of man, a man who would notice things."

"Jeeves!" I said. "Let Jeeves do it! You would, wouldn't you, Jeeves?"

For the first time in our long connection I observed Jeeves almost smile. The corner of his mouth curved quite a quarter of an inch, and for a moment his eye ceased to look like a meditative fish's.

"I should be delighted to oblige, sir. As a matter of fact, I have already visited some of New York's places of interest on my evenings out, and it would be most enjoyable to make a practice of the pursuit."

"Fine! I know exactly what your aunt wants to hear about, Rocky. She wants cabaret stuff. The place you ought to go to first, Jeeves, is Reigelheimer's. It's on Forty-second Street. Anybody will show you the way."

Jeeves shook his head.

"Pardon me, sir. People are no longer going to Reigelheimer's. The place at the moment is Frolics on the Roof."

"You see?" I said to Rocky. "Leave it to Jeeves!"

It isn't often that you find an entire group of your fellow humans happy in this world; but our little circle was certainly an example of the fact that it can be done. We were all full of beans. Everything went absolutely right from the start.

Jeeves was happy, partly because he loves to exercise his giant brain, and partly because he was having a corking time among the bright lights. I saw him one night at the Midnight Revels. He was sitting at a table on the edge of the dancing floor, doing himself remarkably well with a fat cigar and a bottle of the best. His face wore an expression of austere benevolence and he was making notes in a small book.

As for the rest of us, I was feeling pretty good, because I was fond of old Rocky and glad to be able to do him a good turn. Rocky was perfectly contented, because he was still able to sit on fences in his pyjamas and watch worms. And as for the aunt, she seemed tickled to death. She was getting Broadway at pretty long range, but it seemed to be hitting her just right. I read one of her letters to Rocky, and it was full of life.

But then Rocky's letters, based on Jeeves' notes, were enough to buck anybody up. It was rummy when you came to think of it. There was I, loving the life, while the mere mention of it gave Rocky a tired feeling; yet here is a letter I wrote home to a pal of mine in London:

Dear Freddie: Well, here I am in New York. It's not a bad place. I'm not having a bad time. Everything's pretty all right. The cabarets aren't bad. Don't know when I shall be back. How's everybody? Yours,

BERTIE.

P. S. Seen old Ted lately?

Not that I cared about old Ted; but if I hadn't dragged him in I couldn't have got the thing onto the second page.

Now here's old Rocky on exactly the same subject:

Dearest Aunt Isabel: How can I ever thank you enough for giving me the opportunity to live in this astounding city? New York seems more wonderful every day.

Fifth Avenue is at its best, of course, just now. The dresses are magnificent!—[Wads of stuff about the dresses. I didn't know Jeeves was such an authority.]

I was out with some of the crowd at

the Midnight Revels the other night. We took in a show first, after a little dinner at a new place on Forty-third Street. We were quite a gay party. Georgie Cohan looked in about midnight and got off a good one about Willie Collier. Fred Stone could only stay a minute; but Doug Fairbanks did all sorts of stunts and made us roar. Diamond Jim Brady was there, as usual, and Laurette Taylor showed up with a party. The show at the Revels is quite good. I am inclosing a program.

Last night a few of us went round to Frolics on the Roof——

And so on and so forth—yards of it. I suppose it's the artistic temperament or something. What I mean is, it's easier for a chappie who's used to writing poems and that sort of tosh to put a bit of a punch into a letter than it is for a chappie like me. Anyway, there's no doubt that Rocky's correspondence was hot stuff. I called Jeeves in and congratulated him: "Jeeves, you're a wonder!"

"Thank you, sir."

"How you notice everything at these places beats me! I couldn't tell you a thing about them, except that I've had a good time."

"It's just a knack, sir."

"Well, Mr. Todd's letters ought to brace Miss Rockmetteller all right, what?"

"Undoubtedly, sir."

And, by Jove, they did! They certainly did, by George! What I mean to say is, I was sitting in the apartment one afternoon, about a month after the thing had started, smoking and resting the old bean, when the door opened and the voice of Jeeves burst the silence like a bomb.

It wasn't that he spoke loud. He has one of those soft, soothing voices that slide through the atmosphere like the note of a far-off sheep. It was what he said that made me leap like a young gazelle:

"Miss Rockmetteller!"

And in came a large, solid female.

The situation had me weak. I'm not denying it. Hamlet must have felt much as I did when his father's ghost bobbed up in the fairway. I'd come to look on Rocky's aunt as such a permanency at her own home that it didn't seem possible that she could really be here in New York. I stared at her. Then I looked at Jeeves. He was standing there in an attitude of dignified detachment, the chump, when if ever he should have been rallying round the young master it was now.

Rocky's aunt looked less like an invalid than anyone I've ever seen, except my Aunt Agatha. She had a good deal of Aunt Agatha about her, as a matter of fact. She looked as if she might be deucedly dangerous if put upon; and something seemed to tell me that she would certainly regard herself as put upon if she ever found out the game which poor old Rocky had been pulling on her.

"Good afternoon," I managed to say.

"How do you do?" she said. "Mr. Cohan?"

"Er—no."

"Mr. Fred Stone?"

"Not absolutely. As a matter of fact, my name's Wooster—Bertie Wooster."

She seemed disappointed. The fine old name of Wooster appeared to mean nothing in her life.

"Isn't Rockmetteller home?" she said. "Where is he?"

She had me with the first shot. I couldn't think of anything to say. I couldn't tell her that Rocky was down in the country, watching worms.

There was the faintest flutter of sound in the background. It was the respectful cough with which Jeeves announces that he is about to speak without having been spoken to.

"If you remember, sir, Mr. Todd went out in the automobile with a party earlier in the afternoon."

"So he did, Jeeves; so he did," I said,

looking at my watch. "Did he say when he would be back?"

"He gave me to understand, sir, that he would be somewhat late in returning."

He vanished; and the aunt took the chair which I'd forgotten to offer her. She looked at me in rather a rummy way. It was a nasty look. It made me feel as if I were something the dog had brought in and intended to bury later on, when he had time. My own Aunt Agatha, back in England, has looked at me in exactly the same way many a time, and it never fails to make my spine curl.

"You seem very much at home here, young man. Are you a great friend of Rockmetteller's?"

"Oh, yes, rather!"

She frowned as if she had expected better things of old Rocky.

"Well, you need to be," she said, "the way you treat his apartment as your own!"

I give you my word, this quite unforeseen slam simply robbed me of the power of speech. I'd been looking on myself in the light of the dashing host, and suddenly to be treated as an intruder jarred me. It wasn't, mark you, as if she had spoken in a way to suggest that she considered my presence in the place as an ordinary social call. She obviously looked on me as a cross between a burglar and the plumber's man come to fix the leak in the bathroom. It hurt her—my being there.

At this juncture, with the conversation showing every sign of being about to die in awful agonies, an idea came to me. Tea—the good old stand-by.

"Would you care for a cup of tea?" I said.

"Tea?"

She spoke as if she had never heard of the stuff.

"Nothing like a cup after a journey," I said. "Bucks you up! Puts a bit of zip into you. What I mean is, restores you, and so on, don't you know. I'll go and tell Jeeves."

I tottered down the passage to Jeeves' lair. The man was reading the evening paper as if he hadn't a care in the world.

"Jeeves," I said, "we want some tea."

"Very good, sir."

"I say, Jeeves, this is a bit thick, what?"

I wanted sympathy, don't you know—sympathy and kindness. The old nerve centers had had the deuce of a shock.

"She's got the idea this place belongs to Mr. Todd. What on earth put that into her head?"

Jeeves filled the kettle, with a restrained dignity.

"No doubt because of Mr. Todd's letters, sir," he said. "It was my suggestion, sir, if you remember, that they should be addressed from this apartment in order that Mr. Todd should appear to possess a good central residence in the city."

I remembered. We had thought it a brainy scheme at the time.

"Well, it's bally awkward, you know, Jeeves. She looks on me as an intruder. By Jove, I suppose she thinks I'm some one who hangs about here, touching Mr. Todd for free meals and borrowing his shirts!"

"Highly probable, sir."

"It's pretty rotten, you know."

"Most disturbing, sir."

"And there's another thing: What are we to do about Mr. Todd? We've got to get him up here as soon as ever we can. When you have brought the tea you had better go out and send him a telegram, telling him to come up by the next train."

"I have already done so, sir. I took the liberty of writing the message and dispatching it by the lift attendant."

"By Jove, you think of everything, Jeeves!"

"Thank you, sir. A little buttered toast with the tea? Just so, sir. Thank you."

I went back to the sitting room. She hadn't moved an inch. She was still bolt upright on the edge of her chair, gripping her umbrella like a hammer thrower. She gave me another of those looks as I came in. There was no doubt about it; for some reason she had taken a dislike to me. I suppose because I wasn't George M. Cohan. It was a bit hard on a chap.

"This is a surprise, what?" I said, after about five minutes' restful silence, trying to crank the conversation up again.

"What is a surprise?"

"Your coming here, don't you know, and so on."

She raised her eyebrows and drank me in a bit more through her glasses.

"Why is it surprising that I should visit my only nephew?"

Put like that, of course, it did seem reasonable.

"Oh, rather," I said. "Of course! Certainly. Go the limit! What I mean is——"

Jeeves projected himself into the room with the tea. I was jolly glad to see him. There's nothing like having a bit of business arranged for one when one isn't certain of one's lines. With the teapot to fool about with, I felt happier.

"Tea, tea, tea—what? What?" I said.

It wasn't what I had meant to say. My idea had been to be a good deal more formal, and so on. Still, it covered the situation. I poured her out a cup. She sipped it and put the cup down with a shudder.

"Do you mean to say, young man," she said frostily, "that you expect me to drink this stuff?"

"Rather! Bucks you up, you know."

"What do you mean by the expression 'Bucks you up'?"

"Well, makes you full of beans, you know. Makes you fizz."

"I don't understand a word you say. You're English, aren't you?"

I admitted it. She didn't say a word. And somehow she did it in a way that made it worse than if she had spoken for hours. Somehow it was brought home to me that she didn't like Englishmen, and that if she had had to meet an Englishman I was the one she'd have chosen last.

Conversation languished again after that. I had another stab at boosting the session into a feast of reason and a flow of soul.

"Dear old Rocky——"

"Who?"

"Your nephew, you know."

"Oh!"

"He—er—always gave me the idea that you were pretty much the invalid."

"Did he?"

"Bed of sickness, and all that sort of thing, you know."

"Indeed!"

Eight bars' rest. I tried again. I was becoming more convinced every moment that you can't make a real lively salon with a couple of people, especially if one of them lets it go a word at a time.

"Are you comfortable at your hotel?" I said.

"At which hotel?"

"The hotel you're staying at."

"I am not staying at a hotel."

"Stopping with friends—what?"

"I am naturally stopping with my nephew."

I didn't get it for a moment; then it hit me. "What! Here?" I gurgled.

"Certainly. Where else should I go?"

The full horror of the situation rolled over me like a wave. I couldn't see what on earth I was to do. I couldn't explain that this wasn't Rocky's apartment without giving the poor old chap away hopelessly, because she would then ask me where he did live and then he would be right in the soup. I was trying to induce the old bean to recover from the shock and produce some results, when she spoke again:

"Will you kindly tell my nephew's manservant to prepare my room. I wish to lie down."

"Your nephew's manservant?"

"The man you call Jeeves. If Rockmetteller has gone for an automobile ride there is no need for you to wait for him. He will naturally wish to be alone with me when he returns."

I found myself tottering out of the room. The thing was too much for me. I crept into Jeeves' den.

"Jeeves!" I whispered.

"Sir?"

"Mix me a b-and-s, Jeeves. I feel weak."

"Very good, sir."

"This is getting thicker every minute, Jeeves."

"Sir?"

"I feel as if I'd been through a hold-up. Jesse James was an amateur compared with this woman. Captain Kidd wasn't in her class. She's pinched the apartment!"

"Sir?"

"Pinched it lock, stock and barrel, just as it stands, and kicked me out. And, as if that wasn't enough, she's pinched you!"

"Pinched me, sir?"

"Yes. She thinks you're Mr. Todd's man. She thinks the whole place is his, and everything in it. I don't see what you're to do, except stay on and keep it up. We can't say anything or she'll get onto the whole thing, and I don't want to let Mr. Todd down. By the way, Jeeves, she wants you to prepare her bed."

He looked wounded.

"It is hardly my place, sir—"

"I know—I know. But do it as a personal favor to me. If you come to that, it's hardly my place to be flung out of the apartment like this and have to go to a hotel, what?"

"Is it your intention to go to a hotel, sir? What will you do for clothes?"

"Good Lord! I hadn't thought of that. Can you put a few things in a bag when she isn't looking and sneak them down to me at the St. Aurea?"

"I will endeavor to do so, sir."

"Well, I don't think there's anything more, is there? Tell Mr. Todd where I am when he gets here."

"Very good, sir."

I looked round the place. The moment of parting had come. I felt sad. The whole thing reminded me of one of those melodramas where they drive chappies out of the old homestead into the snow.

"Good-by, Jeeves," I said.

"Good-by, sir."

And I staggered out.

You know, I rather think I agree with those poet-and-philosopher Johnnies who insist that a fellow ought to be devilish pleased if he has a bit of trouble. All that stuff about being refined by suffering, you know. Suffering does give a chap a sort of broader and more sympathetic outlook. It helps you to understand other people's misfortunes if you've been through the same thing yourself.

As I stood in my lonely bedroom at the hotel, trying to tie my white tie myself, it struck me for the first time that there must be whole squads of chappies in the world who had to get along without a man to look after them. When you come to think of it, there must be quite a lot of fellows who have to press their own clothes themselves, and haven't got anybody to bring them tea in the morning, and so on. It was rather a solemn thought, don't you know. I mean to say, ever since then I've been able to appreciate the frightful privations the poor have to stick.

I got dressed somehow. Jeeves hadn't forgotton a thing in his packing. Everything was there, down to the final stud. I'm not sure this didn't make me feel worse. It kind of deepened the pathos. It was like what somebody or other wrote about the touch of a vanished hand.

I had a bit of dinner somewhere and went to a show of some kind; but nothing seemed to make any difference. I simply hadn't the heart to go on to supper anywhere. I just sucked down a highball in the hotel smoking room and went straight up to bed. I don't know when I've felt so rotten. Somehow I found myself moving about the room softly, as if there had been a death in the family. If I had had anybody to talk to I should have talked in a whisper; in fact, when the telephone bell rang I answered in such a sad, hushed voice that the fellow at the other end of the wire said "Hello!" five times, thinking he hadn't got me.

It was Rocky. The poor old scout was deeply agitated.

"Bertie! Is that you, Bertie?"

"This is me, old man."

"Then why the devil didn't you answer before?"

"I did."

"I didn't hear you."

"I didn't speak very loud. I'm much narked."

"You haven't anything on me. Oh, gosh! I'm having a time!"

"Where are you speaking from?"

"The Midnight Revels. We've been here an hour and I think we're a fixture for the night. I've told Aunt Isabel I've gone out to call up a friend to join us. She's glued to a chair, with this-is-the-life written all over her, taking it in through the pores. She loves it, and I'm nearly dippy."

Rummy, how one perks up when one realizes that somebody else is copping it also! I began to feel almost braced.

"Tell me all, old top," I said.

He began to push it out at such a speed that I had to ask him to put the brake on, because all I was getting was a loud buzzing noise. The poor old hound was undoubtedly piqued, and even peeved.

"A little more of this," he said, "and I shall sneak quietly off to the river and end it all. Do you mean to say you go through this sort of thing every night, Bertie, and enjoy it? It's simply infernal! I was snatching a wink of sleep behind the bill of fare just now when about a million yelling girls swooped down, with toy balloons. There are two orchestras here, each trying to see if it can't play louder than the other. I'm a mental and physical wreck. When your telegram arrived I was just lying down for a quiet pipe with a sense of absolute peace stealing over me. I had to get dressed and sprint two miles to make the train. It nearly gave me heart failure; and on top of that I almost got brain fever inventing lies to tell Aunt Isabel. And then I had to cram myself into these damned evening clothes of yours."

I gave a sharp wail of agony. It hadn't struck me till then that Rocky was depending on my wardrobe to see him through.

"You'll ruin them!"

"I hope so," said Rocky in the most unpleasant way. His troubles seemed to have had the worst effect on his character. "I should like to get back at them somehow; they've given me a bad enough time. They're about three sizes too small, and something's apt to give at any moment. I wish to goodness it would and give me a chance to breathe. I haven't breathed since half past seven. Thank heaven, Jeeves managed to get out and buy me a collar that fitted, or I should be a strangled corpse by now. It was touch and go till the stud broke. Bertie, this is pure Hades! Aunt Isabel keeps on urging me to dance. How on earth can I dance when I don't know a soul to dance with? And how the deuce could I, even if I knew every girl in the place? It's taking big chances even to move in these trousers. I had to tell her I've hurt my ankle. She keeps asking me when Cohan and Stone are going to turn up; and it's simply a question of time before she discovers that Stone is sitting two tables away. Something's got to be done, Bertie! You've got to think up some way of getting me out of this mess. It was you who got me into it."

"Me! What do you mean?"

"Well, Jeeves, then. It's all the same. It was you who suggested leaving it to Jeeves. It was those letters I wrote from his notes that did the mischief. I made them too good! My aunt's just been telling me about it.

She says she had resigned herself to ending her life where she was, and then my letters began to arrive, boosting the joys of New York; and they stimulated her to such an extent that she pulled herself together and made the trip. She seems to think she's had some miraculous kind of faith cure. I tell you I can't stand it, Bertie! It's got to end!"

"Can't Jeeves think of anything?"

"No. He just hangs round, saying 'Most disturbing, sir!' A fat lot of help that is!"

"But, Rocky, old top, it's too bally awful! You've no notion of what I'm going through in this beastly hotel, without Jeeves. I must get back to the apartment."

"Don't come near the apartment!"

"But it's my own apartment."

"I can't help that. There's a dead line for you at the other end of the block. Aunt Isabel doesn't like you. She isn't clear in her remarks on the subject, but she says something about tea and a wrist watch. When she mentions you at all she refers to you as 'that guffin.'

"She asked me what you did for a living," Rocky went on. "And when I told her you didn't do anything she said she thought as much, and that you were a typical specimen of a useless and decaying aristocracy. So if you think you have made a hit, forget it. Now I must be going back or she'll be coming out here after me. Good-by."

Next morning Jeeves came round. It was all so homelike when he floated noiselessly into the room that I nearly broke down.

"Good morning, sir," he said. "I have brought a few more of your personal belongings."

He began to unstrap the suitcase he was carrying.

"Did you have any trouble sneaking them away?"

"It was not easy, sir. I had to watch my chance. Miss Rockmetteller is a remarkably alert lady."

"You know, Jeeves, say what you like—this *is* a bit thick, isn't it?"

"We must hope for the best, sir."

"Can't you think of anything to do?"

"I have been giving the matter considerable thought, sir, but so far without success. I am placing three silk shirts—the dove-colored, the light blue and the mauve—in the first long drawer, sir."

"You don't mean to say you can't think of anything, Jeeves?"

"For the moment, sir, no. You will find a dozen handkerchiefs and the tan socks in the upper drawer on the left." He strapped the suitcase and put it on a chair. "A curious lady, Miss Rockmetteller, sir."

"You understate it, Jeeves. By the way, Jeeves, you don't happen to know what a guffin is, do you?"

"I am afraid not, sir." He gazed meditatively out of the window. "In many ways, sir, Miss Rockmetteller reminds me of an aunt of mine who resides in the southeast portion of London. Their temperaments are much alike. My aunt has the same taste for the pleasures of the great city. It is a passion with her to ride in hansom cabs, sir. Whenever the family take their eyes off her she escapes from the house and spends the day riding about in cabs. On several occasions she has broken into the children's savings bank to secure the means to enable her to gratify this desire."

"I love to have these little chats with you about your female relatives, Jeeves," I said coldly, for I felt that the man had let me down and I was fed up with him; "but I don't see what all this has got to do with my trouble."

"I beg your pardon, sir. I am leaving a small assortment of our neckties on the mantelpiece, sir, for you to select according to your preference. I should recommend the blue with the red domino pattern, sir."

Then he streamed imperceptibly toward the door and flowed silently out.

I've often heard that chappies, after some great shock or loss, have a habit, after they've been on the floor for a while wondering what hit them, of picking themselves up and piecing themselves together, and sort of taking a whirl at beginning a new life. Time, the great healer, and Nature, adjusting itself, and so on and so forth. There's a lot in it. I know, because in my own case, after a day or two of what you might call prostration, I began to recover.

New York's a small place when it comes to the part of it that wakes up just as the rest is going to bed; and it wasn't long before my tracks began to cross old Rocky's. I saw him once at Peale's, and again at Frolics on the Roof. There wasn't anybody with him either time except the aunt, and, though he was trying to look as if he had struck the ideal life, it wasn't difficult for me, knowing the circumstances, to see that beneath the mask the poor blighter was suffering.

The next two nights I didn't come across them; but the night after that I was sitting by myself at the Maison Pierre when somebody tapped me on the shoulder blade, and I found Rocky standing beside me with a sort of mixed expression of wistfulness and apoplexy on his face. How the chappie had contrived to wear my evening clothes so many times without disaster was a mystery to me. He confided later that early in the proceedings he had slit the waistcoat up the back and that that had helped a bit.

For a moment I had the idea that he had managed to get away from his aunt for the evening; but, looking past him, I saw that she was in again. She was at a table over by the wall, looking at me as if I were something the management ought to be complained to about.

"Bertie, old scout," said Rocky in a quiet, sort of crushed voice, "we've always been pals, haven't we? I mean, you know I'd do you a good turn if you asked me?"

"My dear old lad!" I said. The man had moved me.

"Then for heaven's sake come over and sit at our table for the rest of the evening!"

Well, you know, there are limits to the sacred claims of friendship.

"My dear chap," I said, "you know I'd do anything in reason; but——"

"You must come, Bertie! You've got to! Something's got to be done to divert her mind. She's brooding about something. She's been like that for the last two days. I think she's beginning to suspect. She can't understand why we never seem to meet anyone I know at these joints. A few nights ago I happened to run into two newspaper men I used to know fairly well. That kept me going for a while. They were both a good deal more tanked than I could have wished, but I introduced them to Aunt Isabel as David Belasco and Jim Corbett, and it went well. But the effect has worn off now and she's beginning to wonder again."

I went along. One has to rally round a pal in distress. Aunt Isabel was sitting bolt upright, as usual. It certainly did seem as if she had lost a bit of the pep with which she had started out to hit it up along Broadway. She looked as if she had been thinking a good deal about rather unpleasant things.

"You've met Bertie Wooster, Aunt Isabel?" said Rocky.

"I have."

There was something in her eye that seemed to say:

"Out of a city of six million people, why did you pick on me?"

"Take a seat, Bertie. What'll you have?" said Rocky.

And so the merry party began. It was one of those jolly, happy, bread-crumbling parties where you cough twice before you speak, and then decide not to say it after all. After we had had an hour of this wild dissipation Aunt Isabel said she wanted to go home. In the light of what Rocky had been telling me, this struck me as sinister.

I had gathered that at the beginning of her visit she had had to be dragged home with ropes.

It must have hit Rocky the same way, for he gave me a pleading look.

"You'll come along, won't you, Bertie, and have a drink at the apartment?"

I had a feeling that this wasn't in the contract, but there wasn't anything to be done. It seemed brutal to leave the poor chap alone with the woman. So I went along.

I had a glimpse of Jeeves as we went into the apartment, sitting in his lair, and I wished I could have called to him to rally round. Something told me that I was about to need him.

The stuff was on the table in the sitting room. Rocky took up the decanter.

"Say when, Bertie."

"Stop!" barked the aunt. He dropped it.

I caught Rocky's eye as he stooped to pick up the ruins. It was the eye of one who sees it coming.

"Leave it there, Rockmetteller!" said Aunt Isabel; and Rocky left it there.

"The time has come to speak," she said. "I cannot stand idly by and see a young man going to perdition!"

Poor old Rocky gave a sort of gurgle, a kind of sound rather like the whisky had made running out of the decanter on to my carpet.

"Eh?" he said, blinking.

The aunt proceeded.

"The fault," she said, "was mine. I had not then seen the light. But now my eyes are open. I see the hideous mistake I have made. I shudder at the thought of the wrong I did you, Rockmetteller, by urging you into contact with this wicked city."

I saw Rocky grope feebly for the table. His fingers touched it and a look of relief came into the poor chappie's face. I understood his feelings. Once or twice after a pretty heavy night I've had to touch something solid myself—a lamp-post or something—just to make sure that the world was still there. There come moments in every fellow's life—after farewell dinners to friends about to marry, and what not—when it is not feasible to trust solely to what one sees.

"But when I wrote you that letter. Rockmetteller, instructing you to go to the city and live its life, I had not had the privilege of hearing Mr. Mundy speak on the subject of New York."

"Jimmy Mundy!" I cried.

You know how it is sometimes when everything seems all mixed up and you suddenly get a clew. When she mentioned Jimmy Mundy I began to understand more or less what had happened. I'd seen it happen before. I remember, back in England, the man I had before Jeeves sneaked off to a revivalist meeting on his evening out and came back, having got religion, and denounced me, in front of a crowd of chappies I was giving a bit of supper to, as a moral leper. All because I wouldn't start off with him that night to be a missionary in the Fiji Islands.

The aunt gave me the withering up and down.

"Yes; Jimmy Mundy!" she said. "I am surprised at a man of your stamp having heard of him. There is no music, there are no drunken, dancing men, no shameless, flaunting women at his meetings; so for you they would have no attraction. But for others, less dead in sin, he has his message. He has come to save New York from itself; to force it—in his picturesque phrase—to hit the trail. It was three days ago, Rockmetteller, that I first heard him. It was an accident that took me to his meeting. How often in this life a mere accident may shape our whole future!

"You had been called away by that telephone message from Mr. Belasco; so you could not take me to the Hippodrome, as we had arranged. I asked your manservant, Jeeves, to take me there. The man has very little intelligence. He seems to have misunderstood me. I am thankful that he did. He took me to what I subsequently learned was Madison Square Garden, where Mr. Mundy is holding his meetings. He escorted me to a seat and then left me. And it was not till the meeting had begun that I discovered the mistake which had been made. My seat was in the middle of a row. I could not leave without inconveniencing a great many people; so I remained." She gulped.

"Rockmetteller, I have never been so thankful for anything else. Mr. Mundy was wonderful! He was like some prophet of old, scourging the sins of the people. He leaped about in a frenzy of inspiration till I feared he would do himself an injury. Sometimes he expressed himself in a somewhat odd manner, but every word carried conviction. Even when he described the people of New York as an aggregation of knock-kneed prunes, something seemed to tell me what he meant and how true it was.

"He said that the tango and the fox trot were devices of the Devil to drag people down into the Bottomless Pit. He said that there was more sin in ten minutes with a Negro banjo orchestra than in all the ancient revels of Nineveh and Babylon. And when he stood on one leg and pointed right at where I was sitting, and shouted 'This means you!' I could have sunk through the floor. I came away a changed woman. Surely you must have noticed the change in me, Rockmetteller? You must have seen that I was no longer the careless, thoughtless person who had urged you to dance in those places of wickedness?"

Rocky was holding on to the table as if it was his only friend.

"Y-yes," he yammered; "I–I thought something was wrong."

"Wrong? Something was right! Everything was right! Rockmetteller, it is not too late for you to be saved. You have only sipped of the evil cup. You have not drained it. It will be hard at first, but you will find that you can do it if you fight with a stout heart against the glamour and fascination of this dreadful city. Won't you, for my sake, try, Rockmetteller? Won't you go back to the country to-morrow and begin the struggle? Little by little, if you use your will——"

I can't help thinking it must have been that word "will" that roused dear old Rocky like a trumpet call. It must have brought home to him the realization that a miracle had come off and saved him from being cut out of Aunt Isabel's. At any rate, as she said it he perked up, let go of the table, and faced her with gleaming eyes.

"Do you want me to go back to the country, Aunt Isabel?"

"Yes."

"Not to live in the country?"

"Yes, Rockmetteller."

"Stay in the country all the time, do you mean? Never come to New York?"

"Yes, Rockmetteller; I mean just that. It is the only way. Only there can you be safe from temptation. Will you do it, Rockmetteller? Will you–for my sake?"

"I will!" he said.

"Jeeves," I said. It was next day, and I was back in the old apartment, lying in the old armchair, with my feet up on the good old table. I had just come from seeing dear old Rocky off to his country cottage, and an hour before he had seen his aunt off to whatever hamlet in Illinois it was that she was the curse of; so we were alone at last. "Jeeves, there's no place like home–what?"

"Very true, sir."

"Jeeves."

"Sir?"

"Do you know, at one point in the business I really thought you were baffled."

"Indeed, sir?"

"When did you get the idea of taking Miss Rockmetteller to the meeting? It was pure genius!"

"Thank you, sir. It came to me a little

suddenly, one morning when I was thinking of my aunt, sir."

"Your aunt? The hansom-cab one?"

"Yes, sir. I recollected that, whenever we observed one of her attacks coming on, we used to send for the clergyman of the parish. We always found that if he talked to her a while of higher things it diverted her mind from hansom cabs."

I was stunned by the man's resource.

"It's brain," I said; "pure brain! What do you do to get like that, Jeeves? I believe you must eat a lot of fish, or something. Do you eat a lot of fish, Jeeves?"

"No, sir."

"Oh, well then, it's just a gift, I take it; and if you aren't born that way there's no use worrying."

"Precisely, sir," said Jeeves. "If I might make the suggestion, sir, I should not continue to wear your present tie. The green shade gives you a slightly bilious air. I should strongly advocate the blue with the red domino pattern instead, sir."

"All right, Jeeves," I said humbly. "You know!"

Crisis for a Coxswain

A POST WAR ANECDOTE

THE battleship to which I was assigned was lying at anchor in San Francisco Bay. Returning to the ship early one morning with a liberty party, I noticed that the coxswain of our launch was new and obviously not very well versed in the handling of the craft.

As we approached the battleship, the officer of the deck stepped to the top of the gangway, expecting to receive the traditional salute from the coxswain. But at this point tradition ended. To everybody's astonishment, the launch shot right past the gangway. Valiantly the inexpert coxswain brought it around, only to undershoot the gangway this time.

Then the poor fellow went completely haywire. Back and forth he jockeyed the launch, amidst shouts of encouragement from his passengers and from the hands aboard ship who gathered round the life line to enjoy the fun. Finally, after repeated efforts to reach the gangway had failed, the expression on the coxswain's face was that of a man on the verge of nervous prostration. The stern officer of the deck tried to control his emotion. But at length, as the futile maneuvering showed no signs of coming to an end, he could stand it no longer.

"Coxswain," he roared down at the wretched steersman, "just try to keep the launch where it is! I'll have the ship pull up alongside you!"

—TOM MCKELVIE.

I JUST DON'T UNDERSTAND WOMEN

By RALPH KNIGHT

§ *Women are wonderful, it says here, but don't try to comprehend what they do while shopping. Then, their behavior is nutty, devious, mad, diabolical, bizarre, crafty, sly—and womanly.*

JANUARY 26, 1952

ONE day I dropped into an arrogant men's store and bought a pair of coral-plaid slacks for $24.95, practically $24. The deal took nine minutes, the pants make me happy, and whosoever does not admire them can go look at other legs. But do you know what my wife said? She said, "You could have shopped around and got something really good for half the price. For shame!"

One, two, three, four, five and up to ten. No, I will not analyze my wife in public, for she is a good girl, barring a few normal aberrations. Gentlemen, shall we regretfully permit the ladies to retire to the drawing room while we attack the cigars and benedictine?

Okay, you guys—take an average woman. You will agree that her destiny in life is to have babies and shop. Since she probably is unsurpassed at having babies, let us chat about shopping. And since shopping is a complex science, like relativity or the game of slapjack, observe it first in its embryonic form, the acorn from which the giant sequoia grows.

An average, upper-class, intellectual woman, having coffeed her husband good-by in the morning, reads her newspaper from the back, and on a good day finds an advertisement offering to give away handbags for $9.95. Immediately she goes cuckoo. Granted, she *does* need a new rubbish-and-salary pouch, since the three she does have no longer match any of her gloves. So she leaps like a fireman into her nattiest garments—taking, however, about two hours longer than firemen do. And her expense account for the day follows: suburban train fare into big city 76 cents; subway 15 cents; bag $12.60 because cheaper ones are sold; conscience-stricken lunch at soda fountain instead of planned restaurant $1.10; tip 10 cents; bargain necktie for husband $2.99; taxi to station (good land, it's nearly dinner-time!) 60 cents; tip 25 cents; train fare away from big city 76 cents—grand total cost of $9.95 handbag $19.31. Let us now consider shopping in its more complex or malignant forms.

Consider the word "around," as in "shopping around." One morning on the subway, I remarked to my neighbor Hanko Smith that of course every friend at that hour is normally contemptible, but that he was acting rather like the Evil One in person. He said it was because his wife took him out the preceding noon to select a suit for her, he having inadvertently blurted, when he saw her last new suit, "Black again, to match everything. Too late to change it for a short, tight, scarlet one?"

It seems that they went into a great feminine bazaar and that Mrs. Hanko either pinched or tried on every suit in the museum. Then, thanking the sales damsel heartily, she said that none of them quite suited her; and Hanko was so embarrassed that he tried to crawl through the floor, but couldn't, so they left by the regular door. Consequently they had to take another hour of Hanko's time and ravish another store, but unhappily again departed unsuitable, this time with Hanko's embarrassment trickling off of him in the form of water.

To make a long agony short, I gathered from Hanko's disorganized memoirs that along about five o'clock Mrs. H. sensed through her mania that her husband seemed a little cross and decided that they would have dinner in town, being in town anyway. She ate a simple meal of beefsteak and home fries, to keep in training, and Hanko drank his, four stingers, which took the sting out of being told, when his eyes looked glassy enough, that this was the evening the stores were open until nine o'clock. Being then as high as a suit price, Hanko actually enjoyed the next two stores, pretending that the dame with him was a chorus girl or at least a movie character actor of young matronly roles. But right in the middle of the third store, suddenly he went cold sober, as if somebody had slapped him across the face with a twill skirt, and Mrs. H., seeing the awful way he was glaring at her, got him out of there fast, just before the blast went off.

"Hanko," I exclaimed to him in that subway train next morning, "congratulations! Think of the money you have saved!"

"Ralpho," groaned he, rolling up his newspaper into the shape of a small bomb and dropping it with a disappointing silence on the floor, "she has decided to buy the simple battleship-gray tweed that she liked so much in the first store at a quarter past noon." We then arrived at our station and reeled off to work before he got hysterics. Let us now consider window shopping.

Window shopping—the ladies in the drawing room can't hear our discussion of politics, can they, gentlemen?—window shopping is not, as cartoonists and advertising executives believe, a means of softening up husbands or even unprotected women for the kill. It is an exact, isolated female science or excess having nothing to do with commerce. Men without women do sometimes look into a window, but after two or three minutes they always louse up the idea by going in and buying something.

The idea is to buy eleven thousand dollars' worth of goods and chattels through some windowpanes and wind up with nothing whatever but a weird dose of exaltation.

For example, a young matrimonial apprentice named William, being on his honeymoon and in a temporary hypnosis, agreed to stroll up Fifth Avenue with his bride to savor the fresh air. They took off from 42nd Street at two P.M. and at sundown had mushed clear up to 47-and-a-halfth Street. The bride had paused at every corset, *objet d'art*, diamond, jade ash tray, Louis Quinze kitchen cabinet and handkerchief, and trilled, "Do you like it, dear? Or don't you, really?" William had raved in each instance, "Nice." But when night fell, and they were practically alone on the pike, the way it is evenings in almost any small town, William suddenly revolted. "Those coats? Don't like either the blue mink or the chinchilla."

"Why," cried his startled bride, "either one would go with my black suit!"

"Look, precious," William ventured adoringly, "what we have liked in five blocks would bankrupt the Savings and Loan Association, but I love you."

"But I haven't spent a cent!" the woman pointed out. "Listen, darling. You've just got to adjust to not buying me everything you'd like to. For years and years we've got to live like the Thoreaus on Walden Pond, and as far as I'm concerned, I feel like a million dollars."

William leaned against a forty-story building and whispered, "I'm tired in my mind and legs."

"Darling," glowed his bride, glancing in a window, "let's go someplace and dance the night away!" Wherefore they did, like light-toed elves gavotting on moonlit clover leaves. And since we are still talking about shopping, this brings us to the weaker sex—men.

Tairy Fales for the Fittle Lokes—and Bigger Toople, Peep!

Little Ride Hooding Red

Modern Spoonerism by Colonel Stoopnagle

A LONG time ago, even before Frenjamin Banklin invented the Patterday Evening Soast, a gittle lurl named Ride Hooding Red started out through a fick thorest to take a lasket of bunch to her grick sandmother. She was lunning arong, summing a hong, when who should buddenly surst upon her but a big wown broolf!

"Gare are you whoaing, my mitty little prayed?" said the berocious feast, with a wry file on his ugly smace.

"To my handmother's grouse," said the minnocent aiden, "to take her a sandful of handwiches and some pill dickles. She is very bick in sed with a fie heaver."

"For the sand lakes!" ride the croolf, "in that case, give me the bitty prasket and I will run with it to your cotmother's grammage. Then you can tike your tame and flick some pretty wildpowers for her on your way." So little Red Hiding Rood gave the bass the wolfket and off he went.

Finally, Little Hood Redding Ride reached her Hanny's grouse. The mean, wolfwhile, had somehow disgranned of the poor old spoaze-mother and had bumped into jed with the old naidy's lightgown on.

Hood Riding Red took a grander at what she thought was her gandmother and said, "Oh, grandmother, what igg byes you have!"

"The setter to bee you with, my dear," wed the soolf.

"Oh, granny," ged the surl, "and what tigg beeth you have!"

"The chetter to boo you up with!" said the wafty croolf, and with that, he beeped out of led. Then it was that Red Hiding Rood saw it was grand her notmother, but that woolful awf.

And here, let is brawze peefly to ted a shear for our hair little purrow-in.

But the endy has a happy storing, jadies and lentlemen, for suddenly, out of a steer clye, came seven woodsy huskmen, who not only gatched the little snurl from the daws of jeth, but grabbed the threest by the boat and hopped off his chedd.

Now Hide Red Hooding is en-maged to garry a margent in the serenes, and is harry, harry, vappy. And although she grisses her dear old manny, she is certainly glad that the wolf who told such forrible hibs lies, door as a deadnail, in Fotter's Peeled.

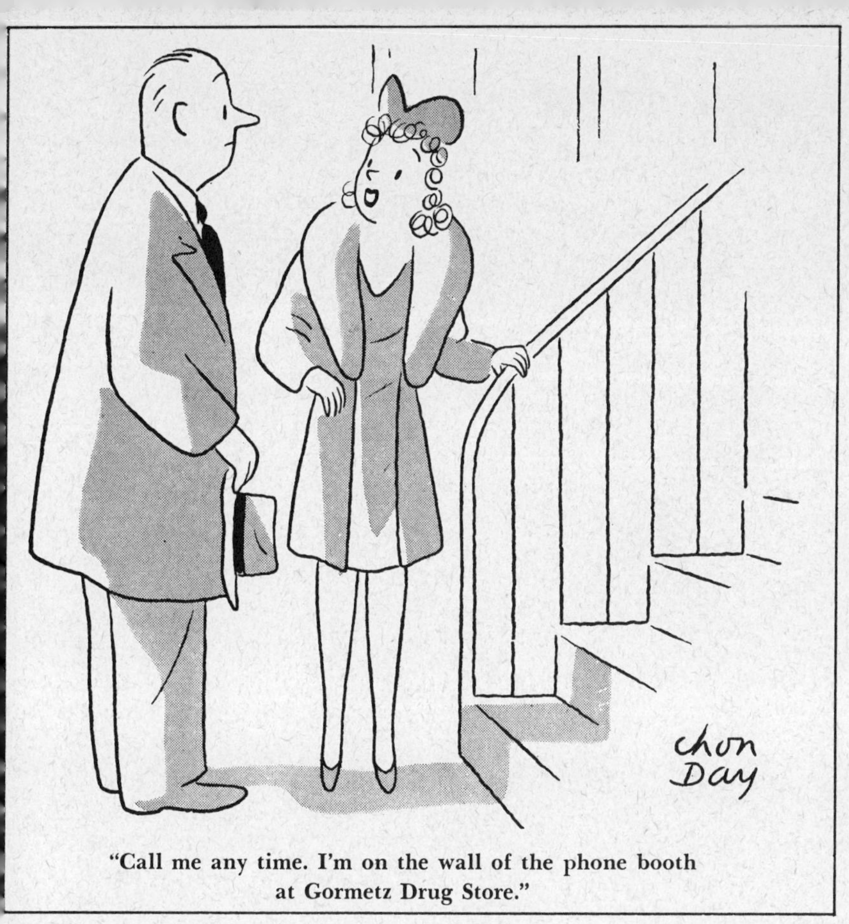

"Call me any time. I'm on the wall of the phone booth at Gormetz Drug Store."

"Come on, baby, defrost a little!"

"We'll leave New York on Monday, spend the night in Virginia, Mississippi by Tuesday, Texas by Wednesday, New Mexico by Thursday and the Grand Canyon on Friday at the latest."

"Did you see what the moths did to my overcoat?"

SEVERE PUNISHMENT.

BERENSTAIN

“But they *sting*!

THERE IS LIFE IN THE OLD GAL YET, AL

By WILL ROGERS

§ *In one of his famous political commentaries on the times, Will Rogers swipes back an unruly cowlick and takes a look at some of his contemporaries and the issues they faced. If you're slightly hazy about what was what at the time, it doesn't matter. Things were a little hazy to our peerless leaders, too, though only Rogers said so.*

JANUARY 19, 1929

DEAR AL: I just thought I would take my pen in hand and drop you a few lines. This is not one of those "Too bad, old boy, we will get 'em the next time" letters. This is from an old friend who ever once in a while drops you a line, and tries to be truthful and lay some facts before you as they are, and Not as Political Leaders tell you they are.

Now, I knew you was pretty busy up to around November, and I dident want to bother you, cause this thing of running for President takes up just as much time on the Democratic side as it would on some side where you had a chance. Now you got time to sit down and think it over, I want to run over some things with you—talk over what we might 'a' done, pass over what we did do, and hold a sort of a Clinic over the old Democratic body and see just how much life there is in the old Gal yet.

Now let's get back and start at the beginning of this Presidential Bee that originally backed up to you and sit down. It was way back in 1920 in Frisco, when the Democrats had met to draft a Victim, and Franklin Roosevelt—who, with yourself, constitute just about the only two that anybody can pick for an All-American Democratic Team—he was just starting in on his nominating career of you for President; that was his maiden nominating speech. He dident have it memorized then, and had to read it. Now, here is something that I want to bring up: If you remember, there was some talk of nominating Hoover at that same convention. He hadent been back from Europe long and nobody knew just what he was. Some of 'em thought, on account of his working over there in such harmony with President Wilson, that he was a Democrat. Well, if they had known anything, that very fact should have showed 'em he was not a Democrat.

Consistent in Bad Luck

He had just made a marvelous record of full feeding some Belgiums, and he looked like a man that, on account of his uncanny ability of providing food where it was impossible to get any, why, the Democrats figured that "here is the man that can provide nourishment for the next four years for us." Any man that can find grub for a Belgian in a war-strewn land, ought to be able to give political sustenance to a Party that looks like it will have the Post Offices shot from under them on November 2, 1920.

Now, while this fellow Hoover had been keeping our sugar down to one lump a day, and had us eating Bran—like a cow—instead of bread—why, if we had stayed on that bran mash for another year we would have sprouted horns—he had been slipping these extra Titbits which he was depriving us of, off to the gaunt and lean Armenians. But after his return over here he had enough spare time to detect that one of the Issues of the coming November Follies would be the League of Nations. Now, in his rambles all over the uncivilized World with his forked switch, which would turn down when it got over a certain piece of ground that needed some engineering feat to make it bear forth pay dirt, he had also stopped long enough to give Human Nature, as well as old Mother Earth's formation, a little study. In other words, his mind was not entirely on his trypod.

After his return over here, he had set up his sextant to get some observations on National Thought. He hadent peeped through the little mechanical gadget long before he discovered that this "pure and holy love" between Europe and ourselves was kinder listed to about forty-five degrees, on both sides of the water. His practical engineering mind showed him that we figured about as follows: We dragged Europe out of a Bog Hole once, but we don't want to have to stand there on the bank the rest of our lives to see if they crawl back in again. We dident mind feeding 'em, but we just dident wish to sign a contract with 'em. We might come over again if we wanted to, but we dident want to have any signed papers to that effect. Who they fought from now on would be their own business; if they over-matched themselves they would have to look out. In other words, we dident mind associating with 'em in a casual way, but we just dident want to get married to 'em.

Now, knowing these facts as he did, and knowing that the League of Nations would be the issue, he also knew that one Political Party would take one side, and the other the other. Now, although he had spent a great part of his life in Siberia and Patagonia, he had kept in close enough touch with American elections to know that in any question that had two sides—and if one side had a lot more people for it than the other—that a Party called the Democrats would pick the side with the fewest votes. Now, he knew that—and even the Siberians and Patagonians knew it. I don't know why it is, Al, but us Democrats just seem to have an uncanny premonition of sizing up a question and guessing wrong on it. It almost makes you think sometimes it is done purposely. You can't make outsiders believe it's not done purposely. For they don't think people could purposely make that many mistakes accidentally. And what makes it funny is we get the first pick. It was practically the Democrats' war; their Administration had carried it through to a successful conclusion, and did a mighty good job of it, and naturally had the first guess as to what most of the people wanted to do after it was all over—did the people want to sign up with Europe or not? Now, it's as I say—the Democrats had their pick; they could have said, "No, people don't want the League." But they said, "Yes, we must have the League." See, they had the first pick and grabbed the wrong side by seven million. Now, Mr. Hoover knew that the Democrats would grab off the minority side, so he pulls his first wise Political move. He dident exactly say that he wasent one of you, but he dident allow you to use his name at the head of your Stationary that year as a Candidate for the Presidency. I really believe, if us Democrats had had anything good in the way of a Vehicle to get somewhere in, that he would have signed up with us. He seemed to have an open mind, but we just dident have any attractive proposition to offer him. If we had been smart, we would have picked him up then and said to him, "Here, write yourself out a Platform; we will turn the whole idea over to you, and all we want is results. We will even forgive you if you Don't mention 'Jeffersonian Principles' and 'Back to Jacksonian Democracy.' All we want out of this thing is to be able to keep on handing out the mail." But no, we couldent see a Big man when he stood right before us. If we had turned our business over to him then, let him do the guessing on what side of a public question to get on, instead of us, we would 'a' been the side that would have got credit for all that Prosperity when everything was so high after the war.

Cold Business and Ideals

All you would 'a' had to do was to just get in and let the Government run itself. We had everything to sell after the war; the world had to buy it. Why, I myself could have taken the Government and Mellon, and made money with it. Then we would have been known as the Prosperity Party. So you see just how a few little wrong moves away back early in the game changes the whole destiny of Parties. If we dident know which side of a problem to get on, why dident we ask the Literary Digest to hold a Poll and find out for us? But No! We had Our Principles, Our Ideals! So we just lost the Post Offices for what looks like the rest of our natural lives. That's why the Republicans always get somewhere—They have No Ideals; It's just Cold Business with those Babies. You don't hear those Guys shouting about, "Get us back to the Lincolnian Principles, or the Taftonian methods." No, Sir, they know this is a fast-moving Country, that the people don't want to "go back" to anything; they want to go forward—or what they think is forward; it may be backward, but if they think it's forward, let 'em have their own way about it. But now to get back to my story: We let Hoover go, and he goes right over and signs up with the opposition as Secretary of Commerce as soon as the election is over. 'Course, it was not much of a job and not much of a Salary, but he showed that he was willing to start at the bottom if he could get in with some going concern. It was really no more than an Auditor's job. All he had to do was to keep track of how much we was buying and how much we was peddling to other Countries. They allowed him to come in and sit with the Cabinet, and several others was there in about the same capacity; and each one read their little reports—Hoover on "Exports—One Billion; Imports, Known —One-Half Billion; Imports, Unknown—Four Billion." Then he was through for the day.

Then Will Hayes would get up and read his: "So many letters sent; so many letters lost; letters received, so-and-so." Then the Secretary of Agriculture would read his little say: "Farms in U. S., Eleven million; Farms mortgaged, Eleven million; farms carrying second mortgage, 10,998,634. The Department reports progress."

Then the Secretary of War would read his Department's record for the last week: "Wars, none; Peace, none; average, 50 per cent." Secretary of the Navy's Cabinet report for the week: "Ships, 950; ships sunk in compliance with Washington Disarmament agreement, 345. Would have sunk more, but run out of ammunition—some were very hard to sink. Cost of sinking, exceeded cost of building; would recommend in next Disarmament Conference that other Nations be asked to bear part of our sinking cost; also have learned from reliable sources—Not Diplomatic—that England and Japan, in accordance with our Disarmament Treaty with them, completed 83 Battleships each. The 5-5-3 Treaty is being strictly adhered to; we sink five in the morning, five in the afternoon, and they build three at night. I am able to report to the President and the Cabinet that on strict investigation I have found we can hold one more Naval Disarmament Conference, but not more. If we held a second one we would have to borrow a boat to go to it."

Jim Davis, Sec. of Labor, responded to the Toastmaster as follows: "Number of people laboring—ten million; people living off people laboring—ninety-eight million—including twenty-three million Government and State Employes. Unemployment is confined practically to College Graduates and Harvard men. No prospect of relief for this type of unemployment until education system is changed to teach them to work, instead of teaching them that with an education they won't have to."

Taking a Little Job Seriously

The Secretary of Interior arose. "On account of some slight Publicity having been attached to some previous leases made by Our Department, we can report nothing but Investigations during the past week." Attorney General responds to the toast: "What's wrong with Justice?" "I won't commit myself. If I did, I would be overruled by four of the Supreme Court, and the other three would vote, as usual, against the four." 'Course, then, that left no one there to talk over affairs of importance, but Sec. of State Hughes, Mr. Mellon, and President Coolidge; Dawes having in the meantime walked out on 'em, saying, as he fondled his old Possum-Bellied pipe: "Hell and Maria, these Cabinet wakes are dryer than a farm-relief Bill."

But this feller Hoover, instead of going out, like the other Cabinet Members, to play Golf when they finished reading their weekly reports, he used to kinder hang around to see what Calvin and Andy and Charley was gabbing about. They dident mind him, and he dident have much to say: In other words, he sorter seemed to take this Cabinet job kinder serious. He kept monkeying around with this Commerce outfit till he got it to amounting to something among Government Departments. So to humor and encourage him, they used to let him stay in the Cabinet meetings after all the others had gone, and listen to what Coolidge, Hughes and Mellon was discussing. He come in mighty handy if they had just got a Note from some foreign Country; he could tell 'em who, and where, the Country was. He knew most of the men personally that they were hearing from Diplomatically. 'Course, if it was from some Republican up in Massachusetts—in the old days, when they had Republicans up there—why, Mr. Coolidge would know who it was from; Hughes would know him if he had ever had a Lawsuit; and Mellon could tell you his Bank rating and all about his politics if he come from Pennsylvania—outside Philadelphia.

Knowing When to Refuse

Then, Hoover, being a great Red Cross man, he picked up a few Tornadoes and Hurricanes to kinder help fill in his spare time, and now and agin a flood to sorter keep his hand in feeding the destitute. The first thing you know he had made himself so valuable at it that it looked like we couldent have a Calamity till he could get there to handle it. A lot of Calamitys that would have happened, we had to hold 'em off just on that account, for the man was booked up.

Then comes the Conventions of the summer of 1924. We better just skip over ours in Madison Square Garden. By the way, that was the only Calamity that Hoover was not put in charge of. He could have done a great relief work there, for there is nothing that ever come under my observations that needed real Humane treatment worse than a Destitute Deligate. So we will get on to the Republican Convention in Cleveland—and there is where Hoover really showed himself a Genius. They wanted him to run for Vice President, and he turned it down; he knew what splendid care Mr. Coolidge took of himself. You see, he dident just grab at the first thing come along. He had an idea in his head, and was willing to wait for it.

What I am a getting at, Al, is this: This fellow is where he is today because he knew when to refuse something that he knew wouldent get him anywhere. He struggled along for eight years just practically as a Bill of Laden Clerk and a First-Aid Kit to Catastrophes, but look where he wound up. You see, all this is right along the line that I wrote you that other letter away back in October, 1927. I was trying to tell you, you got to wait for things till they are ripe; don't just jump into things, just because somebody offers it to you. Look and see if it's going to lead you anywhere. Now, after I wrote you that letter, a lot of your own Party thought I was all wet and dident know anything about it. Now I am not rewriting you any of that letter to rub it in, for you took your defeat in too good a manner. You was a good Sport and dident let out a single Squawk. But I repeat these to try and show not only you but the Party, why do we keep on doing things, elections after elections, that we absolutely know won't get us anywhere.

Here it is word for word, written a year and a half ago:

> I, Al Smith, of my own free will and accord, do this day relinquish any claim or promise that I might have of any support or Deligates at the next Democratic Convention. I don't want to hinder what little harmony there is left in the party; I not only do not choose to run, but I refuse to run. But will give all my time and talents to work faithfully for whoever is nominated by the party.

And the following is the reason I gave you:

"Now, Al, if you will send 'em this letter you will look like you are sacrificing yourself, and in '32 they will nominate you by radio; they can't help it, and you will have a united Party. A half-wit knew you all couldent win in '24. Well, it's the same this year; you couldent put on a revival of Thomas Jefferson and get away with it.

"Even if they don't run Coolidge, they will let it be known that his same Cabinet will be retained. It's that Cabinet you can't beat, Al. But they can't stay in there for ever, and Prohibition, at the present rate of enforcement, will be much more of an Issue than it is this time. Let 'em nominate a Dry Democrat. Naturally he will be defeated, not because he is a dry but because he is a Democrat. Then, that will make your policy twice as strong four years from now. Al, don't let those New Yorkers kid you—this country is dry. Listen: If you think this Country ain't wet, you watch 'em drink; and If you think this Country ain't Dry, you watch 'em vote. When they vote, it's counted; but when they drink, it ain't. If you could register the Voter's breath instead of his ballot, it would be different. Besides, you got no Platform, you got no Issue, you can't ask people to throw somebody out just because somebody else wants in. You meet too many Democratic Leaders—that's what's the matter with the Party—these same Leaders not knowing any more about Public Opinion than they do. That's why they are Democratic Leaders."

Not Enough Votes Per Voter

"Then, you New Yorkers get a wrong prospectus of things. The outsider don't care nothing about New York, and if you think Tammany Hall is an asset, you just run and try to carry them with you, and you will find you have been overhandicapped. Now it ain't that you ain't strong, Al; you are strong—you are the strongest thing the Democrats have had in years. No Democrat could come near you—But it's not a Democrat that you meet in the finals; It's a Republican. Everybody is always asking, 'What's the matter with the Democratic Party?' There ain't nothing wrong with it; it's a Dandy old Party. The only thing wrong with it is the law killed it. It won't let a man vote but once, and there just ain't enough voters at one vote each to get it anywhere. You can't lick this Prosperity thing; even the fellow that hasent got any is all excited over the idea. You Politicians have got to look further ahead; you always got a Putter in your hands, when you ought to have a Driver. Now, Al, I am trying to tell you how to be President, Not how to be a Candidate."

But it's all over, and you made a great race—about six million votes better than anyone else in your Party could have done. And you give the Republicans the Durndest scare they had in years. You Had Mr. Hughes running around speaking every night, and any time anything can keep him up after nine o'clock it is a triple threat. And you got nothing to ever feel downhearted over.

Come and Bring Your Friends

Now, Al, I like you Democrats; you are sorter my kind of people, but I am just sick and tired seeing the whole thing mismanaged. So I have decided to take it over and see what we can salvage out of it. But you all got to take my advice from now on. If I see fit not to start an Entry in '32, why we won't start any. I am tired seeing good men killed off for nothing; I am tired seeing one Party that is not One Bit better than the other, Just Continually outsmart us. Those Guys can be beat, but Not with Jeffersonian and Jacksonian speeches. If a national question comes up, there is no sensible reason why we shouldent be on the Popular side, instead of the Right side all the time. Leave our old Political Leaders in the Senate, where they can't do anybody any good or harm, but hide 'em when a Campaign is on; they been making the same speeches since they was weaned. There is absolutely millions of people in this country who are not even half pleased with the way these Republicans run things, but they prefer 'em to the Democrats' old-fashioned ideas. Now, taken out from under the influence of a lot of these old Mossbacks, you are a pretty progressive fellow, Al, and with you and this fellow Roosevelt as a kind of neclus, I think we can, with a lot of help from some Progressive young Democratic governors and senators and congressmen, why, we can make this thing into a Party, instead of a Memory. Get Raskob back on those Chervolets again. He may know what Wall Street is going to do, but none of those Guys have got a vote. We don't need a Financier; we need a Magician. And let Norris and Blaine and the rest of them go back to where they come from—whereever that was. That is one of the strictest rules I will have in the future: "Don't let anybody join us unless he is bringing somebody with him."

Now, I will see you around New York during the winter—unless you run onto something. I will write you more about my plans soon. They are all practical; they are not New, but they are new to the Democrats. With four years to work on, we may land Coolidge. Things won't look so rosy when he has to look at them from the outside.

Well, I must close, Al. Good luck to you and all the Smith tribe. Met your Daughter the other night at a dinner over at Mrs. Chas. Dana Gibson's. Now, Al, while you ain't doing nothing will you do me a favor and work on that pronunciation of "Radio."

Yours,

WILL.

P. S.: Al, I am going to run this thing like Mussolini—that's what these Democrats need. I will even give 'em Castor oil.

Or in and Bear Left

I DON'T want to be classed among the pedantics,
But next time I visit friends who have moved to the country I want to get together with them on terminology, or semantics.
When you ask them on the telephone how to get there they smilingly cry that it is simple,
In fact you can practically see them dimple—
You just drive on Route 402 to Hartley and then bear left a couple of miles till you cross a stream,
Which they imply is alive with tench, chub, dace, ide, sturgeon and bream,
And you go on till you reach the fourth road on the right,
And you can't miss their house because it is on a rise and it is white.
Well, it's a neighborhood of which you have never been a frequenter,
But you start out on 402 and soon find yourself trying to disentangle Hartley from East Hartley, West Hartley, North and South Hartley and Hartley Center,
And you bear left a couple of miles, peering through the windshield, which is smattered with gnats and midges,
And suddenly the road is alive with bridges,
And your tires begin to scream
As you try to decide which bridge spans a rill, which a run, which a branch, which a creek, which a brook or river, and which presumably a stream.
And having passed this test, you begin to count roads on the right, than which no more exhausting test is to be found,
For who is to say which is a road, which a lane, which a driveway and which just a place where somebody backed in to turn around?
But anyhow, turning around seems a good idea, so there is one thing I don't know still:
Whether that white house where the cocktails are getting warm and the dinner cold is on a ridge, a ledge, a knoll, a rise or a hill.

—OGDEN NASH.

The Octopus

THE Octopus is much misunderstood. He is always judged by his appearance, which leaves him nowhere. In making up their minds about an animal, most people place too much emphasis upon mere external beauty, entirely neglecting such matters as character and inner worth. I have a slight tendency to do this myself, but I'm trying to get over it.[1] Octopuses are not nearly so awful as they are supposed to be. They are shy by nature and prefer to avoid larger forms of life. Shyness can be overdone, of course, but in an Octopus it is a very lovable trait. The Octopus hides among rocks in the sea, waving his arms and attaching them by their suction cups to any object within reach. He is after a square meal of Crabs and other sea food. If he catches you by mistake, it isn't his fault, is it? He has you, however, and he doesn't let go, because that is the way Octopuses are.[2] Never attempt to pry his arm loose from your torso. He has seven other arms. Just squeeze his neck as hard as you can and he'll stop. If this doesn't work, try to think of something else quick.[3] Octopuses are cephalopods, or head-footed mollusks. The head and foot are combined, so that neither is quite what it should be. This would not do for us, as we use our feet a lot and they have to be good. The mouth is near the middle of the foot, which is divided into eight arms, or tentacles, and what looks like the head of the Octopus is the rest of his body. That's why his neck is up where it is. As if that weren't enough, they have blue blood.[4] The Common Octopus is smallish, measuring only a few feet from tip to tip. The Giant Octopus is much larger and I strongly advise you to keep out of his den.[5] The Movie Octopus is terrific. Sometimes a male Octopus goes through a special routine for a lady Octopus he admires. He changes from brown to yellow, red, purple, violet and blue, and flexes his biceps, four or five at a time. After watching this for an hour or so, she turns pink and everybody's happy.[6] Octopuses also fight, tangling all their sixteen arms in a ferocious embrace. When Octopuses embrace, it is really something. They must find it a little difficult to break away.

—WILL CUPPY.

1 I'll let you know how I make out.

2 Octopuses do not develop their minds. They get by, and that's all they care.

3 You'll find his neck a few inches above his eyes. I almost forgot to tell you.

4 This is caused by the presence of hemocyanin instead of the usual hemoglobin. I happen to know this for a fact and I see no reason for keeping it to myself.

5 He may have his better side, too, but you needn't pal around with him. One has to draw the line somewhere.

6 The hen Octopus hangs her eggs on a rock at the bottom of the ocean and squirts water on them until they hatch. I'm not criticizing. I'm just telling you.

Put It This Way

You can't always tell what makes a man tick until you meet his wife. She may be the works.

He who takes no for an answer is usually a parent.

A girl who watches her figure isn't the only one.

—FRANKLIN P. JONES.

SOME LIKE THEM COLD

By RING W. LARDNER

§ It was romance right from the start when "Mr. Man" just happened to sit down beside of a mighty pretty girlie who was waiting to meet her sister from Toledo in the Lasalle st. station . . .

OCTOBER 1, 1921

N. Y., AUG. 3.

DEAR MISS GILLESPIE: How about our bet now as you bet me I would forget all about you the minute I hit the big town and would never write you a letter. Well girlie it looks like you lose so pay me. Seriously we will call all bets off as I am not the kind that bet on a sure thing and it sure was a sure thing that I would not forget a girlie like you and all that is worrying me is whether it may not be the other way round and you are wondering who this fresh guy is that is writeing you this letter. I bet you are so will try and refreshen your memory.

Well girlie I am the handsome young man that was wondering round the Lasalle st. station Monday and "happened" to sit down beside of a mighty pretty girlie who was waiting to meet her sister from Toledo and the train was late and I am glad of it because if it had not of been that little girlie and I would never of met. So for once I was a lucky guy but still I guess it was time I had some luck as it was certainly tough luck for you and I to both be liveing in Chi all that time and never get together till a half hour before I was leaveing town for good.

Still "better late than never" you know and maybe we can make up for lost time though it looks like we would have to do our makeing up at long distants unless you make good on your threat and come to N. Y. I wish you would do that little thing girlie as it looks like that was the only way we would get a chance to play round together as it looks like they was little or no chance of me comeing back to Chi as my whole future is in the big town. N. Y. is the only spot and specially for a man that expects to make my liveing in the song writeing game as here is the Mecca for that line of work and no matter how good a man may be they don't get no recognition unless they live in N.Y.

Well girlie you asked me to tell you all about my trip. Well I remember you saying that you would give anything to be makeing it yourself but as far as the trip itself was conserned you ought to be thankfull you did not have to make it as you would of sweat your head off. I know I did specially wile going through Ind. Monday P.M. but Monday night was the worst of all trying to sleep and finely I give it up and just layed there with the prespiration rolling off of me though I was laying on top of the covers and nothing on but my underwear.

Yesterday was not so bad as it rained most of the A.M. comeing through N.Y. state and in the P.M. we road along side of the Hudson all P.M. Some river girlie and just looking at it makes a man forget all about the heat and everything else except a certain girlie who I seen for the first time Monday and then only for a half hour but she is the kind of a girlie that a man don't need to see her only once and they would be no danger of forgetting her. There I guess I better lay off that subject or you will think I am a "fresh guy."

Well that is about all to tell you about the trip only they was one amuseing incidence that come off yesterday which I will tell you. Well they was a dame got on the train at Toledo Monday and had the birth opp. mine but I did not see nothing of her that night as I was out smokeing till late and she hit the hay early but yesterday A.M. she come in the dinner and sit at the same table with me and tried to make me and it was so raw that the dinge waiter seen it and give me the wink and of course I paid no tension and I waited till she got through so as they would be no danger of her folling me out but she stopped on the way out to get a tooth pick and when I come out she was out on the platform with it so I tried to brush right by but she spoke up and asked me what time it was and I told her and she said she geussed her watch was slow so I said maybe it just seemed slow on acct. of the company it was in.

I don't know if she got what I was driveing at or not but any way she give up trying to make me and got off at Albany. She was a good looker but I have no time for gals that tries to make strangers on a train.

Well if I don't quit you will think I am writeing a book but will expect a long letter in answer to this letter and we will see if you can keep your promise like I have kept mine. Don't disappoint me girlie as I am all alone in a large city and hearing from you will keep me from getting home sick for old Chi though I never thought so much of the old town till I found out you lived there. Don't think that is kidding girlie as I mean it.

You can address me at this hotel as it looks like I will be here right along as it is on 47th. st. right off of old Broadway and handy to everything and am only paying $21 per wk. for my rm. and could of got one for $16 but without bath but am glad to pay the differents as am lost without my bath in the A.M. and sometimes at night too.

Tomorrow I expect to commence fighting the "battle of Broadway" and will let you know how I come out that is if you answer this letter. In the mean wile girlie au reservoir and don't do nothing I would not do.

Your new friend (?)
CHAS. F. LEWIS.

CHICAGO, ILL., AUG. 6.

MY DEAR MR. LEWIS: Well, that certainly was a "surprise party" getting your letter and you are certainly a "wonder man" to keep your word as I am afraid most men of your sex are gay deceivers but maybe you are "different." Any way it sure was a surprise and will gladly pay the bet if you will just tell me what it was we bet. Hope it was not money as I am a "working girl" but if it was not more than a dollar or two will try to dig it up even if I have to "beg, borrow or steal."

Suppose you will think me a "case" to make a bet and then forget what it was, but you must remember, Mr. Man, that I had just met you and was "dazzled." Joking aside I was rather "fussed" and will tell you why. Well, Mr. Lewis, I suppose you see lots of girls like the one you told me about that you saw on the train who tried to "get acquainted" but I want to assure you that I am not one of those kind and sincerely hope you will believe me when I tell you that you was the first man I ever spoke to meeting them like that and my friends and the people who know me would simply faint if they knew I ever spoke to a man without a "proper introduction."

Believe me, Mr. Lewis, I am not that kind and I don't know now why I did it only that you was so "different" looking if you know what I mean and not at all like the kind of men that usually try to force their attentions on every pretty girl they see. Lots of times I act on impulse and let my feelings run away from me and sometimes I do things on the impulse of the moment which I regret them later on, and that is what I did this time, but hope you won't give me cause to regret it and I know you won't as I know you are not that kind of a man a specially after what you told me about the girl on the train. But any way as I say, I was in a "daze" so can't remember what it was we bet, but will try and pay it if it does not "break" me.

Sis's train got in about ten minutes after yours had gone and when she saw me what do you think was the first thing she said? Well, Mr. Lewis, she said: "Why Mibs (That is a pet name some of my friends have given me) what has happened to you? I never seen you have as much color." So I passed it off with some remark about the heat and changed the subject as I certainly was not going to tell her that I had just been talking to a man who I had never met or she would of dropped dead from the shock. Either that or she would not of believed me as it would be hard for a person who knows me well to imagine me doing a thing like that as I have quite a reputation for "squelching" men who try to act fresh. I don't mean anything personal by that, Mr. Lewis, as am a good judge of character and could tell without you telling me that you are not that kind.

Well, Sis and I have been on the "go" ever since she arrived as I took yesterday and today off so I could show her the "sights" though she says she would be perfectly satisfied to just sit in the apartment and listen to me "rattle on." Am afraid I am a great talker, Mr. Lewis, but Sis says it is as good as a show to hear me talk as I tell things in such a different way as I cannot help from seeing the humorous side of everything and she says she never gets tired of listening to me, but of course she is my sister and thinks the world of me, but she really does laugh like she enjoyed my craziness.

Maybe I told you that I have a tiny little apartment which a girl friend of mine and I have together and it is hardly big enough to turn round in, but still it is "home" and I am a great home girl and hardly ever care to go out evenings except occasionally to the theater or dance. But even if our "nest" is small we are proud of it and Sis complimented us on how cozy it is and how "homey" it looks and she said she did not see how we could afford to have everything so nice and Edith (my girl friend) said: "Mibs deserves all the credit for that. I never knew a girl who could make a little money go a long ways like she can." Well, of course she is my best friend and always saying nice things about me, but I do try and I hope I get results. Have always said that good taste and being careful is a whole lot more important than lots of money though it is nice to have it.

You must write and tell me how you are getting along in the "battle of Broadway" (I laughed when I read that) and whether the publishers like your songs though I know they will. Am crazy to hear them and hear you play the piano as I love good jazz music even better than classical, though I suppose it is terrible to say such a thing. But I usually say just what I think though sometimes I wish afterwards I had not of. But still I believe it is better for a girl to be her own self and natural instead of always acting. But am afraid I will never have a chance to hear you play unless you come back to Chi and pay us a visit as my "threat" to come to New York was just a "threat" and I don't see any hope of ever getting there unless some rich New Yorker should fall in love with me and take me there to live. Fine chance for poor little me, eh Mr. Lewis?

Well, I guess I have "rattled on" long enough and you will think I am writing a book unless I quit and besides, Sis has asked me as a special favor to make her a pie for dinner. Maybe you don't know it, Mr. Man, but I am quite famous for my pie and pastry, but I don't suppose a "genius" is interested in common things like that.

Well, be sure and write soon and tell me what N.Y. is like and all about it and don't forget the little girlie who was "bad" and spoke to a strange man in the station and have been blushing over it ever since.

Your friend (?)
MABELLE GILLESPIE.

N. Y., AUG. 10.

DEAR GIRLIE: I bet you will think I am a fresh guy commencing that way but Miss Gillespie is too cold and a man can not do nothing cold in this kind of weather specially in this man's town which is the hottest place I ever been in and I guess maybe the reason why New Yorkers is so bad is because they think they are all ready in H—— and can not go no worse place no matter how they behave themselves. Honest girlie I certainly envy you being where there is a breeze off the old Lake and Chi may be dirty but I never heard of nobody dying because they was dirty but four people died here yesterday on acct. of the heat and I seen two different women flop right on Broadway and had to be taken away in the ambulance and it could not of been because they was dressed too warm because it would be impossible for the women here to leave off any more cloths.

Well have not had much luck yet in the battle of Broadway as all the heads of the big music publishers is out of town on their vacation and the big boys is the only ones I will do business with as it would be silly for a man with the stuff I have got to waste my time on somebody that is just on the staff and have not got the final say. But I did play a couple of my numbers for the people up to Levy's and Goebel's and they went crazy over them in both places. So it looks like all I have to do is wait for the big boys to get back and then play my numbers for them and I will be all set. What I want is to get taken on the staff of one of the big firms as that gives a man the inside and they will plug your numbers more if you are on the staff. In the mean wile have not got nothing to worry me but am just seeing the sights of the big town as have saved up enough money to play round for a wile and any way a man that can play piano like I can don't never have to worry about starveing. Can certainly make the old music box talk girlie and am always good for a $75 or $100 job.

Well have been here a week now and on the go every minute and I thought I would be lonesome down here but no chance of that as I have been treated fine by the people I have met and have sure met a bunch of them. One of the boys liveing in the hotel is a vaudeville actor and he is a member of the Friars club and took me over there to dinner the other night and some way another the bunch got wise that I could play piano so of course I had to sit down and give them some of my numbers and everybody went crazy over them. One of the boys I met there was Paul Sears the song writer but he just writes the lyrics and has wrote a bunch of hits and when he heard some of my melodies he called me over to one side and said he would like to work with me on some numbers. How is that girlie as he is one of the biggest hit writers in N.Y.

N.Y. has got some mighty pretty girlies and I guess it would not be hard to get acquainted with them and in fact several of them has tried to make me since I been here but I always figure that a girl must be something wrong with her if she tries to make a man that she don't know nothing about so I pass them all up. But I did meet a couple of pips that a man here in the hotel went up on Riverside Drive to see them and insisted on me going along and they got on some way that I could make a piano talk so they was nothing but I must play for them so I sit down and played some of my own stuff and they went crazy over it.

One of the girls wanted I should come up and see her again and I said I might but I think I better keep away as she acted like she wanted to vamp me and I am not the kind that likes to play round with a gal just for their company and dance with them etc. but when I see the right gal that will be a different thing and she won't have to beg me to come and see her as I will camp right on her trail till she says yes. And it won't be none of these N.Y. fly by nights neither. They are all right to look at but a man would be a sucker to get serious with them as they might take you up and next thing you know you would have a wife on your hands that don't know a dish rag from a waffle iron.

Well girlie will quit and call it a day as it is too hot to write any more and guess I will turn on the cold water and lay in the tub a wile and then turn in. Don't forget to write to

Your friend,
CHAS. F. LEWIS.

DEAR MR. MAN: Hope you won't think me a "silly Billy" for starting my letter that way but "Mr. Lewis" is so formal and "Charles" is too much the other way and any way I would not dare call a man by their first name after only knowing them only two weeks. Though I may as well confess that Charles is my favorite name for a man and have always been crazy about it as it was my father's name. Poor old dad, he died of cancer three years ago, but left enough insurance so that mother and we girls were well provided for and do not have to do anything to support ourselves though I have been earning my own living for two years to make things easier for mother and also because I simply can't bear to be doing nothing as I feel like a "drone." So I flew away from the "home nest" though mother felt bad about it as I was her favorite and she always said I was such a comfort to her as when I was in the house she never had to worry about how things would go.

But there I go gossiping about my domestic affairs just like you would be interested in them though I don't see how you could be though personly I always like to know all about my friends, but I know men are different so will try and not bore you any longer. Poor Man, I certainly feel sorry for you if New York is as hot as all that. I guess it has been very hot in Chi, too, at least everybody has been complaining about how terrible it is. Suppose you will wonder why I say "I guess" and you will think I ought to know if it is hot. Well, sir, the reason I say "I guess" is because I don't feel the heat like others do or at least I don't let myself feel it. That sounds crazy I know, but don't you think there is a good deal in mental suggestion and not letting yourself feel things? I believe that if a person simply won't allow themselves to be affected by disagreeable things, why such things won't bother them near as much. I know it works with me and that is the reason why I am never cross when things go wrong and "keep smiling" no matter what happens and as far as the heat is concerned, why I just don't let myself feel it and my friends say I don't even look hot no matter if the weather is boiling and Edith, my girl friend, often says that I am like a breeze and it cools her off just to have me come in the room. Poor Edie suffers terribly during the hot weather and says it almost makes her mad at me to see how cool and unruffled I look when everybody else is perspiring and have red faces etc.

I laughed when I read what you said about New York being so hot that people thought it was the "other place." I can appreciate a joke, Mr. Man, and that one did not go "over my head." Am still laughing at some of the things you said in the station though they probably struck me funnier than they would most girls as I always see the funny side and sometimes something is said and I laugh and the others wonder what I am laughing at as they cannot see anything in it themselves, but it is just the way I look at things so of course I cannot explain to them why I laughed and they think I am crazy. But I had rather part with almost anything rather than my sense of humour as it helps me over a great many rough spots.

Sis has gone back home though I would of liked to of kept her here much longer, but she had to go though she said she would of liked nothing better than to stay with me and just listen to me "rattle on." She always says it is just like a show to hear me talk as I always put things in such a funny way and for weeks after she has been visiting me she thinks of some of the things I said and laughs over them. Since she left Edith and I have been pretty quiet though poor Edie wants to be on the "go" all the time and tries to make me go out with her every evening to the pictures and scolds me when I say I had rather stay home and read and calls me a "book worm." Well, it is true that I had rather stay home with a good book than go to some crazy old picture and the last two nights I have been reading myself to sleep with Robert W. Service's poems. Don't you love Service or don't you care for "highbrow" writings?

Personly there is nothing I love more than to just sit and read a good book or sit and listen to somebody play the piano, I mean if they can really play and I really believe I like popular music better than the classical though I suppose that is a terrible thing to confess, but I love all kinds of music but a specially the piano when it is played by somebody who can really play.

Am glad you have not "fallen" for the "ladies" who have tried to make your acquaintance in New York. You are right in thinking there must be something wrong with girls who try to "pick up" strange men as no girl with self respect would do such a thing and when I say that, Mr. Man, I know you will think it is a funny thing for me to say on account of the way our friendship started, but I mean it and I assure you that was the first time I ever done such a thing in my life and would never of thought of doing it had I not known you were the right kind of a man as I flatter myself that I am a good judge of character and can tell pretty well what a person is like by just looking at them and I assure you I had made up my mind what kind of a man you were before I allowed myself to answer your opening remark. Otherwise I am the last girl in the world that would allow myself to speak to a person without being introduced to them.

When you write again you must tell me all about the girl on Riverside Drive and what she looks like and if you went to see her again and all about her. Suppose you will think I am a little old "curiosity shop" for asking all those questions and will wonder why I want to know. Well, sir, I won't tell you why, so there, but I insist on you answering all questions and will scold you if you don't. Maybe you will think that the reason why I am so curious is because I am "jealous" of the lady in question. Well, sir, I won't tell you whether I am or not, but will keep you "guessing." Now, don't you wish you knew?

Must close or you will think I am going to "rattle on" forever or maybe you have all ready become disgusted and torn my letter up. If so all I can say is poor little me—she was a nice little girl and meant well, but the man did not appreciate her.

There! Will stop or you will think I am crazy if you do not all ready.

Yours (?)

MABELLE.

N.Y., AUG. 20.

DEAR GIRLIE: Well girlie I suppose you thought I was never going to answer your letter but have been busier than a one armed paper hanger the last week as have been working on a number with Paul Sears who is one of the best lyric writers in N.Y. and has turned out as many hits as Berlin or Davis or any of them. And believe me girlie he has turned out another hit this time that is he and I have done it together. It is all done now and we are just waiting for the best chance to place it but will not place it nowheres unless we get the right kind of a deal but maybe will publish it ourselves.

The song is bound to go over big as Sears has wrote a great lyric and I have give it a great tune or at least every body that has heard it goes crazy over it and it looks like it would go over bigger than any song since Mammy and would not be surprised to see it come out the hit of the year. If it is handled right we will make a bbl. of money and Sears says it is a cinch we will clean up as much as $25000 apiece which is pretty fair for one song but this one is not like the most of them but has got a great lyric and I have wrote a melody that will knock them out of their seats. I only wish you could hear it girlie and hear it the way I play it. I had to play it over and over about 50 times at the Friars last night.

I will copy down the lyric of the chorus so you can see what it is like and get the idea of the song though of course you can't tell much about it unless you hear it played and sang. The title of the song is When They're Like You and here is the chorus.

Some like them hot, some like them cold.
Some like them when they're not too darn old.
Some like them fat, some like them lean.
Some like them only at sweet sixteen.
Some like them dark, some like them light.
Some like them in the park, late at night.
Some like them fickle, some like them true,
But the time I like them is when they're like you.

How is that for a lyric and I only wish I could play my melody for you as you would go nuts over it but will send you a copy as soon as the song is published and you can get some of your friends to play it over for you and I know you will like it though it is a different melody when I play it or when somebody else plays it.

Well girlie you will see how busy I have been and am libel to keep right on being busy as we are not going to let the grass grow under our feet but as soon as we have got this number placed we will get busy on another one as a couple like that will put me on Easy st. even if they don't go as big as we expect but even 25 grand is a big bunch of money and if a man could only turn out one hit a year and make that much out of it I would be on Easy st. and no more hammering on the old music box in some cabaret.

Who ever we take the song to we will make them come across with one grand for advance royaltys and that will keep me going till I can turn out another one. So the future looks bright and rosey to yours truly and I am certainly glad I come to the big town though sorry I did not do it a whole lot quicker.

This is a great old town girlie and when you have lived here a wile you wonder how you ever stood for a burg like Chi which is just a hick town along side of this besides being dirty etc. and a man is a sucker to stay there all their life specially a man in my line of work as N.Y. is the Mecca for a man that has got the musical gift. I figure that all the time I spent in Chi I was just wasteing my time and never really started to live till I come down here and I have to laugh when I think of the boys out there that is trying to make a liveing in the song writeing game and most of them starve to death all their life and the first week I am down here I meet a man like Sears and the next thing you know we have turned out a song that will make us a fortune.

Well girlie you asked me to tell you about the girlie up on the Drive that tried to make me and asked me to come and see her again. Well I can assure you you have no reasons to be jealous in that quarter as I have not been back to see her as I figure it is wasteing my time to play round with a dame like she that wants to go out somewheres every night and if you married her she would want a house on 5th. ave. with a dozen servants so I have passed her up as that is not my idea of home.

What I want when I get married is a real home where a man can stay home and work and maybe have a few of his friends in once in a wile and entertain them or go to a good musical show once in a wile and have a wife that is in sympathy with you and not nag at you all the wile but be a real help mate. The girlie up on the Drive would run me ragged and have me in the poor house inside of a year even if I was makeing 25 grand out of one song. Besides she wears a make up that you would have to blast to find out what her face looks like. So I have not been back there and don't intend to see her again so what is the use of me telling you about her. And the only other girlie I have met is a sister of Paul Sears who I met up to his house wile we was working on the song but she don't hardly count as she has not got no use for the boys but treats them like dirt and Paul says she is the coldest proposition he ever seen.

Well I don't know no more to write and besides have got a date to go out to Paul's place for dinner and play some of my stuff for him so as he can see if he wants to set words to some more of my melodies. Well don't do nothing I would not do and have as good a time as you can in old Chi and will let you know how we come along with the song.

CHAS. F. LEWIS.

CHICAGO, ILL. Aug. 23.

DEAR MR. MAN: I am thrilled to death over the song and think the words awfully pretty and am crazy to hear the music which I know must be great. It must be wonderful to have the gift of writing songs and then hear people play and sing them and just think of making $25,000 in such a short time. My, how rich you will be and I certainly congratulate you though am afraid when you are rich and famous you will have no time for insignificant little me or will you be an exception and remember your "old" friends even when you are up in the world? I sincerely hope so.

Will look forward to receiving a copy of the song and will you be sure and put your name on it? I am all ready very conceited just to think that I know a man that writes songs and makes all that money.

Seriously I wish you success with your next song and I laughed when I read your remark about being busier than a one armed paper hanger. I don't see how you think up all those comparisons and crazy things to say. The next time one of the girls asks me to go out with them I am going to tell them I can't go because I am busier than a one armed paper hanger and then they will think I made it up and say: "The girl is clever."

Seriously I am glad you did not go back to see the girl on the Drive and am also glad you don't like girls who makes themselves up so much as I think it is disgusting and would rather go round looking like a ghost than put artificial color on my face. Fortunately I have a complexion that does not need "fixing" but even if my coloring was not what it is I would never think of lowering myself to "fix" it. But I must tell you a joke that happened just the other day when Edith and I were out at lunch and there was another girl in the restaurant whom Edie knew and she introduced her to me and I noticed how this girl kept staring at me and finally she begged my pardon and asked if she could ask me a personal question and I said yes and she asked me if my complexion was really "mine." I assured her it was and she said: "Well, I thought so because I did not think anybody could put it on so artistically. I certainly envy you." Edie and I both laughed.

Well, if that girl envies me my complexion, why I envy you living in New York. Chicago is rather dirty though I don't let that part of it bother me as I bathe and change my clothing so often that the dirt does not have time to "settle." Edie often says she cannot see how I always keep so clean looking and says I always look like I had just stepped out of a band box. She also calls me a fish (jokingly) because I spend so much time in the water. But seriously I do love to bathe and never feel so happy as when I have just "cleaned up" and put on fresh clothing.

Edie has just gone out to see a picture and was cross at me because I would not go with her. I told her I was going to write a letter and she wanted to know to whom and I told her and she said: "You write to him so often that a person would almost think you was in love with him." I just laughed and turned it off, but she does say the most embarrassing things and I would be angry if it was anybody but she that said them.

Seriously I had much rather sit here and write letters or read or just sit and dream than go out to some crazy old picture show except once in awhile I do like to go to the theater and see a good play and a specially a musical play if the music is catchy. But as a rule I am contented to just stay home and feel cozy and lots of evenings Edie and I sit here without saying hardly a word to each other though she would love to talk but she knows I had rather be quiet and she often says it is just like living with a deaf and dumb mute to live with me because I make so little noise round the apartment. I guess I was born to be a home body as I so seldom care to go "gadding."

Though I do love to have company once in awhile, just a few congenial friends whom I can talk to and feel at home with and play cards or have some music. My friends love to drop in here, too, as they say Edie and I always give them such nice things to eat. Though poor Edie has not much to do with it, I am afraid, as she hates anything connected with cooking which is one of the things I love best of anything and I often say that when I begin keeping house in my own home I will insist on doing most of my own work as I would take so much more interest in it than a servant, though I would want somebody to help me a little if I could afford it as I often think a woman that does all her own work is liable to get so tired that she loses interest in the bigger things of life like books and music. Though after all what bigger thing is there than home making a specially for a woman?

I am sitting in the dearest old chair that I bought yesterday at a little store on the North Side. That is my one extravagance, buying furniture and things for the house, but I always say it is economy in the long run as I will always have them and have use for them and when I can pick them up at a bargain I would be silly not to. Though heaven knows I will never be "poor" in regards to furniture and rugs and things like that as mother's house in Toledo is full of lovely things which she says she is going to give to Sis and myself as soon as we have real homes of our own. She is going to give me the first choice as I am her favorite. She has the loveliest old things that you could not buy now for love or money including lovely old rugs and a piano which Sis wanted to have a player attachment put on it but I said it would be an insult to the piano so we did not get one. I am funny about things like that, a specially old furniture and feel towards them like people whom I love.

Poor mother, I am afraid she won't live much longer to enjoy her lovely old things as she has been suffering for years from stomach trouble and the doctor says it has been worse lately instead of better and her heart is weak besides. I am going home to see her a few days this fall as it may be the last time. She is very cheerful and always says she is ready to go now as she has had enough joy out of life and all she would like would be to see her girls settled down in their own homes before she goes.

There I go, talking about my domestic affairs again and I will bet you are bored to death though personly I am never bored when my friends tell me about themselves. But I won't "rattle on" any longer, but will say good night and don't forget to write and tell me how you come out with the song and thanks for sending me the words to it. Will you write a song about me some time? I would be thrilled to death! But am afraid I am not the kind of girl that inspires men to write songs about them, but am just a quiet "mouse" that loves home and am not giddy enough to be the heroine of a song.

Well, Mr. Man, good night and don't wait so long before writing again to

Yours (?)

MABELLE.

N. Y., Sept. 8.

DEAR GIRLIE: Well girlie have not got your last letter with me so cannot answer what was in it as I have forgotten if there was anything I was supposed to answer and besides have only a little time to write as I have a date to go out on a party with the Sears. We are going to the Georgie White show and afterwards somewheres for supper. Sears is the boy who wrote the lyric to my song and it is him and his sister I am going on the party with. The sister is a cold fish that has no use for men but she is show crazy and insists on Paul takeing her to 3 or 4 of them a week.

Paul wants me to give up my room here and come and live with them as they have plenty of room and I am running a little low on money but don't know if I will do it or not as am afraid I would freeze to death in the same house with a girl like the sister as she is ice cold but she don't hang round the house much as she is always takeing trips or going to shows or somewheres.

So far we have not had no luck with the song. All the publishers we have showed it to has went crazy over it but they won't make the right kind of a deal with us and if they don't loosen up and give us a decent royalty rate we are libel to put the song out ourselves and show them up. The man up to Goebel's told us the song was O. K. and he liked it but it was more of a production number than anything else and ought to go in a show like the Follies but they won't be in N. Y. much longer and what we ought to do is hold it till next spring.

Mean wile I am working on some new numbers and also have taken a position with the orchestra at the Wilton and am going to work there starting next week. They pay good money $60 and it will keep me going.

Well girlie that is about all the news. I believe you said your father was sick and hope he is better and also hope you are getting along O. K. and take care of yourself. When you have nothing else to do write to your friend.

CHAS. F. LEWIS.

CHICAGO, ILL., Sept. 11.

DEAR MR. LEWIS: Your short note reached me yesterday and must say I was puzzled when I read it. It sounded like you was mad at me though I cannot think of any reason why you should be. If there was something I said in my last letter that offended you I wish you would tell me what it was and I will ask your pardon though I cannot remember anything I could of said that you could take offense at. But if there was something, why I assure you, Mr. Lewis, that I did not mean anything by it. I certainly did not intend to offend you in any way.

Perhaps it is nothing I wrote you, but you are worried on account of the publishers not treating you fair in regards to your song and that is why your letter sounded so distant. If that is the case I hope that by this time matters have rectified themselves and the future looks brighter. But any way, Mr. Lewis, don't allow yourself to worry over business cares as they will all come right in the end and I always think it is silly for people to worry themselves sick over temporary troubles, but the best way is to "keep smiling" and look for the "silver lining" in the cloud. That is the way I always do and no matter what happens, I manage to smile and my girl friend, Edie, calls me Sunny because I always look on the bright side.

Remember also, Mr. Lewis, that $60 is a salary that a great many men would like to be getting and are living on less than that and supporting a wife and family on it. I always say that a person can get along on whatever amount they make if they manage things in the right way.

So if it is business troubles, Mr. Lewis, I say don't worry, but look on the bright side. But if it is something I wrote in my last letter that offended you I wish you would tell me what it was so I can apologize as I assure you I meant nothing and would not say anything to hurt you for the world.

Please let me hear from you soon as I will not feel comfortable until I know I am not to blame for the sudden change.

Sincerely,

MABELLE GILLESPIE.

N. Y., Sept. 24.

DEAR MISS GILLESPIE: Just a few lines to tell you the big news or at least it is big news to me. I am engaged to be married to Paul Sear's sister and we are going to be married early next month and live in Atlantic City where the orchestra I have been playing with has got an engagement in one of the big cabarets.

I know this will be a surprise to you as it was even a surprise to me as I did not think I would ever have the nerve to ask the girlie the big question as she was always so cold and acted like I was just in the way. But she said she supposed she would have to marry somebody some time and she did not dislike me as much as most of the other men her brother brought round and she would marry me with the understanding that she would not have to be a slave and work round the house and also I would have to take her to a show or somewheres every night and if I could not take her myself she would "run wild" alone. Atlantic City will be O.K. for that as a lot of new shows opens down there and she will be able to see them before they get to the big town. As for her being a slave, I would hate to think of marrying a girl and then have them spend their lives in druggery round the house. We are going to live in a hotel till we find something better but will be in no hurry to start house keeping as we will have to buy all new furniture.

Betsy is some doll when she is all fixed up and believe me she knows how to fix herself up. I don't know what she uses but it is weather proof as I have been out in a rain storm with her and we both got drowned but her face stayed on. I would almost think it was real only she tells me different.

Well girlie I may write to you again once in a wile as Betsy says she don't give a dam if I write to all the girls in the world just so I don't make her read the answers but that is all I can think of to say now except good bye and good luck and may the right man come along soon and he will be a lucky man getting a girl that is such a good cook and got all that furniture etc.

But just let me give you a word of advice before I close and that is don't never speak to strange men who you don't know nothing about as they may get you wrong and think you are trying to make them. It just happened that I knew better so you was lucky in my case but the luck might not last.

Your friend,

CHAS. F. LEWIS.

CHICAGO, ILL., Sept. 27.

MY DEAR MR. LEWIS: Thanks for your advice and also thank your fiance for her generosity in allowing you to continue your correspondence with her "rivals," but personly I have no desire to take advantage of that generosity as I have something better to do than read letters from a man like you, a specially as I have a man friend who is not so generous as Miss Sears and would strongly object to my continuing a correspondence with another man. It is at his request that I am writing this note to tell you not to expect to hear from me again.

Allow me to congratulate you on your engagement to Miss Sears and I am sure she is to be congratulated too, though if I met the lady I would be tempted to ask her to tell me her secret, namely how she is going to "run wild" on $60.

Sincerely,

MABELLE GILLESPIE.

F.Y.I., I.L.Y.

(The Note Jotter's Proposal—or its equiv.)

Darling, I take the lib. to put in verse
The things I feel too shy to say in pers.

I love you even more, if poss., than life;
And, for the rec., I hope you'll be my wife.

One visit to the rev., that's all I ask,
To bring us happiness both fem. and masc.

We'll honeymoon on mountaintop or surf–
Whichever's pref. to you, to me is perf.

When we come home, my arms will lift you
in;
Then joy will reach its max., and woe its min.

I'll get a raise–if nec. I'll play the stocks–
To keep a fam. of three or four (approx.).

From Mon. through Sun. my love will never
ebb,
Nor from the springtime to the snows of Feb.

Say yes, my sweet! In gen. I'm loath to beg,
But now I pray your ans. will not be neg.

—HARRY G. NICKLES.

THE LAST OF THE FLATFEET

By RICHARD CONNELL

§ Although the tribal gentleman who is the hero of this story possesses an unpronounceable name consisting of 54 characters—count 'em, 54!—he justifies his existence by submitting to the rigors of civilized education. Occasionally, however, his would-be mentors are shocked when severe attacks of atavism sweep over him from the glorious Flatfoot past.

SEPTEMBER 29, 1923

HIS name was Ugobeecheebuggocheebeepawpawkeepiswiskiweeweechinoobee. In Flatfoot Indian this means, of course, Little-Big-Fat-Brown-Muskrat-Sitting-on-a-Pine-Stump-With-His-Tail-Just-Touching-the-Ground. At the school on the reservation whither he was taken, screaming, at a tender age, the teacher, in the interest of simplicity and patriotism, renamed him George Washington Ug.

After some months had passed, the teacher voiced a regret that he had done this; it hardly seemed fair to the Father of His Country. Closer acquaintance with the young aborigine forced the teacher to conclude that it was entirely unlikely that Ug would ever be first in war, peace, or, indeed, anything. Privately the teacher expressed the opinion that if Ug were to unveil his boxlike head in the open air Ug would be in acute peril from woodpeckers. The juvenile Ug seemed absolutely impervious to the pearls of knowledge with which he was pelted. So the teacher decided to change his name to Walter Muskrat.

It was then that the salient trait of Ug's character shone forth. He refused flatly to be Walter Muskrat. Somehow the idea had seeped through some chink in his cranium that George Washington was, or had been, a great white chief entitled to many feathers and rich in horses, squaws and scalps, for whom it was an honor to be named. Ug announced without passion but with palpable determination that he intended to remain George Washington Ug. What was his, was his, he intimated. Arguments, cajolery, threats left him equally unmoved. He refused to answer to any other name, and he refused to eat. Before his wooden-faced obduracy the teacher at length surrendered; Ug remained George Washington Ug.

To the task of civilizing Ug, the teacher, a zealous soul, gave particular attention. It was a matter of pride with that teacher that the civilizing job should be a thorough one, neat, efficient, and with no rough edges; for Ug, it seemed quite probable, was destined to be the last of the Flatfeet. To civilize a Flatfoot! That was an ambition worthy of any man, thought the teacher. It had never been done; full well the teacher knew this. Had he not been trying for thirty years? He had seen no end of Flatfoot youths issue forth from his schoolroom, to the outward eye finished products, glowing with the high polish of civilization and possessed of well-cultivated tastes for derby hats, bank accounts, a reasonable amount of morality, safety razors, hymns, suspenders, lawsuits and the other essential habiliments of civilization, only to backslide into barbarous practices at the first suitable opportunity that presented itself.

"There's a broad streak of atavism in the Flatfoot," said the teacher. "He reverts to type as easily as the rattlesnake sheds its skin. On Saturday night he may be seen in a derby hat and rah-rah clothes, peaceably eating a nut sundae in a drug store and discussing Ty Cobb, ship subsidies and self-starters with the clerk. On the following Monday, like as not, he is back in moccasins and feathers, doing some forbidden tribal dance, whetting up his hunting knife and wistfully regretting that the Government has such narrow-minded prejudices against a little scalping.

"But," concluded the teacher, "I've got hold of Ug early enough to civilize him so it will stick. The last of the Flatfeet is going to be the best of the Flatfeet. I'll train Ug so that he will never want to take off his derby hat. After all, the derby hat is the symbol of civilization. No man can possibly be wild in a derby hat."

So he labored over Ug. Time passed, as it is apt to, and Ug's chest measurement and appetite increased, and the teacher watched hopefully for signs of mental and moral development. That Ug would ever become a profound thinker, the teacher harbored grave doubts; there was scant indication that the chunky, square-faced boy would ever become a Flatfoot Aristotle. Indeed, in darker moments the teacher sometimes opined that the only way to implant seeds of knowledge in that brown head was by means of a major operation involving trepanning. It was not that Ug preferred sin to syntax; docilely enough, and readily, he accepted the leading facts of an elementary education—to wit: That in 1492 Columbus sailed the ocean blue; that six times nine is invariably fifty-four; that one must spell "separate" with an "a" till one's hair turns gray; that homicide is not only illegal but unethical; that the femur is the longest bone in the human body; that when a fat man gets into a tubful of water the water will overflow. Having accepted them, he forgot them.

"However," said the teacher, "if I can teach him to be a law-abiding member of his community, who will work and keep sober, it will be enough. A man can be civilized without being a mental Hercules."

He continued most earnestly to train Ug in the way, by civilized canons, he should go. When Ug was fourteen a most encouraging event happened. With his own delighted eyes the teacher observed the behavior of Ug that day at recess in the school yard when Ug became involved in a quarrel with Henry James Curly Bear, a sprig of the Blackfoot tribe, and a youth of superior size and brawn. Henry James Curly Bear, whom no amount of effort had been able to redeem from savagery, had kicked Ug roundly in a dispute over the somewhat knotty technical problem of whether Jess Willard was a greater fighter than Ty Cobb was a ball player. Ordinarily such an act meant instant and spirited fistic battle, for traditionally the Flatfeet are of martial cast and care no more for Blackfeet than one male bulldog cares for another male bulldog confined in the same coal bin. The teacher made ready to launch himself into the fray and drag the opponents apart. To his surprise and joy he heard Ug say in ringing tones:

"I will not fight you, Henry James Curly Bear. The teacher says only bad people fight. Good people sue in the courts. If you kick me again, Henry James Curly Bear, when I say my prayers tonight I'll tell our heavenly Father on you, and He'll fix you, Henry James Curly Bear."

Young Curly Bear expressed the opinion that Ug was afraid of him. This Ug gently denied.

"The Good Book," said George Washington Ug, "says that it is wicked to fight; and, anyhow, why don't you take somebody your own size?"

Then, not without a show of dignity, Ug turned his back on young Curly Bear and retired from the scene. The teacher felt the warming flush of pride.

"Score one for civilization," he said.

As he walked toward his home that evening the teacher was decidedly in a self-congratulatory mood; overnight, almost, it seemed that Ug had begun to respond to the efforts of the teacher. With such gratifying thoughts in his brain, the teacher passed a grove of live oaks, a secluded spot. To his ears came sounds. He stopped. Louder grew the sounds, and stranger; they appeared to issue from the grove. Now he heard a wail, shrill and laden with some emotion akin to anger; then he heard a chant, weird, almost frenzied. The teacher cautiously pushed aside some underbrush and peered into the grove. An unpedagogical expression leaped to his lips, for he saw the person from whom the sounds came, and he knew their import.

The chanting lips were the lips of his pupil, George Washington Ug. As Ug chanted he danced—a wild, abandoned dance full of twists, turns, bends and wriggles. Gone were Ug's pants; they hung on a stump; and so did his derby hat. In his black hair stood feathers, plainly the tail feathers of a recently despoiled rooster. In his hand gleamed the blade of a jackknife, and he made menacing gestures at what the teacher thought at first was a bit of red string but which closer scrutiny revealed to be an adult earthworm of the night-crawler variety. A concentrated and bloodthirsty scowl was on the face of Ug as he twisted in the dance, and chanted:

"Koopeekis koopeekis
Bobbochee cheebobo
Toowanda bonda bonda bonda
Bopokum kobokum."

At this point Ug dispatched the earthworm by biting off its head. Chagrin and horror overwhelmed the watching teacher, for he knew that the chant meant:

"Help me, O bloody war spirit, to strangle my enemy, Curly Bear, even as I strangle this serpent. Give me the strength to mash him, smash him, scalp him and cut him into very small bits."

It was the forbidden snake dance. By such heathenish rites, the teacher knew, Flatfoot braves in the unregenerate days of yore had whipped themselves into a fury before going on the warpath.

The teacher descended, outraged, on Ug, confiscated the worm on the spot, and chastised Ug corporeally on another spot. What, demanded the teacher, did Ug mean by this? Ug, frightened, replied that he didn't know. Once, years and years before, when he was little more than a papoose, he had seen his father and the other men of the tribe do this dance in a secret spot. He had not thought of it since; but on this evening, as he was wandering past the grove, smarting under the insults and kicks of Henry James Curly Bear, an earthworm had crossed his path; and suddenly, somehow, the idea had come to him to do the dance. He could not explain why.

"It just came over me, like, teacher, please," he said.

That night the teacher thought long over the problem of civilizing Ug.

"I must do more than make him accept the ways of white men," the teacher said. "I must make him like them. But how? First, I must get hold of his imagination. I must find the secret spring in his nature to which he will respond with genuine enthusiasm."

The teacher was unlike many teachers in this: He did not think that every little Indian was exactly like every other little Indian. He set about the task of prodding for Ug's own particular secret spring. It took days, but he found it at last. It was pride; ardent patriotic pride.

Mostly, when the teacher was talking of fractions or verbs or such things, Ug was in a species of torpor, with dull face. But when the teacher conducted the class in history and civics and spoke of Uncle Sam, Ug, the teacher noticed, straightened his backbone and brightness came into his black eyes. This clew was enough for the astute teacher. He dilated on the power of Uncle Sam and his love for all in the country, but particularly for his wards, the Indians, and most particularly of all for a certain youthful Flatfoot named George Washington Ug. Ug was impressed; that was plain. He became passionately devoted to Uncle Sam; he appeared to derive unlimited comfort and inspiration from the fact that a benevolent old gentleman in a tall gray hat, a star-spangled vest, striped trousers and a goatee was his friend and protector. Though Ug's notions of what a ward is were slightly fog-bound, he was very proud of the fact that he was a ward of Uncle Sam. He rather looked down on the white farmers whose land adjoined the reservation; they were mere citizens; he was a ward. No longer, when larger Indians kicked him, did he plan to massacre them as they slept. Instead, he said, "Just you wait! I'll tell my Uncle Sam on you some day when I see him." And he wrote down their names in a small notebook.

From the day that Ug discovered Uncle Sam he became a changed Flatfoot. Gladly he embraced the ways of the white man. "Uncle Sam won't like you if you don't do this or that," the teacher would say; it would be enough.

No longer with reluctance did Ug wash his ears. He attended church cheerfully; he brushed his derby hat without being told; he contributed an occasional penny to the missionary box; he learned empirically that it is unwise to use the fingers in eating custard and he desisted from doing so; he voluntarily abandoned the notion of keeping a family of pet shunks under his bed; he discontinued the practice of putting grasshoppers down the necks of smaller Indians during Sabbath school; he expressed at various times ambitions to be a railroad engineer, a moving-picture actor and a big-league shortstop; he told lies only when it was necessary, and sometimes not then. The teacher felt that Ug at last was headed in the right direction; the last of the Flatfeet was destined to be completely civilized.

When Ug was twenty the teacher decided that the job was done. It was true that Ug's scholarship was still of dubious quality; he was still under the impression that Utah is the capital of Omaha and that six times six is forty-six. But his devotion to Uncle Sam, his burning patriotism—they were unimpeachable. Love of his country and its institutions was in his blood; it broke out in a rash of small flags in his coat lapels. Ug was given a diploma full of curly penmanship, and a new derby hat, a gift from a proud teacher, and sent forth into the world. He was not worried about his future; Uncle Sam would take care of him. Perhaps he'd raise pigs; that seemed like a genteel occupation and one not involving undue labor. Anyhow, whatever he did, if he was a good Flatfoot, washed his ears regularly, paid his bills, resisted any wayward impulses to commit assault, battery, arson or theft, and in general respected the edicts of his Uncle Sam's representatives, all would go well with him. He had, as one of his most valued possessions, a newspaper picture of the Atlantic Fleet riding the high seas; and, Ug liked to reflect, at a word from him to his uncle, these giant war canoes, with cannons as big as redwood trees, would come chugging up the mountain streams leading to the reservation to protect the rights of Ug and strike terror to the hearts of Ug's enemies. Of course, Ug must merit this protection by leading an unblemished life. This idea was the only thing George Washington Ug carried away from the school in addition to his diploma and his new derby hat; but the teacher was satisfied that it was enough.

There was no doubt about it—Ug was a good Indian, a credit to his teacher and an estimable member of society. His room-and-a-half frame house on the edge of the reservation he painted red, white and blue. He bought a tin bathtub. He planted hollyhocks. He carried a nail file in a leather case and used it openly and unabashed at the gibes of the less refined Indians. He refused to have dealings with traffickers in illicit spirits; indeed, he obeyed all rules, laws, ordinances and regulations punctiliously. On the wall of his dwelling, opposite the rotogravure of the Atlantic Fleet, was a large picture of the Washington Monument, for the teacher, when pressed, had told Ug that this was one of the homes of his Uncle Sam. Ug had sent to himself from Chicago a very civilized suit of blue serge with braid-bound lapels and freckled with small pearl buttons. He wore a rubber collar on Sundays, on formal calls and on the Fourth of July, which he believed to be Uncle Sam's birthday.

He even decided to shatter the best traditions of the male Flatfoot and work a little.

The work he selected for himself was of a sort in keeping with the importance and social position of a ward of Uncle Sam. George Washington Ug became a model. He permitted himself to be photographed by passing tourists, and for this privilege he charged a dime. It was worth it. Ug was a perfect specimen of Flatfoot beauty. His head had sharp corners, because when he was a papoose it had been strapped to a board, this being the Flatfoot contribution to the science of child-rearing. His face was a mocha prairie, with nostrils like gopher holes. He had eyes like bits of new patent leather. In figure Ug was inclined to plumpness; in general outline he resembled a hot-water bag at high tide.

It was natural, as one of the fruits of civilization, that Ug should aspire to be a capitalist. Accordingly he saved his dimes and, after prayer and meditation, invested them in a pig. It was not much of a pig, and it was given to whimpering. Ug had no special fondness for dumb animals, especially pigs; but he kept his charge under his bed and waited for him to increase and multiply. It was Ug's hope and plan that the pig would be the nucleus of a far-flung pig ranch. After consulting his school history book Ug named the animal General Grant.

Then he left the pig to browse about in the chickweed in the back yard and toughen its snout by trying to root under the hog-tight fence, while Ug himself added more dimes to his store by lurking in the vicinity of the railroad station and displaying his charms to the lenses of amateur photographers in passing trains.

The lightning of calamity struck Ug one afternoon at six minutes past five. Returning to his domicile, Ug discovered that General Grant was not snuffling about the back door, as was the General's habit. That the General could have burrowed under the fence was impossible. So Ug searched the house. He looked everywhere—under the bed, in the bathtub, in the phonograph-record case. General Grant had vanished. Ug retained enough hunting instinct to look for tracks, and he found them. They were nail-shod boot tracks and they pointed in the direction of the farm of one Patrick Duffy, white farmer, just across the boundary of the reservation. To him went Ug.

Mr. Duffy came out from his supper with egg on his overalls and fire in his eye. He was a high, wide, thick man, with a bushel of torch-colored hair, a jaw like an iceberg and fists like demijohns. Ug removed his derby hat, bowed, and inquired politely if Mr. Duffy had seen a pig answering to the name of General Grant.

"I have," said Mr. Duffy, grim of voice.

"Where is he, please?"

"In my pen," responded Mr. Duffy.

"I'll take him away," said Ug.

"You will not," said Mr. Duffy.

"But he's mine," protested Ug.

"He was," corrected Mr. Duffy. "Now he's mine."

"Since when, Patsy Duffy?" Ug was growing agitated; he had heard tales of Mr. Duffy.

"Your thievin' pig," declared Mr. Duffy, "come over and et my prize parsnips. I was goin' to show 'em at the state fair. They was worth eleven dollars—to me, anyhow—not countin' the honor an' glory. Now they're et. I'll be keepin' the pig."

"You give me back my pig, Patsy Duffy!" cried Ug.

"You give me back my parsnips," returned Mr. Duffy coldly.

"But General Grant didn't eat your parsnips," said Ug. "He hates parsnips. And, anyhow, he was home all day. You took——"

"Look here, Injin," said Mr. Duffy severely, "I ain't got time to stand out here debatin' with you."

Ug was trembling with an emotion he knew to be sinful and contrary to all moral precepts. An ax lay on a near-by woodpile, and Ug's eyes leaped from it to the bushy head of Patrick Duffy and then back to the ax again; for a second, civilization tottered. Then Ug, with a movement of resolution, replaced the derby hat on his black locks.

"All right, Patsy Duffy," he said with dignity. "Just you wait! I'm going to tell my uncle on you." And Ug turned away.

"You can tell your aunt, too," Mr. Duffy called after him, "and all your cousins. But the pig stays here, and if I ketch you pesterin' around here, Injin, I'll boot you for a gool."

Ug made his way cabinward with cloudy brow. Here was injustice, flagrant injustice. He was a ward of Uncle Sam and he didn't propose to be treated like that, even by Patsy Duffy.

"It's not the pig; it's the principle of the thing," muttered Ug as he tramped along.

It was not that he was sentimentally attached to General Grant; the pig, indeed, had grown to be more of a pest than a pet. But the pig was his property, and another man had dared to take him. Ug shook his fist in the direction of the Duffy house.

"You'll rue the day, Patsy Duffy," said Ug; he had seen melodramas. Then Ug chuckled to himself. He had reached the cabin and his eye had fallen on the picture of the Atlantic Fleet; he was picturing to himself Patsy Duffy shelled into submission by its big guns.

To his teacher, as the nearest representative of Uncle Sam, Ug went and stated the case of the kidnaped General Grant. The teacher listened sympathetically, but he shook his gray head; he knew Patsy Duffy, his gusty temper, his heavy fist, his plethoric bank roll, his political power. He pointed out to Ug that the recovering of kidnaped pigs was not a pedagogical function; furthermore, Ug was no longer a schoolboy, but a man of the world. Ug suggested a direct appeal to Uncle Sam. The teacher said emphatically that that would never do. Uncle Sam was much too busy to be bothered about one pig. He never, the teacher assured Ug, concerned himself personally with any matter involving less than a million pigs; his hired men looked after lesser cases, the teacher said, congratulating himself secretly that "hired men" was a rather good stroke. The law, suggested the teacher, was on Ug's side; his best advice to Ug was to consult the law in the person of Marcellus Q. Wigmore, attorney and counselor, in his office in Timberlake City. Yes, that was the civilized thing to do. Uncle Sam would approve; yes, yes, consult the law by all means.

Ug, a shade disappointed but not at all downhearted, greased his hair, dusted off his derby and walked the sixteen miles to Timberlake City. The majesty of the law, as embodied in Attorney and Counselor Wigmore, was enthroned in two cobwebby back rooms over a hay-and-feed store on Main Street. Ug was permitted to sit in the outer room until he was impressed, and this did not take long, for it was a musty, intimidating, legal-smelling place lined with books of repealed statutes and reports of drainage commissions, important-looking books with bindings suffering from tetter. Then Ug was summoned into the presence of Attorney Wigmore, a lean, dusty man of prehistoric aspect, with a dazzling bald head, an imposing frock coat and a collar like a spite fence.

He pursed shrewd lips and said, "And in what way may I have the honor of serving you, sir?" in a solemn court-room voice.

Ug, overawed, got out, "Patsy Duffy stole General Grant."

"Ah?" said Mr. Wigmore. "Ah?"

"He said he et his parsnips," hurried on Ug. "But General Grant never et them. He hated parsnips—honest."

"Ah," said Mr. Wigmore, "an interesting historical fact. But how, may I inquire, do the tastes of the late general concern me?"

Ug poured out his story of the abduction of his pig. Mr. Wigmore said, to himself, "Patsy Duffy? Ah, yes; ah, yes." Then he addressed Ug, as if he were a jury.

"My dear sir," said Attorney and Counselor Wigmore gravely, "this is indeed a pretty legal problem. Hur-r-rumph! Yes, a pretty legal problem. I hesitate to give an *ex-cathedra* opinion on a question involving so moot a point of jurisprudence. Hur-r-rumph!"

Ug listened, confused but fascinated. The eyes of Mr. Wigmore searched the grimy ceiling.

"Hur-r-rumph!" he said, with a bass judicial clearing of the throat. "Let us put the case in its simplest terms. We have you, the plaintiff, the party of the first part; we have one Patrick Duffy, defendant, party of the second part; we have one General Grant, pig, *casus belli*, party of the third part; we have certain parsnips, party of the fourth part. It is alleged by the party of the first part that the party of the second part did feloniously steal, make away with and confiscate the party of the third part because said Duffy alleges said General Grant did unlawfully eat, devour and consume or cause to be consumed the party of the fourth part. The plaintiff contends that he can prove an alibi for the aforementioned General Grant and that the said General Grant is innocent of the overt act imputed to him by the party of the second part. Is that not correctly stated, sir?"

"Yes, sir," said Ug, by now dizzy.

Mr. Wigmore consulted a book weighing ten pounds. For minutes he regarded the pages darkly. Then he spoke:

"Hur-r-rumph! To speak *ex capite*, your case is not unlike the case of Bullpitt versus Nudd, 67 Rhode Island, 478, in which the honorable court ruled that the unlawful abduction of animals, was *contra bonos mores;* and, if I remember correctly—and I think I do—fined the defendant two dollars and costs. Your case, sir, clearly involves a definition of *meum* and *tuum;* and, speaking *cum grano salis*, it has a precedent, if my memory is not at fault, and I do not believe it is, in the case of the International Knitted Knight Klose Korporation *versus* Gumbel *et al*, 544 South Carolina, 69, although I must warn you that it will be a question of adjudication just how far the doctrine of *caveat emptor* conflicts with that of *cave canem*. You can see that for yourself, can't you?"

Ug, utterly numb of brain, nodded.

Mr. Wigmore thoughtfully rubbed a bony chin with a thumb.

"*Inter se*," he observed, "it will take much study to determine what your remedy is. Your pig was caught *in flagrante delicto*, according to the defendant, which would make him *particeps criminis*, would it not?"

Ug gulped.

"It might," said Mr. Wigmore, "be possible to obtain a writ of *habeas corpus*. Or again we might have the defendant indicted for abduction. Possibly a question of riparian rights is involved. I hesitate to say without consulting an authority on torts. Have you ten dollars?"

Ug had. He produced it and saw it vanish into a recess beneath the tails of Mr. Wigmore's long coat.

"Pray wait here," said Mr. Wigmore, "while I go into conference."

Mr. Wigmore went into the other room and the door closed behind him. He watched the men pitching horseshoes in the street below for ten minutes, and then returned, with grave face, to the sanctum where Ug waited, perspiring freely.

"My dear sir," said Mr. Wigmore blandly, "my advice to you is—drop the case."

Ug stared.

"And not get my pig back?" he quavered.

"What," said Mr. Wigmore philosophically, "is a pig more or less in the cosmic scheme?"

"But he's mine! I want my pig!" Ug was nearly in tears.

"Possession," remarked Mr. Wigmore, showing impatience, "is nine points of the law. You came to me for advice. I gave it to you. You have received it. The law says nothing that would help you. Forget the pig."

"But that isn't fair! He's mine! Patsy Duffy is a thief!"

Mr. Wigmore grew stern.

"Take care, young man," he said. "There are laws against slander. Mr. Duffy is a respected member of this community. His brother is the sheriff, his brother-in-law is the county judge and his son is the district attorney. Good afternoon. What a bright warm day it is, isn't it?"

Ug found himself on Main Street, stunned. He had appealed to the law and it had failed him. It didn't seem possible that so learned a man as Marcellus Q. Wigmore could be wrong, and yet Ug found himself embracing that heresy. It seemed to him that he had a right to get his pig back. He decided to appeal to another of Uncle Sam's representatives, the superintendent of the reservation.

He was a genial soul, the superintendent, who professed often and loudly a love for the Indians. The winds of politics had wafted him from his cigar store in Altoona, Pennsylvania, where Indians, except wooden ones, are something of a rarity, to his present position. He greeted Ug warmly, almost affectionately, slapped his back and asked after his health. Ug replied that he was in a persecuted state of mind, and pigless, and narrated the story of the loss of General Grant. The superintendent was horrified, sympathetic, indignant simultaneously.

"How dare this fellow Duffy take the property of one of my Indians?" he demanded with heat. "I'll show him! Now don't you worry, young fellow. I'll take this matter up myself, personally, see?" And he patted Ug out of the office.

Ug waited a week. But his pig was not returned. He summoned up his courage, bathed his rubber collar, and once more tremulously visited the superintendent. As he approached the office he noted that the superintendent was busy with some visitor. Ug paused in his approach. He could see the visitor now. There was no mistaking that beacon light of red hair and those haystack shoulders. Ug grinned; doubtless at that very moment the superintendent was castigating Duffy for purloining the pig. Then Ug perceived that that could hardly be the case, for Mr. Duffy emitted a bull bellow of a laugh, and Ug heard with dismay that the superintendent laughed with him. Ug crept nearer the window. He saw that on the table between the two men were cards and piles of chips and a brown bottle. Ug departed as softly as he had come. He did not go back to the superintendent again. Somehow he had divined that it would be of no avail.

He went to the teacher. What could he do now? Write to one of the men in Washington to whom Uncle Sam had intrusted the task of looking after the Indians, the teacher suggested. Ug returned to his cabin and struggled with pen, ink and paper all evening. By morning he had produced a smeary note:

Indian Commissioner,
Washington, D. C.

Hon. sir: I had pig—boughten by me for $3.45. His name was General Grant. Patsy Duffy stealed him. General Grant did not et them parsnips. He hates parsnips worse than the dickens. White man has not right to take Indian pig I guess. I want my pig back. Please tell Uncle Sam.

Your loving son,
GEORGE WASHINGTON UG,
Flatfoot Indian.

Having dispatched this missive, Ug waited quietly, and with assurance. From time to time he glanced at the Atlantic Fleet, and reflected with pride that at a word from him that terrible machinery would be set in motion against that redheaded Duffy man. In eleven days he received a letter—a long, important-looking document with an eagle in the corner. Excitedly he tore it open. It read:

Dear sir: In reply refer to No. 73965435, file 4534, section 23x.

Your communication has been received and will be acted upon in due course.

Chief Clerk of the Chief Clerk,
Department of the Interior.

Ug was not entirely pleased by the letter. He had hoped for a short, firm order to Patrick Duffy that would lead to the immediate restitution of his pig. Then, too, there was something so cool, aloof, impersonal about it, considering that he was a relative of Uncle Sam. He wondered how long "in due course" was. When it proved to be more than two weeks Ug, growing restive, wrote a post card to the Indian commissioner:

Hon. sir: How about my pig?
Your loving son,
GEORGE WASHINGTON UG,
Flatfoot Indian.

He received a reply in a week:

Dear sir: In reply refer to No. 656565, drawer; pig.

A careful search of this department has resulted in the finding of no pig, pigs or other animals belonging to you, and we are therefore at a loss to understand your esteemed favor of the nineteenth.

Chief Clerk of the Bureau of Missing Animals.

Ug groaned aloud when he read this. He bought a fresh bottle of ink and gave himself over for two days to the arduous task of literary composition. The letter he sent away to Washington read:

Hon. sir: Now look here please. I am good little Indian. I had pig. Name, General Grant. Patsy Duffy, bad man but white, he steal that pig. He say G. Grant et his parsnips. This is a fib. I keep all laws and teacher says I am sibbleized. Please tell Uncle Sam I want back my pig.

Your loving son,
GEORGE WASHINGTON UG,
Flatfoot Indian.

Ten days later a very fat letter came for Ug, and he took it triumphantly. He even bought a can of condensed milk for General Grant's home-coming party. In his cabin he opened the letter. It read:

Dear sir: In reply refer to No. 4399768554333; section 29, subsection 9.

Your communication has been received and placed on file. Nothing can be done because of insufficient information. Please answer the inclosed questionnaire and return same to above.

What is your full name?

When and where were you born?

What proofs have you that you were?

What are your father's and mother's names, date of birth, age, sex and cause of death, if any?

What is your tribe?

What is your sex?

What is the full name of the pig in this case?

What is its sex?

Has it any distinguishing marks? Send map of same.

Give dimensions of pig, using inclosed measurement chart.

Did you yourself steal the pig in the first place?

If not, inclose bill of sale.

Inclose statement signed by five witnesses proving that pig is not fond of parsnips.

Inclose photograph of pig and sample of parsnip alleged to have been eaten by same.

Inclose full description of Patrick Duffy, giving name, age, sex and photograph—without hat.

Chief Clerk, Bureau of Claims, Flatfoot Section.

It took Ug three days, seven pens, two bottles of ink—one spilled—two smeared shirts and much grunting to answer the questions, but answer them he did. He mailed the letter and waited.

The Indian Bureau replied in two weeks that his communication had been received and given careful attention; but, inasmuch as it appeared to involve a pig, it had been referred to the Department of Agriculture. The secretary to the secretary to the Secretary of Agriculture wrote Ug that the case had been referred to the Bureau of Animal Husbandry. Ug, puzzled, sent a hasty post card to say that General Grant had no husband, but this information was ignored. Instead, he received a letter saying that because of the legal aspects of the case it had been passed on to the Department of Justice. Ug sighed and waited. The Department of Justice referred the case, it notified Ug, to the ninth assistant attorney-general, who gave it some days of study and sent it back to the Commissioner of Indian Affairs, who wrote Ug to know if it was a pig or a rig that he had lost. Ug wrote "Pig, Pig, Pig!" on a post card and sent it to Washington. Day followed day. No letter came to Ug. He finally could stand delay no longer. He decided one night to play his trump card. He wrote to Uncle Sam:

Dear Uncle Sam: You know me. I am George Washington Ug, a very sibbleized good Indian; wear derby hat; go church; say prayers; don't fight. Now this Patsy Duffy, bad white man, took my pig, General Grant, and I don't know how he get that way. Please send large gunboats and make Patsy Duffy give back my pig please.

Your loving neffew,

George,
Flatfoot.

Doubts, worries, irritations melted away as Ug read and reread his letter. It was all up with Patsy Duffy now. Uncle Sam could not resist that letter, even if it did involve less than one million pigs. It involved an injustice to his ward, and Uncle Sam would not permit that. Ug smiled as he wrote on the envelope in his big, round, scraggly hand, "Uncle Sam, Washington, D. C."

The reply came more promptly than replies to any of his other letters; Ug knew it would. He picked up the official envelope almost reverently. He carried it past the other Indians in his hand. He wanted them to see that he, Ug, had received a letter from his Uncle Sam. He postponed the pleasure of opening it, just as a child saves the best cake till last. He opened it after some blissful reverie in his own cabin. As he read it the brown face of Ug became like a cup of coffee to which a great deal of milk has suddenly been added. The letter was short, formal. It was from the Post Office Department, and it read:

No such person as Uncle Sam is known in Washington, D. C. In the future please give full name and street and number.

Ug felt as if he had been tomahawked. He took himself, his dismay and his *café-au-lait* face to the teacher.

"What is Uncle Sam's last name?" he asked.

The teacher didn't know. Ug had caught him in an unguarded moment; the admission had slipped out; the teacher flushed, flustered.

"What is Uncle Sam's street and number?" asked Ug. His small eyes now held suspicion.

The teacher didn't know.

"Ug," he said in his most kindly manner, "you're a grown man now. I think, perhaps, I ought to tell you. Uncle Sam isn't a man; that is to say, he isn't like you or me. He's a sort of—well, a sort of spirit."

"Like God?" asked Ug.

"Oh, no, no, no, no, no! Not like God."

"Like Santa Claus?"

"Yes, yes; that's it," said the teacher hastily. "Rather more like Santa Claus."

"Teacher," said Ug, and his face was as set as a totem pole, "three years ago you told me that there was no Santa Claus."

The teacher looked away from Ug. The subject was very unpleasant to the teacher.

"You've been a good boy, Ug," he said.

"I've tried to be," said Ug, picking up his derby hat.

Homeward through a quiet evening went Ug, very slowly; his square head was bent forward till his chin obscured his rubber collar; the path across the meadow was well defined by the rising moon, but Ug's feet now and then strayed from it; he walked like a man very tired. Not far from his small red, white and blue cabin Ug stopped short. Something was moving in the grass near the path. Ug bent toward it. It was a large, glistening, red earthworm. Ug's hands went up to his head, and when they came down one of them held his derby hat. A sharp motion and the hat went skimming out into the alfalfa. A hen, the property of a white neighbor, disturbed in her beauty sleep, cackled. Ug made other sharp motions. One of them stripped off his blue-serge pants. Another ended the earthly days of the hen by quick and vigorous strangulation. Still another plucked out the feathers; and yet another nipped the earthworm by the nape of its slimy neck before it could slither back into its burrow. Then the quiet night heard sounds—the sounds of a wild martial chant in a barbarous tongue:

"Koopeekis koopeekis
Bobbochee cheebobo
Toowanda bonda bonda, Patsy Duffy,
Bopokum kobobum."

The owls and the gophers, the only witnesses, saw a plump square-headed man, with feathers in his hair, a knife in one hand and a wriggling worm in the other, twisting and turning and dancing a primitive abandoned dance in the moonlight.

Patsy Duffy, smoking his corncob on his porch in the cool of the evening, heard the distant sounds too. He heard them draw nearer. He did not understand what was happening till a fantastic figure bounded, as if it were India rubber, to his porch. He recognized Ug. It was not the Ug he had known.

It was an Ug with eyes that blazed, an Ug that spoke the chopped untutored speech of his ancestors.

"What the devil!" growled Patsy Duffy, starting up.

"White man, you steal um pig! Me heap bad Injun! You give um pig or you catch hell!"

"I'll boot you——" began Patsy Duffy, but he had no chance to finish his threat. Ug was on him, clawing him like a demon; one brown hand gripped the red hair, the other flourished the long-bladed jackknife. Down they went, with Ug on top. A shrill cry like the note of a drunken whippoorwill caught in a buzz saw cut the night; his breath and his spirit deserted Patrick Duffy; he knew that cry; years and years ago it had struck cold fear to the hearts of white pioneers; it was the war whoop of the Flatfeet.

"You let me up!" sniveled Patrick Duffy. "I was just havin' a little joke with you; honest I was, Ug."

Even a braver man might well have been cowed by the ferocity of a Flatfoot on the warpath. Ug rose. He scowled at the prostrate Duffy.

"White man," said Ug, "if I catch you near my tepee I'll scalp you."

But Ug knew from Patrick Duffy's eyes that that eventuality would never occur.

Across the moonlit meadow a figure made its way; in shape it was not unlike a hotwater bag at high tide. Certain feathers in its hair cast grotesque shadows; it went forward with a conquering swagger, and this was no mean feat, considering that the figure held clasped tight in its arms a fat, squirming pig.

Office News

(From Clean Sweep, employees' magazine of The Go-Dust Vacuum Cleaner Co.)

DURING a recent home-cleaner demonstration, Terrence P. (Teepee) Granshaw, Jr. (Sales, door-to-door), suffered a sprained thumb while using our Odd-Corner Attachment. Get well quick, Teepee!

Don't Forget Our Annual Bowling Banquet Friday Nite.

A very smooth vocal recording of Winter Wonderland was made on Vice-President Mumford's dictating machine by three girls from our Typing Department during Tuesday's lunch hour. The artists, who call themselves the Typist Trio, are Grace Janoski, Bimmy Merrill, and Vic Switzer. They recorded the whole song without any musical accompaniment, except for bell sound effects as played by Pelly Pelham (Accounting) who snapped a typewriter bell at just the right places.

Let's Get Behind the Bowling Banquet! Not Like Last Year!

Mrs. Bertha Maddigan, the cleaning lady who comes at night, has asked that all office personnel please be a little more careful about crumbs in their desk drawers, on account of mice.

Office Bowlers: Have You Paid Your Buck?

The Three o'Clock Cola Club has temporarily folded while Homer (Bunkie) Collet (Time Study) is laid up at home with a head cold. Homer, who is the club's Chairman in Charge of Running After Things, is much missed by one and all. Several volunteers tried to take his place fetching ice cream, sodas, and so on, but they either got our orders mixed or else ran into confusion on bottle deposits.

No Platters on Credit at the Bowling Banquet! Pay Now!

Eddie (Haircut) Wingert (Purchasing Dept., Rotating Brushes Division) would like to know who made three out-of-town phone calls to Sumneytown (toll costs, 18 cents) and charged them to his time-card number. Looks like someone lacks that old Office Spirit! One of you isn't Playing the Game! For a lousy eighteen cents, let's not stick Eddie!

See You at the Bowling Banquet.

—W. F. MIKSCH.

"Well, whose jib didn't you like the cut of today?"

HENRY BOLTINOFF

"I, Ebenezer Snodgrass, being of sound body and of sound mind . . ."

"264317856, but my friends all call me 26."

"Well, frankly, if he's in the armed forces, you don't need anything at all!"

"We'll huff and we'll puff . . ."

"The other day I could have sworn he snapped his fingers and said 'I have it!' "

"Guess!"

B TOBEY

"My name is Botts—your wife went home to visit her mother."

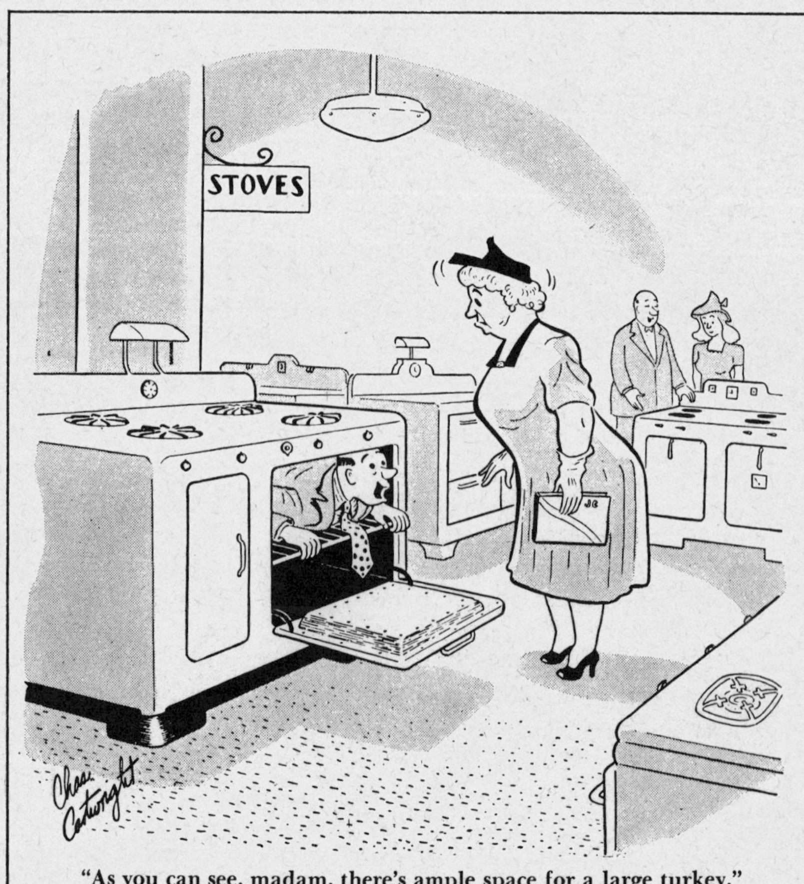

"As you can see, madam, there's ample space for a large turkey."

GYPSIES, NOBLES, PEASANTS, ETC.

By KATHARINE DAYTON

§ *When the subject of opera comes up at dinner parties, or elsewhere, most people know where they stand. They can either take it, or leave it alone. (Incidentally, people on opposite sides are apt to dislike each other.) What's remarkable about the following observations is that you're apt to agree with them, no matter where you stand.*

JANUARY 27, 1923

THERE are certain things that everybody knows about grand opera. Even the man in the street—that amœba of our intellectual and artistic life who is always being invoked by the statisticians and writers of advertisements—can tell you most if not all of the great fundamental principles that govern it.

Roughly speaking—as the man in the street is so apt to be when the subject under discussion is grand opera—he knows that, no matter how much of a moron he may be musically, there are certain things connected with this king of indoor winter sports that nobody could fool him on. As, for instance, that:

1. A coloratura soprano is any lady weighing one hundred and eighty-seven pounds or over, regardless of height, who sings no notes lower than the Ace, King, Queen and Jack, and has a quaint habit of wandering around the stage in her nightgown with her hair hanging down her back. Somewhere along in Act III you are perfectly safe in giving odds that she will go mad and start crying for a flute accompaniment. If the management is wise it will give it to her at once, for she simply won't be happy till she gets it!

2. A contralto, on the other hand, though tipping the scales, as the saying is, almost completely over, never goes mad and, no matter where she may be or what the provocation, she is never accompanied by a flute. It simply isn't done. The contralto's mission in grand opera may be one of two things: She may be either a true friend or a false friend to the soprano. In the first case she will not have to sing much, but she will have a lot of heavy—oh, very heavy!—chaperoning to do. For example, when the soprano—whose name, let us say, is Eldorado—meets her tenor lover Alfredo at midnight in the garden of Manrico's castle near the Piazza della Piccolo, it is up to the contralto to see that the course of true love is not rudely interrupted by Edgardo, who has been warned by the jealous Pinucchi that there is to be dirty work that night at the crossroads. This entails a great deal of running back and forth, listening in the wings, peeking into the bushes, et-

cetera—to say nothing of registering alarm, fright, pity, caution, and the various other emotions that are required of an operatic chaperon. In addition to all this the contralto must catch the soprano whenever she swoons or is stabbed—which, as these little contretemps occur anywhere from eight to eleven times in the course of a really grand opera, makes the existence of a life guard at Atlantic City during the rush season appear a comparatively happy one.

Mortality Statistics of Grand Opera

The alternative for the contralto, the rôle of false friend, requires infinitely more voice, but the action is confined principally to giving the soprano dirty looks and poison.

3. Unhappy endings are, of course, *de rigueur*. A grand opera cannot have a happy ending—unless you consider it a happy ending when all the characters are too dead to sing any longer. Some do.

Ninety-eight and seven-tenths per cent of the deaths in grand opera can be traced to only three causes—suicide, murder and *opera mortuis*. The majority of operatic suicides are to be found among tenors, according to the best available vocational suicide statistics. This is not so deplorable a condition as it may appear at first sight, when one takes into consideration the fact that if there were fewer tenors who commit suicide there would probably be more murders, with the final result practically the same.

Opera mortuis takes the heaviest toll. This disease will attack the healthiest of singers during the last act of any opera. For instance, Raimundo—a barytone apparently in the pink of condition—is walking along by the glue factory on the outskirts of Sienna when he trips over the body of the beautiful Maddelena, who has been murdered by Rodolfo, Raimundo's stepbrother on his mother's side, in the belief that she is Esmeralda, who had been abandoned by a band of gypsies in their flight from Umbria at the close of the war. Raimundo, overcome by his grief, falls upon the body, rolls over and, after coming up twice for arias, dies. Just like that!

A bare one-half of one per cent of operatic villains and villainesses—which is to say, bassos and contraltos—die of remorse. The accepted theory is that in their frequent gnashing of teeth and biting of nails, bits of enamel are swallowed, which irritate the delicate lining of the intestines, with satisfactorily fatal results.

4. German opera may be readily distinguished by the merest tyro by the number of poor relations occupying the boxes. In a way, this is the easiest kind of opera to follow because everything in it, whether sung or merely barked in the quaint Wagnerian manner, is repeated at least three times. This custom probably owes its origin to the fact that the majority of German operas were composed, oddly enough, for the German people. The thing distinctly has its advantages. It's rather a satisfaction, in a way, to feel that in a world where things happen as swiftly as they do in ours nowadays, one can snatch one's forty winks while Wolfram von Edelweiss is defying the Goddess Helga at the entrance to her cave in the Forest of Thuringia, secure in the knowledge that twenty minutes later one may awake greatly refreshed to find one hasn't missed a thing—for there stands Wolfram in exactly the same spot on the stage, and still defying away through his beard like anything!

The operas of Wagner are especially easily grasped by the layman—as we sometimes affectionately refer to the man in the street—due to the use of the motif. A motif is the particular noise made by the orchestra to denote the different characters, their entrances and exits, their emotions, and even, sometimes, their little personal belongings. As, for instance, when you hear things happening in the stringed instruments that sound as if something had got itself caught in the swing door you may be sure that the lady entering at the right, snugly wrapped against the chill of the night air in about three dozen white automobile veils, is Umlaut, Princess of Zweibach—soprano—who has forgotten her last name and has come to ask the powerful god Pilsner—basso—what it is. A blow-out in the horns gives us the motif Umlaut's Last Name; a back-firing among the bass viols denotes the pink transfer given to Umlaut by Bertha—contralto—which she has lost on her way hither; while the entire orchestra joins in an imitation of New Year's Eve at Times Square for the magnificent and soul-stirring theme of Pilsner's Anger at Being Given the Wrong Number.

Although it is very nice to be familiar with the various motifs in these operas it is not strictly necessary, for there is almost certain to be a lady in the row ahead, or somewhere adjacent, who will be explaining them loudly to her husband.

5. Italian opera—well, your nose knows! The minute you enter the opera house and see the standees are six deep, and it comes over you suddenly that seven-tenths of the audience had garlic for dinner and enjoyed it thoroughly, you know you are going to have a good time. You know you are going to hear a lot of corking songs you really know—oh, not personally, of course, but phonographically—and that you won't be able to resist the prevailing enthusiasm, and will applaud a great deal, and perhaps shout "*Bis*" and be ashamed of it afterwards, when the tenor leaves the rest of the cast flat and comes running down to the footlights to fling the highest note in the world right at you—well, it's just what you'd call really grand opera!

So much for the things that everybody knows. But what about the things that everybody doesn't? Which brings us right at the start to that noble, though nameless, company of Gypsies, Nobles, Peasants, Friends, Guests, Etc., with which this article is chiefly concerned, and which is so casually dismissed by the average operagoer as the chorus.

Essential Etceteras

Without this brave band of etceteras, grand opera, as such, could not be given; nor, perhaps we may add, forgiven. Can you think of Aïda without its Priests, Soldiers, Ethiopian Slaves, Prisoners, Egyptians, Etc.—and their march? How much would you give to see Faust without the Soldiers' Chorus? Or Trovatore without its Gypsies and their anvils? Think of all the operas you have ever heard, as well as of all those you haven't, and try to imagine them without their full quota of Monks, Bandits, Guards, Courtiers, Matadores, Villagers, and—above all—Etc. It's unthinkable! Yet do we ever give them any credit? Do we ever even give them any applause? Personally we admit with shame that, let the tenor blat no matter how sharp a B flat, or the prima donna shrill no matter how flat a C sharp, our response has always been courteous and immediate. We were brought up like that. But with the chorus, no matter how excellent its work, we have always just sat back and let it exit amid silence after it has done its bit to make grand opera safe in a democracy. We always have—but we never will again. Because, to lay aside our operatic generalities and become personal, we have lately seen the most famous Gypsies, Nobles, Peasants, Friends, Guests, Etc., in the world—in other words, the chorus of the Metropolitan Opera Company—in rehearsal.

Now, a regular routine rehearsal at the Metropolitan is all very thrilling and fascinating in theory, but it is not particularly impressive just at first sight—at least, the one we saw wasn't. The great auditorium was dark and, except for a little knot of three or four men about a third of the way back, quite empty. The orchestra pit was empty, also. On the stage apron which juts out over it, with their backs to the footlights—which were not lighted—were four substantial-looking gentlemen seated upon as many unsubstantial-looking little gilt chairs, and each with a music rack, with its green-shaded lamp, before him. These were the conductor, the chorus master, and two assistant conductors. Over at one side stood an upright piano. The big barnlike stage itself was littered with various odds and ends of scenery, rolls of carpet, and an assortment of chairs that ranged all the way from thoroughbred kitchens to the wabbly mongrel gilt affairs aforementioned, while overhead lights shone with singularly dismal effect upon twelve solemn, serious, sack-suited Latin gentlemen who were seated in a row upon a small raised platform in the center. A thirteenth gentleman, at the moment we entered, was addressing them in a mixture of Italian, French and English. Unfortunately, or perhaps not, though our English is flawless we always have to go into second to make the grade in French, and in Italian we run on only one cylinder, so although we could not catch the trend of his conversation our native wit led us to identify him as the stage director. And thus it proved.

The Dumb-bell Dozen

But who were the sad-faced twelve? As we asked ourselves the question the stage director clapped his hands as one who should say "Now, children, all ready for the lesson!"

One of the assistant conductors seated himself at the piano, the man at the extreme left of the row grasped a property bowl and pitcher, and they were off. We use the phrase advisedly. They certainly were off—way off—but not for long! A smart rapping on the conductor's desk, a moan of pain from the director—the piano stops, and with it the Dumb-bell Dozen. Back they go to the starting post. During the ensuing ten minutes of intensive pleading on the part of the director we rack our brains to recall an opera where twelve unusually gloomy gentlemen sit on a platform and pass a bowl and pitcher. They look like a jury—but of course we know better than that! Are they gypsies—nobles—peasants—friends—guests?

"*Voici le pain*," sings the first, handing his neighbor the bowl.

"*Et le sel*," sings another. To our astonishment, these are words we know. If they keep this up, we say to ourselves, we'll soon get the hang of it. Are they soldiers—matadores—guards? "*Voici le miel.*" The stage director signals frantically but fruitlessly to the man holding the pitcher, who apparently in a fit of acute depression has gone off into a trance and rouses himself just two and three-quarters seconds too late to sing "*Et voici l'eau.*" Again everything stops. The young *répétiteur* at the piano fills in a painful interval by gently strumming some operatic equivalent for Over the Fence is Out, the gentleman with the pitcher tries to look as if the eleven others were really responsible, the stage director has a good cry and seems to feel better afterwards, and everything begins all over again.

What opera is it? Are they courtiers? Villagers? Monks? Monks! Oh, now we know! Monks, of course! Only we had never paid any attention to them before. Who does, in Thaïs? What Farrar or Jeritza will or, rather, will not wear, the Meditation—these are the things in Thaïs that have always focused our interest, not the Opening Chorus of Cenobites.

And right here the rehearsal became impressive. Impressive, because we became conscious for the first time of the tremendous effort, the enormous expenditure of energy, time, money and brains involved in what we are accustomed to thinking of as a detail in a Metropolitan production. For one solid hour we watched the twelve earnestly and gravely pass imaginary bread and honey, and greet the returning Athanael, whose rôle was assumed for the moment by the stage director, who sang like—well, like a stage director—and who set himself the almost superhuman task of simultaneously depicting the distraught monk and disciplining his brother Cenobites, who persisted in exiting in the wrong direction, sitting in the wrong seats, kneeling when they ought to stand, and vice versa. Do you remember how hard you had to work at the last Christmas entertainment of the Maple Avenue Baptist Church, pushing and pulling those little boys into a formation that would eventually spell "Merry Christmas"? Well, multiply that by forty-seven, divide by twelve, take away what you first thought of and you will have a faint idea of this rehearsal.

Saying It with Music

But this is a slight affair compared with one that employs the full chorus—one hundred and twelve Italians, Frenchmen and Americans, whose number is frequently augmented by picked members from the chorus school. When you see Tannhäuser this winter you will enjoy the Pilgrims' Chorus even more if you will pause and reflect how they got that way. And in Act II, where the Nobles, Knights and Ladies —— But perhaps you've forgotten Tannhäuser since the war, and we'd better explain that Act II is The Hall of Song, which is rather like a German equivalent for the covered grand stand at the Polo Grounds, and where there is about to take place one of those song contests which, strangely enough, come under the head of sport with the German people. The Nobles and Knights, all looking as if they had lost their election bets, and the Ladies, dressed—oh, well, you know how the German nobility always did dress—have turned out in full force and every seat in the bleachers at the right of the stage is taken. The game in this instance is to see whether Wolfram or Tannhäuser can sing the longest and the loudest about love.

Wolfram wins the toss, and begins. Betting on him seems to be heavy among the Nobles, Knights, Ladies, Etc., and you yourself begin to think you have rarely listened to a longer song. In a nutshell its plot is that love is great stuff, and at its conclusion, after a matter of thirty minutes, you can see he has the crowd absolutely on his side.

Then Tannhäuser rises. Instead of letting sleeping dogs lie, he takes issue with Wolfram. He mentions, very favorably, a lady named Venus—who was to mythology what Theda Bara is to movies—and right away things take a turn for the better and it looks as if a rather dull song contest would end in a good old-fashioned knock-down-and-drag-out fight. And now comes the part we particularly want you to notice!

"Away! Away! Nor near him stay!" sing the Ladies—in German, of course, so it sounds even worse than that—running in horror from the hall while the Knights, Nobles, Etc., flourishing their swords, rush towards Tannhäuser and the footlights.

"*Entsetzlich! Scheusslich! Fluchenswerth!*" they sing—which is not, as might be supposed, a hastily composed cheer of greeting to the newly elected president of the Hay Fever Association, but "Disown him! Curse him! Banish him!"

"Well," you say, "what's so wonderful about that?"

And we would be the first to agree with you if we hadn't seen it rehearsed for two hours. Have you ever tried to get out of one door of a subway train at Times Square, for instance, when a lady near you decided to get out another? Do you remember what happened? Well, just multiply it by one hundred and twelve, and see if you don't change your mind about it. And take into consideration, too, that these people are singing—and singing beautifully and correctly. Have you ever tried a running broad jump while singing, say, a second to I've Been Workin' on the Railroad? Then try jumping over six or eight rows of benches at top speed and, as you land, sing "*Entsetzlich! Scheusslich! Fluchenswerth!*" on the right note at the right moment. Go on, try! We dare you!

Let's Not Worry

YOU bump into a great many people, these days, who are worriers. They are worried all the time. This is entirely unnecessary and causes them a great deal of travail that could be avoided. I used to be like that myself, and out of the sympathy I feel for men and women in that fix, am glad to pass along my advice. The thing to do, if you are one of these unfortunates, is to look on the bright side. There are always two sides, you know. There is the bright side, the dark side, and the even darker side you don't even suspect.

Just because the house is full of sharp knives, it doesn't necessarily follow that the baby will get one. Just because there is water boiling on the stove, it doesn't necessarily follow that the baby will get a chair (as we know he does) and climb up to spill it on himself. Just because everything dangerous is put on the back burners or the mantel, doesn't necessarily mean the dangerous items will be the most attractive. Common sense tells you they will be, but you could be wrong—on a real lucky day.

The icebox could be making that peculiar noise and still not be getting ready to break. (I'll give three to one that it does.) The smoke you smell may *not* be your house on fire—it could be the one next door, which will spread to yours. The screens might hold out another year. That pain in your side may be on the wrong side for appendicitis. Probably it is only a touch of something that has been attacking the chickens in Maryland. If you start shedding your feathers, medical science will be powerless to help, but you will be of great interest to the Department of Agriculture.

The dog across the way may not be as vicious as he looks. The chances are it will *not* turn out he bit three children before moving here from Nesselrode, New Jersey. As for the tobacco that spills from your cigarette when you tap it, the chances are the baby will not put a flake in his eye, on a day when the doctor is playing golf. There is also a chance that you are *not* smoking too much. Lots of people have smoked just as much, and some of them are still alive.

There is some reason to suppose that the tires *will* hold out for this trip, except for one, and what do you need with four tires? Besides, you can always replace them, and it would cost only a small fortune. Incidentally, do you think it would be better to get the cigarette lighter disconnected, before the baby puts his finger in it? And yells, and kicks the car out of gear, so you are all in the ditch? And have to wire the office for money, on a day when the banks are closed?

There is no sense in letting little things bother you. That burning sensation in your stomach may very well *not* be ulcers. The fact that you are the nervous, worrying type is, of course, not in your favor, but you may be the exception. You must learn to look for these little rays of sunshine. You won't need dark glasses either.

Just look at it this way: the postman isn't *necessarily* bringing bills. He may be bringing a post card from two relative strangers who will be here Tuesday with three bored children, to spend the week. The trick is to cultivate a hopeful outlook. Take the lawn, for instance. Sure, it will need a little attention, come summer. But probably it could be put in wonderful shape for around four hundred precious dollars. And with food prices what they are today, what's four hundred dollars? Lots of people have four hundred dollars. Are they worried?

Possibly you worry about things at the office —how you stand there, the boss' attitude, trifles like that. The trouble with a worrying man is that he assumes the worst. He puts the gloomiest possible construction on every set of facts. Mention the atom bomb, and right away he thinks of explosions. Mention rattlesnakes, and he thinks of getting bitten. Where were we? Oh, yes, the office. Now there is every chance they may like you there. There is some chance they may think you are doing good work. Well, fair work, anyway. A high mediocre. But you, you think they are getting ready to fire you, so you worry. There isn't a chance they'll fire you. Not until next Christmas Eve. Just when you are putting up the tree.

As a matter of fact, the office may be fixing to give you a raise, a raise you haven't dared ask for. Stranger things have happened, and Ripley had a picture of them. I'd be willing to bet you are aces all around with your employers. Want to bet? Here's my one. Just lay down your twenty.

What else do you worry about—your health? The way to get over that is to go see some good doctor and get a thorough checkup. Just tell him your symptoms, if you can get an appointment, and get them off your mind. He will probably make a few simple suggestions, like giving up eating, drinking, smoking, walking, talking and looking at girls, and tell you you will live fifty years. Well, in your case, fifty days. But fifty something, you see, and then you know where you stand. The chances are you are in much better shape than you think. Any good doctor can tell you in five minutes. That's five minutes after four months of examinations. It'll cost a little money, but it's money well spent. What was that noise? I guess it was just a backfire. There have been quite a few robberies in the neighborhood lately, and it gets you a little jumpy.

I'll tell you what you ought to do—I'm assuming the doctor lets you do anything. But I think he will, for you look pretty good to me. A little peaked, maybe, and sallow, and I don't think you get enough sleep. A doctor friend of mine told me, he said the best thing in the world for insomnia is eight hours of sound sleep. He also told me to cut down on my coffee. It's made a new man out of me. Would you mind holding a match for me? Every time I try to light a cigarette I burn my nose.

As I was saying, what a fellow like you needs is a hobby. You see, you're too engrossed in your work. Take up something, like trout fishing. I'll bet there's a trout stream not five hundred miles from your door. Get up early in the morning, put on your waders—you'll have to buy those—and get out there, say, by seven o'clock, and see how many you can land. I tried it myself, and while I still limp a little from stumbling over those rocks, it got my mind right off my business, where it was needed.

Or a workshop. I don't care for it myself, but I know a guy who has everything you can get in the way of a shop. We call him Old Three Fingers.

But you get the idea—the idea is to get your troubles off your mind, so you won't worry so much. It's this constant worry, worry, worry that makes people worry. Just say to yourself, "What have *I* got to worry about?" You'll be surprised the difference it will make, and the list too. Why don't I get you the name of this psychiatrist that straightened a friend of mine out? It cost two thousand dollars, but he's in the chips, so what does he care? This psychiatrist, he's regarded as tops, or else he's a quack, I forget which, but anyway, he knows his stuff. You know what he told this friend of mine? He said, "Look, you know what the trouble with you is? You worry too much. Be happy!"

—ROBERT M. YODER.

Men I'm Not Married To

No matter where my route may lie,
  No matter whither I repair,
In brief—no matter how or why
  Or when I go, the boys are there.
On lane and byway, street and square,
  On alley, path and avenue,
They seem to spring up everywhere—
  The men I am not married to.

I watch them as they pass me by;
  At each in wonderment I stare,
And "But for heaven's grace," I cry,
  "There goes the guy whose name I'd bear!"
They represent no species rare,
  They walk and talk as others do;
They're fair to see—but only fair—
  The men I am not married to.

I'm sure that to a mother's eye
  Is each potentially a bear;
But though at home they rank ace-high,
  No change of heart could I declare.
Yet worry silvers not their hair;
  They deck them not with sprigs of rue.
It's curious how they do not care—
  The men I am not married to.

L'ENVOI

In fact, if they'd a chance to share
  Their lot with me, a lifetime through,
They'd doubtless tender me the air—
  The men I am not married to.

—DOROTHY PARKER.

YOU COULD LOOK IT UP

By JAMES THURBER

§ Magrew's ball club couldn't seem to shake the worst slump it had ever been in. The manager's temper got so foul no one could stand him, except an amazing midget named Pearl du Monville who might have been a girl, but wasn't. Thus began the strange friendship that was to end in some of the craziest antics ever witnessed in the history of America's favorite pastime. In case you don't believe the story, well, "You could look it up."

APRIL 5, 1941

IT ALL begun when we dropped down to C'lumbus, Ohio, from Pittsburgh to play a exhibition game on our way out to St. Louis. It was gettin' on into September, and though we'd been leadin' the league by six, seven games most of the season, we was now in first place by a margin you could 'a' got it into the eye of a thimble, bein' only a half a game ahead of St. Louis. Our slump had given the boys the leapin' jumps, and they was like a bunch a old ladies at a lawn fete with a thunderstorm comin' up, runnin' around snarlin' at each other, eatin' bad and sleepin' worse, and battin' for a team average of maybe .186. Half the time nobody'd speak to nobody else, without it was to bawl 'em out.

Squawks Magrew was managin' the boys at the time, and he was darn near crazy. They called him "Squawks" 'cause when things was goin' bad he lost his voice, or perty near lost it, and squealed at you like a little girl you stepped on her doll or somethin'. He yelled at everybody and wouldn't listen to nobody, without maybe it was me. I'd been trainin' the boys for ten year, and he'd take more lip from me than from anybody else. He knowed I was smarter'n him, anyways, like you're goin' to hear.

This was thirty, thirty-one year ago; you could look it up, 'cause it was the same year C'lumbus decided to call itself the Arch City, on account of a lot of iron arches with electric-light bulbs into 'em which stretched acrost High Street. Thomas Albert Edison sent 'em a telegram, and they was speeches and maybe even President Taft opened the celebration by pushin' a button. It was a great week for the Buckeye capital, which was why they got us out there for this exhibition game.

Well, we just lose a double-header to Pittsburgh, 11 to 5 and 7 to 3, so we snarled all the way to C'lumbus, where we put up at the Chittaden Hotel, still snarlin'. Everybody was tetchy, and when Billy Klinger took a sock at Whitey Cott at breakfast, Whitey throwed marmalade all over his face.

"Blind each other, whatta I care?" says Magrew. "You can't see nothin' anyways."

C'lumbus win the exhibition game, 3 to 2, whilst Magrew set in the dugout, mutterin' and cursin' like a fourteen-year-old Scotty. He bad-mouthed everybody on the ball club and he bad-mouthed everybody offa the ball club, includin' the Wright brothers, who, he claimed, had yet to build a airship big enough for any of our boys to hit it with a ball bat.

"I wisht I was dead," he says to me. "I wisht I was in heaven with the angels."

I told him to pull hisself together, 'cause he was drivin' the boys crazy, the way he was goin' on, sulkin' and bad-mouthin' and whinin'. I was older'n he was and smarter'n he was, and he knowed it. I was ten times smarter'n he was about this Pearl du Monville, first time I ever laid eyes on the little guy, which was one of the saddest days of my life.

Now, most people name of Pearl is girls, but this Pearl du Monville was a man, if you could call a fella a man who was only thirty-four, thirty-five inches high. Pearl du Monville was a midget. He was part French and part Hungarian, and maybe even part Bulgarian or somethin'. I can see him now, a sneer on his little pushed-in pan, swingin' a bamboo cane and smokin' a big cigar. He had a gray suit with a big black check into it, and he had a gray felt hat with one of them rainbow-colored hatbands onto it, like the young fellas wore in them days. He talked like he was talkin' into a tin can, but he didn't have no foreign accent. He might 'a' been fifteen or he might 'a' been a hunderd, you couldn't tell. Pearl du Monville.

After the game with C'lumbus, Magrew headed straight for the Chittaden bar—the train for St. Louis wasn't goin' for three, four hours—and there he set, drinkin' rye and talkin' to this bartender.

"How I pity me, brother," Magrew was tellin' this bartender. "How I pity me." That was alwuz his favorite tune. So he was settin' there, tellin' this bartender how heartbreakin' it was to be manager of a bunch a blindfolded circus clowns, when up pops this Pearl du Monville outa nowheres.

It give Magrew the leapin' jumps. He thought at first maybe the D.T.'s had come back on him; he claimed he'd had 'em once, and little guys had popped up all around him, wearin' red, white and blue hats.

"Go on, now!" Magrew yells. "Get away from me!"

But the midget clumb up on a chair acrost the table from Magrew and says, "I seen that game today, Junior, and you ain't got no ball club. What you got there, Junior," he says, "is a side show."

"Whatta ya mean, 'Junior'?" says Magrew, touchin' the little guy to satisfy hisself he was real.

"Don't pay him no attention, mister," says the bartender. "Pearl calls everybody 'Junior,' 'cause it alwuz turns out he's a year older'n anybody else."

"Yeh?" says Magrew. "How old is he?"

"How old are you, Junior?" says the midget.

"Who, me? I'm fifty-three," says Magrew.

"Well, I'm fifty-four," says the midget.

Magrew grins and asts him what he'll have, and that was the beginnin' of their beautiful friendship, if you don't care what you say.

Pearl du Monville stood up on his chair and waved his cane around and pretended like he was bally-hooin' for a circus. "Right this way, folks!" he yells. "Come on in and see the greatest collection of freaks in the world! See the armless pitchers, see the eyeless batters, see the infielders with five thumbs!" and on and on like that, feedin' Magrew gall and handin' him a laugh at the same time, you might say.

You could hear him and Pearl du Monville hootin' and hollerin' and singin' way up to the fourth floor of the Chittaden, where the boys was packin' up. When it come time to go to the station, you can imagine how disgusted we was when we crowded into the doorway of that bar and seen them two singin' and goin' on.

"Well, well, well," says Magrew, lookin' up and spottin' us. "Look who's here. . . . Clowns, this is Pearl du Monville, a monseer of the old, old school. . . . Don't shake hands with 'em, Pearl, 'cause their fingers is made of chalk and would bust right off in your paws," he says, and he starts guffawin' and Pearl starts titterin' and we stand there givin' 'em the iron eye, it bein' the lowest ebb a ball-club manager'd got hisself down to since the national pastime was started.

Then the midget begun givin' us the ballyhoo. "Come on in!" he says, wavin' his cane. "See the legless base runners, see the outfielders with the butter fingers, see the southpaw with the arm of a little chee-ild!"

Then him and Magrew begun to hoop and holler and nudge each other till you'd of thought this little guy was the funniest guy than even Charlie Chaplin. The fellas filed outa the bar without a word and went on up to the Union Depot, leavin' me to handle Magrew and his new-found crony.

Well, I got 'em outa there finely. I had to take the little guy along, 'cause Magrew had a holt onto him like a vise and I couldn't pry him loose.

"He's comin' along as masket," says Magrew, holdin' the midget in the crouch of his arm like a football. And come along he did, hollerin' and protestin' and beatin' at Magrew with his little fists.

"Cut it out, will you, Junior?" the little guy kept whinin'. "Come on, leave a man loose, will ya, Junior?"

But Junior kept a holt onto him and begun yellin', "See the guys with the glass arm, see the guys with the cast-iron brains, see the fielders with the feet on their wrists!"

So it goes, right through the whole Union Depot, with people starin' and catcallin', and he don't put the midget down till he gets him through the gates.

"How'm I goin' to go along without no toothbrush?" the midget asts. "What'm I goin' to do without no other suit?" he says.

"Doc here," says Magrew, meanin' me—"doc here will look after you like you was his own son, won't you, doc?"

I give him the iron eye, and he finely got on the train and prob'ly went to sleep with his clothes on.

This left me alone with the midget. "Lookit," I says to him. "Why don't you go on home now? Come mornin', Magrew'll forget all about you. He'll prob'ly think you was somethin' he seen in a nightmare maybe. And he ain't goin' to laugh so easy in the mornin', neither," I says. "So why don't you go on home?"

"Nix," he says to me. "Skiddoo," he says, "twenty-three for you," and he tosses his cane up into the vestibule of the coach and clam'ers on up after it like a cat. So that's the way Pearl du Monville come to go to St. Louis with the ball club.

I seen 'em first at breakfast the next day, settin' opposite each other; the midget playin' Turkey in the Straw on a harmonium and Magrew starin' at his eggs and bacon like they was a uncooked bird with its feathers still on.

"Remember where you found this?" I says, jerkin' my thumb at the midget. "Or maybe you think they come with breakfast on these trains," I says, bein' a good hand at turnin' a sharp remark in them days.

The midget puts down the harmonium and turns on me. "Sneeze," he says; "your brains is dusty." Then he snaps a couple drops of water at me from a tumbler.

"Drown," he says, tryin' to make his voice deep.

Now, both them cracks is Civil War cracks, but you'd of thought they was brand new and the funniest than any crack Magrew'd ever heard in his whole life. He started hoopin' and hollerin', and the midget started hoopin' and hollerin', so I walked on away and set down with Bugs Courtney and Hank Metters, payin' no attention to this weak-minded Damon and Phidias acrost the aisle.

Well, sir, the first game with St. Louis was rained out, and there we was facin' a double-header next day. Like maybe I told you, we lose the last three double-headers we play, makin' maybe twenty-five errors in the six games, which is all right for the intimates of a school for the blind, but is disgraceful for the world's champions. It was too wet to go to the zoo, and Magrew wouldn't let us go to the movies, 'cause they flickered so bad in them days. So we just set around, stewin' and frettin'.

One of the newspaper boys come over to take a pitture of Billy Klinger and Whitey Cott shakin' hands—this reporter'd heard about the fight—and whilst they was standin' there, toe to toe, shakin' hands, Billy give a back lunge and a jerk, and throwed Whitey over his shoulder into a corner of the room, like a sack of salt. Whitey come back at him with a chair, and Bethlehem broke loose in that there room. The camera was tromped to pieces like a berry basket. When we finely got 'em pulled apart, I heard a laugh, and there was Magrew and the midget standin' in the door and givin' us the iron eye.

"Wrasslers," says Magrew, cold-like, "that's what I got for a ball club, Mr. Du Monville, wrasslers—and not very good wrasslers at that, you ast me."

"A man can't be good at everythin'," says Pearl, "but he oughta be good at somethin'."

This sets Magrew guffawin' again, and away they go, the midget taggin' along by his side like a hound dog and handin' him a fast line of so-called comic cracks.

When we went out to face that battlin' St. Louis club in a double-header the next afternoon, the boys was jumpy as tin toys with keys in their back. We lose the first game, 7 to 2, and are trailin', 4 to 0, when the second game ain't but ten minutes old. Magrew set there like a stone statue, speakin' to nobody. Then, in their half a the fourth, somebody singled to center and knocked in two more runs for St. Louis.

That made Magrew squawk. "I wisht one thing," he says. "I wisht I was manager of a old ladies' sewin' circus 'stead of a ball club."

"You are, Junior, you are," says a familyer and disagreeable voice.

It was that Pearl du Monville again, poppin' up outa nowheres, swingin' his bamboo cane and smokin' a cigar that's three sizes too big for his face. By this time we'd finely got the other side out, and Hank Metters slithered a bat acrost the ground, and the midget had to jump to keep both his ankles from bein' broke.

I thought Magrew'd bust a blood vessel. "You hurt Pearl and I'll break your neck!" he yelled.

Hank muttered somethin' and went on up to the plate and struck out.

We managed to get a couple runs acrost in our half a the sixth, but they come back with three more in their half a the seventh, and this was too much for Magrew.

"Come on, Pearl," he says. "We're gettin' outa here."

"Where you think you're goin'?" I ast him.

"To the lawyer's again," he says cryptly.

"I didn't know you'd been to the lawyer's once, yet," I says.

"Which that goes to show how much you don't know," he says.

With that, they was gone, and I didn't see 'em the rest of the day, nor know what they was up to, which was a God's blessin'. We lose the nightcap, 9 to 3, and that puts us into second place plenty, and as low in our mind as a ball club can get.

The next day was a horrible day, like anybody that lived through it can tell you. Practice was just over and the St. Louis club was takin' the field, when I hears this strange sound from the stands. It sounds like the nervous whickerin' a horse gives when he smells somethin' funny on the wind. It was the fans ketchin' sight of Pearl du Monville, like you have prob'ly guessed. The midget had popped up onto the field all dressed up in a minacher club uniform, sox, cap, little letters sewed onto his chest, and all. He was swingin' a kid's bat and the only thing kept him from lookin' like a real ballplayer seen through the wrong end of a microscope was this cigar he was smokin'.

Bugs Courtney reached over and jerked it outa his mouth and throwed it away. "You're wearin' that suit on the playin' field," he says to him, severe as a judge. "You go insultin' it and I'll take you out to the zoo and feed you to the bears."

Pearl just blowed some smoke at him which he still has in his mouth.

Whilst Whitey was foulin' off four or five prior to strikin' out, I went on over to Magrew. "If I was as comic as you," I says, "I'd laugh myself to death," I says. "Is that any way to treat the uniform, makin' a mockery out of it?"

"It might surprise you to know I ain't makin' no mockery outa the uniform," says Magrew. "Pearl du Monville here has been made a bone-of-fida member of this so-called ball club. I fixed it up with the front office by long-distance phone."

"Yeh?" I says. "I can just hear Mr. Dillworth or Bart Jenkins agreein' to hire a midget for the ball club. I can just hear 'em." Mr. Dillworth was the owner of the club and Bart Jenkins was the secretary, and they never stood for no monkey business. "May I be so bold as to inquire," I says, "just what you told 'em?"

"I told 'em," he says, "I wanted to sign up a guy they ain't no pitcher in the league can strike him out."

"Uh-huh," I says, "and did you tell 'em what size of a man he is?"

"Never mind about that," he says. "I got papers on me, made out legal and proper, constitutin' one Pearl du Monville a bone-of-fida member of this former ball club. Maybe that'll shame them big babies into gettin' in there and swingin', knowin' I can replace any one of 'em with a midget, if I have a mind to. A St. Louis lawyer I seen twice tells me it's all legal and proper."

"A St. Louis lawyer would," I says, "seein' nothin' could make him happier than havin' you makin' a mockery outa this one-time baseball outfit," I says.

Well, sir, it'll all be there in the papers of thirty, thirty-one year ago, and you could look it up. The game went along without no scorin' for seven innings, and since they ain't nothin' much to watch but guys poppin' up or strikin' out, the fans pay most of their attention to the goin's-on of Pearl du Monville. He's out there in front a the dugout, turnin' handsprings, balancin' his bat on his chin, walkin' a imaginary line, and so on. The fans clapped and laughed at him, and he ate it up.

So it went up to the last a the eighth, nothin' to nothin', not more'n seven, eight hits all told, and no errors on neither side. Our pitcher gets the first two men out easy in the eighth. Then up come a fella name of Porter or Billings, or some such name, and he lammed one up against the tobacco sign for three bases. The next guy up slapped the first ball out into left for a base hit, and in come the fella from third for the only run of the ball game so far. The crowd yelled, the look a death came onto Magrew's face again, and even the midget quit his tomfoolin'. Their next man fouled out back a third, and we come up for our last bats like a bunch a schoolgirls steppin' into a pool of cold water. I was lower in my mind than I'd been since the day in Nineteen-four when Chesbro throwed the wild pitch in the ninth inning with a man on third and lost the pennant for the Highlanders. I knowed something just as bad was goin' to happen, which shows I'm a clairvoyun, or was then.

When Gordy Mills hit out to second, I just closed my eyes. I opened 'em up again to see Dutch Muller standin' on second, dustin' off his pants, him havin' got his first hit in maybe twenty times to the plate. Next up was Harry Loesing, battin' for our pitcher, and he got a base on balls, walkin' on a fourth one you could 'a' combed your hair with.

Then up come Whitey Cott, our lead-off man. He crotches down in what was prob'ly the most fearsome stanch in organized ball, but all he can do is pop out to short. That brung up Billy Klinger, with two down and a man on first and second. Billy took a cut at one you could 'a' knocked a plug hat offa this here Carnera with it, but then he gets sense enough to wait 'em out, and finely he walks, too, fillin' the bases.

Yes, sir, there you are; the tyin' run on third and the winnin' run on second, first a the ninth, two men down, and Hank Metters comin' to the bat. Hank was built like a Pope-Hartford and he couldn't run no faster'n President Taft, but he had five home runs to his credit for the season, and that wasn't bad in them days. Hank was still hittin' better'n anybody else on the ball club, and it was mighty heartenin', seein' him stridin' up towards the plate. But he never got there.

"Wait a minute!" yells Magrew, jumpin' to his feet. "I'm sendin' in a pinch hitter!" he yells.

You could 'a' heard a bomb drop. When a ball-club manager says he's sendin' in a pinch hitter for the best batter on the club, you know and I know and everybody knows he's lost his holt.

"They're goin' to be sendin' the funny wagon for you, if you don't watch out," I says, grabbin' a holt of his arm.

But he pulled away and run out towards the plate, yellin', "Du Monville battin' for Metters!"

All the fellas begun squawlin' at once, except Hank, and he just stood there starin' at Magrew like he'd gone crazy and was claimin' to be Ty Cobb's grandma or somethin'. Their pitcher stood out there with his hands on his hips and a disagreeable look on his face, and the plate umpire told Magrew to go on and get a batter up. Magrew told him again Du Monville was battin' for Metters, and the St. Louis manager finely got the idea. It brung him outa his dugout, howlin' and bawlin' like he'd lost a female dog and her seven pups.

Magrew pushed the midget towards the plate and he says to him, he says, "Just stand up there and hold that bat on your shoulder. They ain't a man in the world can throw three strikes in there 'fore he throws four balls!" he says.

"I get it, Junior!" says the midget. "He'll walk me and force in the tyin' run!" And he starts on up to the plate as cocky as if he was Willie Keeler.

I don't need to tell you Bethlehem broke loose on that there ball field. The fans got onto their hind legs, yellin' and whistlin', and everybody on the field begun wavin' their arms and hollerin' and shovin'. The plate umpire stalked over to Magrew like a traffic cop, waggin' his jaw and pointin' his finger, and the St. Louis manager kept yellin' like his house was on fire. When Pearl got up to the plate and stood there, the pitcher slammed his glove down onto the ground and started stompin' on it, and they ain't nobody can blame him. He's just walked two normal-sized human bein's, and now here's a guy up to the plate they ain't more'n twenty inches between his knees and his shoulders.

The plate umpire called in the field umpire, and they talked a while, like a couple doctors seein' the bucolic plague or somethin' for the first time. Then the plate umpire come over to Magrew with his arms folded acrost his chest, and he told him to go on and get a batter up, or he'd forfeit the game to St. Louis. He pulled out his watch, but somebody batted it outa his hand in the scufflin', and I thought there'd be a free-for-all, with everybody yellin' and shovin' except Pearl du Monville, who stood up at the plate with his little bat on his shoulder, not movin' a muscle.

Then Magrew played his ace. I seen him pull some papers outa his pocket and show 'em to the plate umpire. The umpire begun lookin' at 'em like they was bills for somethin' he not only never bought it, he never even heard of it. The other umpire studied 'em like they was a death warren, and all this time the St. Louis manager and the fans and the players is yellin' and hollerin'.

Well, sir, they fought about him bein' a midget, and they fought about him usin' a kid's bat, and they fought about where'd he been all season. They was eight or nine rule books brung out and everybody was thumbin' through 'em, tryin' to find out what it says about midgets, but it don't say nothin' about midgets, 'cause this was somethin' never'd come up in the history of the game before, and nobody'd ever dreamed about it, even when they has nightmares. Maybe you can't send no midgets in to bat nowadays, 'cause the old game's changed a lot, mostly for the worst, but you could then, it turned out.

The plate umpire finely decided the contrack papers was all legal and proper, like Magrew said, so he waved the St. Louis players back to their places and he pointed his finger at their manager and told him to quit hollerin' and get on back in the dugout. The manager says the game is percedin' under protest, and the umpire bawls, "Play ball!" over 'n' above the yellin' and booin', him havin' a voice like a hog-caller.

The St. Louis pitcher picked up his glove and beat at it with his fist six or eight times, and then got set on the mound and studied the situation. The fans realized he was really goin' to pitch to the midget, and they went crazy, hoopin' and hollerin' louder'n ever, and throwin' pop bottles and hats and cushions down onto the field. It took five, ten minutes to get the fans quieted down again, whilst our fellas that was on base set down on the bags and waited. And Pearl du Monville kept standin' up there with the bat on his shoulder, like he'd been told to.

So the pitcher starts studyin' the setup again, and you got to admit it was the strangest setup in a ball game since the players cut off their beards and begun wearin' gloves. I wisht I could call the pitcher's name—it wasn't old Barney Pelty nor Nig Jack Powell nor Harry Howell. He was a big right-hander, but I can't call his name. You could look it up. Even in a crotchin' position, the ketcher towers over the midget like the Washington Monument.

The plate umpire tries standin' on his tiptoes, then he tries crotchin' down, and he finely gets hisself into a stanch nobody'd ever seen on a ball field before, kinda squattin' down on his hanches.

Well, the pitcher is sore as a old buggy horse in fly time. He slams in the first pitch, hard and wild, and maybe two foot higher 'n the midget's head.

"Ball one!" hollers the umpire over 'n' above the racket, 'cause everybody is yellin' worsten ever.

The ketcher goes on out towards the mound and talks to the pitcher and hands him the ball. This time the big right-hander tries a undershoot, and it comes in a little closer, maybe no higher'n a foot, foot and a half above Pearl's head. It would 'a' been a strike with a human bein' in there, but the umpire's got to call it, and he does.

"Ball two!" he bellers.

The ketcher walks on out to the mound again, and the whole infield comes over and gives advice to the pitcher about what they'd do in a case like this, with two balls and no strikes on a batter that oughta be in a bottle of alcohol 'stead of up there at the plate in a big-league game between the teams that is fightin' for first place.

For the third pitch, the pitcher stands there flat-footed and tosses up the ball like he's playin' ketch with a little girl.

Pearl stands there motionless as a hitchin' post, and the ball comes in big and slow and high—high for Pearl, that is, it bein' about on a level with his eyes, or a little higher'n a grown man's knees.

They ain't nothin' else for the umpire to do, so he calls, "Ball three!"

Everybody is onto their feet, hoopin' and hollerin', as the pitcher sets to throw ball four. The St. Louis manager is makin' signs and faces like he was a contorturer, and the infield is givin' the pitcher some more advice about what to do this time. Our boys who was on base stick right onto the bag, runnin' no risk of bein' nipped for the last out.

Well, the pitcher decides to give him a toss again, seein' he come closer with that than with a fast ball. They ain't nobody ever seen a slower ball throwed. It come in big as a balloon and slower'n any ball ever throwed before in the major leagues. It come right in over the plate in front of Pearl's chest, lookin' prob'ly big as a full moon to Pearl. They ain't never been a minute like the minute that followed since the United States was founded by the Pilgrim grandfathers.

Pearl du Monville took a cut at that ball, and he hit it! Magrew give a groan like a poleaxed steer as the ball rolls out in front a the plate into fair territory.

"Fair ball!" yells the umpire, and the midget starts runnin' for first, still carryin' that little bat, and makin' maybe ninety foot an hour. Bethlehem breaks loose on that ball field and in them stands. They ain't never been nothin' like it since creation was begun.

The ball's rollin' slow, on down towards third, goin' maybe eight, ten foot. The infield comes in fast and our boys break from their bases like hares in a brush fire. Everybody is standin' up, yellin' and hollerin', and Magrew is tearin' his hair outa his head, and the midget is scamperin' for first with all the speed of one of them little dashhounds carryin' a satchel in his mouth.

The ketcher gets to the ball first, but he boots it on out past the pitcher's box, the pitcher fallin' on his face tryin' to stop it, the shortstop sprawlin' after it full length and zaggin' it on over towards the second baseman, whilst Muller is scorin' with the tyin' run and Loesing is roundin' third with the winnin' run. Ty Cobb could 'a' made a three-bagger outa that bunt, with everybody fallin' over theirself tryin' to pick the ball up. But Pearl is still maybe fifteen, twenty feet from the bag, toddlin' like a baby and yeepin' like a trapped rabbit, when the second baseman finely gets a holt of that ball and slams it over to first. The first baseman ketches it and stomps on the bag, the base umpire waves Pearl out, and there goes your old ball game, the craziest ball game ever played in the history of the organized world.

Their players start runnin' in, and then I see Magrew. He starts after Pearl, runnin' faster'n any man ever run before. Pearl sees him comin' and runs behind the base umpire's legs and gets a holt onto 'em. Magrew comes up, pantin' and roarin', and him and the midget plays ring-around-a-rosy with the umpire, who keeps shovin' at Magrew with one hand and tryin' to slap the midget loose from his legs with the other.

Finely Magrew ketches the midget, who is still yeepin' like a stuck sheep. He gets

"Mamma, may I poison somebody?"

ESCALATOR UP

ODS

SWEATERS

WOOLENS · ARGYLES

temes

"Wipe your feet!"

FAMOUS LAST WORDS

"I know it isn't much of a job to start with, young man, but there are great chances for advancement."

"I suppose it can happen to one couple in every three billion or so."

"Well, if we're going to play Cowboys and Indians, *somebody* has got to be the Indians!"

"Will it be difficult to breathe?"

"Well, it's about time—I've been playing golf for three months now, and I was beginning to think I'd never make a hole in one."

"MCMXIII–MCMXIV–MCMXV–
MCMXVI–MCMXVII–"

"I don't raise my hand enough."

holt of that little guy by both his ankles and starts whirlin' him round and round his head like Magrew was a hammer thrower and Pearl was the hammer. Nobody can stop him without gettin' their head knocked off, so everybody just stands there and yells. Then Magrew lets the midget fly. He flies on out towards second, high and fast, like a human home run, headed for the soap sign in center field.

Their shortstop tries to get to him, but he can't make it, and I knowed the little fella was goin' to bust to pieces like a dollar watch on a asphalt street when he hit the ground. But it so happens their center fielder is just crossin' second, and he starts runnin' back, tryin' to get under the midget, who had took to spiralin' like a football 'stead of turnin' head over foot, which give him more speed and more distance.

I know you never seen a midget ketched, and you prob'ly never even seen one throwed. To ketch a midget that's been throwed by a heavy-muscled man and is flyin' through the air, you got to run under him and with him and pull your hands and arms back and down when you ketch him, to break the compact of his body, or you'll bust him in two like a matchstick. I seen Bill Lange and Willie Keeler and Tris Speaker make some wonderful ketches in my day, but I never seen nothin' like that center fielder. He goes back and back and still further back and he pulls that midget down outa the air like he was liftin' a sleepin' baby from a cradle. They wasn't a bruise onto him, only his face was the color of cat's meat and he ain't got no air in his chest. In his excitement, the base umpire, who was runnin' back with the center fielder when he ketched Pearl, yells, "Out!" and that give hysteries to the Bethlehem which was ragin' like Niagry on that ball field.

Everybody was hoopin' and hollerin' and yellin' and runnin', with the fans swarmin' onto the field, and the cops tryin' to keep order, and some guys laughin' and some of the women fans cryin', and six or eight of us holdin' onto Magrew to keep him from gettin' at that midget and finishin' him off. Some of the fans picks up the St. Louis pitcher and the center fielder, and starts carryin' 'em around on their shoulders, and they was the craziest goin's-on knowed to the history of organized ball on this side of the 'Lantic Ocean.

I seen Pearl du Monville strugglin' in the arms of a lady fan with a ample bosom, who was laughin' and cryin' at the same time, and him beatin' at her with his little fists and bawlin' and yellin'. He clawed his way loose finely and disappeared in the forest of legs which made that ball field look like it was Coney Island on a hot summer's day.

That was the last I ever seen of Pearl du Monville. I never seen hide nor hair of him from that day to this, and neither did nobody else. He just vanished into the thin of the air, as the fella says. He was ketched for the final out of the ball game and that was the end of him, just like it was the end of the ball game, you might say, and also the end of our losin' streak, like I'm goin' to tell you.

That night we piled onto a train for Chicago, but we wasn't snarlin' and snappin' any more. No, sir, the ice was finely broke and a new spirit come into that ball club. The old zip come back with the disappearance of Pearl du Monville out back a second base. We got to laughin' and talkin' and kiddin' together, and 'fore long Magrew was laughin' with us. He got a human look onto his pan again, and he quit whinin' and complainin' and wishtin' he was in heaven with the angels.

Well, sir, we wiped up that Chicago series, winnin' all four games, and makin' seventeen hits in one of 'em. Funny thing was, St. Louis was so shook up by that last game with us, they never did hit their stride again. Their center fielder took to misjudgin' everything that come his way, and the rest a the fellas followed suit, the way a club'll do when one guy blows up.

'Fore we left Chicago, I and some of the fellas went out and bought a pair of them little baby shoes, which we had 'em golded over and give 'em to Magrew for a souvenir, and he took it all in good spirit. Whitey Cott and Billy Klinger made up and was fast friends again, and we hit our home lot like a ton of dynamite and they was nothin' could stop us from then on.

I don't recollect things as clear as I did thirty, forty year ago. I can't read no fine print no more, and the only person I got to check with on the golden days of the national pastime, as the fella says, is my friend, old Milt Kline, over in Springfield, and his mind ain't as strong as it once was.

He gets Rube Waddell mixed up with Rube Marquard, for one thing, and anybody does that oughta be put away where he won't bother nobody. So I can't tell you the exact margin we win the pennant by. Maybe it was two and a half games, or maybe it was three and a half. But it'll all be there in the newspapers and record books of thirty, thirty-one year ago and, like I was sayin', you could look it up.

The Perfect Squelch

TWO teen-age girls, dining out in style and doing their best to appear sophisticated, got into a sharp argument. With a grand gesture, one pushed away her plate, flipped out a cigarette and lighted up.

Her companion, more composed, continued eating. As the smoke haze from the annoyed one enveloped her, she leaned forward in her most ladylike manner and asked in a voice audible throughout the restaurant, "I hope you don't mind my eating while you're smoking?"

"Not at all," her companion replied, "provided I can still hear the orchestra."

—M. GORDON BEVERLEY.

Money Came in Thick and Fast

A *POST* WAR ANECDOTE

AFTER the morning sermon at the post chapel at Camp Roberts, California, a lanky, redheaded soldier diffidently handed the chaplain an envelope, explaining that he wanted to make a donation.

"That's fine," approved the chaplain. "We can always use money to fix up the chapel." But when he opened the envelope and, to his astonishment, drew out five ten-dollar bills, he added slowly, "That's a lot of money, isn't it, private?"

The soldier shifted his weight and finally blurted out, "To tell the truth, sir, I won it."

"H'm," mused the chaplain. "Don't you think it would be better to give it back to the men you won it from?"

"No, I don't think so," demurred the private. "'Besides, they've shipped out."

"Well, I'll accept it then," the chaplain agreed. "I suppose it will do some good."

Twice after that the soldier brought in similar donations, and twice the chaplain accepted them to apply to chapel improvements, after futile attempts to have the winnings restored to the losers. But when the soldier again showed up—this time with $100—the chaplain decided to call a halt.

"Now, look here," he said sharply, "this has gone far enough. Gambling is a mighty bad habit. And what's more, giving all your winnings to the church doesn't excuse it in the least."

"Oh, I'm not giving it all to the church," the soldier hastily explained. "I'm giving a tenth. After your swell sermon about the Lord providing when people tithe, I tried it. Boy, He sure does!"

—GLENN P. HOLMAN.

O'MEARA AT TROY

By DON MARQUIS

§ *Who ever said Apollo was a Greek god? His real name was O'Pollo, of course, and Olympus was actually run by a sturdy band of emigrants from the Emerald Isle. You don't have to be Irish to appreciate this story, but it helps.*

JUNE 21, 1930

IT'S a queer thing, as many singers as the Irish have had," Terence O'Meara said to his father, "that they have never produced a very great singer, such as Shakspere or Dante."

His father gave him a glare of contempt.

"Don't ye ever give utterance to such ignorant words annywhere ye might be overheard by a real scholar," said the senior O'Meara. "The greatest poet of all time—famed, noted and renowned the wide world over wherever poetry is read—was an Irishman. Homer, he is called."

"Homer?" Terence's tone was incredulous.

"Homer he is called nowadays," said Mr. O'Meara solemnly, "but there shouldn't be anny letther H at the beginning of it—that H was put there by the English, like as not, for they're always putting H's where they shouldn't be and laving thim off where they should be. This name Homer is a diginirate corruption of the name O'Meara—he had the same name as me own, who am discinded from him. A great warrior he was, too, though he says nothing about that in his songs, being a modest man, as all us O'Mearas have ever been."

Mr. O'Meara loved to dwell upon the ancient glories of Ireland, although he had been born in America and had never even seen the green island of his ancestors. He had spent most of his life in Brooklyn, where he had been a prosperous building contractor for many years. His sons had found they could stimulate him into strange narration by pretending to underrate Irish prowess, and that was what Terence was at now. After a little more goading, the old gentleman jumped into his tale.

II

The history books don't tell ye where the Greeks came from—said Mr. O'Meara to his son—but I can tell ye. For the story has been handed down in the O'Meara family from father to son for thousands of years. They originated as sicond-string Irishmen, thim Greeks did.

In all the old mythologies, as ye would know yoursilf if ye were not uneducated because of your indolence towards learning, there is always the story of some green and golden island far in the western seas that is the land of the blest. And thim stories was not fables entirely; thim stories was legends that had truth in thim, and the land of heroes they had reference to was Ireland.

In the young days of her early glory there came a time whin Erin found hersilf terrible thronged with surplus population, and the kings and chiefs says there must be either more emigration or less propagation. So they put wan of these referindums up to the peasantry, and the peasantry voted as wan man to increase emigration and not diminish propagation. A couple of millions of the lower classes emigrated to the mainland of Europe, and afther wandering hither and yon for a thousand years, went down over the hills and streams and took possession of the islands and peninsulas of Greece. They was the inferiors of the betther classes in Ireland, but at that they was the superiors of annywan else they met.

And that's how the Greeks got started. Somewhat changed they was in their migrations, by contact with thim Scythians and bohunks and other furriners; but the memories of the heroes of ancient Ireland was still in thim, faded and dim afther manny centuries, and they carried with thim the story they was discinded from the gods. The warriors and sages and minstrels left behind in Ireland was pagan deities to their minds. Thim Trojans was a similar people. Indade, wan of thim Trojans in particular comes to me mind who called himsilf Æneas; he wasn't nothing but wan of the Innis boys who'd forgot his right name.

Wan day the High King of all Ireland—Timothy O'Meara was his name, the same as me own—was thinking how the country was being overrun by peace and prosperity to a disgraceful extint, whin wan of the O'Neills says to him:

"Tim, Your Majisty, you're not giving us anny of your songs these days."

"There's no great deeds anny more to be singing about," says King Timothy. "Thim Scots and Britons and Gauls has been subjugated and civilized and dicimated ag'in and ag'in by me and you lads, till there's occasion for nayther song nor slaughter left in thim."

"Seaumas O'Kelly passed through yesterday with the tale of a ruckus down around some place called Troy," says The O'Neill. "I thought I might get a gang of the lads together and go see what 'tis all about. It has been a long time," says this O'Neill, looking at his fist, "since The Red Hand of Ireland has had anny action. Maybe ye would like to be coming along with the rest of us lads, Your Majisty."

"Come along with ye, O'Neill?" says King Tim, getting off his throne and hitching his sword near to his hand. "If ye go, 'twill be under the King's command, and 'tis well ye know that, O'Neill. Or if ye doubt it, O'Neill, do ye and that Red Hand of yours step out on the front lawn and I'll convince ye."

For at that day and date, if ye was going to be a king in Ireland 'twas a continual necessity to be showing anny wan in the world wide ye was the betther man. Were ye not a real leader and chieftain, soon there was another king in Ireland. O'Neill of the Red Hand looked King Tim in the eye and kept his own fist away from his sword hilt.

"Fair enough," says he; "and whin do we be sailing?"

The upshot of that was that within a few weeks King Timothy O'Meara and a score or more of his best men dropped anchor and took possission of an island seven or eight miles off the coast of Troy, where thim so-called Greeks and Trojans was bickering. There was The O'Keefe, with his blue shield that had the golden hands and the prancing lion on it; there was The

Hennessy, The McCarty, The O'Dwyer, The O'Toole; there was Seaumas O'Kelly, whose jaw was ever like blue steel with the beard under the skin, and the anger of his eyes in battle was like the thrust of spears; there was The O'Reilly and The O'Rourke; there was The O'Neill, with the two red beasts and the three red stars above the green sea with the white fish in it; there was The Hickey and The Caroll, The O'Donnell and The Rooney; The O'Brien with his motto, *Lambh laidir an nachtar;* The Ryan was there and The O'Sullivan and The Cavanagh; The O'Connel flaunting his shamrocks and his deer and the cry of *C'eall agus neart;* The Regan came along, and The Nolan; there was Duffy with his golden lion against the green; there was Keogh with the wild boar for his crest, and wan of the mightiest of the Murphys with his legend: To Conquer or to Die! Men and mottoes known, noted and feared wheriver the yells of battle and the ring of steel resounded. Bright green was Tim's twenty-oared ship, which he had named The Shamrock, and she had a sharp bronze beak; and all thim heroes' shields along the gunnels made her the gay sight going through the wather.

"Now thin, me lads," says Tim, whin the anchor was down, "there's the war over there in front of us. Which side is it your notion we should be coming in on?"

"Which side would be the most Irish?" says Duffy.

"Which side would be needing us the most?" says O'Neill.

"Arrah, the side that would be needing us the most," says Murphy, says he, "would not be the side that was the most Irish."

"There's logic in that, Murphy," King Tim says, "and it makes the choice difficult."

"Which side is in the right, and which is in the wrong?" says O'Rourke.

"Now don't ye be codding us," says O'Donnell. " 'Tis not nicessary there should be anny right or wrong to it; 'tis just a war."

"Mesilf," says McCarty, "I'm always for the under dog."

"How could we be for the under dog?" says Hickey. "The instant we join wan side or the other, that instant will it cease to be the under dog."

"Well, lads," says King Timothy O'Meara, "I've brought ye down here for the frolic, and ye'd betther be making up your minds—here's a war will be going to waste right forninst us, and us not in it."

"Did but wan side or the other insult us," says Cavanaugh, "the choice would be aisy."

"They're both afther insulting us," says O'Brien, "by ignoring us—here's a war going on, and we've not been asked in by annybody."

"But both sides has aquelly insulted us that way," objicted Regan, "and that laves us where we was."

"Seaumas O'Kelly," says King Tim, "what is this war all about, annyhow? Ye've been in these parts before, and ye should know."

"Some quane or other," says O'Kelly. "Some wan stole her away from some wan, and so the trouble started. But don't ye lads be underrating this war, nayther. There's wan of me own distant relations in it is a divil with edged tools; O'Kelly is his right name, but it's been corrupted to Achilles. And there's a fella by the name of O'Day—Odysseus they are afther calling him in these ignorant parts—is a strong man of his hands and a crafty fella for strategy. There isn't annything the matther with this war excipt these Trojans and Greeks is superstitious beyond all belief. Ivery now and thin they'll get to fightin' like divils, and the rumor will start as wan of the pagan deities they believe in has joined on wan side or the other, and with that they'll scuttle away like hares."

"Such superstitions is beyond the comprehinsion of me mind," says O'Sullivan.

"Ye must remimber that these people is not altogether enlightened people," says O'Kelly. "The learning they brought away from Erin ages ago is diluted and contaminated by Asiatic communications."

" 'Twould be great sport," says O'Reilly, "for us lads to pretind we was some of thim deities oursilves!"

King Timothy O'Meara was doubtful about this. It somewhat appealed to the mirth of his amusement, but 'twas not entirely a dignified procedure, to his mind. The wise prophets of Erin had foretold that there wasn't going to be anny religion in the world worth the trouble of an Irishman's attintion for a couple of thousand years yet, and the Irish was soberly waiting for its appearance and kaping thimsilves free of all manner of heathen foolishness in the meantime. But the more he thought of it, the more it struck him that O'Reilly's suggestion might hilp cure these people of their terrible superstitious belief in thim pagan deities of Olympus, who niver existed annywheres—the lads might pretind to be deities, and wallop them about a bit in that character, and thin get thim together and lesson thim in the foolishness of such ignorance.

"Well, well, boys," says Tim, considering, "so ye do not let the sport diginerate into mere horse play, I have no objections to a little fun of that nature, for a week or two annyhow."

III

But 'twas all too aisy, that jest, and it worked all too well. There worked with it the ancient, age-long memories of thim Greeks and Trojans. O'Kelly or O'Brien or wan of the others would come ashore from their island in a small boat and disembark in wan of the numerous coves screened by sand dunes, and suddenly appear in the midst of a combat, and thim pagan Greeks and Trojans would cry out 'twas a heathen deity in their midst. The appearance and bearing of the heroes from Erin, their superior craft and courage, made thim just like the tales of the gods had been going the rounds for centuries. They'd say, the Greeks or the Trojans would, that Zeus, the chief heathen, had joined the battle, or maybe Ares, the god of war, or Phœbus O'Pollo, and whole troops and squadrons would flee from wan Irishman.

Tim's lads would sit around their own camp fire at night and shake dice to see who would be on which side the next day; and Tim used to call that the council of Olympus, and put it all down in that poem he wrote about the fracas, which he called The Iliad. Now and thin contintions broke out amongst Tim's lads.

"That Hector," Duffy would say to O'Kelly, "could wallop ye to a fare-ye-well, Seaumas, was he not firmly convinced ye are an Olympian. Ye have nothing on him at all, at all, excipt for his superstitions."

"Ye lie, Duffy," would be the natural answer of blue-jawed O'Kelly; and Tim would have great ado to prevint the sudden death of wan or the other. Within a week there was a score of rows like that started.

And the war itsilf, beneath the city walls and along the plain, got to be less and less of a war between human Greeks and Trojans and more of an affair where, if the so-called deities did not urge wan side or another forward, there was nothing doing. So King Timothy O'Meara, out of patience with the situation, sat down wan day with a quill pen and a sheet of parchment and drew up an ultimatum which went like this:

PROCLAMATION

To All Ye Greeks and Trojans

Oyez! Oyez! Oyez! Hereafther and from now on us deities from Olympus will take no notice of the brawls and contintions of ye Greeks and Trojans unless so be ye make thim snappier.

Ayther ye are at war, or else ye are not. If ye are, us deities would like to see some action we don't have to be starting oursilves. If ye are not, 'tis time ye dropped the foolish pretinse of it.

'Tis our intintion to hold oursilves aloof for the space of three weeks and give ye the final chance to fight to a conclusion as real warriors should, without fear nor favor from anny of us deities. If so be ye have not the guts to take up with this fair offer and go through with it, at the end of the three weeks us deities will gang up and utterly destroy both armies.

A word to the wise is sufficient, and ye can take it or lave it.

Who do ye think ye are, annyhow, that ye should monopolize the exclusive attintion of us deities that may have important business elsewhere that ye know nothing about?

Signed. ZEUS, head heathen; ARES, deity of battle; HADES (X) his mark; POSEIDON, deity of the sea; HERMES; PHŒBUS O'POLLO, et al., and company.

Olympus, Greece, June seventeenth, 1589 B. C.

"Now thin," says Tim, "we'll make a couple of dozen copies, and me and some of you lads will slip into town tonight and post some of thim up on the street corners, and others we will tack to the Greek ships."

IV

But instead of inspiring thim to action it seemed to paralyze the Greeks and Trojans. Day afther day wint by and nothing started. The truth was, they'd niver got anny communications from Olympus in black and white before, and they was perturbed in their minds.

Wan day Tim went ashore alone from his island where the Shamrock was moored, and sat down in a nook of rocks fronting the beach. His harp was with him, and above him and behind him to landward was the dunes of sand. He was thinking this whole expedition was a failure, and he'd be hard put to it aven to get a good ballad out of it all for Tim niver thought much of that stuff he called The Iliad himsilf—when he heard the padding of horses' hoofs muffled in sand, and the soft slur of wheels, not very far away.

He judged a chariot had driven by on the sandy plain on the landward side of the barrier of dunes, and thought no more of it. But afther a few minutes a woman emerged from behind a hill of sand, not thirty yards from him, and ran down to the sea to bathe.

A bit of a scrap of a wan-piece bathing suit she was wearing, and a gleam of brightness she was as she raced and plunged into the sea and battled through the surf. Had it been early dawn instead of afthernoon, ye might have thought she was a ripple of the rose-and-golden morning moving on the dark blue wathers.

"By the powers," says Tim to himsilf, he says, "it may be there's something in the heathen superstitions of these parts afther all; for ayther that's a goddess swimming there or else me eyes need the expert attintion of a physician."

And his hand fell upon the strings of his harp, though he scarcely knew it, and his harp began to talk. "Are ye but a crest of golden foam upon a green-blue wave?" says the harp. "Come hither, foam upon the wave! Are ye goddess, are ye woman, are ye creature of the sea? Have all the tides of all the wathers of the world gathered their gleaming beauty to wan point, to thrust it like a spear's point through the heart of me? Come hither; here is my heart, point of the spear of beauty! All the seas of life are breaking in me soul and all the surf is beauty; and all the seas of all the world are ringing all the coasts with song; and all the waves of all the seas are an army of strong warriors, and ye are the sharp sword they have plunged through the heart of me! Come hither, woman, if ye be woman! Goddess, come hither! Gleaming arrow from the curved bow of the ocean, bright arrow from the twanging string of ocean, ye are sped to pierce the heart of me."

'Tis such nonsense as that a harp will be speaking when 'tis left alone with a young fella under such circumstances—and always 'tis "Come hither!" will be the burden of its speech.

Out in the wather the woman heard. She swam farther out, as if to be beyond the reach of it. Thin she turned and floated and listened ag'in. For a minute the music stopped; betwixt his lifted finger and the strings a moment's silence gathered, and farther out ag'in she swam. And thin the song—for Tim had no consciousness that he had annything to do with it himsilf personal—the song, like a queer fisherman, reeled her slowly in, and she drifted ashore like wan in a dream.

Straight up to him she walked, and he rose; and the dream and bewilderment of the music was on both of thim.

"Are ye a god?" says she. Considering the looks and bearing of the man, and the woman's superstitions, 'twas an entirely logical question. "Are ye a god?" she says, simple and frank and in all good faith.

"Do ye judge of it," says Tim, aquelly simple and direct, and dropped an arm about her and kissed her.

"Ye are!" she says, says she, afther a moment or two, with a long breath.

"I've had me moments of feeling like wan," says Tim, quite sincere, "but niver before a moment like this."

"I niver knew before," says she, sizing him up in wonder and admiration, "that there was anny red-headed gods. Are ye Pan—ye with your music—or are ye O'Pollo?"

"Which would ye rather, mavourneen?" says Tim, always anxious to plaise the ladies, and this wan in particular.

"If ye're not a god," says she, looking a little worried, " 'tis terrible unconvintional and indiscreet me kissing ye like this, for I'm a married woman mesilf. I'd rather ye was O'Pollo."

"Thin ye can call me O'Pollo, mavourneen," says Tim, with a smile.

"Oh! Oh!" she cries, alarmed by his smile and his tone of voice. "Ye're not a god at all! Ye're a man! And ye've tricked me by your music into a most unconvintional situation! What will ye be thinking of me? Oh, I hate ye for it!"

"Arrah, now mavourneen," says Tim, he says; "make your mind aisy. I'll prove to ye agin that I am wan."

Which he did.

"Yes, oh, yes!" she says, says she, with a sigh, "ye are wan; I know ye must be wan now—and the most convintional woman is hilpless entirely agin the gods!"

"Of course," says he; "let your mind be at rest."

"It is," says she. She gave him a wondering look. "I'm sure ye are wan," she says, "but 'tis strange that, too. 'Twas always in me mind a god would be a little different from this, somehow."

"How?" says Tim.

"More like a ghost, maybe, some way," she says. "More kind of loose and mistylike in the material he's made of," she says. She wiped her lips where he had kissed the salt wather from thim, with the back of her hand. "Ye're not misty at all, at all," she says. "Ye're more like a god would be if so he was a man at the same time," says she.

"Tell me about yoursilf, colleen," says Tim, charmed with the childish simplicity of the creature. "Are ye maybe wan of the goddesses of these parts?"

"I'm related to a number of thim," says she, so solemn that Tim saw she really believed that ignorant superstition. "I come from over there," says she, pointing across the wather in the gineral direction of

Greece. "But at prisint," she says, "I'm living in the city down yonder." She motioned towards the towers and walls of Troy, swimming in the sunlight half a dozen miles down the coast.

Tim O'Meara had a sudden mind.

"And next," says he, he says, "ye'll be coming with me to Erin! Get yoursilf dressed and we'll be off at wance!"

"Dressed?" And thin she cried: "Oh, ye're not a god at all, at all! 'Tis a man ye are! No god would be afther noticing the kind of clothes I was wearing!"

All wan blush of anger and confusion she was; and whin he tried to speak ag'in, she snatched up his sword which he had unhooked from his belt and laid on the ground, and banged him across the face with it. Lucky for Tim, 'twas in the scabbard. "I hate ye!" she cried, and flung the weapon at him and turned and ran. She was up and over the line of sand dunes in an instant, and him feeling of his face and wondering was his nose broken.

"The wild cat!" he says. But he liked thim like that. He stood for some minutes looking towards the town of Troy in the distance, and already forming a plan to take it. Of a sudden a pebble rolled from the top of a sand dune and bounced and pinged agin the strings of his harp. He turned and looked up. There she was, in her proper street clothes, gazing down on him with a countenance all lighted up with curiosity.

"Where is that Erin ye spoke of?" she says.

Before he could give her that lesson in geography she had vanished ag'in. Tim struggled to the top of the dunes, but she was scampering towards a chariot with two attindants that was waiting fifty yards away. She jumped in and the horses was off at a gallop towards Troy. 'Twas ayther the breeze of their gallop or her own hand that waved a bit of a bright scarf back at Tim.

V

That night Tim reconnoitered. And the next day at dusk he was in the town of Troy himsilf, in the guise of a profissional minstrel. There was a canal cut inward from the sea through which the Trojans got the greater part of their supplies; and this entry was definded by great ballistas and catapults. The Greeks had sea force enough to harry and discommode this commerce, but not enough to stop it entirely. Nor had the Trojans the superior naval force to sally out and destroy the entire Greek fleet. The war had been a queer kind of a stand-off. The Greeks controlled the plains in the near vicinity of the city, and had destroyed all the crops there and taken all the livestock, but at a distance the allies and countryfolks of the Trojans still carried on and slipped materials into the town in barges.

'Twas through this wather gate to the city that Tim entered, with his harp and in a small boat. He played some chunes to the guards and cracked thim some jokes, and they passed him on from station to station. Whin he had tied his boat to a wharf and begun to wander through the streets wan of the first things he noticed was long lines of people waiting at the wells of the town. Officers were rationing out wather very carefully.

Terrible thronged was that big town, and ivery male person Tim saw from fifteen to sixty was bearing arms. The city was laid out like a great wheel; at the center, where the hub would be, was King Priam's citadel. It stood upon a height of rocky land and was both a palace and a fortress. Terraces led up to it from the city streets, and ivery terrace was capable of definse. Long streets, splendid, and so broad that six chariots might drive abreast, radiated like spokes of the wheel from the citadel to the gates in the walls; and at each gate was a watch tower. Tim judged the price of real estate in that town was high, for the tindincy in building had been to go up in the air. Ivery building had its tower, or became a tower itsilf, like we're putting thim up in New York and Brooklyn today; and manny families lived in each building.

In the blue dusk, with lights flaring high above in the manny windows, and the whole city crowned and adorned by King Priam's lofty citadel with its own flares here and there upon its scarps and battlemints, and billows of shadow and cloud rolling in from the sea, perhaps the town seemed taller than it was. For to Tim's mind it seemed to thrust itsilf up towards the yellow moon and early stars that hung above it; 'twas hard to tell where city left off and sky began, and that gave it all a touch of shifty magic to his eyes. Indade, wance or twice he had the feeling, as he took his way towards the citadel, that he had built it all himsilf out of the music of his harp, for the amusement of his own fancy, and could tumble it into nothingness ag'in with a slam of discontented discords. The dream of that woman was strong upon his soul, and the mood of his intellect glimmered with the extravagance of poetry and love.

"I'm the minstrel that King Priam sint for," he said to the guards, and all of thim was impressed by the port of the man and the conquering glamour that walked with him, and into the citadel he went. He was sure that the lady he'd met on the seashore would be somewhere about the King's palace, for there was quality in ivery line and look of her.

And she was the first thing Tim seen whin he entered the King's council hall. A great and lofty room that was, with a high vaulted roof. At the far end was a dais, with a great fat man upon a throne and a fat woman upon another throne near him. A group of half a dozen others stood or sat near King Priam and Quane Hecuba; and this woman of Tim's was by Quane Hecuba's throne. A man's voice said, as Tim entered and strode up the hall:

"Your Majisty, suppose we lave that point to Helen hersilf."

Tim's colleen opened her mouth as if to speak. Thin she seen Tim and recognized him. She closed her mouth ag'in, and stared at Tim and said nothing. With that, all prisint turned and stared. Tim stepped forward boldly.

"Your Majisty," he says, says he, bowing mannerly to King Priam, "I'm the minstrel was brought the word ye wanted me at the palace here this night."

King Priam opened his eyes wide and rubbed his forehead. "I don't quite remimber ye," he says, "but sit down somewheres, minstrel, and I'll spake to ye prisintly."

Tim sat down quietly and pretinded to be studying the condition of his harp, and they all give him a long look. Calm and placid he received it, and prisintly they wint on with their hot argumint ag'in, and ignored him—all excipt Helen, and kape her eyes from him she could not.

They was all so heated with the business in hand, excipt King Priam himsilf, that in a minute they forgot Tim. King Priam was robed in fine white wool trimmed with purple and clasped with gold. Tim, as the argumint wint on, might have thought most of the time that the King was aslape; for his eyes was mostly shut and his head drooped forward so that his crown was tilted crooked on his white poll. But his hands was clasped over his enormous stomach and now and thin ye could see he was twiddling his thumbs. And now and thin he opened both his eyes and mouth and aimed at a golden cuspidor was set convenient to the throne; for the King was chewing betel nut—a most unroyal habit he'd picked up from a wandering Hindu sage. Quane Hecuba was a red-cheeked ould dame like a dumpling, with manny gems that twinkled and a blond wig was all awry. With a pair of bronze knitting needles she was clicking away at a stomach band for wan of her numerous grandchildren.

By the look on Helen's face, where she stood near Quane Hecuba's chair, she was wondering wance more was Tim a god or not. She was pale and red by turns, and her breath was quick. She was in a bad enough jam before Tim strolled in, as he seen whin he realized who the others were. There was Paris, whom she had eloped from Sparta with. There was Menelaus, her former husband, whom she had run away from. There was Hector, Paris' brother. There was King Agamemnon, Menelaus' brother, with his ferocious visage and the yellow fangs that showed whin he opened his mouth.

"Helen should come back and mind her house like an honest woman," says this King Agamemnon. "If she does not come back, we must have an indimnity in place of her. Is that not right, brother?" he says to Menelaus.

This Menelaus was a boyo with a bull neck set on heavy shoulders, and a twirl of hair on his forehead was altogether like a bull's. He glared at Helen and nodded to his brother.

Tim had walked in on an attimpt to settle the whole war.

"Ye've not been able to take her, ye dog face!" says Hector to Agamemnon. And Paris laughed and trifled with a golden-plated spear.

"Now, boys, don't be afther calling names!" says King Priam, with his eyes closed. "Remimber this is a peace parley and not wan of your famous contists of strength and skill."

"Himsilf there," says Quane Hecuba, nodding towards Priam, "is getting nigh his dotage, or he would tell ye that the gods is tired of all this strife—'tis themsilves has said as much. For me own part, does Helen go or does Helen stay, it matthers little to me. The wan thing I want is the end of this war."

" 'Tis well I know ye'd be glad to be getting rid of me, Quane Hecuba," said Helen, with a glance at Tim.

"Sorrow came with ye," says the Quane, still knitting and placid, "and the divil can take ye, for all I care. I'm not the kind of woman has trouble with anny of me daughters-in-law as a rule, but afther ye strife follows, as plague follows drought. Howiver, if 'tis so decided we kape ye here, kape ye I will, and spake ye civil whin ye spake me so."

"Nobody loves me," says Helen; and ag'in her voice was for Tim. "Nobody wants me!"

"I do!" says Paris and Menelaus in wan breath.

"Ye do not, nayther of ye!" flares Helen. Maybe she was anxious Tim should get the rights of the story. "The only reason Menelaus wants me back is because I'm Quane of Sparta in me own right, and he'll niver feel aisy on his throne unless so be I reign beside him! He was niver the man to come storming across the seas for the love of anny woman, not him. And as for ye, Paris," she says, says she, turning on that handsome lad; " 'tis often ye say ye love me, but whin did ye ever have the nerve to face Menelaus here and fight for me with your own hand?"

"Always there was wan of thim Olympian deities on his side," says Paris, smiling and waving his hand, airy and graceful. "Ye know full well, mavourneen, I'd fight anny man in the world for ye, so none of thim Olympian deities comes meddling into the matther."

Menelaus says to Paris, with a scowl, dropping his hand to his sword: "All thim Olympian deities is laying off this war right now, and you and me can sittle this affair in wan minute."

"Ye spake so bold because ye know I can't fight ye now," says Paris; "and ye here under word of honor and flag of truce."

"Now thin," says Agamemnon; "it's got to the place where ye can no longer sittle it personal—ye two. Too manny others has become involved. King Priam, here is me terms to ye: Give us Helen and ten thousand head of good cattle and fifty of your best ships, and we go in peace. Or kape Helen, and give us twinty thousand head of cattle and wan hundred ships."

" 'Tis exorbitant, dog face," says Hector, "aven if ye were in a military position to demand it, which ye are not. The walls of this town is still intact."

"And the wells is all but dry," says Agamemnon.

"And your own people back in Greece is half of thim rising in revolt agin ye," retorts Hector.

King Priam nodded and took a little golden box from the bosom of his royal robe and hilped himsilf to another chew of betel nut.

"Himsilf here does nothing all day long but sit and chew and let the world go by," sighs Quane Hecuba. "Ye fools all!" she cried suddenly, and laid down her knitting. "Stop this war!" she says. "Both the human sinse of mortal intellect and the warnings of the gods tells ye the wan thing—stop this war!"

"There's something in what hersilf here says," King Priam remarks, his chew in his cheek and his thumbs twiddling. "I didn't want anny war, nor anny Helen nayther—there was none more surprised than mesilf whin Paris comes bouncing home with her, expicting iverywan in Troy to be as plaised as he was himsilf. And now there's no doubt the gods is all stirred up inimical to all of us. Agamemnon, I'll settle with ye on the basis of the *status quo ante*—take Helen, and be off with ye, and be damned to ye!"

"No!" cries Hector, jumping to his feet. "Our Trojan honor demands we keep her!"

"We'll take her, and we'll have ships and cattle too!" says Agamemnon.

"I hate ye all!" cries Helen, so vehement that Quane Hecuba dropped her knitting and King Priam swallowed his betel nut. "All of ye I hate! Ye pass me back and forth, and bargain for me with cattle, like I was a prize cow mesilf—and me a quane in me own right! I hate ye all!" And with that she turned and ran from the room through a door was back of the thrones, and slammed the door afther her. But before she slammed it she give wan look at Tim.

The discussion rose high and loud ag'in, promising annything but peace, and Tim watched his chance and slipped unnoticed from the hall. He had the intuition she'd be making for the open air. And 'twas on wan of the terraces he found her, high above the flare and rattle of the city. She was at the base of a bronze statue, leaning agin it; and whin Tim came up to her she was beating her head against the bronze and weeping—maybe she'd seen him coming, and annyhow, the thick hair on her head protected it from real injury.

Tim slipped an arm about her.

"Lave me die, redhead," she says, says she; "niver before was woman or quane humiliated as I have been, and there's nothing left but death!"

And she give her head a real bang, and maybe it hurt her more than she intinded, for she left off that diversion.

"There's me left," says Tim. "And there's Erin left, mavourneen."

"Is it like Olympus?"

"Practically the same," says Tim.

"And which wan of the gods are ye?" she says. For the certainty he was wan had returned to her in full force. "Are ye O'Pollo?"

"Listen, mavourneen," says he; "I love ye so much I must be truthful with ye. I ain't anny deity at all, at all. I'm an Irishman."

"That must be the same thing, darlint," she says. " 'Tis no use your telling me ye're a mortal man; for mortal men I have been married to, and I know the difference. Oh," she says, all wan blaze of rapture from head to foot, " 'twas the dream of me girlhood to be abducted by a deity, and now the dream's come true! All us girls in Greece used to talk about it," she says, "but I'm the only wan it's happened to! Whin do we start for Erin?" she says.

"Now," says Tim.

But 'twas not to be that aisy. Wan of the palace doors had opened soft behind thim and Quane Hecuba came out, walking fat and quiet-footed in her sandals. There was half a dozen respectful guards behind her, and wan of her grandchildren was suffering with the colic laid stomach down across the muscle of her left arm. The Quane looked at thim two lovers and chuckled scornful, and the child she was jiggling gurgled in a most knowing way, and the Quane said to Tim, very skeptical and pointed:

"So ye're a minstrel, are ye? Minstrel! Huh!"

Tim looked at her guards, and he looked down the slopes toward the city streets. A company of a hundred spearmen was coming up the terraces toward their barracks in the citadel. 'Twas too manny, aven for Tim O'Meara. He did not reply to the Quane; he murmured, quick, to Helen: "Be at this spot two hours before daybreak."

With that he was off through the dusk before Quane Hecuba could make up her mind to shout to the soldiers to stay him.

VI

Tim was out of the canal with his rowboat and back at his island with his Irish lads in but little more than an hour. He told thim the situation, and they got their gear and arms in shape as quick as might be, and 'twas not long afther midnight the Shamrock was under way for the shore. 'Twas Tim's idea him and his Irish would presint thimsilves at the Skian gate as deities, and as deities march to the palace and carry off the girl.

But things had took a turn. Whilst they was still five miles out at sea, Seaumas O'Kelly cried out: "By the powers, Tim, Your Majisty, there's something doing yonder!"

A fire was burning by the Skian gate. While they looked, from the top of the watch tower at the gate there suddenly spouted a burst of flame; 'twas on fire inside. And thin a flame within the town leaped higher, so that they saw it above the walls. In a few minutes more they began to hear a confused great noise and the shouts of men and the clanging of arms.

"The Greeks are in the town!" cried Tim, and they all bent to their big oars.

The parley had broke up in a row. 'Twas scarcely over before that Greek O'Day, who called himself Odysseus, appeared at the Skian gate with a big wooden horse on wheels, and the tale that 'twas intinded as a prisint to Quane Helen from her loving Spartan subjicts overseas, who continued to regret her absence—and for all he knew what 'twas for, says this O'Day, she could use it to dry clothes on or something. Whilst he parleyed with the doubtful guard, his men wheeled it agin the gate itsilf, which was made of great oaken beams braced and reënforced with bronze. Thin this wily divil O'Day sets fire to its tail, which was made of tow soaked in oil, and steps back. In a minute there was an explosion like ye had thrown a torch into a room full of celluloid collars; for the inside of that wooden horse was filled with hundreds of gallons of naphtha and oil. The burning fluid was flung all over the beams of the gate thimsilves, and they was dry as tinder, for 'twas a hot, rainless summer. The Skian gate was a good mile distant from the salt-wather canal, and the only well near was almost dry. Whin the charred beams weakened, a thousand Greeks crashed thim and forced their way through the flaming breach; and thin they rushed a long row of wooden barracks near the gate and set fire to thim. The alarm was given in all quarters of the town, but the Greeks were pouring through the Skian gate by the hundred, and lancing deep into the city, and fires climbing and spreading iverywhere, long before Tim and his Irish beached the Shamrock and made their own way into the doomed capital.

VII

'Twas a mad town that Tim and his Irish entered, with bells clamoring and trumpets screaming and the shouts of warriors and the shock of arms and the yells and squeals of chariot horses and the whirl and roar of racing fires. For the Greeks carried fire to ivery house they took and ivery street they assaulted, and the Trojans had to fight agin both the Greeks and the fires. The wather shortage licked thim from the start. Some of the buildings was masonry, and some tile with stucco over it, and some made part of wood and plaster, but whativer the outside material, the inside of all was braced and lined and floored with wood. Tall towers they was, and that was their undoing; for whin a building caught inside, it became just wan terrible high and roaring chimney.

Tim, as he entered mixed up with a streaming tide of Greeks and unnoticed amongst thim for the moment, saw a company of Trojan cavalry flanked by chariots trying to form in wan of the broad streets for a dash at the thick of the Greeks. But just as the horsemen got the word to charge, a big tower came roaring down right across the street and the whole company disappeared amidst the smoke and thunder. Out of the crash squirmed wan hurt horse with its hind quarters smashed, and Tim himself put his sword through its heart out of pity, for 'twas screaming like a woman. More and more Trojans was hastening from ivery quarter, and more Greeks surging through the gate; and 'twas a terrible street-to-street and house-to-house struggle, with aven the girls and women flinging down crockery and brass kettles upon the invaders, and iverywhere a most eruptive tumult like hell, saving your prisince, was sick at its stomach.

In wan compact body like a steel fist, Tim and his Irish hammered their way straight across the turmoil toward the citadel—not that they had to do much hammering at this stage of the game, nayther. For iverywhere they was seen, under the heave and swing of those fiery skies, the cry would go up: "The gods! The gods!" And whether 'twas Greeks or Trojans, all men that saw thim scampered from before thim.

'Twas through strange scenes they approached the citadel. Horses raced loose and riderless, cattle milled and clashed their horns and bellowed, dogs ran here and yon, singed cats wailed and scurried, and rats from the falling houses, red-eyed and insane, kept pace, fearless, with the cats—all these, and men and women no less mad, were before thim, and behind thim the main strife of battle and the Greeks advancing and the jumping fires. Wan small boy Tim saw astride a white bull; he'd nothing on but his undershirt, and was blowing a trumpet and having the time of his life. And there kipt pace with the Irish for a mile or more an old woman gone mad, who'd saved a mattress from her burning home. A drunken trooper came from a wine shop and took it from her; he stood befuddledlike with it for moment and thin cast it to the pavement and laid down on it. And the old woman reached down and took the drunkard's sword and plunged it in hersilf, instead of him, as if with the loss of the mattress the world was at its end.

VIII

And madness was in the citadel itsilf. Tim and his men slashed their way through a moil of broken regiments that was trying to re-form in the plazas and parks and open spaces at the foot of the citadel, and up and into the hall he'd left but a few hours before; and there he came on a dozen of the Trojan leaders in a council. Paris was there, and Æneas and Hector, and Helen, sitting dumb at the foot of King Priam's throne, and ould Priam himself, sprawled in fat slumber with his kingdom toppling.

"We'll make a stand below," Hector was saying, as Tim came in; "and if we lose, we'll burn the palace oursilves, and perish with it. And Helen too!" he cried, with an angry look at her who was the author of all their woes.

"Helen too!" says Æneas. And Paris said nothing, but looked around him, running his tongue along his dry lips, as if seeking his own way out.

With a gust of gray smoke from the burning town, and the red fires behind thim, the Irish swept into the hall.

" 'Tis the gods! The gods!" cried a Trojan chief, and all the warriors shrank back. But Helen jumped up with a cry, and was in Tim O'Meara's arms.

"Gods or not," cried Hector, beside himsilf with desperation, " 'tis me own hall and me father's!" And with that, with a most magnificent bravery, he loosed a javelin at Tim O'Meara—a courage more than mortal was his, for he thought 'twas more than mortal man that he assailed.

The spear glanced from Tim's shield. It swerved and laid open the blue jaw of Seaumas O'Kelly. The red blood spurted. There was a roar wint up.

"Not gods but men!" cried the Trojans. "Not gods! They bleed!"

With that, the fight was on.

"There's some satisfaction in this!" says McCarty, hanging sword and sword with that Æneas. " 'Tis no fun at all, at all, unless they stand up to ye!"

"Right ye are, Mac," says O'Reilly, putting ten inches of steel through a Trojan's neck. "There's the makin's of a sweet little brawl here!"

Tim drove straight at Hector; and that splendid warrior whirled up his sword and met him halfway. The most distinguished swordsman the world iver saw was Timothy O'Meara—me ancestor he was, and your own, but ye are not worthy of him! 'Twould have been pleasant pastime for Tim to have given him a fencing lesson before he disposed of him, but 'twas no time for mere diversion now, and Tim regretted the necissity for haste, aven as he laid him low with a thrust under the arm.

"So ye'd burn the lady, would ye, Hector?" he says, as the toughest Trojan of thim all fell clashing to the marble floor. But aven as he spoke an arrow pinged agin his breastplate, and an instant later another wan splintered on his helmet. 'Twas that Paris, peering from behind his father's throne and shooting with a horn bow. Helen had located him before Tim had, and as Tim cut down two spearmen and strode toward him, she slipped a spear through him.

"That's me sicond husband, Tim," she says, looking down on him. "He was niver anny good, and I'm glad to have me freedom back nice and legal."

"Arrah, darlint, here comes your first wan!" says Tim. 'Twas so. For into the hall burst Menelaus, and Agamemnon was with him, and Ajax and Achilles, and a score more of thim Greek lads. The vanguard of the Greeks had lanced through the Trojans in the streets below, and up into the palace, seeking Helen hersilf. What Trojans was left was still shouting: "Not gods! Not gods but men!" and the Greek lads took the tip at wance, and came rushing at the Irish.

What had gone before was child's play to

what happened now, for the Greeks was wild with victory and crazy with the wine of bloodletting. 'Twas a strange fight. All about the palace the wild city reeled and roared, and the great slashing blades of fire tore at the dark heart of the night; thousands of the Trojans still battled in the courts and streets below, and there was the constant thunder of the falling buildings; all up and down the terraces the warriors strove, and all up and down the sky blue shadows and yellow flame twined about each other like serpents and bit and struck. The citadel itsilf was afire now, and smoke and flames was within the great hall—and that queer fat king huddled in his throne and sleeping through it all.

With the Trojan leaders trampled under foot, the Irish turned to meet the Greek rush.

"This was worth waiting for," says Duffy to Regan, smiling happy as he took that big Ajax to pieces, neat and scientific.

"Give them the point; they ain't used to it," advised Cavanagh to O'Brien.

"Hark to King Tim singing!" says O'Neill to Murphy. "That means the boss' blood is getting up, indade!"

Tim was. 'Twas a way he had whin he was happy in battle; and happy he was now, for Menelaus was in front of him, and he hadn't liked that man from the first minute he set eyes on him. He pleasured himsilf in the job, and took pains to make the combat interesting—for was not Helen hersilf looking on?

"Don't fence wide, Tim," warned Keogh; "that boy ye have there is not without the rudiments of the art himsilf."

"King Tim's showing off," laughs O'Toole to O'Connel, as he freed his blade from the throat of Agamemnon.

"King Tim's in love!" laughs O'Donnell to Nolan. "King Tim's in love!" laughs Nolan to Rooney, and Rooney laughed and lifted the head from a Spartan prince with a backhand sweep; and Hickey and O'Sullivan laughed, and all the Irish laughed—and a terrible thing for their foes to hear is that Irish laughter whin it rises from the din of battle.

"Gods afther all!" said Menelaus, whin he heard that laughter. Thin Tim killed him quick, lest his superstitions come back on him and spoil the fight.

"There's your first husband, mavourneen," he says to Helen. "And we'll be out of here quick." For parts of the citadel itsilf was beginning to crash and fall.

"I'm glad both thim fellas has passed on," says Helen to Tim, looking from Paris to Menelaus. "It makes no doubt of me being a legal widow, darlint. I've always been a convintional woman," she says, says she, "and discreet."

"I admire ye for it," says Tim, proticting her with his shield, as he slashed his way at the head of the Irish towards the outer door. 'Twas just at the door itsilf that O'Kelly put the finishing touches to Achilles.

"I could have made something of that man, with a month's tuition," says Seaumas O'Kelly, looking down on him regretful. "Well, good-by, cousin," he says, says he; " 'tis too late now!"

Down the slope the Irish cut their way, and through the blazing town, with Helen in their midst. Plunderers and drunkards was abroad in the burning ruins, and there was the cries of women and all the hell of a sacked and taken city. Three or four times Tim had to stop and face about and fight off bands of Greeks that hung upon their flanks or disputed their way; and of more than a score of Irish that wint into the town that night there was but twelve came out ag'in, and all of thim was hurt.

'Twas dawn whin they reached the seashore and found the Shamrock. Red dawn came up out of Asia behind the red city, for now the citadel itsilf was blazing high, and 'twas like two terrible red roses of destruction was flaring in the heavens.

"Ye have fine flowers for yer wedding day, Helen," says Tim, pointing to thim.

"Yes," says she, contentedlike; "aren't they beautiful? Oh, Tim darlint, I'm so happy! And it all goes to show," she says, says she, "that does a girl cling to her ideals, and always seek for the finest and the best, she'll be rewarded in the end," she says.

Just thin they seen ould Quane Hecuba, sitting on the sand, staring with queer eyes out at the wather; and she was alone, excipt the child she'd comforted the night before was sleeping in her lap.

" 'Tis wan of Hector's little boys, Tim," says Helen, good-natured. "Let's take thim along with us."

But the ould Quane gave her a glare of hate, and rose and clasped the child to her bosom, and stumbled off along the sand.

IX

"Well, dad," said Terence O'Meara to the narrator, "that shows where our ancestor, Homer, got the material for the Iliad. But how about the Odyssey?"

The old gentleman reflected for a moment. Then: "Two or three years later," he explained, "comes that O'Day, that called himsilf Odysseus, to Ireland. He'd been wandering here and yon, and got himsilf mixed up with a woman somewheres, and he was afraid to go home, for he could not think of annything to tell his wife. So Tim, he sits down wan afthernoon and writes him the Odyssey, so he could go home with a good story for Mrs. O'Day."

The Perfect Squelch

WEALTHY young George hated to part with money for any reason. But he was especially allergic to tipping the bellboys at the resort hotel he frequently visited.

Knowing his habits, the bellboys tried to avoid answering his calls. However, they couldn't escape delivering telegrams to his room, and each time they did this they were greeted with the growled order, "Just slide it under the door. I'm busy."

When one bellboy was given a fourth telegram to deliver to George in a single afternoon, he rapped smartly on the door and said, "Telegram, sir."

"Just slide it under the door, boy," George answered him as usual.

"Sorry, sir," the bellboy said firmly, "but I can't."

"You can't?" George demanded. "Why not?"

"It's on my tip tray."

—EDWARD C. MORGAN.

ECONOMICS SIMPLIFIED

Good times are the periods in which you create the debts that you can't pay off in bad times.

—HERBERT V. PROCHNOW.

THE ARTFUL MR. GLENCANNON

By GUY GILPATRIC

§ Casually mention the words "Saturday Evening Post" to a group of the magazine's dyed-in-the-wool readers and you are apt to get the response "Glencannon" from at least half of them. That's the sort of impression the chief engineer of the S.S. Inchcliffe Castle has made on grateful readers who have relished the more than fifty Glencannon stories spread over some two decades of Post *publishing. In this one, Captain Ball desperately needed a picture painted by an artist named Churchill—Winston Churchill, that is. It just happened that Glencannon could help the Captain out—although not without profit, of course.*

AUGUST 23, 1947

IT WAS an August morning, as bright and blue and beautiful as only a Mediterranean morning can be. Along the Quai St. Pierre, on the inner harbor of Cannes, fishermen lay sleeping, smoking or scratching themselves in the shade of their boats while their wives and daughters trundled dripping barrows of the night's catch up the hill to the market or squatted in the scorching sun to mend the long brown nets stretched out on the sidewalk to dry. The scene was quaint, colorful and inspiringly picturesque, and here and there along the quay, artists had set up their easels to record it. Its aesthetic qualities were lost, however, upon two gentlemen who sat engaged in acrimonious converse beneath the awning of the Café des Pêcheurs. The one with the walrus mustache and the whisky breath was Mr. Colin Glencannon, chief engineer of the S.S. Inchcliffe Castle. The other, who was scowling into a cup of tea, was Mr. Chauncey Montgomery, the vessel's first mate. The Inchcliffe Castle herself—an ancient Clyde-built freighter of some thirty-five hundred tons, flying the house flag of Clifford, Castle & Co., Ltd., of London—lay moored at the long granite jetty which extended from the far end of the street.

"Foosh! How do ye explain what's worriting him, then?" Mr. Glencannon was demanding accusingly. "Obviously the puir Auld Mon's had something on his mind ever since they called him to the office that day in London. It looks vurra much to me as though ye'd been up to some o' yere usual dirty wurrk—by whuch I mean ye've been telling lies to the owners behind his back and trying to steal his job."

"No, blarst it, no!" Mr. Montgomery protested hotly. "I've told yer twenty times I didn't say a word about 'im to nobody at the office—er—at least, not this trip. Oh, I won't pertend I don't think Captain Ball is a silly old pot, incompetent to command the ship, nor that I don't think I ought to 'ave 'ad 'is job long ago. But if, as yer believe, the owners 'ad 'im up on the carpet and gave 'im a dressing down—welp, it wasn't none of my doing!"

Mr. Glencannon shrugged skeptically and turned his eyes in the direction of the ship. "H'm! Look yon; here comes Jessup. Pairhops he picked up some information through his private London grapevine and can give us a lead. I'll broach it to him—vurra discreetly, o' course, and in a roondaboot monner. . . . Ho, there, Jessup! Come on ower!" he called. "Muster Montgomery wants to treat ye to a beer."

"Oh, thank y', sir! That's very kind indeed, sir!" The steward seated himself diffidently on the edge of a chair. "Heh-heh-heh!" he simpered, shifting his eyes from one to the other of them. "Charming weather, ain't it, gempmen?"

"A-weel, yes and no; it's a motter o' opinion," said Mr. Glencannon, getting to work on him. "Whether the weather is guid or bod is always a controvairsial subject, because the weather itsel' is always subject to —er—to—er——"

"To change, sir?"

"Eh? Change, did ye say? Why, Jessup, how vurra odd that ye shud bring that up! Are ye hinting that ye heard rumors in London aboot some changes on the ship or in the line?"

"Oh, that! D'yer mean abaht Captain Ball getting the job as shore superintendent and orl?"

Mr. Montgomery started violently. "What?" he cried. "Ball? As shore superintendent? Oh, sweet Fanny Adams! I never thought I'd live to see the day when an old chump like 'im would——"

"Shish and pish-tush!" Mr. Glencannon admonished him. "Spare us yere clashmaclaver until Jessup can tell us exockly what he heard."

Jessup took a sip of his beer and cleared his throat importantly. "Welp, gempmen, it so 'appens that my missus lives at Number Six, Catsmeat Yard, Lime'ouse, right next door to that lolloping fat widder 'oo's the charlady of our owners' offices. Veronica O'Halloran, 'er nyme is. Welp, a couple of days before we left London on this 'ere voyage, Veronica O'Halloran 'eared Mr. 'Azlitt and Sir John Castle discussing abaht picking a successor for old Captain 'Igginson, the shore superintendent, 'oo's planning to retire at the end of the year. They went through a list of orl the senior captains of the line and finally narrered it down to two —our skipper and Captain Flynn, of the Marlecliffe Castle."

"Hmph! So that's the way it is, is it? Well, Flynn's a good man," growled Mr. Montgomery. "Wot I mean, 'e's got brains, appearance and personality, instead of just a belly. I 'ope 'e gets the job!"

Mr. Glencannon peered at him incredulously. "Eh? Ye do? But why, ye gowk?" he demanded. "If Captain Ball is chosen, won't ye finally get yere wish and commond the Inchcliffe Castle? Though for mysel', I can only breathe a fervent 'God forbid!' "

Mr. Montgomery spread his hands in a gesture of frustration. "Wot good would it do me to command the Inchcliffe, with Ball lording it over me as superintendent of the 'ole ruddy line? Why, I'd be even worse off than I am now!"

"Blosh and fuddlesticks!" scoffed Mr. Glencannon. "The bald truth is either that ye're afraid to assume the respunsibilities o' commond, noo that ye find them staring ye in the face, or that ye hate Captain Ball so bitterly that ye'd be willing to cut off yere nose to spite it!"

Jessup coughed. "Welp, gempmen, it ain't settled yet—not by a long chalk," he reminded them. "Sir John and Mr. 'Azlitt was sayin' as 'ow a shore superintendent 'as got to be a bit of a politician and diplermat—'ow 'e 'as to wear posh clothes, meet posh people, read 'is reports before the board of directors, and orl like that. Then they got to discussing Captain Flynn—'is brains, appearance and personality, just like wot Mr. Montgomery mentioned. And while both of 'em seemed to 'ave a very 'igh opinion of Captain Ball, they was wondering if 'e wasn't a bit too much of a—well, a rough diamond."

"Diamond? Hmph! They meant neck!" Mr. Montgomery sneered. "Anyway, 'ow are they going to settle it, Jessup?"

"Welp, Veronica says they called in Captain Ball and Captain Flynn and told 'em wot the situation was. They explained to 'em that being shore superintendent of Clifford, Castle and Comp'ny, Limited, calls fer a damn sight more get-up-and-go-get-it than it takes to command a ship. They said that between now and the end of the year, they'll watch both captains very careful, and the one 'oo shows the most jump and ginger will win the prize coconut."

"Well," said Mr. Montgomery, "at least they both know exackly wot they're up against."

"Ah, but they don't, sir! The most important part is wot Sir John and Mr. 'Azlitt didn't tell 'em! You see, they're going to think up certain special tasks—test jobs, so to speak, quite outside the ord'n'ry line of juty—and spring 'em on the captains when and where they'll least expect it!"

Mr. Glencannon nodded solemnly and tapped out his pipe bowl against the heel of his shoe.

"A-weel, Jessup has vurra lucidly revealed what Captain Ball has got on his mind. Aye, and it's just as weel the auld fellow doesna ken the whole o' it! Even as it is, he's sitting on tenterhooks, lik' a Hindu on a couch o' nails. And so, for that motter, am I."

"You? Why, wot in blazes 'ave you got to worry about? Just think of me!"

"I am—and that accounts for exockly half o' my worry. The thocht o' having to sairve under ye as captain is enough to curdle my liver, but the alternative thocht o' Captain Ball not getting the job is enough to break my heart!"

Mr. Montgomery's lip curled with sarcasm. "My word, yer insides are in a 'orrid mess, ain't they?" He gulped his tea and turned upon Jessup. "Orl right, you, beggar orff and do yer marketing! D'yer think Clifford and Castle are paying yer good wages to 'ang around guzzling in pubs?"

For a while the two officers sat brooding in silence; then Mr. Montgomery stirred, glowered at his watch and stood up. "Eleven o'clock," he said. "We'd better be getting back aboard before old Bean Belly lets the Boy Scouts or somebody steal the ship out from under 'im. . . . No, no, don't larff!" he insisted. "Why, when I came back aboard yestiddy arfternoon, blyme if there wasn't a gang of kids playing follow my leader all over the ship, scratching the paint orff with their 'ob-nailed boots. Just as I was about to give a couple of the narsty brats a taste of my belt, the Old Man barges out of his cabin, orders me to turn 'em loose and then gives me a lecture about live and let live and love thy neighbor. Yus, 'e did, so 'elp me! Is that the way to run a ship? Is it? Is it, I arsks yer?"

As they continued out upon the wide stone jetty, the mate's mood waxed blacker and blacker. He champed on his pipestem, clenched and unclenched his fists, and muttered horrid curses.

Some fifty yards from the Inchcliffe Castle's bow, an artist in a linen dust coat and a wide-brimmed straw sun hat was standing at his easel. Apparently he had just applied the finishing touches and now was appraising his handiwork; he stepped back, cocked his head from side to side and nodded approvingly, meanwhile giving off gusty sighs of satisfaction with a work well done. The pair came to a halt behind him and looked over his shoulder at the picture.

"Phew! Oh, 'orrors!" cried Mr. Montgomery. "Did yer ever set eyes on such a ruddy mess o' muck as that there daub is? Why, if 'e 'adn't painted 'Inchcliffe Castle' on it, I wouldn't know whether it was supposed to be the Rock of Gibraltar or the back side of Waterloo Station!"

"H'm—weel, noo, I dinna think it's quite as bod as all that," said Mr. Glencannon mildly. "I've no' had a great deal o' experience in looking at pictures, but I knew it was meant to be the ship the moment I saw it. He's spelled 'Inchcliffe Castle' correctly, hasn't he? And aren't those sea gulls or fishing boats or whatever they are in the background really vurra lifelik'?"

"Yus, yus, but look 'ow 'e's got the 'ull orl lopsided! Look 'ow that port 'awse 'ole is set cockeyed, and 'ow 'e's left out every single rivet in 'er plates! Oh, kick me gently, mother! If I——"

"Sh-h! Pairhops we're distoorbing him." Mr. Glencannon took Mr. Montgomery by the arm and led him, still sputtering, away.

The artist swung slowly around and stood staring after them as though in a daze; then he turned to the picture. With an explosive snort and a mighty heave, he sent it scaling through the air like a boomerang.

Meanwhile, the two art critics were proceeding toward the Inchcliffe's gangway, Mr. Glencannon chiding Mr. Montgomery on the violence of his temperament. "Watch yersel', mon—watch yersel'!" he warned. "Any competent psychoanolysist wud agree wi' me that ye're a classic exomple o' the headstrong, impulsive, hyper-snotty emotional type. Instead o' flying off the hondle at the slichtest provocation, as ye did just noo, ye ocht to foorce yersel' to emulate some weel-bolanced, sweet-natured, kindly Christian gentlemon such as—— Weel, tak' me, for exomple! Noo, whenever I——"

"Dammit!" Mr. Montgomery jabbed him with his elbow and pointed a tense forefinger. "Look there!" Shuffling down the gangway came an Algerian peddler, crimson tarboosh on his head, fake Oriental rugs draped over his shoulders and in his hand a stick festooned with chaplets of tin jewelry.

"Cheerio, Jack!" he addressed them jointly, grinning from ear to ear. "Looka-looka! Very fine roog! Very fine jewelry! Very chip price!" He stepped down onto the jetty to display his wares. "Captain of ship just now buy very fine necklace for take home to Ingleesh lady very chip!"

"Oh, 'e did, did 'e?" Mr. Montgomery's lips retracted in a grin so ghoulish that a hyena, witnessing it, would have demanded to see his union card. "Now, ain't that just too charming? Well, you putty-colored son of a mangy camel, ye're about to learn wot 'appens to riffrarff that comes snirking aboard British ships when they ain't been invited!" His right hand whisked back to his hip pocket and came up with a slim leather blackjack.

Mr. Glencannon threw himself upon him and pinioned his arms to his sides. "Ho, for shame!" he cried. "Have ye no control at all ower yere brutal possions, mon?"

"Leggo! Lemme at 'im!" Mr. Montgomery pleaded hoarsely.

As they struggled and swayed, the Arab darted past them. A bottle dropped from under his robe and crashed on the pavement with an explosive pop. In the midst of the shattered glass and widening brown pool, the label lay intact. It read: DUGGAN'S DEW OF KIRKINTILLOCH.

"Foosh!" roared Mr. Glencannon, flinging Mr. Montgomery to one side and plunging after the Arab. "Stop! Stop, thief! Stop, I say!"

The peddler, although laden down with merchandise, showed a surprising turn of speed, but Mr. Glencannon soon drew within effective boot range and throughout some fifty yards subjected him to a running fire of kicks in the seat of the *djellaba.* Dripping and breathless, Mr. Glencannon retraced his steps, wistfully savoring the aroma of whisky borne to him on the breeze.

"Domn, what a colomity," he muttered. "I'm positive I locked my door, so the scoondrel must have reached it through the open porthole. . . . Er—exockly what are ye laughing at, may I osk?" he demanded of Mr. Montgomery. "Really, my guid mon, I can see no cause for levity."

"Oh, haw-haw-haw-haw-ho! Can't yer? Welp, fer a well-balanced, sweet-natured, kindly Christian gempman, you put on the jolliest imitation of Doctor Jekyll, Mr. 'Yde and Tarzan of the Apes that I ever set me eyes on! Yer gave me the best larff I've 'ad since—since—since—— Oh, ha-ha-haw-ho-ho!"

Mr. Glencannon's face assumed an expression of extreme severity. "Muster Montgomery, I dinna approve o' yer ottitude. It seems to me that when common snick thieves go roaming at will aboot a vessel, plundering its officers o' the vurra necessities o' life, something ocht to be done aboot it."

"Right-o, old chap! Yer never spoke a truer word! It's slack, it's sloppy, it's wrong! But ain't that exackly wot I've been telling yer orl morning . . . and wot I've been trying to tell the Old Man fer ten years? But—oh, 'ell, wot's the use? The captain knew that A-rab was aboard, but instead of kicking 'im orff, 'e actually bought some jewelry from 'im!"

"H'm—a-weel—yes, so it wud appear. But why canna we mak' sure that strangers dinna come aboord in the feerst place? Why dinna we have a sign, Keep Off, richt here on the gangway, lik' all other ships?"

Mr. Montgomery shrugged. "Arsk the Old Man that one too! I've suggested it to 'im fifty times, including yestiddy, and 'e orlways huffs and puffs and changes the subjick. The truth is, 'e's afraid the owners would think a 'omemade sign wouldn't look shipshape, and 'e won't spend ten shillings on a regular painter, fer fear they'd 'ave 'im up on the carpet for extravagance."

Mr. Glencannon turned and gazed ruefully at the puddle of whisky evaporating in the sun. "Weel, noo that the necessity for a sign has been brocht so painfully hame to me, I'll undertake to paint one with my ain fair honds. I gorontee to mak' a braw neat job o' it too!"

"Well, yer done them initials on yer suitcase very nicely, I must say—or was it yer 'ope chest, dearie? Ha-ha-ha! The responsibility for the sign is orl yours, though!" Mr. Montgomery turned and mounted the steep incline toward the deck, pausing for a moment to peer down into the gap between the jetty and the ship's side to see if the fenders were properly in place. " 'Ullo, 'ere's a bit of luck!" he exclaimed. "That bit of plywood floating for'ard there —it looks just about the right size for yer sign. Wait a mo'; I'll nip down and fetch it." Returning, he shook the water from it and turned it over. "Well, well, well, look 'oo's 'ere!" he cried, waving the panel on high. "Blarst me, if it ain't our old friend the picture of Gibralterloo Inchcliffe Station, drifted in with the rest of the garbage! I don't know 'ow it found its way 'ome, but it's exackly made to order fer yer!"

He brought it up on deck. Mr. Glencannon examined it, approved it and set it in the sun to dry. "I'll paint it white all ower, letter Keep Off on one side, for use in civilized countries, and—er—the French equivalent on the other. I can go ower yonder to the other jetty and copy it off that French ship."

Later that afternoon Mr. Glencannon strolled across the Pantiero to the opposite side of the harbor and out upon the Jetée du Casino, where the French vessel was berthed. She was the Pascal Paoli, of Ajaccio, spick, span and shining from a refit in the Ciotat yards. A sign—DÉFENSE FORMELLEMENT DE MONTER À BORD—hung from the rail at the foot of her gangway.

Mr. Glencannon produced pencil and paper and set about copying it. "It's a domned lang-winded way o' saying, 'Keep Off,' " he grumbled. "I can see where painting my sign is going to be more o' a job than I bargained for." He examined the hooks by which the panel was attached. "H'm! Why, ye can sumply lift it off. How vurra hondy!"

He looked up at the ship and very slowly ran his eye along her length. Save for half a dozen seamen leaning over her rail, well aft, her decks were deserted. The seamen were watching an artist—the linen-coated, straw-hatted artist of the morning—at work on a picture of the Pascal Paoli's stern. He was surrounded by a little group of spectators.

With an elaborate show of feeling the heat, Mr. Glencannon loosened his necktie, unbuttoned his collar and mopped his face and neck with his handkerchief. He took off his jacket and draped it over the sign for a moment while he stooped to slacken his shoelaces. When he stood up and retrieved the garment, the sign came with it. Assuring himself that all but its edges were concealed, he shaped a course toward shore.

"Haw!" he chuckled. "All's clear ahead and I hope all's weel behind!"

Just to make sure, he turned his head very casually and looked back over his shoulder. What he saw—and now he saw it for the first time—caused his eyes to bulge and his heart to miss a beat. It was the face of the artist—a ruddy, square-jawed, jovially British face. It wore a contented smile from which jutted a chair-leg cigar. It was the face of The Right Honorable Winston Spencer Churchill.

Mr. Glencannon made for the Inchcliffe Castle under forced draft. He reached it, winded, dripping and spent. The picture was still on deck, exactly as he had left it.

"Thonk heavens!" he gasped, snatching it up and hurrying aft to his room.

Something less than an hour later, Mr. Montgomery found him seated on the doorsill, diligently plying a paintbrush.

"Well, 'ow's it coming?" he inquired.

Mr. Glencannon held the sign up for his inspection. "Judge for yersel'," he invited grumpily. "I did the French side feerst because it was the hardest. Noo I'm just starting on the 'Keep Off.' But, domn it all, mon, canna ye see I'm busy? Please go away and lean on something, and allow me to concentrate."

As a matter of fact, Mr. Glencannon had realized that the picture, now safely hidden beneath his bunk, presented a highly complex problem. He was certain that any painting from the brush of Mr. Winston Churchill must be worth a considerable sum of money, but how could he prove this picture's authenticity?

He was still cudgeling his brains over this problem three days later, when Mr. Montgomery came into his room. The mate wore a conspiratorial air which Mr. Glencannon found extremely irritating.

"I say, 'ave yer seen Old Blubberguts this arfternoon?" he asked eagerly.

"I've no' had the pleasure," said Mr. Glencannon. "By the way, Muster Montgomery, I think ye owe our commonding officer a wee bit more respect. Noo go ahead and speak yere piece and leave me to my privacy."

Mr. Montgomery grinned, closed the door and settled himself on the edge of the bunk. "Welp, the plot is thickening!" he said. "This morning 'e 'ad me up in 'is cabin, giving me 'is usual asinine orders, when Jessup come in with a special-delivery air-mail letter. The Old Man grunts, nods to me to wait a minute and starts to read it. I could see by the stationery it was from the London office. Welp, I wish yer could 'ave seen 'is face! It turned orl the colors of the rainbow and 'is 'ands were shaking so bad 'e could 'ardly 'old the letter. For a minute or so 'e just sat there, puffing out 'is cheeks; then 'e looks up at me and stammers, 'I'll t-t-talk to you l-later, M-Mr. Mate. I've g-g-got to go ashore.' "

"Weel, what then?"

"Well, then 'e went, and 'e's just come back now. I was on deck watching 'im come along the jetty, and I give yer my word 'e was talking to 'imself and gesturing with 'is 'ands like 'e'd gone orff 'is chump. Suddenly 'e spotted yer nice new sign, which 'e 'adn't noticed when 'e went ashore. 'E scowls at it for a minute, looks up at me, and 'ollers, 'Wot the flaming 'ell is this?' 'Why, it's a sign, sir. It means "Keep Orff," ' I explains to 'im, very polite. 'Huhn?' he bellers. ' "Keep off?" 'Oo the 'ell says I've got to keep off? I'm still captain of this ship, ain't I?' Yus, 'still'—that's exackly 'ow 'e said it, Mr. Glencannon! Welp, with that 'e yanks down the sign, smashes it across the rail and chucks the pieces into the water!"

"He did? Tsk, tsk, tsk! What do ye suppose was in that letter to upset him so?"

"Well, my guess is that Mr. 'Azlitt put one of them special test jobs up to 'im that Jessup was telling us about. Yus—ha-ha!—and it's my guess the old fool foozled it too —wotever it 'appened to be!"

Mr. Montgomery made his exit, chuckling sardonically.

Mr. Glencannon was deep in troubled cogitation when there came a tap on the door and Jessup's voice said, "Captain's compliments, sir, and 'e'd like to see yer in 'is cabin as soon as convenient."

The old gentleman was in his undershirt, sitting with his elbows on his desk, his chin supported in his cupped hands. His face, normally as round and ruddy as the setting sun, was pale, drawn and haggard.

"Ah, Mr. Glencannon, please sit down," he said wearily. "It's good of you to come up so promptly."

"I am always hoppy to be o' sairvice, sir," the engineer murmured.

"Yes, I know you are, Mr. Glencannon, and I want you to know that I appreciate it." He smiled sadly. "Well, if ever a man was in need of help, you see him sitting right here before you! Mr. Glencannon, I am in hell's own fix!" He slumped back in his chair and spread his hands helplessly.

"Oh, indeed, sir? I'm vurra distressed to hear it. Exockly what's the trooble, captain?"

"Well, the net of it is that Hazlitt, the damned old weasel, has got his ax out for me again. I'll explain about that later, but first, just take a look at what I got from him this morning." He shoved a letter and a four-column picture, clipped from a newspaper, across the desk.

Mr. Glencannon took up the picture and started so violently that he almost bit through his pipestem. There, smiling genially beside his easel, was Mr. Churchill. On the easel was his painting of the Inchcliffe Castle, distinct and unmistakable. In the background loomed the bow of the vessel herself, her name clearly visible.

The text beneath the picture read:

A STATESMAN RIDES HIS HOBBY

Mr. Winston Churchill, now enjoying a well-earned holiday at Cannes, on the French Riviera, was caught by our photographer while engaged in his favorite pastime. His paintings, coveted no less for their artistic merit than because of their illustrious authorship, are occasionally presented by him as gifts to his distinguished friends or to charities for whose benefit they are sold at auction to private collectors. Inevitably, a few have found their way into the open market, where their prices are understood to range upwards from 500 guineas. In our photograph it is notable—although wholly characteristic—that Mr. Churchill has chosen for his subject a typical British freighter, the S.S. Inchcliffe Castle, owned by Messrs. Clifford, Castle & Co., Ltd., of London.

Mr. Glencannon replaced the clipping on the desk and tried to think of something to say. The best he could manage was a long-drawn "Whoosh!"

"Yes, and it's in all today's French papers too," said Captain Ball miserably. "I saw 'em when I was ashore a while ago. But now go ahead and read the letter."

Mr. Hazlitt's letter read:

Dear Ball: Enclosed is a cutting from the London Daily Mail which you will readily see is of extraordinary interest to Clifford, Castle & Co., Ltd. We have already ordered a thousand prints of the photograph for distribution among our present and prospective clients, but we realize that the original painting, hanging in our Board Room, would be an almost priceless asset in prestige to the line. We have ascertained through inquiry that Mr. Churchill ordinarily is a difficult man to approach in the matter of disposing of his paintings; it has been suggested, however, that in the present relaxation of his holiday, he might be amiably inclined toward the British captain of the British ship which is the subject of this painting. You are, therefore, directed to request the British consul at Cannes to put you in touch with Mr. Churchill's secretary, and convey to him the following proposition:

In exchange for the painting of the Inchcliffe Castle, including rights for its use in our advertising and publicity, Clifford, Castle & Co., Ltd., will contribute the sum of £750 to any charity or other worthy cause which Mr. Churchill may designate.

The Board of Directors consider this matter as of the very greatest importance and I think I should warn you that the manner in which you handle it will have a decisive bearing on their choice of a shore superintendent at the end of the year.

"Shore superintendent? Haw! Weel, weel, weel, what a pleasant surprise!" Mr. Glencannon thrust a horny hand across the desk, grasped the captain's limp one and wrung it heartily. "Pairmit me to be the feerst to congrotulate ye!"

Captain Ball shuddered, withdrew his hand and looked away. "No!" he begged. "No, please don't! Oh, I won't say I didn't have some hopes this morning! But now—but now—— Well, let's face it, Mr. Glencannon. I'm sunk!"

"Oh, come, sir! What has hoppened?"

Captain Ball half closed his eyes and drew a long breath. "I went up and saw the consul," he said, in a hollow voice like that of a trance medium. "Mr. John Smythe-Browne, his name is—I've known him for years on account of transacting the ship's business with him. I showed him Hazlitt's letter. He said he had no objection to acting as intermediary in a matter involving charity, and he put through a call to the villa where Mr. Churchill is visiting. He got the secretary on the wire, introduced me and handed me the phone. Well, I'd no sooner put it to my ear than a voice—that voice—his voice—said, 'Churchill here!' Oh, phew, Mr. Glencannon!" Captain Ball swayed back and forth, the sweat pouring out of him. "D'you remember that morning coming up through St. George's Channel, with the Stukas diving down on us, our decks all bloody and the water all churned up with bullets and bombs, and—and suddenly we heard that voice on the loud-speaker saying, '. . . we shall fight them on the beaches, we shall fight them on the landing grounds, we shall fight them in the fields and in the streets, we shall fight in the hills; we shall never surrender'?"

"Aye," said Mr. Glencannon. "Aye, captain, I remember!"

"Well, here was that very same voice coming to me over the wire. I was so nervous, so scared, that when I started to tell him who I was and all, I stuttered and stammered like a ruddy schoolboy. He was very patient and polite, and he kept saying, 'Yes, yes, captain. . . . Quite so, captain,' trying to help me out. Just as I'd finally managed to say, 'Now, sir, Mr. Churchill, sir, concerning your picture of the S.S. Inchcliffe Castle,' there came a loud snort, a bang that almost knocked my ear off and then . . . silence! He'd—he'd hung up!" Captain Ball buried his face in his hands.

Mr. Glencannon was confronted with a momentous decision. Without a word, he arose and strode from the room. Captain Ball raised his head and stared at the door in wide-eyed disbelief. "Deserting me! Him

. . . of all people!" he said tragically. "Ah, well, the rats and the sinking ship!"

He was still brooding over the vileness of man and the putridness of life in general when the engineer breezed in again, carrying a wooden panel, some eighteen inches by twenty-four, partially concealed within a bath towel.

"Here, captain!" he cried, unveiling it with a dramatic flourish. "What do ye say to this?"

Captain Ball said nothing at all. He couldn't. Then, little by little, he regained control of himself and finally managed to enunciate a fervent "I'll be damned!"

"No, ye won't, sir; ye'll be shore superintendent!" Mr. Glencannon corrected him jovially.

Captain Ball was still a trifle groggy. "But tell me about this, Mr. Glencannon! Tell me—er—how you got it. I mean to say—kerhem—is everything strictly—er—regular?"

"Obsolutely, captain! I give ye my wurrd o' honor that this picture was given to me."

"Eh? You mean—you mean——"

"I hoppened to come alang the jetty just as he was finishing it, and I made some favorable comments aboot it," Mr. Glencannon explained with perfect accuracy.

"Well, I'll be damned!" said Captain Ball again. "So he gave it to you, did he? But—but am I to understand that you're actually giving it to me?"

"If ye'll do me the honor o' accepting it, sir!"

"But the thing is valuable, man—tremendously valuable!"

"Aye, captain, but no' half so precious as yere friendship throughoot our years together in the ship!"

Captain Ball opened his mouth, shut it again and thrust out his hand dumbly. When at length it was free, he reached into the lower drawer of the desk and came up with a bottle and glasses.

"It's Duggan's Dew. The occasion demands it," he said vibrantly. "I bought it off an A-rab who came aboard the other morning, and it's a bit of the right stuff!" They drank. They drank a second. They were about to have triplets when Captain Ball's face suddenly clouded again. "Look here, Mr. Glencannon," he said. "You've been no end noble about this thing, but I just happened to think about the letter I've got to write to Hazlitt when I send him the picture. What can I tell him? How can I explain how I got it—especially for nothing? What can I say about Mr. Churchill?"

"Ye can tell him the truth, sir; no more and no less. Ye must sumply say that the picture was presented to ye by an auld pairsonal friend—a gentlemon whose name wud be vurra familiar to him, but who wishes to have it withheld."

"But he'll think I mean Mr. Churchill!"

"Weel, will that be yere fault . . . and will it do ye any harm?" Mr. Glencannon poured another drink, picked up the newspaper photograph and studied it thoughtfully. "Ye say the French papers are carrying this picture today, sir?"

"Yes, I saw 'em on all the newsstands, over in the Rue d'Antibes."

"H'm!" Mr. Glencannon arose. "If ye'll pairdon me, captain, I think I'll just stroll ashore and pick up half a dozen."

"Half a dozen? What do you want that many for?"

"A-weel, before we send the painting off to London, I'm going to hire some young artist here in Cannes to knock oot six copies o' it. These I shall offer for sale in New York, Buenos Aires, and wherever we hoppen to be. Obviously, I'll need a newspaper picture to go with each copy, to prove it's a genuine, original Churchill."

He stepped out on deck and paused for a moment to watch the sun sink grandly behind the peaks of the rocky Estérel. Mr. Montgomery was returning shipward along the jetty. He walked slowly, with his head slumped forward, scowling at a picture on the front page of a newspaper. He moved over to the edge of the wall and shifted the scowl to the usual collection of flotsam and jetsam below. Mr. Glencannon followed his gaze and saw two jagged-edged white objects which he recognized as the fragments of his shattered sign. Even as he watched, Mr. Montgomery ripped his newspaper in two, crumpled the pieces into a ball and hurled it violently into the water.

"Ho, there!" Mr. Glencannon called to him gaily. "What are ye doing, Muster Mate—contemplating the beauty o' the Mediterranean sunset?"

"Hunh?" Mr. Montgomery looked up, startled. "Oh! Er—why, yus." His face contorted in a sheepish, sickly grin. "Lovely evening, ain't it?"

"Aye!" said Mr. Glencannon. "It's almost as pretty as a picture!"

The Tactful Admiral

A *POST* WAR ANECDOTE

EARLY in the war, the Netherlands naval vessel Jan van Brakel acquired a distinctive new camouflage job of which her officers and men were very proud. And well they might be, for the nautical artists who decorated this convoy-escort craft had created a masterpiece that would have made a surrealist painter green with envy.

The theme of this terrific paint job was deceptive rather than concealing—the vessel was literally a nightmare of lightninglike slashes of brilliant blue and glaring white. The result may have been exceptionally confusing to a German U-boat captain, but it certainly was a fact that to others she hit the eye like a fat woman in a striped bathing suit.

One day the spectacular Jan van Brakel steamed into a British port for the first time since the artists had made her their masterwork. Her appearance attracted everybody's attention as impellingly as if she had come in blowing whistles or firing guns. Surely every man not asleep or on watch below decks aboard the English vessels was spellbound by this majestic entrance.

Shortly after dropping the hook, the skipper of the Jan van Brakel radioed proudly over to the senior British officer, "How do you like our camouflage?"

There was a pause. Then the English admiral tactfully inquired, "Where are you?"

—LOUIS H. BRENDEL.

A Child's Garden of Curses;

or, The Bitter Tea of Mr. P.

OUTSIDE of a spring lamb trotting into a slaughterhouse, there is nothing in the animal kingdom as innocent and foredoomed as the new purchaser of a country place. The moment he scratches his signature on the deed, it is open season and no limit to the bag. At once, Nature starts cutting him down to size. Wells that bubbled over for two hundred years mysteriously go dry, stone walls develop huge fissures, and chimneys sag out of plumb. Majestic elms which have withstood the full fury of the hurricane and the Dutch blight begin shedding their leaves; oaks dating from the reign of Charles II fade like cheap calico. Meanwhile, the former owner is busy removing a few personal effects. He rolls up the lawn preparatory to loading it on flatcars, floats the larger trees downstream, and carts off the corncrib, woodshed and toolhouse. When I first viewed my own property, my dewy naïveté was incredible—even Dewey Naïveté, the agent who showed me around, had to suppress a smile. What sealed the choice was a decrepit henhouse occupied by a flock of white Wyandottes. According to my estimate, it needed only a vigorous dusting and a small can of enamel to transform it into a snug guest cottage. Shading my eyes, I could see a magnificent wistaria, heavy with blooms, creeping up a lattice any fool could construct with ten cents' worth of nails. As soon as I took possession, though, I discovered it must have been on casters, for all that greeted me was a yawning pit trimmed with guano and eggshells.

This baptism, however, was merely a prelude to the keelhauling the natives had in store. Like any greenhorn from the city, I used to choke up freely at the sight of the man with the hoe. Every bumpkin I encountered reminded me of Daniel Webster; his dreariest platitude had the dignity and sweep of Walt Whitman's verse. Selecting one noble old patriarch, who I was sure had served with John Brown at Harpers Ferry, I commissioned him to paint the barn. Several days later, he notified me that forty-seven gallons were exhausted. "No use skimpin'," he warned. "A hickory stump, a widow woman and a barn has to be protected from the weather." I was chuckling over this bit of folk wisdom without quite understanding it when I detected a slight bulge under his coat similar to that caused by a five-gallon drum. He intercepted my glance and informed me fluently that he usually picked a few cranberries during his lunch hour. Apparently he lunched on Cape Cod, five hundred miles to the north, but since he never took more than half an hour, I overlooked it and ordered more paint. A week afterward, his barn burst forth in a shade of red identical with mine.

"Looks like yours, don't it?" he grinned. "Darned if I can tell 'em apart." I knew what he meant.

I have been taken to the cleaners since by some notable brigands, but the most brazen of the lot was the kinsman of Jesse James who repaired our road. Edward Mittendorf and his merry men spent a fortnight lounging about in well-cut slacks, pitching quoits and reading Swinburne. Occasionally one of the more enterprising would saunter over and deposit a pinch of gravel daintily in the ruts. Whenever my wife passed by, they critically appraised her charms, whistling and clucking spiritedly. I entered a mild demurrer and received the following instructions: "You tell 'em, corset; you've been around the ladies." The day of settlement dawned on schedule, and with Mittendorf watching me beadily, I began to examine his bill. It was a closely typewritten document resembling the annual report of the Federal Reserve. Among other items he listed depreciation on shovels, lemonades for the men, and some bridgework his niece had ordered.

"Who's Ed Mittendorf?" I inquired, indicating a salary in excess of Cary Grant's.

"My cousin—the little fat feller," he explained.

"Is he the same as Eddie Mittendorf?" I asked.

"No, that's my dad," he returned smoothly, "and Ned Mittendorf there, he's my uncle. I'm Edward—got that straight?"

"I should," I snapped. "Your name's down here twice."

"It is?" he gasped. "Well, I swan."

I swanned also on reading the total, but I paid through the nose, a locale which was rapidly taking on the aspect of a teller's window. If you ever drive up the lane, be careful. Those diamonds raise hell with your tires.

—S. J. PERELMAN.

You Pays Your Money . . .

HAVING turned six, my small daughter Ferna has now become interested in boys. I am perfectly willing that she should show a normal interest in the opposite sex. I do not even mind when she presents me with a list of twelve people she wants for her next party and they are all of the male gender.

What disturbed me recently were reports from the field that Ferna not only liked boys but was very aggressive about it, given to chasing them as they fled panic-stricken down the streets. In fact, Ferna's teacher hinted that a number of boys were staying out of school in deadly fear of my small siren, and would I please have a talk with her? . . . With Ferna, of course. Her teacher is a bit afraid of boys.

I had several talks with Ferna. I told her the ancient and still valid theory of courtship was that the girl waited, poised and polite, for the boy to chase her. I reminded Ferna of certain penguins who bring small pebbles to their lady loves. I told her of the bower bird who builds a nest which he decorates with colored paper and bits of thread for the female's pleasure and delight. I told her about certain insects who wafted perfume and brought honey to their girl friends. I spoke gently and in my usual winning manner.

When I had concluded, Ferna seemed suitably impressed.

I find, however, that things are not what they seem to be. Ferna came running into my study after school with a roguish smile on her face that usually meant either she had found a lollipop or had succeeded in kicking her sister's shins. Not so this time.

"If I tell you something, will you promise not to tell mummie?" she began, rolling her big blue eyes.

"Sure. But what's so bad you can't tell mummie?"

"Well—uh—I got a new boy friend. Frankie Havens."

"So what?" I said nonchalantly. "The week is up. It's time for a new one."

"Well . . . I—I kissed him."

I narrowed my eyes and then relaxed. "It isn't a very good idea to go around kissing boys."

"Don't tell mummie," she begged again.

"It isn't a good idea, it isn't anything mummie's going to be terribly angry about. Why shouldn't I tell mummie that you kissed Frankie Havens?"

"Because," she said, "it cost me five cents!"

Why don't the teachers take charge of this sort of thing? What am I paying taxes for?

—ROBERT FONTAINE.

SHIPPING THE CLARET TO PORT

By FRANK WARD O'MALLEY

§ *It is hard now—indeed, for many it is impossible now—to recall the dear, departed days when the three-mile limit was so important to American citizens, whatever their ancestry. Prohibition confused many an issue, including this one.*

NOVEMBER 18, 1922

I SHALL touch on the matter of booze aboard and abroad in its turn. Be patient. Let me first at least start the ship in my own way. On the night before my departure last summer, Fire Chief Frank Pettit, of our Brielle Volunteer Fire Department and Chemical No. 1., came to me apologetically during one of the happiest periods of the big social and lap supper held in my honor in Fire House. The Borough of Brielle, as readers in touch with recent social happenings of wide interest will doubtless recall, was that night tendering to one of the biggest men in all Brielle a farewell lap supper.

Music and games were indulged in until a late hour, and a delightful evening of pastime was voted by each and every one and all present.

Among those present were Mr. and Mrs. Fire Chief Frank Pettit, Mr. and Mrs. Justice of the Peace Bowdish Pearce, Mr. and Mrs. Draw Tender Bickford Pearce, Postmaster Kroh, Lute Pearce, Jr., and Miss Gazelle Umpleby, of Asbury Park—ah, there, Lute, you little rascal!—Mr. and Mrs. President of the Borough Council Orville Kroh, Lawyer Benton Pearce and Mrs. Lawyer Pearce, little Warren G. Harding Pettit and his older cousin, William Howard Taft Pearce, Shem Longstreet and Shem Pearce.

The guest of honor and his handsome missus were presented with a handsome combination parlor lamp-phonograph that must have set the donors back a bunch of money, and a delightful time was had by all.

But speaking about the time I was abroad, Fire Chief Frank Pettit came up to me, as I was saying, at the height of the lap supper and apologetically asked me my age. I told him the truth, and Chief looked thoughtfully for a moment into his beaker of apple.

Enough to Cover Tips

"Well," said Chief, "if you have now reached that age you may sail for England tomorrow confident of the fact that you are now eligible to the benefits of Fire Company's Old Firemen's Free Death and Insurance Benefit Association. You should worry!"

A small thing, you say? Far from it. In case I died abroad the widow would get one hundred dollars, or more than enough, so I was to learn later, to balance the tips shelled out to ship's stewards, one way. Furthermore, in case my body were brought back to America I'd get one coffin of best yellow oak, a motor-driven hearse and the regulation floral offering—a big fireman's hat in red, white and blue immortelles and lilies, I to take the big floral fire hat with me to the hereafter.

I did not die abroad, but the free-funeral offer still stands. Pretty soft, eh?

But on the morning after the lap supper I awoke in low spirits. Throughout my hot journey up the Jersey coast from Brielle to the Hoboken pier I gloomed over the fact that at last I had been definitely doomed to the aged and exempt vet's class forever.

"Europe," said I mournfully, passing through Perth Amboy, "will have to go some to work up another thrill in me."

I was wrong. There was still one thrill left. But it took something of cataclysmic importance to stir it.

Once, about two years ago, I had an invitation to spend a week-end in Flatbush, Brooklyn, but was unable to go. Up to the morning I went aboard ship recently I had never been east of Eleventh Avenue. And so the last thrill left in me rose and gripped my throat, squeezed tears from my eyes, when suddenly I noticed from my high perch on the boat deck that the great shedded pier below, massed solidly with cheering humanity, seemed slowly, almost imperceptibly, to be gliding westward past our still, apparently, motionless ship.

We were off!

The chatter and cacklings of shrill last messages from pier to ship and ship to shore exploded into one magnificent yell. Deadened oom-pahs and the faint boom of a bass drum of the ship's brass band tried bravely to come to the surface of the sea of noise.

Impulsively I clasped the hand of a matron standing beside me on the boat deck—an absolute stranger who turned out to be, I learned, a prominent New York woman named, as I recall it, Mrs. Eisenschutz.

I was a first tripper and wanted to soak my soul with the ecstasy of the first actual move toward somewhere east of Eleventh Avenue. European summer trips had long since become a necessary bore to Mrs. Eisenschutz and her lovely daughter, who was standing there arm and arm with mother, idly gazing down upon the ecstatic pier. Besides, Mrs. Eisenschutz was the sort of mother who would not permit an earthquake to interrupt her praises of her young.

"And this sweet baby of mine," Mrs. Eisenschutz was saying while still we were barely moving, her arm now circling the waist of thirty-year-old Flapper Eisenschutz, "is the best, the dearest, the most modest daughter——"

Chanteys by My Shipmates

The good ship, made in Germany, selected this moment to take a more determined spurt out of her slip toward that dear Fatherland which, to mix the metaphor or sex, gave her birth.

Roars increased. Flapper Eisenschutz, the modest, blushingly stepped a yard or two in advance of mother's disconcerting, loudly spoken praises.

There was thrill on thrill. Massed on the river end of the long pier was a great group of male singers. Stalwart American lads they were, many of them able to sing in English. And they it was who gave the needed big dramatic and patriotic punch to our departure.

One of the singers, a husky American lad in his shirt sleeves, who carried in his arms the grand old flag, risked his brave young life climbing high on the pier rail.

Always shall I remember the picture he made to us on the ship as his muscular young American arms rhythmically began to wave over the heads of the singers the glorious old banner, its three-barred and imperial stripes of black, white and red snapping in the breeze on Hoboken's shore.

And then from the lusty lungs of those American lads we had left behind came the stirring words of the national anthem:

Es braust ein Ruf wie Donnerhall,
Wie Schwertgeklirr und Wogenprall:
"Zum Rhein, zum Rhein, zum Deutschen Rhein!
Wer will des Stromes Hüter sein?"

Himmel! It gripped our own American hearts with the fierceness of Lew Fields choking Joe Weber in an old-time Weber-Fields show.

And then the last glorious outburst as we headed down the Hudson toward the upper bay.

Lieb Vaterland, magst ruhig sein!
Lieb Vaterland, magst ruhig sein!
Fest steht und treu die Wacht,
Die Wacht am Rhein!
Fest steht und treu—hoy—oi
Die Wa-a-acht a-a-a-m-m Rhei-i-i-n!

Gott! It beautiful was! It was a final yell of patriotism so intense that it loosened the rivets on the bronze Liberty Lady's clothes, far down the bay, until she was all but forced to step down behind her towering pedestal of granite, blushing a deeper bronze, and borrow a crowbar for purposes of pinning up.

Doubtless the reader will better understand the patriotic inwardness of our farewell when it is recalled that the vessel on which I was a passenger went to Germany as well as to England and France. Plymouth and Cherbourg are visited, but the great final objective is Bremen.

A Distinguished Company

Furthermore, the second-class quarters of our particular ship that day were all but filled with German-American master bakers in convention assembled. They were all headed for that dear Vaterland, rather, to do their annual convening on German soil. Hence our imperial farewell.

Followed a tedious lull after the excitement of actual departure. I suppose there was nothing slower last summer than the creeping of a boat from an American wharf to a point three miles out from the Constitution of the United States.

It was blazing midday of the hottest day of the hottest stretch of weather of the entire summer. If one had torn any page of the printed passenger list, German blood would have spurted forth, from the Adelsohns all the way back to the Zookmans. And lashed on an open stretch of deck aft, all in plain sight and scent of second-class as well as first-class passengers, were barrels and barrels and barrels of beer. Real German beer it was, made in Bremen. Barrels of it, I say—not mere kegs. And, heavens, mates, the day was hot!

Slowly, even more slowly at times, the big liner inched her way past Quarantine, the Narrows, and at last stood out to sea.

The feel of ominous tenseness aboard tightened. Something seemed about to begin to commence. The heat grew more withering.

In pairs and groups the passengers began to mass themselves to leeward of the great piles of scenty draft beer, all breathing deeply through the nose. The long, long dry years were all but passed! With everybody huddled behind the beer barrels far aft, the forward third of the ship, including the first few feet of the keel, stuck high out of water.

The heat grew terrifying.

There was a movement, sharp hysterical cries among the closely packed hophounds rigidly pointing their kill. Stewards, it seems, had begun to drag great cakes of ice across decks toward barrels of German beer. Ice approached beer, beer approached

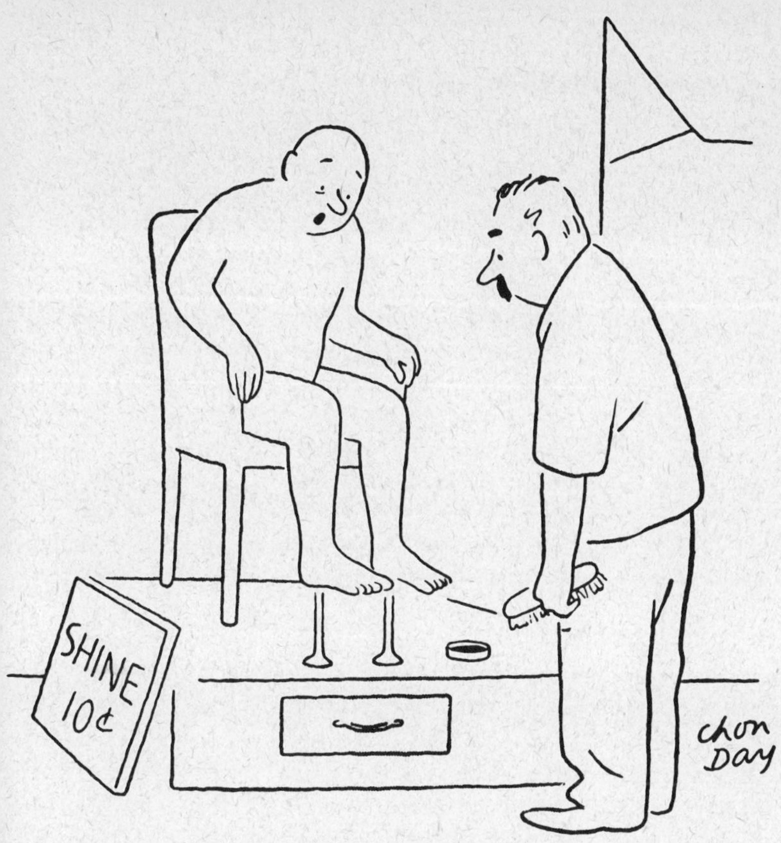

"Why, bless me—so I haven't."

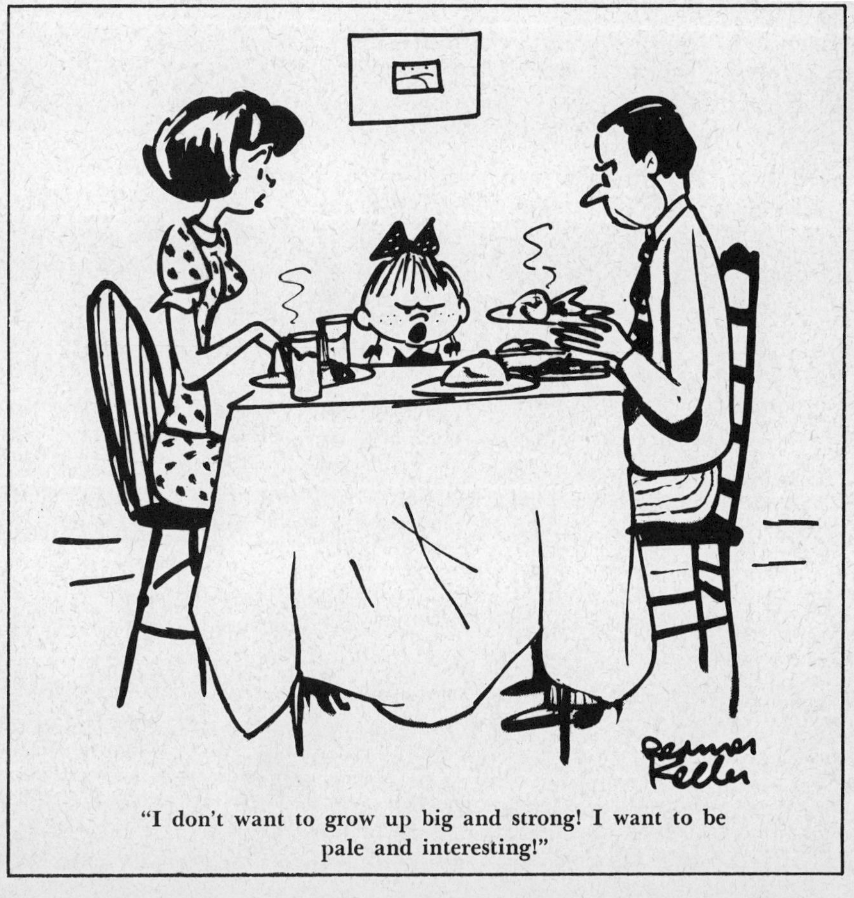

"I don't want to grow up big and strong! I want to be pale and interesting!"

"—so, after you fired me from the chief accountant's job, I went and applied for this job with the Government. Well, down to business, eh, Mr. McElroy?"

FAMOUS LAST WORDS

"Let's go; only a home run could save us now . . . and this joker coming up couldn't hit one out of the park if his life depended on it."

"Oh, no! . . . Not another old Army buddy!"

"Oh, boy! Payday again!"

"I feel inferior to other people, doctor."

"Mr. Barnes here will attend to the fitting."

ice. The ice touched the wood. Then the ship slowed down—stopped! Worse, she perceptibly began to ride back toward America on the swift flood tide.

Now it is well known that the chief hot-weather indoor sport of the great German people is suicide by gas. Out back of the beer barrels they had no gas, but there was the sea. Master baker after master baker had a foot on the rail, only to be dragged back by more level-headed and still more masterful bakers.

The arrival of a tug that the liner had been awaiting caused a diversion. It seems that a noted young man—writer, publicist and close friend and associate of one of our presidents—had that morning thoughtlessly left his passport on a Broadway counter while buying a new straw hat. He had to go back for the passport and missed the ship. Hence the slow-up to permit him to climb aboard the liner from his taxi tug.

Famous as he was and is, John Callan O'Laughlin and new straw hat were received with great outbursts of glum Teutonic silence. Not a cheer. Not one good old American "*Hoch!*" did he get. He deserved none. Knowing, as he must have known, the miserable time an eastbound liner makes these days out to the three-mile line, he might have strolled easily from Broadway to Coney Island, rowed out to the channel leisurely in a skiff and still have had a long wait until the liner showed up. But instead he wasted hours hunting up a taxi tug.

With John and his hat safely aboard we got under way again. At the same moment a ship's bellhop came along the decks distributing dainty little booklets.

"The passenger list," said someone, reaching for one of the booklets.

I opened my copy without glancing at preambles and began on the A page the always interesting study of the names of one's fellow passengers.

Aldegunder, Palmberg. Alfer, Herrenberg.
Alsheimer, Sonnenberg.

"All particularly masterful master bakers," I mused, "who no doubt can afford to travel first-class."

Lightly my eye glanced at a name here, another there:

Berncastler, Reisling.
Deidescheimer, Nueberg.
Duerkheimer, Reisling.
Haig & Haig.
Hennessey, John.

I flipped the pages feverishly:

Jameson, John. MacDonald, Sandy.
Walker, Johnny.

It was unbelievable! Could it be possible that so many celebrities—at least one man of international fame topping any letter grouping one turned to—were aboard one ship? Perhaps just one of the Haig boys might be with us, yes; but certainly common business sense, especially common Scotch business sense, would cause the Haig family to see to it that one of the boys stayed safely ashore while the other was risking the dangers of the sea.

I turned back to the booklet cover for enlightenment. The big block printing on the cover explained all:

WINE LIST
ALSO
SPIRITS, LIQUEURS, COCKTAILS
AND
BEERS

"Queer people, you Americans." Thus I began tentative acquaintanceship with the man, also reading the wine list, in the deck chair at my right. He was a prominent New York business man named Mr. I. A. Kettz—Ignatius Aloysius Kettz, I think, although my mere guess about his given names may be all wrong.

"Have we reached the three-mile limit yet?" was Mr. Kettz's only comment.

"No, not yet," drawled a lanky New Englander sprawling all over the deck chair to my left. The lanky New Englander was, if memory does not trick me, a Mr. Abromawitz, of Boston, and he was in men's underwear—his business, I mean.

Mr. Finnigan Introduces Himself

"Gentlemen," boomed a big voice from the chair to the left of Mr. Abromawitz's, "if I may introduce myself, my name is Finnigan—Michael Finnigan."

I did not know at the instant that Michael Finnigan and I were to be inseparables throughout the rest of the trip. All I was conscious of was that the mere name, Michael Finnigan, aroused in me an overwhelming atavic complex of remote caveman origin. I jumped to my feet with the hot purpose of dragging Michael Finnigan down to my chair and smothering him with one long passionate kiss. But his bristling red beard calmed me. Gripping myself I shook his hand.

"It's impossible, gentlemen," began the lanky New Englander, Mr. Abromawitz, "to run a transatlantic passenger service without a smoking-room bar. As a business man I ask you how——"

That was as far as he got. Wild-eyed men suddenly began to run past us, crying out excitedly. Women were crying out in terror and pointing hysterically toward the opposite, or port side of the ship.

It seems that one of the breed that is always ready to yell "Fire!" on the slightest pretext in a crowded theater was aboard. The idiot—he was a rangy Middle Westerner named Splitzenheim, from Pittsburgh, I believe—had not yelled "Fire!" He had done worse. He had spread the ghoulish story that the skipper had, half a mile or so on the bad, or land side of the three-mile limit, pointed the ship more and more to the northeast until now the liner, still inside the three-mile limit, was running parallel with the Long Island coast.

Rumors piled high. The skipper was born and raised in Maine, someone recalled. What was Maine? A rock-and-rye ribbed coast girding the first state in the Union to go dry, the American birthplace of prohibition. This captain was one of them!

All passengers now were jammed on the port decks, gazing toward the too close coast of Long Island. Indeed, to all appearances the ship and Long Island appeared to be racing along together, with the bow of Long Island so far ahead of the ship's bow that a day might elapse before we could get a three-mile lead on Long Island.

Mutinous talk began to rumble.

"Gentlemen!" at last shouted a tall Southerner whose broad shoulders loomed large above the angry crowd jamming the port deck—the indignant Southerner was, as I recall the name, a Mr. Geltsticker, of Gumbo, Louisiana—"I propose, gentlemen," continued the dashing Southern colonel, "that a committee of protest right away go quick up to the captain and—and——"

Speechless, the distinguished-looking Southerner faltered, stopped. Just what it was that the hot-blooded Southerner's committee was to tell the captain never was learned. Rigidly he stood at gaze, high on the deck chair on which he had climbed, his eyes looking steadily through a porthole just opposite where he stood. And next, with a maniacal cry, half sob and half terrible laughter, he flung himself down on the astounded mob and fought and clawed his way toward a smoking-room entrance close to the porthole through which he had been looking.

At the height of his exordium from the deck chair, it seems, Mr. Geltsticker had seen the entire roster of the starboard and port bartenders' first dogwatch file into the smoking room, unlock the bar and pipe all hands to grog.

Little remains to be told.

Let me merely add that never shall I forget that first rush. Among all its wild scenes always, too, I shall remember how a wide, raw-boned Texan of obvious frontiersman type—we learned later he was a Mr. S. Pincus, of Curley Wolf, Texas—became wedged at the hip pockets in the smoking-room entrance, blocking all traffic. Kicking him from behind only wedged him the tighter. Strong men behind him screamed and wept in their desperation.

"Around to the other porch of the ship, men!" rang the gallant cry of a New Yorker. I forget his name—it doesn't matter.

Round the ship they raced, galloping forward the length of the port deck and then doubling back on the opposite deck to a starboard entrance to the smoking room, far aft. Their parched tongues hung out as they raced. It was pitiful.

Just to keep the record straight I should like to be able to give here the name of the winner of that round-the-ship sprint, but the name escapes me. I think he was a college athlete; at any rate he was a student from New York City.

It was three o'clock in the afternoon precisely when the hot-blooded Southern orator, Mr. Geltsticker—why is it these old Southern boys of the blood are all born orators?—saw the bar opened. By 3:02 o'clock the smoking-room cash registers were ringing with the uninterrupted steadiness of a railroad crossing's warning bell. Another two minutes later the smoking room was as solidly stuffed as a Philadelphia ballot box always was stuffed on the Sunday night before the Tuesday after the first Monday in November, back in the old days.

In those first moments of German frightfulness one with a name like mine of course stood no chance. How Michael Finnigan secured a good place, his right resting on the bar itself, I could not understand; at least not then.

I could see him inside a few feet from where I stood outside.

The best I got was a place at a smoking-room porthole, but outside looking in. I was one of a long waiting list. We could stand and wait, but were not served. As hour after hour after hour passed, the sun blistering our necks on deck, the slosh and splash of the ice-cold real thing in Pilsener coming to us through the open portholes from within, we who panted for admission to the exclusive club inside prayed that a club member would drop dead, and thus create a vacancy.

Late in the afternoon we had new cause for hope. A grizzled sailorman lugging a stout piece of canvas—the canvas was just about large enough to wrap round a bloated human body, we noted—came to a halt outside the entrance to the smoking room and spread the canvas on deck. Hope jumped to the zenith when the sailorman next brought forth stout sail needles and coarse threads.

We cheered when finally the old salt stepped aft a bit and promptly returned with weighty lumps of scrap iron, of the sort used to sink a body buried at sea.

Goody, goody! Somebody indoors who couldn't handle the stuff had died!

For two hours and forty minutes by our watches the sailorman stitched and stitched. As dusk was settling on the sea he had sewed the canvas to a shape roughly the length and possibly the breadth of a man who had died from guzzling Pilsener from three o'clock in the afternoon until late summer sunset.

The sailor's hard afternoon of work completed, he dragged canvas and weights toward what remained of the barrels of beer on deck and tried to fit the canvas jacket over the cakes of ice piled on top of the beer barrels. The canvas covering for the ice was too small. Chagrined, the sailorman wrapped the scrap iron in the canvas, chucked the afternoon's work overboard and proceeded aft to take up his next important duty.

One man did drop in his tracks just as darkness set in. Unfortunately he was merely another of the overflow standing outside looking in. And oddly enough the venerable gentleman who dropped dead—he was a member of an old New Orleans creole family named Schlippenpfatz, we learned—was the ship's total abstainer.

In justice to the poor old man it should be explained that his doctor was sending him to a German spa to take the cure, because of an illness that had absolutely forced him to go on the wagon. But in spite of great age and illness, he had given the blistering afternoon and evening to climbing furtively, secretly, from the depths of the E deck to the hurricane deck, from stem to stern, on some sort of fruitless search.

Finnigan to the Rescue

I asked him, a moment before he expired in my arms, what he had been seeking. With the last energy left in him he turned his head from side to side, peering about cautiously before answering.

"Dammit all," were his last words, "I was trying to find on this ship a good, reliable, sea-going German bootlegger who would take a chance and slip me a glass of plain water."

At midnight that night, with a nautical "Heave!" and a "Ho!" and a farewell "Attaboy!" we flipped the old boy over the side.

But enough of the tragedies of the sea.

Some time after the midnight funeral good old Finnigan saved my life. I had felt since the bar opened that if help were to come to me the good Finnigan—who, with the sole exception of myself, was the only passenger aboard with a name like that—alone would help me. Kind flocks to kind.

Following the midnight funeral I had resumed my vigil outside the porthole nearest the smoking-room bar, waiting for someone inside to resign or die, when Finnigan turned and saw me gazing in wistfully only a few feet from where he stood. And immediately Finnigan began to push his way along the bar toward my porthole, cautiously, and always careful not to lose his front-row status. Once during his cautious progress he came close to serious mishap. Someone pushed him so roughly that he all but lost his grip on the edge of the bar—and he told me later he couldn't swim a stroke. Finnigan halted only when he had reached the extreme end of the bar nearest my porthole. He had an idea, and it was wonderful.

"Listen!" he called guardedly across the short space—short but, oh, how long!—separating us. "Borrow the captain's cap and then come back here and I'll tell you how to work it."

The captain, I learned after racing to the bridge, had turned in for the night hours before. The only bluejacket in sight absolutely refused to leave the wheel and rout the captain out of bed. The best that the blue-clad boy at the steering wheel could do for me was to lend me his own sailor cap.

Placing the cap on my head in a jaunty way that made one think of the Prince of Wales, I hurried back through the darkness to my smoking-room porthole. Immediately good old Finnigan directed me to climb up on something, stick my head inside the porthole as far as possible and receive final instructions.

I received them and then proceeded to let loose Finnigan's magnificent idea. For a man with a name like Finnigan he had a sane head.

"Mates!" I yelled to the startled drinking club indoors, my head pressed into the porthole farther, much farther than I could possibly have pressed it on any morning after thereafter. "Mates, attention! I desire officially to announce that the same draft beer you've been drinking here all day and night is being sold at five cents the seidel less in the second-class smoking room. And at even a greater proportionate reduction, mates, the second-class smoking-room bargains on our fine stocks of Kentucky ryes and bourbons, Haig and Haig—"

I myself couldn't hear the rest of my announcement. Probably in the instant panicky rush toward first-class smoking-room exits no one indoors heard even as far as the name of the second of the Haig boys. There is nothing so excitedly irresistible as a bargain sale to us thrifty old Yanks.

On to Bremen

Before the rest of the patient waiting list out in the dark could think, I was inside the now all but vacant smoking room and anchored beside good old Mike Finnigan at the bar. Thereafter, or until I landed at Plymouth, we never were separated for a moment. On the nights that the smoking room was closed for a bit of airing Finnigan and I, being the last to be thrown out, always got sleeping places on deck closest to the smoking-room entrance and slept there, Finnigan athwart the starboard sill and I athwart the port.

Consequently we two, of course, always led the port and starboard rushes that converged and met at the bar the moment the smoking-room doors were unlocked for business each morning. Hunger often during the week drove even the most patient standees behind us to the dining saloon, but never Finnigan and me. Finnigan and I were content with the bar sandwiches. Munching between drafts day after day, we two settled question after question of love and life and death. The old, old days were back again.

Naturally I took it for granted, since Finnigan had said that he was headed for his boyhood home in the old country, that he was going ashore at Plymouth. But on the last morning, with the tender waiting alongside, he still clung to the bar. He would not even step over to the port side of the smoking room to gaze out upon the beautiful soft farmland hills rising high beyond Plymouth harbor. Remembering his name, it occurred to me that perhaps he had suddenly decided he would not dirty his boots with the hated soil of the oppressor, and I suggested as much.

But he merely shook his head, gave me his card in parting and turned back in silence to his beer. He was going on to Bremen.

Regretfully we parted. He hadn't bought once on the way over, I recalled while the tender was gliding smoothly toward the near shore of England, but I cared not. Of more importance was the fact that he was the only passenger with a name like mine aboard, and racial blood at times is thicker than Pilsener.

I am not ashamed to confess that it was with misty eyes I read the card he had handed me. It was one of Mike's business cards, and it ran:

MICHAEL HERMAN PFENNIGHANN, PRES.
PFENNIGHANN & PFLEITZ BAKING COMPANY
MFRS. OF "THAT DIFFERENT" P. & P. BRAND
VIENNA BREADS, COFFEE CAKES
AND PRETZELS
OFFICES AND FACTORY
BROWNSVILLE, BROOKLYN, N. Y.
TELEPHONE, SLAUGHTERHOUSE 0786

So I stepped ashore, tapped my feet reverently on British soil, and cried with a half sob, "Well! Well! So this is England."

Any person who can fold up a road map is entitled to a driver's license.
—HERBERT V. PROCHNOW.

MR. POPE RIDES AGAIN

By WALTER BROOKS

§ Take a Sunday afternoon, a neighbor's attractive wife, a deserted back road or two, mix well with an incredible talking horse named Ed who drinks beer and likes peace and quiet, add one advertising executive named Wilbur, and you've got all the ingredients for one of Walter Brooks' best humorous repasts.

JULY 4, 1942

THIS Wilbur Pope had a horse named Ed that he used to go riding on Sundays. Mr. Pope was an advertising account executive five days a week, and on Sundays he liked to get a little peace and quiet, so, after he had had breakfast and read the paper, and before his wife's friends began dropping in, he would saddle Ed and take to the hills. There are plenty of back roads around Mt. Kisco if you know where to find them, and lots of taverns full of ice-cold beer too. Ed liked peace and beer and quiet as much as Mr. Pope did, so it was a nice arrangement.

Well, there was an abandoned orchard a couple miles from Mr. Pope's house, and after they had had enough exercise and beer, they used to go up there and take a nap in the shade. And one Sunday when they came ambling through the gap in the stone wall they saw a buckskin pony tied under their favorite tree, and beside him in the grass sat a girl.

"Hell!" said Mr. Pope, and started to turn Ed to go back, but the girl jumped up and waved and called, so he thought he had to go over.

"Why, Wilbur Pope!" said the girl. "Isn't this nice? I was just wishing someone would come along and talk to me, but I hadn't hoped it would be you!"

Ed turned around and rolled his eyes at Mr. Pope, but Mr. Pope pretended not to see him.

"I didn't know you rode, Mrs. Niles," he said.

"I haven't for years," she said, "but now that tires are so scarce, Richard won't let me use the car Sundays when he plays golf, so I got this pony."

"Didn't I hear he was on one of the tire-rationing boards?" said Mr. Pope. "He ought to have tires."

"He has six brand-new ones in the garage," said Mrs. Niles, "but he doesn't feel he should use them yet. . . . But why so formal?" she said, smiling at him. "My friends call me Nita."

Well, Mr. Pope was not any special friend of the Nileses', although they lived just over the hill back of his house. But he had met them at several parties which had been anything but formal, and for all he knew, he might have got on quite disrespectful terms with them, for it wasn't always easy to remember exactly what had happened at parties. So he said, "Sorry, Nita. The formality, I guess, was merely a recognition of the fact that you might not want to be disturbed here."

"That's very subtle of you, Wilbur," said Mrs. Niles, "but whether you disturb me or not, I leave to your intuition." And she smiled at him with her eyes, which were large and blue.

Well, Mr. Pope had no objection to talking to a pretty girl, but he had come out in search of peace and quiet, and, after all, by this time on Sunday afternoon his own home would be full of pretty girls, if that was what he wanted. Not to mention Mrs. Pope, who was one of those dark Spanish types that are so terrifying to men, or would be, if the men knew anything. So he said he was afraid he must be getting back.

So Mrs. Niles said she must, too, and she would ride back with him. And she did, and Mr. Pope wasn't bored at all, because she had a trick of turning everything he said into a compliment to herself, and that was a kind of back-handed flattery that made him feel how clever and fascinating he could be even when he didn't try. Ed was pretty bored, though. But of course he couldn't say anything, because he never did to anybody but Mr. Pope, and nobody else even suspected that he could talk.

Well, Mrs. Niles left them at her gate, and they rode on toward home, and neither of them said anything for half a mile. And then Ed said disgustedly, "Pah!"

"Pah yourself," said Mr. Pope. "What's the matter, Ed?"

"Oh, you make me sick," said Ed, "sitting up there gloating over your conquest."

"What conquest?" said Mr. Pope self-consciously.

But Ed just shrugged his shoulders so Mr. Pope's hat fell over his eyes, and then they were home.

Well, the next Sunday when they turned into the orchard, there was Mrs. Niles under the apple tree, and Mr. Pope didn't see how he could get away without being impolite, so he sat and talked to her quite a long time. He tied Ed on the other side of the tree, but, although the horse couldn't see, he could still snort derisively, and every time Mr. Pope said anything, he did. Mrs. Niles didn't think anything about it, except to wonder once if Ed had a cold, but anybody who has ever suspected a kid brother behind the davenport while handing out his best line will know how Mr. Pope felt. He was pretty short with Ed on the way home.

On the following Sunday, when Mr. Pope led Ed out of the barn, the horse said, "Hey, look, Wilb, if you're going to meet the girl friend again, take the car and leave me home, will you? Because I just can't take it."

"You can't take what?" said Mr. Pope.

And Ed said, "That fancy talk you hand out, and where you get it I don't know—you sound like a third-rate Maugham novel."

"I'll pass over that crack," said Mr. Pope, "because I haven't any intention of running into Mrs. Niles today, if I can help it, and I thought we'd go up past Jerry's and through Patten's Woods."

"You mean that?" said Ed, and Mr. Pope said, "Of course I mean it, for I want to have a nice quiet time as much as you do."

"O.K.," said Ed; "then I'll hold my fire."

Well, they had some beer at Jerry's, but just as they were coming out, Mrs. Niles came cantering along, and then it was just like last Sunday. And the three following Sundays were the same. Mr. Pope said he didn't like to be impolite, and of course they had to go past the Nileses' to reach most of the back roads, and what could he do? Ed told him, but Mr. Pope didn't do anything about it.

And then one Sunday, Mrs. Niles looked worried. "Oh, Wilbur," she said as she pulled up alongside him on the road back of her house, "I'm glad we met. Oh, dear, it's just too silly for words, but Richard has found out about us, and he's frightfully angry."

"Found out?" said Mr. Pope. "But what is there to find out?"

"Oh, why, nothing, of course," said Mrs. Niles, "but—well, we have been meeting in that remote place, haven't we? And you know how Richard is!"

"No," said Mr. Pope. "How is he?"

"Well," said Mrs. Niles, "he went and phoned Carlotta about it yesterday."

"Well, I don't think Carlotta will be much disturbed," said Mr. Pope, smiling.

Mrs. Niles gave him a wide blue stare and said, "Of course, you would know whether she should be or not. And I do like your being so sure of yourself, Wilbur."

"Oh, don't be stuffy," said Mr. Pope. "You know what I mean."

"What do you mean?" said Mrs. Niles.

Well, Mr. Pope didn't have any idea what he meant, but he felt he had to say something—I don't know why—and so he opened his mouth to say it, but just then Ed decided it would be a good thing to stumble, and he did, and Mr. Pope's hat fell over his eyes and he bit his tongue, and all he said was, "Hell!"

And Mrs. Niles laughed merrily and said, "Let's go up to the orchard and talk it over."

Mr. Pope didn't want to, but he was mad at Ed for stumbling, so he said, "Let's."

So they rode up and sat under the apple tree, and Mrs. Niles said, "Oh, Wilbur, dear, what are we going to do?" and Mr. Pope said, "Well, if Richard doesn't like your riding with me, perhaps you'd better stop it."

But Mrs. Niles turned her eyes on him full strength, and the tears welled up, but she blotted them before they ran down and eroded her make-up, and she said, "Oh, you are so hard!"

"No, I am not hard," said Mr. Pope, "and it has been very pleasant riding together, but——"

"Oh, don't say it!" burst out Mrs. Niles. "Don't talk about common sense! I am sick of common sense!" and she began a sort of low sobbing, which, to Ed, behind the tree, seemed pretty artificial, but to Mr. Pope, rather touching. For, after all, she was sobbing for him, and to have anybody sob for you gives you a pretty strong shot in the ego.

So he moved closer and patted her shoulder comfortingly. But he looked around first to see where Ed was. For Ed had once leaned over his shoulder and kissed a girl, and the girl had thought it was Mr. Pope and it had caused quite a lot of trouble. And he felt that a kiss from Ed at this juncture would be a large-scale disaster.

"There, there," he said, and he reflected that it was rather pleasant to comfort a girl who was crying. For Mrs. Pope only cried when she was mad, and if you tried to comfort her then, you would probably lose an eye.

So he went on patting, and Mrs. Niles went on sobbing and talking, and she made it pretty plain that whatever her husband said, she wasn't going to stop seeing Mr. Pope. She seemed to take it for granted that Mr. Pope felt the same way. Mr. Pope didn't, but he had a kind of antiquated chivalry toward women which made it ungallant to inform them in so many words that you did not care to see them if it might mean a poke in the nose. So, like a darn fool, he put his arm around her and said, "But really, Nita, I do think we'll have to stop seeing each other."

And they were sitting like that when Mr. Niles came panting up from where he had left his car in the road at the foot of the hill.

Mr. Niles was mad, all right. He grabbed Mrs. Niles by the arm and pulled her to her feet and said, "You get on your horse and go home! . . . And as for you, Pope——" he said.

"Oh, don't be an ass, Niles," said Mr. Pope. "Nita was just telling me that you had misunderstood our meetings—which have been entirely by chance and——"

"Yeah," interrupted Mr. Niles. "I saw her telling you," and he advanced threateningly.

Mr. Pope had no intention of getting into a fight over somebody he didn't care if he never saw again, and he felt pretty silly too. He couldn't figure out how he had ever got into such a situation. He tried not to look as guilty as he felt—for, after all, he had been sitting with his arm around the guy's wife—and he said, "I don't mean anything in Nita's life. We've happened to meet—— Hey, quit, you fool!" he shouted, side-stepping a furious right swing that Mr. Niles had aimed at his jaw.

Well, Mr. Niles towered half a foot above Mr. Pope, and Ed, who had been peeking around the tree, decided it was time for a diversion. So he hauled off and kicked the buckskin pony in the ribs. The buckskin reared and smacked Ed on the nose, and it was several minutes before Mr. Niles and Mr. Pope got the squealing animals separated. Then Mr. Pope prudently mounted.

Mrs. Niles was weeping bitterly with one eye and watching the two men with the other, and Mr. Niles was feeling of his shoulder, where one of Ed's hoofs had grazed him, and he said, "You watch your step, Pope; I warn you."

"Oh, come, Niles," said Mr. Pope. "Don't be medieval. You can't stop my riding."

"I can stop your riding with my wife," said Mr. Niles, "and don't you forget it."

"Well," said Mr. Pope, "I gather you encouraged Nita to ride to save wear on your tires, and if you wouldn't be such a hog about your car and would let her use it, she probably wouldn't have much interest in riding, and then she certainly wouldn't meet me. But as there are only a certain number of dirt roads around here——"

"What arrangements I make with my wife are my business."

"And my opinions are mine," said Mr. Pope, "and I must say that a man who has six brand-new tires tucked away and still won't let his wife use his car——"

"Who told you that?" shouted Mr. Niles; and Mr. Pope said, "Oh, a little bird," and rode quickly off.

"You kicked Niles in the shoulder, Ed," he said as they ambled home. "You ought to be more careful; you might have killed the guy."

"Yeah," said Ed, "and then you could have got a divorce and married your Nita."

"Don't talk nonsense," said Mr. Pope. "I wouldn't marry her if she were the last woman on earth."

"Yeah?" said Ed. "Well, you certainly acted like she was the last woman on earth. Gee, I can't figure you out, Wilb," he said. "You mean you ain't making a play for her?"

"Certainly not," said Mr. Pope.

"Then maybe it's as well I didn't hit the guy's head, like I intended," said Ed. "But if that's so, you certainly missed your cues."

Mr. Pope asked, "How so?"

And Ed said, "Well, my guess is she ain't making a play for you either. Not a serious one, anyway. She wants to use that car, and if old whoosis can be made to think her riding is just a blind to meet some guy she wants to build a nest with——"

"Could be," said Mr. Pope.

"Is," said Ed. "And what's more," he said, "if you really make a good strong play for her, she'll be scared pointless. And we'll have our orchard back," he said.

But Mr. Pope thought it was a terrible idea. "If you think I'm going all out to try to scare her off," he said, "you're crazy."

"You think maybe you'd be stuck with her?" said Ed. "Well, you're stuck with her now, for what do you bet we run into her again next week?"

Mr. Pope didn't answer and they rode

home. And there was more trouble. For, as they rode up the drive, they saw Mr. Pope's car, and some people looking at it, and well they might look at it, for the right front fender was smashed and the front tires looked as if they had been chewed by lions.

Mrs. Pope ran up to Mr. Pope, and said, "Oh, Wilbur, I am afraid I have wrecked our front tires, for I ran off the road and into a barbed-wire fence."

Mr. Pope said, "Oh," and looked at the tires, and then he said, "Well, that ends our jolly motoring days for the duration; for, as you know, I have only the one spare."

"Well, I said I was sorry," said Mrs. Pope defiantly, "and you might ask if I'm all right."

So Mr. Pope did, and Mrs. Pope said she was, and Mr. Pope asked how it happened.

"Well, I had Jed Witherspoon with me," said Mrs. Pope.

"Ah," said Mr. Pope, "and were you driving with one hand or something?"

"Well, in a way," said Mrs. Pope, "because I had to slap his face, and we were on a curve and I sort of lost control."

"Couldn't you have waited until pulling up before slapping him?" said Mr. Pope.

"No," said Mrs. Pope, "because he would have misunderstood if I had stopped the car."

"Well, it's too bad," said Mr. Pope, "and I still think it might have been simpler to have pulled up and then to have removed his misunderstanding, than to have spoiled two perfectly good tires."

"Oh, you do!" said Mrs. Pope angrily.

And Mr. Pope said firmly, "Yes, I do!"

And Mrs. Pope said, "Well, you're a good one to talk! Running about and making a spectacle of yourself with that little Niles creature every Sunday!"

So Mr. Pope rode Ed over to the barn.

"Well, Ed," he said, "I guess you'll have to take me to the train mornings now. I haven't a car any more."

"Yeah?" said Ed. "And where do you park me—in that lousy garage of Duffy's?"

"Oh, it won't be so bad," said Mr. Pope, "and you'll probably hear a lot of good stories."

"There's only three good stories, and I know them," said Ed, and he began to complain.

But Mr. Pope was sore about the car, and he said, "Don't give me an argument. Maybe later I can get some retreads, but until then we ride."

"You might apply to Niles' rationing board," said Ed.

"You're a big help," said Mr. Pope.

Well, Mr. Pope spent an unpleasant evening, during which it became plain that Mr. Niles had indeed talked to Mrs. Pope, and with considerable imaginative detail. In the morning he went out to saddle Ed to ride to the station. And there in the middle of the barn floor were two brand-new tires.

"Hey, Ed," he said. "What's this?"

"Oh, them?" said Ed in an offhand way. "Oh, those tires. Yeah. Well, what do you know!"

"What do you know?" said Mr. Pope.

And Ed said, "Oh, Wilb, I might as well tell you. I sneaked over to Niles' place last night and picked 'em up for you."

"Good Lord, Ed," said Mr. Pope, "you mean you stole them? And how'd you get in his garage?"

"Well," said Ed, "I sort of leaned against the door, and it flew right open, and then Niles came out to see what the noise was, but I'd pulled the door to, and I just sort of joined two cows that were standing in the next field, till he went in the house. Then I went back and stuck my head through a couple tires and brought 'em over. . . . Now look," he said, as Mr. Pope started to blow up. "Don't be a sap, Wilb. Get those tires on and drive to the station, and nobody'll ever know the difference."

"You darned fool," said Mr. Pope. "Those tires have got serial numbers on 'em, and anyway, I don't drive with stolen tires.

We'll have to get 'em back somehow." He glanced apprehensively out of the barn door, and then picked up the tires and rolled them into the harness closet. "Well," he said, "I haven't time to think about it now. Come on; I'm late for the train as it is."

Well, that evening Mr. Pope made Ed promise to take the tires back, and he and Mrs. Pope went off to the movies with the Brintons. When the Brintons brought them home, it was late, and they were just starting into the house when they heard a pounding out in the barn, and they went out to see what it was. As they got nearer they heard muffled shouting, and it seemed to come from the harness closet, so Mr. Pope switched on the light and unlocked the harness-closet door, and out tumbled Mr. Niles.

Well, that was quite a surprise. Mrs. Pope screamed, and Mr. Pope said, "Well, for heaven's sake!"

And Mr. Niles, who gave the general effect of having been well shaken up in an ash can, put his face close to Mr. Pope's and said between his teeth, "You're going to regret this, Pope, till the last day you live!"

Well, Mr. Pope could see that the two tires were no longer in the harness closet, and they weren't in sight anywhere around the barn either. Ed was in his stall, munching away stolidly on a wisp of hay.

"I don't know what you're talking about," he said, "and perhaps you'd better explain why I find you skulking in my harness closet."

"Skulking!" yelled Mr. Niles. "Skulking!" and his voice rose to a shriek, and then he got hold of himself and said, "I don't know how much you know about this, Mrs. Pope, but I don't propose to drop it, even if your husband returns the tires he stole from my garage last night, and while I am sorry to embarrass you, I don't intend to let him out of my sight until I can get the police here."

"Oh, come," said Mrs. Pope. "Why should you think Wilbur would steal your tires?"

"He was the only one who knew I had them," said Mr. Niles. "My wife told him, and that was why I came here to look for them."

"Ah, yes, your wife," said Mrs. Pope thoughtfully. "Well, Wilbur might try to steal your wife, but I don't think he'd steal your tires."

"But I found them here," said Mr. Niles.

"Yeah?" said Mr. Pope, who had just received a reassuring wink from Ed. "Well, where are they?"

"Wherever you hid them after you shoved me into that closet," said Mr. Niles, "and if you want to——"

"Just a minute," interrupted Mrs. Pope sharply. "Wilbur couldn't have shoved you into any closet, because we've been at the movies all the evening. But I'd like to get this thing cleared up myself, and so you can watch Wilbur if you want to, while I go in and phone the police." And she left the barn.

Well, it was half an hour before a police car turned into the driveway, and it was an unpleasant half hour for Mr. Pope, for Mr. Niles just stood and glared steadily at him, without saying a word. Mr. Niles' story was that he had driven over and found the missing tires in the harness closet, and he had just rolled them out when somebody slammed the door on him and locked him in. "It was Pope all right," he said, "because I heard him laugh, and he came back a couple of times and laughed at me, and I suppose we will find the tires hidden somewhere around here, officer."

"Well, it don't seem to me——" began the trooper, scratching his head, and then he said, "You say you were at the movies, Mr. Pope?"

"With Mr. and Mrs. Brinton," said Mrs.

Pope, "and you can easily phone them and check up."

"No," said Mr. Pope; "let him make a complete search. Then, when I sue Niles for making this charge, as I certainly intend to do, we'll have a complete story."

So the trooper searched. He examined the tires on Mr. Pope's car and he searched the house and the barn and every bush and tree on the place.

And while he was searching, Mr. Pope took a measure of oats in to Ed.

"Where are they?" he whispered, and Ed said, "Make him look in his garage. I took 'em back. Boy, did the guy use scurrilous language!" he said with a giggle. "After I shoved the door to, I had to sit against it until I could turn the key with my teeth, and my, my, such talk!"

Well, pretty soon the trooper and Mr. Niles came back, and the trooper was good and angry, and he said, "Well, Mr. Pope, Mr. Niles may have seen those tires here, but they aren't here now, and I've checked with Mr. Brinton on the phone, and you certainly couldn't have locked Mr. Niles into the closet. So what do I do now?"

Mr. Pope said it seemed obvious to him that Mr. Niles suffered from delusions and that perhaps they'd all better go over and look in the Nileses' garage. So Mr. Niles got into his car, which he had left out in the road, and the trooper took the Popes in the police car, and they drove over. And sure enough, there were all of Mr. Niles' six tires in a neat pile in the corner of his garage.

Well, Mr. Niles didn't have much to say, but Mr. Pope had plenty. "Well, there you are, officer," he said, "and if you ask me, hoarding of this kind is pretty darned unpatriotic—particularly in a member of a tire-rationing board."

"I bought those tires long before rationing started," said Mr. Niles, but in a rather subdued voice.

"Who's to say?" said Mr. Pope. "You might be as mistaken about that as you were about where they were. . . . Eh, officer? Not a nice story, if it got around locally." The trooper shook his head and looked with disgust at Mr. Niles. "Now, you take me," said Mr. Pope. "You saw my car. I've had to quit using it. And here's a member of the board who has six new spares. Six! Don't seem fair, does it?"

The trooper said it didn't.

"Now, of course," Mr. Pope went on, "I wouldn't have been justified in stealing two of these tires. But if I told you that I offered Mr. Niles fifteen dollars apiece for two of them and that he refused to let me have them——"

"You never tried to buy any tires of me!" exclaimed Mr. Niles.

"You see?" said Mr. Pope, and the trooper nodded.

"Oh," said Mr. Niles, looking at Mr. Pope with his eyes narrowed, "I begin to see too." He thought for a minute. "I don't get this thing at all," he said. "I don't know how you did it, or why. But you can make things unpleasant for me. All right, Pope. I won't apologize, but you can have two of those tires."

"That's fine," said the trooper. "That's fine. And you gentlemen——"

"We're satisfied, I think," said Mr. Pope, pulling out his checkbook.

"Yes," said Mr. Niles grudgingly, "and thank you, officer. I'm sorry I called you out. If there's anything I can do for you any time——"

The trooper grinned. "I'll remember that," he said, "whatever else I forget."

Well, the following Sunday, Mr. Pope and Ed went out as usual. Ed felt pretty good, because he wasn't going to have to spend most of the week in Duffy's garage, waiting for Mr. Pope to come back from the city, and he wanted to celebrate, so Mr. Pope had stuck a bottle of whisky in his pocket. Ed hadn't wanted to go up to the orchard, but Mr. Pope said he'd be darned if he'd be driven out of such a peaceful spot by any darned girl, and anyway, he said, after the bawling-out Niles gave her, she wouldn't try it again. Ed wasn't convinced, but he wanted to get at the bottle, so they went up and sat under their tree and passed the bottle back and forth and had a nice time.

By early afternoon they were pretty well oiled, and they sang and shouted and carried on until the orchard sounded like a reunion of the class of 1910. But Ed was still kind of nervous, and finally he said, "Maybe we're making too much racket, Wilb, if that pest is galloping around on her pony."

"Pooh!" said Mr. Pope.

But Ed said, "Pooh all you want to, but she won't give up so easy."

"She don't want me," said Mr. Pope.

"She wouldn't leave her happy home for you," said Ed, "but I know her kind. She's a scalp hunter, and until she's tore your scalp off, she won't quit."

"You mean if she knew she could get me," said Mr. Pope, "she'd have no further interest?"

"Sure," said Ed.

And Mr. Pope said, "Well, that's easy. If she shows up, I'll tear off my own scalp and hand it to her, and then we can go on drinking."

"Is that a promise?" said Ed.

And Mr. Pope said, "Sure. Pass the bottle."

Well, they had hardly had two more drinks when Ed said, "Oh-oh!" and pointed with one hoof to the gap in the stone wall, and Mr. Pope looked, and there was Mrs. Niles on her pony.

"Why, Wilbur," she said, dismounting, "how nice! I thought maybe after what Richard said——"

"Who's Richard?" said Mr. Pope, and he shook his head to clear it. "My, Nita," he said, "you're purry as a pitcher!"

"Am I your Nita?" said Mrs. Niles lightly.

"One man's Nita 'nother man's poison," said Mr. Pope.

"Why, Wilbur, I believe you're tight!" she said, and she looked at the bottle, and then at Ed, who had rolled over and was lying in the grass with his eyes shut. "And your poor horse!" she said. "He's tired out!"

She led her pony around the other side of the tree to tie him, and Ed opened one eye.

"Remember your promise," he whispered.

Mr. Pope frowned. "Oh, now listen, Ed," he began, but Ed put his mouth close to Mr. Pope's ear.

"You keep this up," he muttered, "and you'll have to slug it out some bright Sunday with Nilesy. Be a man, Wilb."

"Yeah," said Mr. Pope, "but——"

"O.K.," said Ed, jumping up, "then I'm leaving and you can walk home."

Mr. Pope caught at the bridle, but missed it.

"Oh, all right," he said.

"What did you say?" asked Mrs. Niles, coming back and sitting down beside him.

"Just addressing my charger," said Mr. Pope. "Poor old Ed," he said, "I've ridden him pretty hard today." Then he shook his head sadly. "But I can't help it," he said. "I'm about at the end of my rope, Nita."

"Why, what do you mean?" she said.

And he said, "Well, we can't go on like this."

Mrs. Niles screwed up her eyes and looked at him.

"What on earth are you talking about?" she demanded.

"Talking about us," said Mr. Pope. "Two loving hearts serrated by a few words mimbled by a munister—I mean mumbled by a minister. Nice word, 'mimbled.' I remimber—I mean, I remember when we were married, the minister——" He stopped as Ed gave a loud snort, and then said, "Well, anyway, there's too many *m*'s in that, and as I was going to say, I told Carlotta last night that you and I——"

"You what?" shouted Mrs. Niles. "Oh, Wilbur, you fool! You don't mean you went and——"

"Sure, I did," said Mr. Pope; "I went and did. Well, we got to accept the ineffable, haven't we? And what we got to do, we got to go tell Richard right away."

"Tell Richard!" screamed Mrs. Niles, jumping to her feet.

"Sure, sure," said Mr. Pope. "We go to him hand in hand and tell him frankly and freely—— Why, Richard's a human being just like us," said Mr. Pope—"in many respects, that is—and after all, if we really want to marry each——"

"You're drunk!" interrupted Mrs. Niles harshly. "Why, I never heard such a lot of nonsense in my life! Good heavens, just because I stop and talk to you once in a while——"

"Why, Nita," said Mr. Pope, "you distinctly said——"

"Well," said Mrs. Niles, untying the pony's reins, "I'll distinctly say now that you're a conceited fool, and—why, I wouldn't marry you if you were the last man on earth!"

"You and her too," said Ed, opening one eye as Mrs. Niles cantered off.

"Yeah," said Mr. Pope. "Well, Ed, the orchard's ours again."

"Yeah?" said Ed, sitting up.

"What do you mean, yeah?" said Mr. Pope. "You heard the line I handed her."

Ed yawned and sat up. "Dear me," he said, "I must have dropped off. Same old line, was it, Wilb?" Then he grinned. "Oh, I won't kid you, Wilb; I heard it all, and you done fine. I didn't think you had it in you. And maybe you wouldn't have had it in you if you hadn't had a lot of good whisky in you too. Yeah," said Ed, "some folks take women for their inspiration, but me, I take whisky. Pass the bottle, Wilb."

The Perfect Squelch

AT A WEEKLY meeting of the Three-Quarter Century Club, composed of men and women in St. Petersburg, Florida, who are seventy-five or over, an affable elderly gentleman arrived early and decided to wait outside on one of the city's numerous green benches. A woman came by and sat on a bench facing him.

"Are you a member of the Three-Quarter Century Club too?" the man asked pleasantly.

"Indeed not!" the woman replied. "I'm nowhere near seventy-five. The idea!"

"Please forgive me," the man said apologetically. "I'm eighty-three, and we old-timers kind of like to brag about our age. Now where the fair sex is concerned," he chuckled, "you can't always be so sure. By the way, how old are you?"

Glaring at him, the woman snapped, "A woman's age is her own business."

"Well," said the man, as he rose from the bench to go. "I can see you've been in business a long time."

—A. D. SCHOENLEBER.

THE ETERNAL DUFFER

By WILLARD TEMPLE

§ *Maybe you never thought golf could be ghostly, but Willard Temple's nimble typewriter proves that the spirit world operates as well on the links as in drafty, deserted houses. In a classic of* Post *humorous fantasy, Mr. Temple has created a couple of lovable and unforgettable gentlemen in Barnaby Jessup and Pete Tyson. The problem? Well, when Barnaby arrives in Heaven, he looks the place over and promptly reaches this decision: He would much rather carry golf clubs than a harp.*

MAY 18, 1946

THE funeral was mighty impressive. It was bound to be in the case of a man like Barnaby Jessup. Most of the town had turned out, and after it was all over, one of the pallbearers looked up at the sky and murmured, "Be a nice afternoon for golf."

That remark might be considered to bear on the sacrilegious, in view of the occasion, but none of the other pallbearers objected, and they were all old friends of Barnaby Jessup, men in their sixties or higher, all but one of them, and Barnaby Jessup had been seventy-six when they laid him to rest.

The six pallbearers walked back across the gravel path to the car to take them back to town, and on the sidelines their names were spoken in hushed tones. For one of them, some years before, had been a candidate for president of the United States, one was a great surgeon in the land, a third, the young man of the lot, was a lean and tanned golf professional, winner of the Open, and it was he who had made the remark about golf.

The men got into the car and, as was natural, they talked about Barnaby Jessup on the ride back to town. But they did not reminisce about the time back in the 20's that Jessup had made a million in the stock market, nor about the way he had juggled railroads; it was of quite different matters that they talked.

The man who had almost become president, said, "I was with Barnaby the day he put eight straight balls in the lake hole."

The surgeon, his eyes reflective, said thoughtfully, "I played with him the day he took a twenty-seven on a par-three hundred-and-ten-yard hole."

The mildest man of the group, the man who was simply the head of one of the late Jessup's holding companies, said, "I saw him wrap all of his clubs around a tree one afternoon," and no one commented, because that had been commonplace.

The car hummed across the black ribbon of road and there was a silence while the men privately considered their friend, and then finally the golf professional looked up at the warm blue sky and spoke quietly.

"I hope Barnaby finds a golf course," he said.

The gate before which Barnaby Jessup found himself was highly ornamental, of a curiously intricate wrought iron, and the pillars were of marble, but a marble which Jessup had never seen, marble with the luster of a pearl.

"Ought to look into this," Jessup said. "The trustees could use it for the art museum."

And so saying, he passed through the gate and was presently standing in the registrar's office, where in due time he gave his name to the clerk, who wrote it down in gold letters.

"Glad to have you with us, Mr. Jessup," the clerk said. "A good many of the inmates like to know why they've been able to come here. In your case—"

Jessup stopped him with a wave of the hand.

Like many men who have achieved great wealth and prominence, he was inclined to be autocratic. "I left an art museum behind," he said. "I divided my fortune among colleges and institutions—"

"Not for any of those things did you enter here," said the clerk.

Jessup was momentarily startled. "Well," he said, "I built the finest hospital in my state, equipped it with the best that money could buy, and brought some of the greatest medical men in the world—"

The clerk said, "That is entered on page three thousand one hundred and forty-nine under the heading Superficial Trivia."

Jessup was jarred right down to his heels by that one. He thought a minute and then began a recital of what he had done with his money, the charities he had supported, and before he had gotten under way with the list the clerk was shaking his head negatively.

"You remember Jim Dolan?" said the clerk.

Jessup thought back down the years. "Jim Dolan," Jessup said slowly. "Must have been thirty years ago, that was. He was a caddie at the club. Killed in an accident."

"You went to see his mother," the clerk said, reading aloud from a page in the ledger. "You had a meeting that was worth thousands to you, and you turned it down to go and see his mother."

"I didn't give her a dime," Jessup said. "Just called to pay my respects and tell her what a fine boy Jim had been. That's all I did."

"That's all," said the clerk gently, and smiled, and Barnaby Jessup scratched his head and wondered, but not for long, because he was a man of action and unaccustomed to being introspective.

"Look, son," he said, "all my life I've been on the go. I don't mean any offense, but tell me this, do I have to sit around on a cloud? I mean, just sit? And I've no ear for music, I can't play a harmonica, let alone a harp."

"Why, no," the clerk said. "You can do about anything you like; anything within reason, that is."

Barnaby hesitated and said in a low voice, "No golf courses in these parts, I suppose?"

"No country clubs," the clerk said. "There's no discrimination up here. But we have a very fine public course."

Barnaby Jessup smiled and then said, "I didn't bring my clubs. I—"

"Last door down on your left," the clerk said.

Barnaby had another question, but he kept it back because he didn't like to take too much of the clerk's time. And likely Pete Tyson wouldn't be up here anyway.

"Oh, Milton, try to think. Was it about us?"

THE LATE BUS.

"Aha! Just what I always suspected!"

" 'Little elves shaking out feather pillows'? Why, what a delightful conception!"

"Don't worry, Edith. Why, just the wedding presents alone will furnish our apartment."

"Of course, the Chronicle has a sounder editorial policy, but the Herald seems a little warmer."

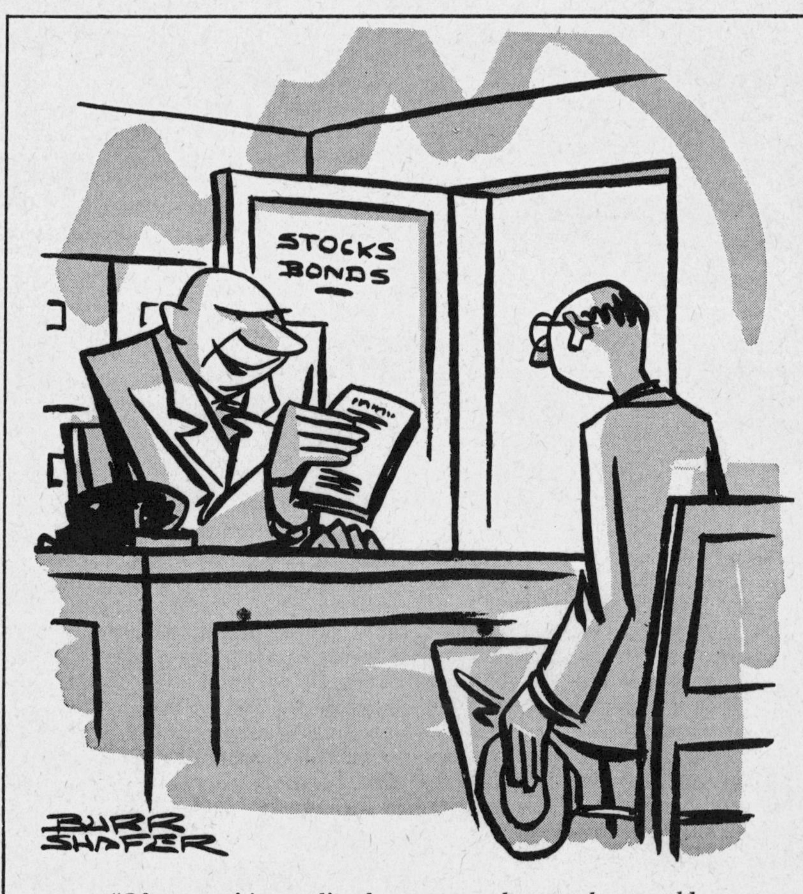

"Of *course* it's not listed on any exchange—that would let in too many people."

Barnaby and Tyson had been business competitors and had fought each other with no rules and no holds barred, but most of all they had battled on the golf course. Ten years before, Barnaby had fought back the tears while he watched the clods go down over the mortal remains of his dearest enemy and closest friend.

He'd sure like to see old Pete. But a man can't have everything, he thought, and he went on down the hall to the last room on the left. A man sat at a bench inside and Barnaby stopped and stared, for he had never seen so many golf clubs. They lined the walls, clubs of every description.

"Help yourself," the man at the bench said without looking up.

Barnaby thanked him and selected a likely-looking driver from a case along one wall. It had the right feel with the weight in the head where he liked it. He tried the rest of the clubs and found them perfectly matched, and finally he put the set in a golf bag and a half dozen balls in the pocket.

"What do I owe you?" he said, taking out his wallet and extracting two one-hundred-dollar bills, for these were hand-designed bench-made clubs and he was ready to pay two hundred for all he had there, but not a penny more because he had always made it a practice not to let people take advantage of him because of his wealth.

"No charge," the man said. "They're your clubs. Look on the shaft."

Barnaby glanced down and saw his name stenciled there. "Well," he said in wonder, "but look here, I want to give you something. I don't doubt all employees up here are well treated, but just the same——"

The man squinted down the shaft of a club. "I'm no employee," he said. "I'm a permanent resident and a busy man."

Barnaby Jessup thanked him, walked to the door, then said, "Can you tell me how to reach the course?"

"Six miles due north."

"Is there a cab for hire?"

Barnaby couldn't understand what he said, it sounded like "Fly," and he didn't repeat the question, for the man was plainly eccentric, although a genius at his craft. He went outside to look for a cruising taxi and then he felt something at his back when he slung the golf bag over his shoulders and discovered that the strap was tangled up with a protuberance growing out of his shoulders.

He wiggled his shoulder blades, and the next thing he knew he was three feet off the ground and treading air, with both wings flapping.

"Well, I'll be," Jessup said, then sighted on the sun, got a bearing on what he considered to be due north, and took off, flying at a steady, even clip about ten feet above the ground. It was a trifle awkward; he got out of balance somehow while trying to shift the golf bag and went into a tailspin and landed on his chin in a gully, but it didn't hurt, and presently he was airborne again, and then finally he saw a long stretch of green ahead of him and he flew over the entire eighteen holes, surveying the layout.

When he had finished he knew he had just seen the ultimate in golf courses. The fairways were gently undulating, lush with grass, the greens like huge emeralds. It was a sporty course, too, not too flat, and yet not too hilly.

Getting quite excited, he flew back to the first tee, eager to swing a club, for although he had been one of the world's most successful men, it is said that no man achieves everything he wants in life and Barnaby Jessup had been a success at everything he turned his hand to with the exception of golf. A not inconsiderable part of his fortune had been spent on the game, but he had remained a duffer. He had in his home a comprehensive library of golf from the earliest works down to the most modern tomes. He had studied under the greatest professionals in the world and had built in the cellar of his home a cage where he could practice on such days that inclement weather kept him off the course. But he had remained a divot digger and a three putter down the years.

He made a neat two-point landing on the tee and as if by magic a caddie bobbed up, a small freckled boy with a missing front tooth who relieved him of his bag and handed him his driver.

"Howdy, Mr. Jessup," the boy said. "Nice day for it."

Jessup stared at him. "Jim Dolan," he said. He couldn't see any mark on the boy from the truck. "Well, Jim," he said. "Like old days."

"Smack 'er out there, Mr. Jessup," the boy said.

Jessup stood at the tee, addressing the ball and sighting toward the green, four hundred yards distant. Then he ran through the rules, cautioning himself not to press, to keep his head down, to start the club back low to the ground, to let the left arm do the work, to cock his wrists, and to shift his weight to the right foot with most of the weight on the heel.

He thought of all these things and then struck the ball, wincing a little as he always did, expecting either a hook or a slice. But he heard a musical little click, and the ball bounced on the fairway about two hundred and sixty yards away.

"Good shot," Jim said.

"Best one I ever hit," Jessup cried. "By juniper, I had it that time. I think I've figured this game out."

They walked forward to the ball and Jessup selected a brassie, sure that he was going to miss because never in his life had he put together two consecutive good shots.

He swung the brassie and that click sounded again and Jessup rubbed his eyes and said in awed tones, "It's on the green."

The caddie was already walking forward, handing Jessup his putter.

"I never made a par in my life," Jessup said. "I have a chance for a birdie. Oh, well, I suppose I'll three-putt."

On the green he surveyed the situation, noticing the slope toward the pin. He jabbed at the ball, tightened up, but it rolled forward and fell into the cup.

Barnaby Jessup mopped his brow with a handkerchief and sat down on the apron at the edge of the green.

"Well," he said finally, "accidents will happen. Let's go, Jim. But maybe, at that, I will break one hundred today."

The second was a water hole. The lake sparkled a bright sapphire in the sun and the distance across the water was a hundred and eighty yards.

Jessup selected a spoon. "I should have brought more than six balls," he said. "Don't know why I didn't. I lose at least six every time I play. I'll put at least three in that lake."

He swung, then listened for the whoosh as the water received his offering, but he failed to hear it and neither did he see drops of water splashing upward.

"Lost sight of it," Jessup said.

"Good shot," the caddie said. "It's in the cup. It's a hole in one, Mr. Jessup."

"Now wait a minute, Jim," Jessup said. "You're not supposed to lie up here. Besides, I'm an old man and—"

"It's in the cup," the boy repeated.

Jessup was looking for a path around the lake when the boy took off and flew across, and Jessup sailed after him. They landed on the green and sure enough the ball was in the cup.

He was too shocked to say anything, but assumed that every once in a while this kind of thing happened to everyone, a superlatively good day, but of course he'd go blooie any minute; he always had, he always would.

The next hole was three hundred and eighty yards and his drive was straight and far. They came up to it and the caddie handed him a seven iron.

"I usually use a five this far away," Jessup said.

"You can make it with the seven," Jim said.

Jessup didn't think so, but although he invariably took the hide off people who tried to advise him at business, he'd never somehow been able to disregard a caddie's advice.

Meekly he took the seven and swung. The ball landed on the edge of the green, bounced twice, rolled forward and fell into the cup. Jessup removed his glasses, blew on them and put them back on.

"You're playing a nice steady game," the caddie said. "Even two's at this point."

"I am not," Jessup said. "Don't be ridiculous, Jim. I can't possibly have played three holes and only taken six shots. Nobody could, no golfer in the world."

He took the scorecard from the boy and counted it, and counted it again on his fingers, and the boy was right, there was no disputing it. He had a three and a one and a two. There was no getting away from it. It wasn't possible, but there it was. He was even two's.

He had started out with the eternal hope of breaking one hundred. Now he was afraid to think about it. But still, he told himself, he'd go blooie any moment now.

And when they stood on the fourth tee he was sure of it. Despite the fact that he was in heaven, this hole might have been designed by the devil himself.

The fairway was perhaps forty yards wide with a dog leg in the distance. On the left was a gorge, the fairway ended abruptly, and beyond it was a vast nothingness; he could see clouds below it. A hooked ball was a goner.

"What happens to the ball if you hook it over the gorge?" Jessup said.

The boy's face was serious. "It goes all the way down," he said. "All the way."

"To the earth?" Jessup said.

And Jim Dolan shook his head. "All the way down."

Jessup took a second look and the clouds parted and he got a faint whiff of brimstone and saw a red glow burn madly for a moment.

"The only golf balls they get are the ones hooked over that gorge," the caddie said. "Poor devils."

Jessup placed his ball on the tee. On the right were the densest woods he had ever seen, and the fairway itself was sprinkled with traps. He took careful aim at a grassy spot between two traps and swung. He was afraid to look, and automatically he was reaching in his hip pocket for a second ball when the caddie said, "Nice shot."

And there was the ball, dead in the middle of the fairway.

They walked toward it and Jessup was shaking as though he had the ague, although it was as nice a day as a golfer could find, no breeze and not too hot, just warm enough to make a man's muscles feel loose.

They had almost reached the ball when they heard a sound in the woods to the right and a moment later a handful of dirt and pebbles came down out of the sky and then a ball dropped out of nowhere and landed in front of them.

Barnaby stopped and looked around at a lean lank figure coming out of the woods. He had a turned-down mouth and a bald and wrinkled pate and he was talking to himself. "By Saturn," he said, "by Venus, that was a shot."

Barnaby stared in amazement and then finally he found his tongue. "Pete Tyson, you old horsethief," he said.

"Well," Tyson cackled, "I never expected to see you here. What did you do, bribe the authorities?"

They shook hands and grinned at each other and then Tyson addressed his ball and he hadn't changed at all, Barnaby saw. Tyson wound himself into a pretzel until he was next door to strangling himself, then the club came down and the ball hopped across the fairway and disappeared over the edge of the gorge and down toward the licking red flames.

But his old partner had become philosophical, Barnaby had to admit that. "If it weren't for me," Tyson muttered, "they'd have a hell of a time down there." And he took another ball from his hip pocket, placed it on the turf and hit it toward the pin.

It was like old times playing with Pete Tyson, and Barnaby was so puffed up he could hardly wait to hit his ball. He could hardly contain himself, waiting to see the look on Tyson's face when he showed him how he was hitting the ball now.

Jim Dolan handed him a brassie and Barnaby stepped up and swung, and when he raised his head the ball was lying on the green. He turned and looked at his friend and waited for him to say something.

But Tyson hadn't even opened his mouth. He just grunted and moved on down the fairway, and Barnaby stared at him, his face getting red.

They went along to the green and Barnaby sank a forty-foot putt and he looked up, and still Tyson didn't say a word, and that was the last straw.

They went toward the next tee and Barnaby exploded. "Why don't you be a man?" he said. "I always knew I was the better golfer and now I've proved it. Why can't you be man enough to admit it? Just standing there and sulking like the cantankerous old goat you are."

"Hit the ball," Tyson growled. "If there's anything I hate it's a gabby golfer. You always did talk too much."

His face purple now, Barnaby stepped up without another word and hit the longest drive ever seen in the solar system. The ball went practically out of sight, then came down on the green and Jim Dolan handed him his putter.

And still Tyson's expression hadn't changed. Barnaby stood there, choking, while Pete hit his usual hundred-yard drive into the rough. They plodded along and Barnaby couldn't figure how Tyson had gotten up here, but it was obviously a mistake, and somebody had slipped up somewhere; some mix-up in the celestial filing system that probably explained it. And instead of being grateful Tyson was more ornery here than he'd ever been down below, which was saying a good deal. And maybe Tyson wouldn't admit it, but anyway, Barnaby was going to beat the tar out of him.

And he did. They finished the first nine and Barnaby totted up his score.

Pete Tyson said, "Gives me a sixty-three. Couple of bad holes, but I'll do better on the back nine. Let's have an ambrosia before we start out."

They walked up to the terrace and a waiter flew out with two tall and misty-looking glasses.

Barnaby put his score card down on the table. "I have a twenty-three," he said defiantly. "The caddie will vouch for it. I'll shoot about a forty-five for the eighteen."

He shoved the card under Tyson's nose, but the old goat just yawned and said nothing.

Barnaby sat there and told himself that he was the champion golfer of the universe. But somehow it left him cold, and suddenly he felt old and tired and even the ambrosia tasted flat. He sighed, put down his half-empty glass and got up slowly from the table.

"In a hurry?" Tyson grunted.

Barnaby said sadly, "Sorry, Pete, but somehow I don't feel so good. I'm going to turn in my clubs. Don't think I'll play any more golf." And he thought that even if Tyson had congratulated him, he still wouldn't want to play any more.

Pete's wise old eyes squinted up at him and he chuckled dryly.

"Barnaby, you old fool," he said, "I shot a forty-six myself the first round I played here. It's one of the house rules."

"House rules?" Barnaby said, bewildered.

"They let you have up here what you don't get below," Tyson said. "You always wanted to be a perfect golfer. So did I. But somehow, most of the residents prefer to go back to being themselves. You can make your choice."

Barnaby didn't have to think twice for the answer to that one. And suddenly the sun came out and his loneliness was gone and he was itching to get out on the tee again.

"Tell you what," Tyson said. "On this back nine I'll play you for the ambrosia at the nineteenth. I'll give you three strokes."

"You'll give me strokes!" Barnaby's face was purple again.

"You've gotten hogfat since I saw you," Tyson said. "And besides, I've had lessons from Macpherson."

"Sandy Macpherson is up here?" Barnaby said in a whisper, for his was a name to conjure with.

"And where else would he be?" said Tyson. "So it's only fair I give you strokes. I wouldn't take advantage of you."

Barnaby's jowls shook with his laughter. "You'll give me strokes! Do I look like a man takes candy from a baby! I never saw the day when I had to take strokes from a string bean of a man put together with baling wire. Strokes! Come on," he said. "I'm playing you even!"

"Man, you'll rue the day," said Tyson, and their scowls wavered for a minute and became broad grins as the love they had for each other came through.

The caddies came up and they hurried across to the tenth tee. "Start it off," Barnaby said. "Give me something to shoot at if you can."

Tyson wound up and he missed the ball on his first try and swung again and got himself bunkered behind the ladies' tee.

"If I couldn't do better than that," Barnaby chuckled, "I'd quit."

He took his stance and then saw a stranger watching him, a hawk of a man with a blade for a nose, a man with sandy red hair, and shrewd gray eyes, and a pipe in his mouth and a contemptuous dour look on his face.

"Meet Sandy Macpherson, our pro," Tyson said.

"Too bad we didn't meet earlier," Barnaby said. "I'd have liked a lesson from you, but I'll not be needing one now, for I've finally grooved my swing."

"Then swing, laddie, and dinna talk sae much," said Macpherson.

Barnaby waggled his club over the ball and ran over the rules in his mind and started back with the left hand and kept his eye on the ball and pivoted with the hips and shoulders and did everything according to the book—or so he thought. But there was a whooshing sound like a wet sock falling on a concrete floor and the ball blooped into the air and came down in a meadow to the right of the fairway.

"You'll have to hit another," Tyson cackled. "The Elysian fields are out of bounds."

Hit another he did, a topped dribbling shot and he turned to Sandy Macpherson.

"I'd better have a lesson tomorrow," Barnaby said. "I must have done something wrong."

"Something!" said Macpherson with a laugh like a rusty safe door opening. "Ye dinna keep yere head doon."

"No, sir," said Barnaby, humble and ashamed.

"Ye swing like an old witch wi' a broomstick."

"I suppose I do," Barnaby said meekly, bowing his head for shame.

"Hoot," said Macpherson, "I'll hae to throw yere game away, mon. I'll hae to start from scratch and see if there's aught to be done wi' ye. Ten o'clock sharp tomorrow."

"Yes, sir," said Barnaby, "I'll be there."

He grinned at Tyson, who was grinning back at him, and then started out to hunt for his ball in the Elysian fields, whistling a tune of his youth, and happy as a lark.

Fables for All Ages, Especially the ATOMIC

By ROBERT M. YODER

How Hamilcar Wilts Prepared for Everything and Got It

THERE never was a more careful man than Hamilcar Wilts. Hamilcar would have walked the streets of heaven keeping an eye cocked for falling cornices. Although the only river in his vicinity was two feet wide and looked badly in need of water, Hamilcar kept a rowboat on his roof in case of a flood. In the rowboat there was a raft, in case the boat leaked, and the raft's equipment included needles for sewing furs, in case Hamilcar was carried to the far north, and an auger for opening coconuts, in case he was carried to the tropics. There wasn't much against which Hamilcar wasn't prepared.

He had studied his neighbors carefully, and they seemed prudent people. The only daredevil in the block kept a few guppies, but they did not seem likely to run amuck. When Hamilcar got home, consequently, he could relax. He allowed nothing poisonous or inflammable; his medicine cabinet contained remedies for everything he might have encountered on the streetcar or in crowds, from measles to butter slicer's squint, which is a form of eyestrain affecting the pygmies who cut butter pats for restaurants. Once inside this fireproof stronghold, with plenty of fire extinguishers, lightning rods and an elephant gun, Hamilcar felt safe. He could rest warily, and sometimes sip a sterilized glass of boiled beer.

Eight miles across the city there lived a dolt named Boggle. Boggle was recuperating; he had tested what some scaredy cat told him at the factory—that it is dangerous to play catch with bottles of sulphuric acid while standing on a rickety stepladder with oil on your shoes. Bored at home, Boggle set out to open a can of gasoline with a blow torch. There was a quiet rustle, then a terrific "bam!" and the house blew apart. Boggle was thrown seventy feet into a warehouse filled with 4000 pillows, landing so gently that it barely knocked the ashes off his cigarette.

In Hamilcar's haven the explosion sounded like something happening in one of his trees. He hurried out. Boggle's stove, describing a perfect arc, hit Hamilcar just as he emerged. He saw something tumbling his way, but not clearly. With the lineman's gloves he was wearing in case of live wires, he couldn't pull off his bee veil in time. . . . Scientists said it was a combination of circumstances that wouldn't happen again in 543,000 years.

THE MORAL: The chances of getting eaten by a leopard on Main Street aren't one in a million, but once is enough.

How Hard Work Got an Eager Beaver Just What You'd Expect

ONCE upon a time there was an ambition-ridden clerk named Barnsether, who was determined to forge ahead by hard work and solid merit. "When opportunity knocks, I will be ready," he vowed. "In fact, I will put in a doorbell." Pleased with this remark, he filed it mentally, for a speech he would deliver sometime in the successful future to young men eager for his guidance.

Carefully studying the joint where he worked, he observed that the boss, a Mr. Dillhoughton, did not like arithmetic. It reminded Dillhoughton of his income tax and his alimony, and made him nervous. Barnsether practiced nights until he could make most certified public accountants look hesitant. And one day he found Dillhoughton staring glumly at a page of involved calculations. "Can I help with that?" said Barnsether.

"You sure can," said Dillhoughton, and a smile of gratitude wreathed the great man's mismated though avaricious features.

There worked in the same establishment a happy hayhead named Middlesworth, who looked upon work as the dull preface and unsuccessful sequel to lunch. His goal in life was to run 50,000 on the pinball game in the cigar store. He, too, knew that Mr. Dillhoughton was weak on arithmetic, but all this sloth did about it was to pad his expense account. "Pad" isn't the word; this baby's expense accounts were quilted. He put down sixty dollars for a moose call when visiting Mooseheart, Illinois, and forty dollars for carfare to Girlsie, which he explained was a suburb of Boise.

One day both young men were in Dillhoughton's private office with the mother-of-pearl push buttons, the rich leather chairs and the beautifully furnished secretary, when the Government asked for an immediate report on the working hours above thirty-three and one third put in by employees under thirty-five before taxes.

"Beats me," said the shiftless Middlesworth. "I have to use pencil and paper to figure out how many musicians it would take to play a cornet solo."

But Barnsether stepped forward. "I'll do it," he said.

"Bless you, my lad," said Dillhoughton. "We'll get out, to make sure you're not disturbed. . . . Come, Middlesworth, to some desolate golf course."

A few weeks later an opening developed for a new executive vice-president, and without a moment's hesitation Dillhoughton awarded the post to Middlesworth, in whom he had discovered a kindred soul having trouble with approach shots as well as mathematics. But in reward for his ability to do hard, painstaking work, Barnsether gets first crack at all the hard, painstaking work that comes along.

THE MORAL: Opportunity knocks but once, and it is pleasanter waiting on the country-club veranda.

To the Stars, and Back, With Launcelot Briggle

LAUNCELOT BRIGGLE regarded this as a world where it's dog eat dog, and it must be admitted that he had many natural qualifications for such a struggle. Girls limping home from the Junior Prom reported that Launcelot showed up in spiked shoes. It probably isn't true that in kindergarten the precocious tot was caught using loaded blocks. Still, when first told he could write a letter to Santa Claus, the happy tyke sent the butter-hearted old gentleman a six-page list of costly gifts, signing it "The Briggle Quintuplets." Even then, Launcelot was out to win. "A man's got to look out for himself," he was fond of saying.

In business, some doubted if Launcelot could have sold water to a slow-witted sponge. Still, he came up with many a good idea. This puzzled their real authors, especially before they learned that the slot marked "Suggestion Box" fed into Launcelot's office. Working with Robert Fulton, he would have given Fulton full credit for the steamboat whistle. And he would have borrowed your secretary to dictate a complaint that you were behind in your correspondence.

In brief, Launcelot was just a great big grown-up Teddy Bear, and his associates loved him like an open elevator shaft. Still, it worked. There came a day when only one rival stood in Launcelot's way, and Launcelot knifed him by mailing comic valentines to the board of directors from the fellow's suburb. Poor Charlie Smith, the victim, could find no job except a chancy one trying to interest the country in a ridiculous new idea called electricity. Launcelot felt a brief twinge of pity for Charlie's three kids, but as Launcelot always said, a man has to look out for himself. And Launcelot was clearly a success, in a sure-fire business, making a product people could never do without. Thinking how he had guaranteed his future, he smiled as brightly as one of the popular kerosene lamps his company made.

THE MORAL: The same Fate that can make you head bartender can bring in local option.

Why Lester Laches Quit Finishing People's Sentences

ONCE upon a time there was a man named Lester Laches who always knew what you meant. You might tell Lester that you ran out of cigarettes last night, but you'd get no further. "I know what you mean," Lester would say. "Just about drives you nuts. You wouldn't think smoking would be that important." Mention parking, and Lester knew what you meant. "You spend an hour looking for a place to park, so you can run a five-minute errand. Makes you grumpy all day." If your wife remarked it was sometimes pleasant to eat in restaurants, Lester knew what she meant too. "Nice to feel you can walk away and let somebody else wash those dishes."

A fun-loving man named Hamptrangle often visited Lester's city. He had told a girl named Miss Threnody Thrunk that he was a wealthy bachelor, intended to marry her, and would take her away to his big rayon plantation near Duluth. Miss Thrunk discovered one day that Hamptrangle was, in fact, a furniture salesman from Syracuse, where he had a wife and three children. This good-natured prank made Threnody as sore as a bee on a paper rose, and she set out to find the bounder. En route she bit a mounted policeman on the ankle and slugged a mailbox just to warm up. As she passed, radios missed a beat and chickens went to roost. Hamptrangle saw her coming and fled into a grocery store. Lester was telling the grocer what the grocer meant when he said he hated to wear new shoes. Seeing Hamptrangle stopped behind a display of dog food, he went right over. "Hiding from someone?" he asked.

"Blow," Hamptrangle whispered, "I'm ducking a babe, and this kid is trouble."

"I know what you mean," said Lester. "You want me to go away, so I won't give away your hiding place." It was the last time Lester ever interpreted other people's thoughts. For Threnody had spotted Hamptrangle in flight and let fly with a .32 as he sprinted for the icebox. Her aim was as bad as her intentions, and she missed him. But she drilled a No. 6 can of sliced pineapple, a box of soap flakes and Lester.

THE MORAL: A good man is hard to find, and if his girl discovers he was only kidding, he'd better be.

MR. DIGBY AND THE TALKING DOG

By DOUGLASS WELCH

SAVANT SAYS DOG THINKS, *ran the Daily Informer's headline.* ALEXANDER, SUPER-DOG, ASTONISHES PSYCHOLOGISTS. *The Informer's ace photographer just craved to catch the super-dog in a compromising position. He did —with results that not even the dog could foresee.*

OCTOBER 12, 1946

SAY," cried the eager young man with the camera, "aren't you Happy Digby, of the Central City Daily Informer?"

"Drop dead," said Mr. Digby.

"I guess you don't remember me, Mr. Digby. I'm Hack Harris, of the Bugle here."

"Beat it," said Mr. Digby.

"I met you over at the state fair at Waterville last year."

"Blow," said Mr. Digby. "You bother me."

"I've just been making some pictures of the mayor frying eggs on city-hall steps. Hot here today, isn't it?"

"Write me a letter," said Mr. Digby, "so's I can throw it away without I read it."

"What kind of a story are you covering here in Silverton?"

"I ain't going to tell you," said Mr. Digby.

"It must be pretty big or they wouldn't send you," said the eager young man. "I guess any time Happy Digby shows up on a story, it's a pretty big one."

"It's big, all right," said Mr. Digby. "It's so big you wouldn't understand it. It's so big I don't understand it myself."

"Gosh, I hope I don't get scooped in my own town."

"You got nothing to worry about," said Mr. Digby. "If you went back to your office with this one, they would prolly punch you right in the nose."

"Why don't we get out of this heat and have a beer somewhere? I'd like to talk to you about some of the great pictures you have made lately."

"I got to go," said Mr. Digby.

"What's the hurry?"

"I got to follow that dog which he just come out of the public library."

"You're kidding."

"All right, I'm kidding. Still I got to follow him."

"Say, wait a minute!" cried the eager young man. "I've seen that dog before! Or I've seen pictures of him! Your pictures, too! Isn't that Alexander the Great, the famous talking dog?"

"Could be," said Mr. Digby. "Could be."

"What's he doing here?"

"I don't know," said Mr. Digby. "I ain't

asked him. I am only supposed to follow him."

"But you must have brought him here!"

"I don't bring him nowheres," said Mr. Digby. "Him and me, we don't get along too good. I don't have nothing to do with where he goes. He just gets on the train at Squirrel Hill in the morning, and he gets off anywhere he takes a notion. Then he catches the afternoon train back home. Today he gets off at Silverton. Yesterday he got off at Barkerville. The day before it was Williams Lake. Me, I got nothing to say about it. I only follow him."

"As long as he's here in Silverton," said the eager young man, "I've got to get some pictures of him myself. I don't want to horn in on your story, but——"

"Go ahead," said Mr. Digby. "Who cares?"

"What places has he visited here already?"

"What's the difference?" said Mr. Digby. "You can make up any kind of a story you want. He ain't going to care. The only thing he wants is that you should mail him a clipping."

"What kind of a story are you going to tell your office about his being in Silverton?"

"I tell them the truth," said Mr. Digby.

"What's the truth?"

"I tell them he come over here to inspect the water system."

"The water system?"

"Yes," said Mr. Digby. "I tell them we go from one hydrant to the next."

Ordinarily, the dogs of that giant breed known as the St. Bernard are benign, easygoing, good-natured and, politically, well to the right of center. For a thousand years they have been trained to a tradition of truth and tolerance and helpfulness, and not one in a hundred thousand has ever sampled the juicy tenderness of a retreating letter carrier or barked at anyone but a burglar. Their mission in life, when not romping across Alpine snows with a portable bar, is to pose for pictures at dog shows with Chihuahuas.

In Central City there was, however, an atavistic St. Bernard which had no respect for the noble tradition, a sly and cunning animal with a subverted disposition and the social consciousness of a cutpurse. His habitual expression was that of a dog which had tarried too long the previous night at the corner bar, and his manner was in keeping. He was an intellectual dog, and, like many intellectuals, was disenchanted.

Alexander the Great was known to the city staff of the Central City Daily Informer and to the Informer's two hundred thousand readers as "The Talking Dog of Squirrel Hill." He did not, of course, actually talk in the sense that humans talk, but this was only because he saw no necessity for it. He possessed, or believed he possessed, an intelligence superior to that of most humans he had thus far encountered, and he simply preferred not to chitchat with what he regarded as inferior minds. He contented himself with making his wants and thoughts known by barking, howling and snapping, and by an extraordinary gesturing and posturing.

The readers of the Informer were told that Alexander could count up to ten even before he was weaned, and that by the time he qualified for an adult dog license he was solving the simpler algebraic equations such as x is to ten as six is to twelve. His master, the agent of the Squirrel Hill suburban station of the Pacific Great Western Railway, claimed that Alexander could make change, and that he could, on demand, extract the proper pasteboard from the ticket rack for any point on the division.

Alexander also served as train announcer at Squirrel Hill and seemed to know, when an oncoming train was yet a mile or two distant, whether it was a freight or passenger, and whether it would stop or roar on through. He had also been trained by the agent, a simple and incautious soul, to hoop up train orders to passing crews who took their instructions on the fly, and he did this from a tall stepladder which the agent would set up alongside the track,

When Alexander's superdog activities were first chronicled in the Informer, hundreds of letters poured in from readers; most of them in lavish praise of him, a few in criticism. Among these latter, not directed to the Informer but to the agent, was an indignant note from the general manager of the railway that Alexander's hooping-up of train orders was in direct violation of Interstate Commerce Commission regulations, and that, unless the dog immediately disassociated himself from matters of train operation, both he and the agent could start looking for other employment.

It was a moot question among members of the Informer's editorial staff as to who was the more disenchanted, Alexander the Great or Mr. Robert H. (Happy) Digby, whose permanent assignment it was to attend this remarkable animal and produce one good picture-feature story each week.

The editors of the Informer, to be sure, invested Alexander with none of the human qualities and capabilities claimed for him by his master and by the paper's professional dog-loving readers. They only cared that he made good copy and that the response was immense. The fact that Alexander always bit Mr. Digby whenever the two met bothered them not at all.

It had never been definitely established why Alexander took such a violent dislike to Mr. Digby, but it was often suggested that Alexander may have noted and been offended by Mr. Digby's conduct at dog shows. Mr. Digby had a way of remarking, and loudly, whenever he was assigned to attend a dog show, that the dogs looked a whole lot smarter than the people who were exhibiting them.

This infuriated exhibitors, as Mr. Digby intended it should, and the Informer always lost a considerable number of subscribers after each show. However, dog lovers could not follow the exploits of that wonder dog, Alexander, without reading the Informer, and sooner or later they would drift resignedly back.

City Editor Edward Wood tried to discover what deep-seated reason might lie behind his man's hostility toward dogs and dog lovers.

"I talked to Happy," he reported to the managing editor, "and, as nearly as I can make out, this thing is rooted in some personal controversy with his wife. It seems a neighbor's dog has more or less adopted the Digbys, and Mrs. Digby, I gather, makes quite a fuss over it. Happy says his wife calls it Itty Bittums or Itto Bitty and feeds it often from a chair at the dinner table. Happy became pretty grim as he told me about it, and I thought it best not to press him for details."

"All right," said the managing editor, "maybe he's got a reason, but tell him to button up his mouth hereafter when he goes to dog shows."

"Now, John," protested the city editor, "you know better than that. You know that nobody tells Happy anything. He's already quit twice this month, and I simply can't think up arguments enough to bring him back if he quits again. As long as the publisher thinks, as long as we all think, that Happy is the best news photographer in the Middle West, I don't much care what his opinions are or where he airs them."

"Okay," said the managing editor. "Say, by the way, what kind of a dog is this Itty Bittums?"

"A Chihuahua," said Mr. Wood.

Alexander the Great was yet a puppy when he and Mr. Digby met for the first time in the Informer's city room.

"Happy," said Mr. Wood, "I want you

to meet Mr. John Jarvis, the station agent at Squirrel Hill. This is his dog, Alexander. I think there is a good story for us here in Mr. Jarvis and his dog. Mr. Jarvis claims his dog can talk or that he at least can understand human conversation and bark a reply. He also claims that Alexander can count up to ten. Mr. Jarvis has given us a little demonstration, and I must say we are all astonished. It appears that Alexander really can count up to ten."

"If he's so smart," said Mr. Digby, "it ain't going to be no time at all before he's working on the city desk. That's all we need around here to make the joint perfect—a St. Bernard for city editor."

"What I want you to do, Happy," said Mr. Wood, "is to take Mr. Jarvis and Alexander out to the university and have that professor of psychology, old Doctor Wharton, examine Alexander and tell us whether Alexander really can understand what people say, whether he can actually think as humans think, and whether he really can count up to ten."

"Why don't you just have the dog call the professor up on the telephone?" said Mr. Digby. "Maybe they can work it out together, without no help from us."

"I'm thinking of the pictures," said Mr. Wood firmly.

"I give the dog my camera," suggested Mr. Digby, "and he can make his own pictures. Any dog as smart as him don't need no photographer around. Leave him go to the university and make his own pictures, and I will stay here and bark."

"Mr. Digby," said the agent, "I should like to introduce you to Alexander formally. We sort of think of Alexander, you know, as a—well, as another person."

"What do you want I should do?" demanded the photographer. "Get down on my hands and knees and exchange cards?"

"Just shake hands with him," said the agent. . . . "Alexander, this is Mr. Digby, a photographer. We are going with Mr. Digby and a reporter to the university to talk with a professor. Won't that be fun? I want you to shake hands with Mr. Digby, Alexander, and tell him how glad you are to make his acquaintance."

"Now I seen everything," observed Mr. Digby.

The dog left his master's side, approached Mr. Digby tentatively and sniffed his hand.

"He's waiting for you, Mr. Digby," urged the agent.

"I ain't going to do it," said Mr. Digby. "I done some silly, stupid things for this paper in my time, but I ain't going to get myself introduced to no dog. I got no time to be playing games."

Alexander the Great suddenly lunged, and his teeth closed over the photographer's forearm. Mr. Digby, startled, stepped back and tumbled over a desk.

"I am afraid you offended him by what you just said," the agent chided. "Alexander understands what people say, you know."

"I offended him!" screamed Mr. Digby. "He pretty near torn my arm out of the socket! How would you like a punch in the nose for you and him both?"

"Now, Happy," said Wood. "The dog's only a puppy, and he didn't hurt you. He was only playing."

"Say you are sorry, Alexander," commanded the agent. The dog barked twice, then sneered. "You see, Mr. Digby. He said he's sorry."

"It don't sound to me like he's sorry," said the photographer. "And he don't look like he's sorry, either. I never seen a dog with such a mean puss. Why ain't he hustling around outside with a barrel on his neck, like he's suppose to do, instead of coming into newspaper offices and counting up to ten?"

"That will do, Happy," said the city editor. "You had better get started for the university."

Doctor Wharton was an elderly and gentle scholar and a man of much dignity, preeminent in his field, the author of a six-volume work on behavioristic psychology which was acclaimed throughout the whole world of higher education. His patient research had won him honorary degrees from seven foreign universities. Now, at the peak of a brilliant career, he found himself staring into the face of a talking dog.

"But, gentlemen," he said, "I am not sure I understand. Exactly what is it you want of me?"

"All's we want, doc," said Mr. Digby, "is to grab off a shot of you asking this dog some questions."

"I do feel the university is under very great obligation to your newspaper," said the professor, "but really! I shall be laughed at from coast to coast. This sort of thing simply isn't done."

"We'll handle the yarn in a very scientific manner," the reporter said.

"I guess Alexander is probably the most intelligent animal you've ever seen, professor," said the agent proudly. . . . "Alexander, I want you to count up to ten for Doctor Wharton. Now, one . . . two . . . three . . ."

An expression of deep pain spread slowly over the scholar's face.

"Be looking right into his kisser while he's barking, doc!" commanded Mr. Digby. . . . "Okay, I got it. Now, how about another one, of you and him reading a book together?"

"I am sorry," said the psychologist, "but this is a good deal more than I bargained for. I shall be drummed out of the Faculty Club by noon tomorrow, at the very latest."

"Doctor," said the reporter, "do you think it is possible for an animal—a dog, say—to think like a human?"

"I think he is a very handsome animal," said Doctor Wharton. "Yes, very handsome, surely."

"But do you think he can think like a human?"

"I am sure he's a very intelligent dog too," said Doctor Wharton.

"But can dogs think?"

"I am sure I don't know," said the psychologist miserably. "There is very little literature on the subject."

"I heard about a professor once," offered Mr. Digby, "which he rang a bell and made a dog's mouth water. What do you say we get a bell and try a shot of that?"

"Gentlemen, please!" said Doctor Wharton. "I would far rather pose without my trousers."

"What about whether dogs can think?" persisted the reporter.

"I don't say it is impossible," said the professor, "but I do say it is highly improbable."

"But it is still possible?"

"In view of what is happening to me now," said Doctor Wharton, "I no longer feel that I can say anything is impossible."

"Well, okay, thanks," said the reporter. "We may want to do a follow-up story after this one. Will we be able to reach you here tomorrow?"

"No."

"Where will you be?"

"Far, far away," said Doctor Wharton. "In the hills. Hiding."

SAVANT SAYS DOG THINKS, the Informer told its readers the following day. ALEXANDER, SUPER-DOG, ASTONISHES PSYCHOLOGIST. " 'This is a good deal more than I expected,' said the distinguished Dr. Ernest K. Wharton. 'After what I have just seen, anything is possible.' "

And so Alexander made his public debut. Presently he was a fixture in the town's civic life and a familiar figure on its streets, to be pointed out to strangers. He carried baskets in his mouth and solicited funds for the Red Cross and the many veterans' drives, and he sold bonds. Sometimes he marched in parades and rose to his hind legs and saluted briskly as he passed the reviewing stand. He became the mascot of the ball team and a member of the mayor's official greeting committee.

In addition to his public appearances, Alexander managed in many other ways to impinge upon the public mind. He had his picture made smoking a pipe and reading the front page of the Informer with a knowing look, and he barked out an Informer comic strip to the kiddies every Sunday morning on a radio program. A few of the Informer's readers went quietly mad, but most of them read and reread every line, and saved all Alexander's pictures, for heaven knows what.

It was inevitable that a dog of Alexander's talents would someday find Central City too confining. When he took to boarding the morning train at Squirrel Hill and spending the day in communities a hundred miles or more down the line, Mr. Digby was not surprised, but he was outraged when the Informer directed him to accompany the great dog on all such excursions.

"How do I know where he's going to go or when he's going to go?" demanded the photographer. "It means I got to haul my pants over to the Squirrel Hill station every morning to see does he get on the train or doesn't he get on the train. And if he gets on the train, I got no idea where he will get off or when he is coming back. He don't tell nobody.

"And let me tell you something else, Wood!" screamed Mr. Digby. "Every time I go out of town with him, it means I get no lunch. He ain't interested in stopping at no restaurants for no lunch or even for a cup of coffee. He just puts his head into a butcher shop and barks or salutes or something, and the guy throws him a raw pot roast. He eats good and I eat nothing. I'm losing weight, and my ulsters are coming back."

"Can't you entice him into a restaurant while you have lunch?" asked the city editor.

"Listen to him!" shouted Mr. Digby. "I don't entice him nowheres. He don't want no part of me, ever, and he's always running down alleys or crawling under fences to throw me off."

"I am sorry it works out that way, Happy," said Wood, "but there isn't much we can do about it. Your pictures of him are the talk of the state, and there isn't a community within two hundred miles that isn't anxiously awaiting Alexander's first visit."

"You make just one little mistake when you say there isn't anything we can do about it," said Mr. Digby, "because there is something I can do about it, all right, and that is I can always go back to my old man's barbershop and help him lather up the customers and sweep the hair off the floor Saturday night, which is a lot better work than I get around here."

On the train one day Mr. Digby was approached by the conductor.

"Tickets, please."

"I got no ticket," said Mr. Digby.

"Where do you want to go?"

"I don't know where."

"If you don't know where you want to go," demanded the conductor, "why did you get on this train? If you stay on this train, you've got to make up your mind where you want to go, and you've got to have a ticket."

"I can't buy no ticket," screamed Mr. Digby, "until I know where I want to go! So you will have to wait and sell me a ticket when I get off!"

"Now, just a moment, my friend," said the conductor, reaching for the bell cord. "You either buy a ticket or get off now."

"All right," said Mr. Digby. "You sell me a ticket to the next station, and then you keep coming back and sell me tickets to each station that comes along next."

"Indeed I will not," said the conductor. "You make up your mind right this minute."

"Go ask that big dog sitting in the smoker," said Mr. Digby. "I get off where he gets off."

"You mean the dog of Mr. Jarvis, the agent at Squirrel Hill?" said the conductor. "What's he got to do with it?"

"I got to follow him around and grab off his picture."

"Why, you must be that photographer named Digby on the Informer!" said the conductor, beaming. "I want to tell you, Mr. Digby, how much my wife and I admire some of the pictures you have made of Alexander. We cut one of them out and had it framed, and we have it hanging in our living room. And the expression on that dog's face, Mr. Digby, I do declare I don't think I have ever seen——"

"Drop dead," said Mr. Digby.

Someday, the photographer promised himself, *I get even with that dog good. I grab off a shot which he is biting some blind man or looking over the transom into a powder room. I maybe even catch him chasing some cat up a tree which all the cat lovers in town they will scream their heads off when they see it.*

But until the night of the big pile-up at the Squirrel Hill station, Alexander the Great offered him no such opportunity; the big dog was too canny.

On the day he met the eager young man with the camera in Silverton, Mr. Digby arrived wearily home at nine o'clock in the evening. He was in an ill temper, and his first act, after shedding his clothes about the living-room floor and peeling down to his undershirt, had been to brush Itty Bittums, the gregarious Chihuahua, from a dining-room chair.

"Robert H. Digby!" shouted Mrs. Digby. "You stop slapping that nice little dog around, you great big bully, you! And you march right back into the living room and put your clothes on. You are not going to sit at my dining-room table half naked! And I'll tell you something else too. If you think for one moment that you can stomp into this house at this hour of night and expect short-order service like you would get in a restaurant, well, I'm going to tell you you're sadly mistaken, and, furthermore, I want to say if you think you can——"

"Shaddap," said Mr. Digby, "and bring me some supper."

At that moment, fortunately, the telephone jangled. It was Wood with an urgent summons.

"Happy," he said, "I want you to get right out to Squirrel Hill. There's a big story there. A train wreck of some kind, and the agent telephoned us a minute ago that——"

"What's the matter with the night man?" demanded the photographer. "Why ain't you send him? Listen, Wood, I ain't eat anything since seven o'clock this morning, and I ain't even eat my dinner yet. I have to follow that blasted creeping dog clean to Silverton and back today, and I don't feel like going to Squirrel Hill or nowhere else."

"I would send the night man, Happy," said Wood, "except that Alexander is involved in this. Jarvis says the dog was a hero tonight, and that's in your department."

"Look, Wood," said Mr. Digby, struggling to be patient. "I ain't got my hero camera with me tonight. You probably ain't going to believe this, but do you know something? Any picture I grab off of Alexander tonight is going to look just like any other picture I made of him, so all's you got to do is go into the morgue and find a shot I made before and have the artist draw the word 'Hero' on it, and you got it."

"No, I'm afraid not, Happy," said Wood. "I want a picture of Alexander against the wreck as a background. It's too late to send a reporter out there tonight, so we'll cover it by telephone. And it's too late to use your pictures tonight, so we'll use them Wednesday morning. Try to pick up some additional details for a follow-up story to run with your art, will you?"

"I ain't have to pick up any details," said Mr. Digby. "That Alexander, he is pro'ly writing a by-line story hisself right this minute."

"Here's all we know about it so far, Happy: It seems there was a freight stopped at the depot, and Alexander began barking loudly and tugging at somebody's coat, and finally he managed to convey the idea that another freight was coming up behind. So they got the first train started and had it moving about ten miles an hour when the second train hit them. It gave the head-end crew of the second train time enough to slow down to the point where they could jump off."

"Why, that ain't hardly nothing at all," said Mr. Digby sourly. "I thought at first, the way you was talking, that maybe Alexander get into one of them engines and start it off hisself."

Mr. Digby grimly made his way through the wreckage west of the station to the depot platform, where Alexander, the agent, the crews of the two trains, the general manager and half a hundred wide-eyed and delighted Squirrel Hill folk awaited the arrival of the wrecking crew.

"Smartest dog I ever see," said one of the engineers, fondly stroking Alexander's head. "If we had listened to you when you first told us, there wouldn't have been any wreck at all."

"Never mind that!" said the general manager savagely. "What I want to know is how does a thing like this happen? . . . Why are you stopped here," he said to the first engineer, "and why didn't you whistle back your flag when you stopped? . . . And why"—he turned to the second engineman—"why did you come booming in here when you knew there was a movement a few minutes ahead of you?"

"Because I got a green eye on the board here," said the second engineer smugly. "That's why."

"The board is always green at this time of night!" snapped the general manager. "The station is closed and the operator is off duty, and he always leaves it green, and you know it!"

"Yea, I know that," said the engineer, "but I saw it go to green from red. The board was working. I figured they wouldn't drop it to green from red unless the first section had already gone through."

"It couldn't have cleared from red to green!" stormed the general manager. "The station was closed, the agent was upstairs in his quarters!"

"All I know," said the engineer, "is that we were back there on the hill, about two mile, I figure, and I spotted a red eye on the board here. Bill Hawkins, my fireman, he called out 'Red eye,' too. So I gave her a service application, figuring to come in here slow for a stop. And then, while we were watching and wondering why the station was open, we got a green eye. I figure the first section has already gone through. We get down on the flats, we can't see the board any more because of the trees, and I didn't see the markers on his caboose until we come around that curve back there."

"And how do you account for the fact that the board is working in a station that is closed, when the operator is upstairs asleep?"

"I don't try to account for it. I just know what I saw."

"And what's your story?" said the general manager to the first engineer. "Let's see if you can make it better than his."

"When I come in here," said the first engineer, "the board is against me, red. I know the station is closed, but the rules say I can't proceed until the board is cleared. So we stop and back up and get the agent down. He's got no idea why it's red. So we're talking, and the dog barks and warns us something is coming along behind, the agent clears the board, and I get out of here as fast as I can. But I got to pump off my brakes first, and I can't pick up seventy-eight cars under my arm, you know, and start running with them. It takes time. And I did whistle out my flag. He started walking back, and he was watching the board all the time over his shoulder, and when he saw the agent clear it for us, he turned around. What I figure happened, Mr. Eldridge, is this: I figure when the agent cleared the board for me, the crew back on the hill naturally figured he cleared it for them."

"You are sure you left the board green tonight when you went off duty?" the general manager asked the agent.

"I certainly did, Mr. Eldridge," protested Jarvis. "I always clear the board, and then I walk outside and look at it to make sure. And Number Thirteen went through here twenty minutes after I closed, and they didn't stop, so the board must have been green for them."

"What kind of a lever have you got in there?"

"One of the oldest kinds on the system," said the agent. "It works in a slotted casting in the floor. I have been after them for five years to give me a modern one of the wall or ceiling type, but, no, they've always got some better place to spend the money."

Mr. Digby had heard enough. The hour was late, and the mechanics of railroad signaling and station-block systems interested him not at all.

"I ain't got time to listen to any more of this double talk," he announced. "Some of you dummies stand out of the way while I grab off a shot of them engineers shaking hands with the dog."

"There will be no pictures made around here tonight," said the general manager. "And I will ask you to leave railroad property at once."

"If you spend a little more time worrying about how to keep your trains on the track and not running into each other," suggested the photographer, "you ain't have to worry so much about somebody making a picture of what a lousy railroad you got."

"Are you looking for trouble?" demanded the general manager.

"Why, no," said Mr. Digby. "I don't never go looking for trouble, but I don't never run away from it, neither. Do you maybe figure on trying to make me a little?" He set his camera down.

"Take this man and throw him out of here," said the general manager to a wrecking-crew foreman who had just come up with his gang.

"This is something," said Mr. Digby joyously, "which I got to see!"

For once, the constitutional guaranty of freedom which the press traditionally enjoys was flagrantly infringed. Mr. Digby was seized, battered, booted and dragged on the seat of his trousers over a good quarter mile of the Pacific Great Western's rock-ballasted right of way, and tossed into a drainage ditch. The photographer made a frightful uproar throughout the process, and managed to inflict semipermanent injuries on at least four of his assailants. Alexander, meanwhile, romped alongside, barking deliriously. It was the hysterical quality in the dog's voice which Mr. Digby first recalled when he regained consciousness. The beating he dismissed as one of the natural hazards of his profession. But Alexander's frenzied delight he couldn't forget.

"I go back and get my camera," he muttered grimly as he crawled up the embankment, "and then I measure that no-good dog for a rug. I teach him a trick he ain't learned yet. I give him a little boost and I teach him to jump clean over the depot."

The crowd had left the platform and

had gone down the track to watch the wrecking crew—all but the general manager and another man, who stood talking, with their backs turned, near Mr. Digby's camera. The photographer crept along the front of the station and paused in the deep shadow of the operator's bay. And then, out of the corner of his eye, through the windows of the dimly lit bay, he saw a remarkable thing. He saw Alexander, the wonder dog, alone, with the signal lever in his teeth, cunningly disengage the lever and let it back from the green to red position. And overhead outside the counterweighted board responded by moving slowly up and gleaming brightly red. Perhaps Alexander had learned to do this by observation, perhaps his incautious master had once taught him to do it on command. Almost at once the dog drew the lever back again and notched it into the green position. Then he stood off and proudly wagged his tail.

Mr. Digby did not at first entirely comprehend what he had just witnessed, and then the enormity of it struck him.

"How d'ya like that," he muttered. "A train wrecker! A no-good, dirty low-down train wrecker!" He paused and began to chuckle. "And me," he said, "I'm just a natural-born stool pigeon. This I tell all over the joint."

Mr. Digby stepped out of the shadow toward the general manager. The dog, suddenly aware of him, barked and raced for the waiting-room door.

"Say, Eldridge," began Mr. Digby, "I think maybe I can tell you something about that train wreck. I think maybe I got the answer you been looking for."

The general manager wheeled. "I thought I had you thrown out of here once tonight!" he screamed. "When I tell you to go, I mean to go!" and he kicked out impulsively, not at Mr. Digby, but at Mr. Digby's camera. There was a sickening crash of broken glass. Mr. Digby lunged, but Alexander got there first.

Whatever his master's superiors might choose to do to Mr. Digby as an individual bothered the great dog not at all. But here before his very eyes was a man reducing to wreckage the instrumentality through which Alexander had become a celebrity, the device that had caused his likeness to be reproduced, to be admired, to be clipped out and treasured in a hundred thousand homes. The superintelligent dog, outraged, sprang at the general manager's throat. Eldridge, falling, rolled over on his stomach and face, and the dog, relinquishing his hold, turned his attention to a more expansive and prominent target. He bit wisely and deep, then backed away with the entire seat of the official's trousers.

Stunned and bewildered, Mr. Digby helped the general manager's companion pull the animal away. The general manager raced madly out of the station yard, calling loudly over his shoulder, "Joe, you'd better drive me to a doctor and have him look at this and give me a shot! I might get hydrophobia!"

Alexander the Great, still growling, picked up the broken camera and laid it at Mr. Digby's feet.

"How d'ya like that!" said Mr. Digby. "This I saw, but I don't believe! This, it couldn't happen!"

And suddenly Mr. Digby, despite his better judgment, felt a wave of compassion for the big dog. For the first time he saw Alexander as he really was—an animal of sound instincts and capable of the finer feelings. Maybe, he reasoned, Alexander had never wanted to be a superdog; it had been forced on him. Maybe he had only wanted to bury bones and chase cats and be a dummy like other dogs.

The station agent, puffing wildly, came running up. "Who was fooling with that semaphore lever?" he demanded. "I was down there at the wreck and I was looking up this way, and I saw it go red, then green again."

"I got something to tell you," said Mr. Digby, "and you ain't going to like to hear it, but it's something you really ought to know. And it's just between us. I don't tell nobody else."

Briefly he recounted what he had seen through the bay window, and Alexander's attack upon the general manager. The agent was horror-stricken.

"I just can't believe Alexander would do a thing like that," he said slowly. "What will people say when they hear he caused a wreck?"

"Maybe they hear how he bit Eldridge," said Mr. Digby, "but they don't have to find out about the signal unless you tell them yourself, because I give Alexander a break. I don't tell nobody."

"Mother," said the station agent to his wife the next morning, "we've got to give Alexander away. We've got to give him to somebody who loves him and will give him a good home."

"Itty Bittums, eat up the nice custard," said Mrs. Digby.

"Ah, shaddap," said Mr. Digby. "Stop talking to that mouse like he was some kid."

"Don't you dare tell me to shut up, Robert H. Digby!" said Mrs. Digby. "I'll have you understand that I don't have to take that kind of talk from you. And, furthermore, any man who comes home the way you did early this morning, with his clothes all torn and dirty, and your camera smashed—— I suppose you were fighting somewhere again, and probably drinking——"

"Shaddap and answer the doorbell," said Mr. Digby.

"Get up and answer it yourself," she said.

Mr. Digby rose reluctantly from his chair. Standing on the porch outside with his nose stoutly pressed into the doorbell was the superdog, Alexander the Great. As the photographer opened the door, he saw a car pull away from the front of the house, in it the station agent and his wife.

Alexander walked with stiff dignity through the front hall and paused briefly at the entrance to the living room. Hung from a loop of string about his neck was a note addressed to "My New Master." Alexander gave Mrs. Digby and the Chihuahua in her lap a brief scrutiny, then bared his teeth and growled. With two leaps the little dog was out the nearest open window and legging it for home. Mrs. Digby rose abruptly and stood on the davenport. In every line of Alexander's bearing there was evidence of his immediate distaste for her and everything she probably stood for.

"Robert H. Digby!" she shouted. "You get that big, nasty brute out of here."

"Well, come in, big boy!" said Mr. Digby jovially. "Come in and make yourself to home!"

Many an overworked housewife would like nothing better than to strike while the iron is hot.

—THOMAS A. GOODER.

HOW I PUT DOWN THE REDSKINS

By J. H. PECK, M.D.

§ *Somebody had to save the white settlers. After the big Victory dance in the pool hall they felt too bad to be scalped. Here's the story of a white Medicine Man—and a Utah hero—who braved danger armed only with dried peaches.*

OCTOBER 23, 1948

NOBODY ever asks me if in my days in Western Utah I ever fought Indians. This is discouraging, for I figured in what I believe was the last expedition against the Indians. As a matter of fact, I commanded the expedition, with the full force and authority of the United States Government behind me, and it was just like the movies, with some exceptions.

In the movies, the expedition is a detachment of cavalry, led by a poor but handsome hero on a horse. My expedition was led by a doctor—myself—and the commander's wife insisted on going along, not to be at her hero's side in time of danger, but to see about a bassinet the Indians were making for her. You can tell a movie hero, in a scene of this sort; he looks like a hero. I looked like a visiting grocery salesman, for I had to begin by passing out dried peaches. Just the same, it was a real Indian uprising, and probably the last of those dramatic events. It was my mission to persuade the Indians not to invade the valley below and scalp the white settlers. We white men had five of the Indian chiefs as hostages. This made us unpopular with their followers, though popular with the chiefs; there was a strong chance they would refuse to go home if we let them loose. I will set out the details of this insurrection with some care to show what we pioneers, of about 1918, put up with. It also shows what the Indians put up with.

Those were hopeful days, and a construction company was building a railroad branch from the Western Pacific at Wendover, Utah, to the little town of Gold Hill, Utah, so that when Gold Hill became a great mining district it could pour its wealth out to the world, and vice versa. Gold Hill had 150 inhabitants and could sneer at towns like Callao, which had only about thirty-five. In a sixty-mile circle around Mt. Ibapah—there's where the action is going to take place—you wouldn't have rounded up more than 500 people, white or Indian. At least 200 of them were Indians, living on the mountain in the Goshute Indian Reservation. Goshute is not a bad pun, although it may seem so as this narrative unfolds. At any rate, there you have Gold Hill: 150 people, a copper mine, a train twice a week to Wendover, a telephone line to the same city. For company there were coyotes, all rabied, and liquor was available fifteen miles away across the Nevada state line. The map said the famous Lincoln Highway went through our county. During July and August it did, anyway, and you could get over it, if it didn't rain.

The war was under way in Europe—World War I—but we in Gold Hill were keeping calm about it, even when we heard anything about it. Two or three of the young men had volunteered, and I was waiting my call to the Medical Corps. A far livelier topic was the copper boom. Brokers back East were advertising mining shares at rock-bottom prices, and to show they were on the level, they organized excursions to let the investors see the ore itself. The Gold Hill owners had the job of making these visits interesting. They did this one day before the excursion arrived by scattering a load of peacock copper ore, which is as beautiful as the name implies, around on the mine dump. The bait was carefully picked up and stored in a safe place when the investors left, and the town was somewhat split on the ethics of this. Some maintained that the investors should be allowed to take the samples home with them. This would have involved getting a new load for the next sale, however, instead of using the same one over, and the conservative element prevailed.

It was into such peaceful surroundings that word came one day that the Indians on the Goshute Reservation had been ordered to register for the draft, and I was ordered to go examine them. Everybody thought this very funny—I don't know why—except the Indians, and it made them sore. They were wards of the Government, which means they were stepchildren. They couldn't vote, they had no say in the management of their community. The agent furnished by the Indian Department decided everything. They were the same as white men in only one respect: if they had sheep that they pastured on Government land, they had to pay the same fee. Otherwise the agent ran the tribe and paid the Indians for the work he assigned them; it was one long 1918 version of the WPA.

Well, the Indians got a lot of orders from Washington through the agent, and the orders never seemed to make much sense, so they decided to disregard this new one, like the rest. They said that if we didn't want our canoes sunk in the ocean, we should keep them out of there, and when it was pointed out that they were supposed to go kill Germans they said they had never seen one. A German was a man across the ocean who was against our Government, it was explained. In that case, the Indians said, he had their sympathy; so were they. But the Indian agent had a German name, and they made a generous counteroffer. In case it was open season on Germans, they would kill this one for nothing.

The case involved a total of from three to four Indian boys of draft age, and that's all, but when the news of their insurrection reached Washington, it threw our national leaders into a worse case of jitters than if Stalin had been found working in Oak Ridge. The Interior Department appealed to the War Department. The War Department, in turn, issued orders to the 20th Infantry, then stationed at Fort Douglas, Utah. The 20th was to organize an expedition and go up the mountain and stamp out this rebellion and arrest the chiefs, all five of them. The 20th was alerted, and volunteers were called for, for a hazardous mission which was also top secret, probably on the theory it would play havoc with the nation's morale, on the off-chance that anybody heard about it.

A hundred brave or bored men volunteered, and they found out what "hazardous" meant; they all got frostbite.

The local whites, except me, were not told about the expedition, because their sympathy was all with the Indians. As a draft doctor, I was a Government employee. So I was given the job of securing local transportation for the troops. Then, too, being on the end of the telephone line, I could notify the agent in time for him to get out. To get automobiles, I told people another trainload of suckers was coming in from Pittsburgh to buy coppermine stock. Everyone was glad to assist in swindling the city slickers, so I had plenty of cars. When the suckers arrived, and turned out to be infantrymen, I was the subject of many unkind remarks. But I was on my way to warn the agent.

History chooses unfortunate times of the year for her big moments, and it was bitter cold—in fact, it was the coldest day of a cold February. I was proceeding by a Model T, the top of which had been removed a few nights earlier by a hungry burro. To drive the Model T up the mountain, I had to keep it in low gear, naturally, and the wind whistling in around the clutch froze my foot about the same time the radiator froze. I was five miles from my destination, but a rancher named Kelly volunteered to go on by horseback. We removed the radiator, put it behind Kelly's kitchen stove to thaw, and I took up a position out in the road. The idea was to prevent any wandering Indians from passing. Some of them were camped in the valley. It was the idea that seeing so many cars coming down the mountain pass in one night—an unusual sight, too—would alarm them, and one Indian might slip up to the reservation and give the alarm that the troops were coming. So, with a borrowed deer rifle, I stood guard. It was two o'clock in the morning, in a mountain pass 7000 feet high, with a thirty-mile wind blowing and the temperature near forty below zero. That is a fine time to meditate, but even so, I could not figure what I would do if an Indian appeared. They were my friends and patients, so I couldn't shoot one. On the other hand, I couldn't let one pass. So it was a relief to see the cavalcade of nearly frozen soldiers approaching while Kelly and the agency people rode down from the other direction.

The campaign was a complete success. By daylight, all the chiefs were rounded up and warrants had been read to them. To think how many soldiers it took to capture them made the prisoners feel very good, and so did the prospect of a trip to Salt Lake City with free meals. The expedition's return trip was without incident, except for frosted noses and ears, and was made enjoyable by a stop at the Sheridan ranch, where the ladies of the valley had prepared breakfast for the whole army.

Well, it hadn't exactly been a battle, but it was an occasion, and what do you do on an occasion? You give a party. In our absence, the wives of Gold Hill had taken over the town's biggest building, the pool hall, and waxed the floors. They were giving a big post-Christmas, pre-Easter Victory Ball, celebrating the fact that their husbands had gone up the mountain and got down again without falling. A fiddler came in after a swell supper, and we had Gold Hill's first dinner dance. Refreshments for the evening included one wash boiler full of coffee, two washtubs of sandwiches, and a bountiful supply of a drink known locally as panther milk.

The beauty and chivalry of Gold Hill was there, just like in the poem by Lord Byron, and the lamps shone o'er fair women and brave men. The evening was a striking success. About three A.M. the local bootlegger grew too confused to mix any more of his compound, but the general store leaped into the breach with a case of lemon extract. The troops performed bravely; although they had had no sleep the night before, they stayed up all night, eating and dancing. The only shortage was that of women; there weren't enough to give every man a dancing partner. Some deep thinker proposed a solution: "Let's get the Indians out of jail and put skirts on them." It was given serious consideration, but vetoed. They were prisoners, and it was felt that the Government had not gone to all this expense just to take the chiefs to a fancy-dress ball. Besides, a drunken Indian in some lady's old housecoat would be too much of a good thing. We compromised by taking them coffee and sandwiches so they, too, could celebrate their arrest.

Morale was high as this party came to a close. You could not blame us for feeling that if the rest of the nation handled its assignments as efficiently as we had handled the Gold Hill, Utah, branch of World War I, then victory was a cinch. But the next morning there came dire news. It was a bad morning for it, too, for Gold Hill was in no shape to be solving any more of the Federal Government's problems. But a runner brought word from Ibapah that the 195 Indians left there had thought things over and were upset about our snitching their chiefs. They thought some of burning down the agency buildings and then going down into the valley to get themselves some hostages, as we had done. The warpath, you see. Luckily, we had the Army still on hand, so we turned the whole problem over to the soldiers. They said no. Their orders were to capture the chiefs. This they had done. Their orders said nothing about hanging around to prevent scalping. Thanks for a strenuous evening. Now they were going home.

Somebody ought to do something. A council of war was held, and some great tactician had a brilliant idea. There was one man, he figured, the Indians weren't sore at. That man had been warming his feet in Kelly's kitchen when the chiefs were arrested. If that man had a hang-over, what of it? He was a doctor, wasn't he? So I was elected the Great White Father. Furthermore, I would get fifty dollars mileage from the Government. So I was the logical hero. I needed that fifty dollars too.

Before leaving on this suicidal mission, I interviewed the captives and asked if there was any word they wanted taken to their wives. They had just eaten bacon and eggs, dried-peach pie and coffee, and were in a fine frame of mind. The Army would have had far more trouble losing them than they had had capturing them. The chiefs said they wished their loved ones could have some of those delicious dried peaches. When the male population heard this, it was unanimously voted to buy out all the dried peaches in the store and to warn the merchant firmly against ever stocking them again. We were pretty tired of dried peaches, and besides, the store cat used them for a bed.

I was not allowed to be a hero single-handed. The lone wolf's wife had to tag along. The Indians were making a bassinet for her, out of willow reeds and buckskin, and she wanted to see how they were doing. Her brother came along, too, bearing his shotgun. There were some warm springs on the road and he hoped he might attack a mallard stopping to warm its feet. That is a pretty dastardly trick in that kind of weather, come to think of it. I also had the press along. A reporter from the Salt Lake Tribune got left on purpose when the other newspaperman went home with the troops. He went with me in the forlorn hope there'd be some news.

I was not slain or even scalped upon arrival, and distributed the peaches among the five grieving wives. All the Indians turned out for a mass meeting. They are just as big hams as their white brother, and here was a chance to sound off before a reporter and get their names in the paper. Well, they talked all day. But the principal speaker was Antelope Jake, the tribal wise man. He was about ninety years old and as wrinkled as my dried peaches. I am sorry to say he did not wear a feather bonnet and war paint.

He wore a pair of blue jeans like the rest. But after talking to his tribesmen, he gave me a neat summary of local opinion.

"The white medicine man," he said, "is good to come and comfort us while we are in trouble and our hearts are sad. But many years ago, when Jake was a little boy, the white soldiers come and say, 'You must fight no more. Live on the reservation and the Government will take care of you. Fight and you will go to jail and break rocks. Even if your neighbor steals your pony or your wife, you must not fight him. Come and tell the agent.' All of Jake's life the Goshute have been peaceful. Never have we gone on the warpath. Now the white soldiers put our big men in jail because we don't fight. White men must be crazy."

I have had a good many years to think this over, and I grow more and more persuaded that A. Jake had something there. In fact, when, in later years, I had to act as peacemaker in hospital-personnel squabbles, I used to wish I had old Jake along. I was saved by the dinner bell. Ladies of the tribe —this was one of the eatingest engagements I ever took part in—broke up the gabble to say firmly that dinner was on the table. That took the first bravery on my part. They called it rabbit stew, but I knew that one of their favorite dishes was stewed ground squirrel.

It came my time to talk. I told them the whole thing probably was a mistake. It was, too; the Indians of draft age enlisted and served with honor in that war, as their sons did in this one. I said the absent chiefs probably would be home within ten days. And I added a little white lie: I told the chiefs' wives that the peaches came from their husbands, instead of the male population of Gold Hill. That was a mistake. Husbands don't send gifts home unless they are having a good time. The chiefs' wives glared.

The purpose of the expedition was to save the settlers in the valley. Not a settler was scalped, so the expedition succeeded. I wish I could say that the Indians agreed reluctantly to spare the white men's lives, won by my oratory. The fact is, they were so busy hamming for the reporter that they didn't mention it. They didn't even show any interest in keeping me as a hostage, although I was already on hand. So I gathered up my expedition and went home. I learned later that I had done the chiefs a dirty trick. It took the courts two weeks to discover that there was no reason to detain them, and the chiefs didn't get home in the ten days I predicted. They didn't get home for seventeen. I don't know the Goshute words for "Where were you those other seven days, you bum?" but I know what kind of reception was accorded them.

One Indian told me the chiefs applied to the Army to be readmitted into custody, for a little peace, but this Indian was not reliable. No reliable man would tell narcotics agents from Salt Lake, as he did, that a bale of marijuana found in his bedroll was used only for bath salts.

My wife got the bassinet, anyway, and that was a success; after it served its white papoose, it did duty for many years as a clothesbasket. The soldiers who captured the chiefs went on to war, and since then their sons have fought another one in foreign lands, and are worried about a third. About the only thing that stands up just as well today as it did then is that remark of Antelope Jake's. "White men," he said, "must all be crazy."

THE CASE OF THE MISSING SOURCES

By ***DICK ASHBAUGH***

§ *Due to the confusion on Capitol Hill these days, the so-called "informed sources" seem to have mysteriously vanished.*—News Item.

AUGUST 10, 1946

STOPPING casually at the solid mahogany door, I flicked a speck of dust from the name plate. "Frederick Foame," it said and, underneath, the simple words, "Criminal Investigator."

Entering the lush suite, I padded softly to the desk where my secretary, Woo Woo Higginbottom, a ravishing blonde fresh out of high school, sat buried to her wrists in a Ouija board. "What goes, Gorgeous?" I asked, chucking her under the chin and taking a fast saddle Oxford on the ankle.

"Plenty," she said huskily. "The outer office crowded with clients, the Andrews Sisters singing in the powder room and a man in the hall named Eli Whitney who says he invented the cotton gin."

"Make 'em wait," I yawned.

I glided through the steel door of my private office, and shot the bolt. The thin man seated stiffly in the love seat looked vaguely familiar.

I narrowed my eyes to mere slits and then opened them again because I couldn't see a thing. "Strudel, the T-man!" I gasped. "How did you get past my secretary?"

"Came as the mailman. Women are suckers for a uniform."

"Okay," I said, "make it snappy."

"You're coming to Washington, Foame," he said, and his voice was like chipped marble.

"What's the pitch, Strudel?" I asked, reaching in my jacket pocket, where I keep a change of expression.

Woo Woo came in with my morning coffee. "Here you are, chief," she said adoringly. "All sugared and stirred and saucered and blowed."

"It's blown, Woo Woo," I said. "Get your notebook."

Strudel spoke rapidly, "Strange doings in the nation's capital, Foame," he said. "First we began to notice little things. The Washington Monument gone, the roof missing from the Senate, street signs changed; then, last week, seals in the Tidal Basin."

"Odd, but not highly suspicious," I said. "Go on."

"Key figures began to disappear. First it was the Informed Circles, then the Informed Sources. Now they're getting the Usually Reliable Sources. Last week, four of them vanished without a trace."

There was a moment of dead silence, broken only by the click of Woo Woo's eyelashes. "Pack our bags, Woo Woo," I said quietly. "We're going to Washington."

The minute we walked out of the Union Station, I knew we were being followed. "We're being followed, Woo Woo," I said tensely. "Small man in a belted burberry. Take out your compact and case him."

"It's Strudel," she said shortly. "He's just slipped on an Indian headdress and melted into the crowd."

"He's tailing us," I said. "We've got to have a free hand. You duck around that Southern senator standing over there. I'll meet you on the other side and we'll make a break for a cab." She was gone, leaving a faint trace of mimosa.

Speeding into the city, I slipped on a false beard and Woo Woo changed her nail polish. We passed Strudel once, tearing in the opposite direction, fighting the driver with one hand and holding the flag down with the other.

Claggett, chief of the Bureau of Sources, met us at the inner door of his office. "Glad you could come, Foame," he said. He was a big man with a florid face. He was worried.

"I am worried, Foame," he said. "Not so much about the Reliable Circles—they're a dime a dozen. But last night"—he lowered his voice—"last night an Informed Source Close to the White House received a threatening note."

Woo Woo drew a sharp breath. "We're not playing with kids, chief," she said.

"Any clues?" I asked Claggett.

He pulled out a drawer of his desk. "Only the usual," he said. "Bobby pins, lipstick, two kinds of face powder, notebook, tire-repair kit, jade cigarette holder, chewing gum, keys, coin purse, check stubs that don't balance and—er—this." He held up a filmy object with lace inserts.

I lowered my eyes, but Woo Woo crossed rapidly to the desk. "Nightgown," she said. "Size fifteen, and a beauty. Never been worn. Price tag still attached. This collection could only have come from a woman's purse, chief."

"It means one thing," I said. "We've got to find the woman in Washington carrying an empty purse." Woo Woo looked at me with fright in her eyes. "Any suspects?" I asked Claggett.

I ran down the list he handed me. "Kitty O'Toole, Government girl. Hotsauce Holden, a model. Olga Hammerschlager, an eyelet trimmer. Henrietta Helsingsfors, a simple peasant girl. Bring them to my hotel," I said. Claggett nodded grimly, and we were gone.

We had adjoining rooms at the hotel. I paced the floor deep in thought while Woo Woo tried the gadgets. "Look, chief," she said, "ice water!"

I said, "Yes," and turned at a knock on the door. "Come in," I barked, and wasn't sorry.

Hotsauce Holden—for I knew it was she—crossed the room slowly, placing one shapely ankle before the other. Her footprints in the deep carpet behind her trailed little wisps of smoke. She wore a smoke-blue cocktail dress, carried a smoking cigarette in a jade holder and surveyed the room with smoky gray eyes.

I measured the distance to the fire extinguisher and managed a slight smile. "You've a nerve, Miss Holden," I said, "coming here alone."

"Alone my smoky gray eye," she said. "There are eight marines waiting in the lobby, a sugar baron in the bar, and two Indian princes dueling in the corridor. I've got men to burn."

I moved backward and turned off the steam radiator. "Where are the rest of them?" I asked. "Kitty O'Toole, Olga Hammerschlager, Henrietta Helsingsfors?"

"Mere pawns," she said. "Innocent children caught in the mad whirl of power politics."

"Okay," I snapped. "Out with it. Obviously you've come to make a clean breast of the affair. What do you know of the disappearance of the Informed Sources?"

"I know everything about the Informed Sources," she said. "I am the woman with the empty purse."

"Take this down, Woo Woo," I said. "It's a confession."

"Yes," she said wearily. "It's a confession. It was revenge I wanted. You see, my brother was a radio commentator. A shy, lovable boy—all the family I have. When he first came to Washington he did very well with his radio program, and then he fell among Usually Reliable Sources. From there, he sank lower and lower. Next it was Occasional Sources, and then Rumors. Next it was Unidentified Spokesmen, and then Cocktail Bars and Doormen. He was through——" Her voice broke.

"Come, come," I said quietly and patted her shoulder.

At the desk, Woo Woo's pencil point snapped. "Oh, fudge!" she said.

"I vowed revenge," continued Hotsauce. "One by one, I lured the Reliable Sources to a deserted estate across the river. You'll find them there—locked in the basement." She was silent for a moment. "Well," she said, "that's it. What are you going to do with me?"

"Tear up the confession, Woo Woo," I said, "and get Claggett on the phone. There's no case here. . . . You may go, Miss Holden," I said.

She stood up, swaying slightly toward me. "I'll never forget you," she said and started a long, smoldering glance. In a flash, Woo Woo threw herself between us, taking the full force of the look. I was unhurt but shaken as I heard the door close.

"Someday," said Woo Woo, "you're going to get one of those right in the kisser."

As the German Prisoner Said . . .

A *POST* WAR ANECDOTE

SOMEWHERE in Germany just before V-E Day a gang of German prisoners, enlisted men, were put to repairing a road rendered impassable by bombing. The American officer immediately in charge explained carefully to them how the repairs were to be made, then left to perform other duties.

Some time later, another American officer came along, paused to observe the repair work, ended by expounding his theories on how the job should be done, and went his way. By and by, a third officer came strolling by, stopped curiously to see what was going on, and finally gave a discourse on how he thought the repair problem should be solved.

When the third counselor was safely out of earshot, one of the prisoners tore off his cap, cast it vehemently on the ground, and cried out in high emotion, "Damn it to hell! They're all alike, no matter what army they're in!"

—JANE SAWYER.

A Child's Garden of Curses;

or, The Bitter Tea of Mr. P.

THERE is nothing like a farm, a mountain lodge or a seashore bungalow to bring out the latent mechanic in a man. Once the deed is filed and he stands alone at last with his utilities, he is Cortez on a peak in Darien. Of course, if your name is Cortez and you live on a peak in Darien, Connecticut, your problem is simple. You call in a plumber from Danbury and forget about it. I couldn't; when I returned to the soil, I had a ten-cent screwdriver and the mechanical skill of a turtle. Today, thanks to unremitting study, I can change a fuse so deftly that it plunges the entire county into darkness.

The neighbors call me "the boy Steinmetz" and things like that (the other things are shorter). The power company has offered me as high as fifteen thousand dollars a year to stay out of my own cellar.

The other night, for example. I had invited some guests to dinner at Hysteria Hall and we were grouped around the groaning board. The board was groaning because one end was supported by a chair until I could replace the missing caster. Halfway through the meal, a strident clanking began under our very feet, as though somebody were striking the furnace with a length of chain. I raised my voice to drown it out, but I could see my audience was woolgathering. At first I suspected my wife, who will resort to the most shameless devices to spoil an anecdote. Then I realized she was flinching in concert with the company as the noise redoubled. "Sounds like chains, doesn't it?" I stammered desperately. "You know, this house was a station on the Underground Railway, and there's an old legend——"

I was interrupted by a bubbling effect, as of water seeping through a dining-room floor, and looked down to find an inch or two of moisture lapping at my oxfords. Before I could explain that we had chosen a low, marshy situation to remind us of the English lake country, my wife rose through a jet of live steam like the devil in Faust and placed a monkey wrench beside my plate. I pretended it was part of the meal, a pantomime which threw my guests into gales of silence, and slunk off into the cellar.

As one who flunked trigonometry four times, it took me only a moment to detect the source of the trouble.

That little square business on the electric pump—I forget just what they call it—had worked off. This in turn disengaged the stopcock or the bushing (it was a bit too dark to tell which) in such a way that the hot water was feeding into the coal bin instead of the storage tank, or flange. The whole thing was clearly the work of a master criminal, perhaps Professor Moriarty himself, who had further anticipated my movements and laid a carpet sweeper athwart the stairs. I sidestepped neatly, but my head encountered a low rafter and I sustained a trifling bruise no larger than a robin's egg; in fact, by contrast with a robin's egg that chanced to be lying on a shelf, it was almost tiny. Luckily, I am as tough as nails, and picking myself up at the bottom of the steps, I set to work. By exerting a slight leverage, I succeeded in prying off the gasket, or outer jacket of the pump, exactly as you would a baked potato. I describe this simply so that even the layman can understand. This gave me room to poke around the innards with a sharp stick. I cleaned the pump thoroughly, laid all the different wheels and cams on a board where the plumber could find them and, as a final precaution, opened the windows to allow the water to drain off down the slope.

On the way upstairs, I found my passage blocked by a jug of peach brandy, and after some difficulty managed to squeeze past it. Either it was stuffy in the basement or I had given too freely of my strength, for when I rejoined the party, I felt dizzy. My wife said later it wasn't so much the bric-a-brac I smashed as the language I used. It cost me a quart of perfume to square the rap, to say nothing of a new electric pump. However, the old one was nearly played out. Anybody could have seen it with half an eye—and I had that.

—S. J. PERELMAN.

Squaw Trouble

RECENTLY we recovered from Camp Wa-Wa-Natchee (Girls, ages 8-15) a nine-year-old daughter, who had successfully completed the summer season.

This shy, winsome child was torn from the arms of her parents sometime last June, her clothes properly marked and her buttons reinforced with fine steel wire. Yesterday a tanned, long-legged blonde walked in, casually dropped a hand-stitched leather rucksack and looked around. "How," she said. "What's the word from Glocca Morra?"

"Where are the rest of your clothes?" asked her mother faintly.

"Here," said Diana the Huntress, producing an odd plaid object from her bag. "They sort of fell apart, so I made 'em into a throw rug. It's for my room."

"Thanks," said her mother vaguely. "What about your shoes and the more solid objects?"

Blithely ignoring the question, she plunged again into the rucksack and unreeled presents. A pickled grass bath mat, a small wood-burning fireplace, a corncob peace pipe and several dozen beaded articles. "Woodcraft," she said absently, and handed them around in the manner of an early Hudson Bay trader. "Guess I'll scout the reservation," she added, vaulting lightly through an open window, and leaving behind a parchment scroll proclaiming that henceforth she should be known as "Daughter of the Moon, Nakomis."

Twenty minutes later, while I was quietly choking over the peace pipe, my wife swept back into the room. "Moonchild won't come in for lunch," she announced. "We have to beat on a drum of dried skins."

"She can starve," I roared, a thoroughly aroused paleskin.

"You starve her then," said my squaw, backing ignominiously toward the kitchen. "She's out on the back porch with a hatchet. Says more air should be let into the place."

The porch was empty, but from the rear of the garage the pale column of a campfire climbed into the air.

"Cooking out?" I asked casually.

"Ugh," she replied, without looking up.

"Message came by runner short while ago," I remarked. "Party named Poodles asked where you were. Said tribe meeting at movie this afternoon. First hundred kids get free bubble gum."

Silently she arose, watching me narrowly, and then slipped around the corner of the garage. In exactly eight minutes, something in sweater and skirt flashed by. "Creepers," I heard her say as she disappeared up the street. "Free bubble gum!"

"What was that?" asked my wife in fright.

"Moonchild," I said, carefully depositing the peace pipe on the campfire behind the garage. "She's back in the groove."

—DICK ASHBAUGH.

TALLEYRAND PENROD

By BOOTH TARKINGTON

§ If you don't know Booth Tarkington's Penrod, you are about to meet a boy millions hold in a fond affection that few characters ever have aroused. The townspeople refer to "that Schofield boy!"—with an exclamation point—and Penrod's parents may sigh with relief when he finally gets to bed, but basically Penrod is a very fine person. You'd like to have him around, and quite probably, under another name, you have.

JUNE 21, 1913

"ONE-TWO-THREE; one-two-three—glide!" said Professor Bartet, emphasizing his instructions by a brisk collision of his palms at "glide." "One-two-three; one-two-three—glide!"

Round and round the ballroom went the seventeen struggling little couples of the Friday afternoon dancing class. Round and round went their reflections with them, swimming rhythmically in the polished, dark floor—white and blue and pink for the girls; black, with dabs of white, for the white-collared, white-gloved boys; and sparks and slivers of high lights everywhere as the glistening pumps flickered along the surface like a school of flying fish. Every small pink face—with one exception—was painstaking and set for duty. It was a conscientious little merry-go-round.

"One-two-three; one-two-three—glide! One-two-three; one-two-three—glide! One-two-th—— Ha! Mister Penrod Schofield, you lose the step. Your left foot! No, no! This is the left! See—like me! Now again! One-two-three; one-two-three—glide! Better! Much better! Again! One-two-three; one-two-three—gl—— Stop! Mr. Penrod Schofield, this dancing class is provided by the kind parents of the pupilses as much to learn the manners-s of good societies as to dance. You think you shall ever see a gentleman in good societies to tickle his partner in the dance till she say Ouch? Never! I assure you it is not done. Again! Now then! Piano, please! One-two-three; one-two-three—glide! Mr. Penrod Schofield, your right foot—your right foot! No, no! Stop!"

The merry-go-round came to a standstill.

"Mr. Penrod Schofield and partner"—Professor Bartet wiped his brow—"will you kindly observe me? One-two-three—glide! So! Now then—no; you will please keep your places, ladies and gentlemen. Mr. Penrod Schofield, I would puttickly like your attention; this is for you!"

"Pickin' on me again!" murmured the smoldering Penrod to his small, unsympathetic partner. "Can't let me alone a minute!"

"Mister George Bassett, please step to the center," said the professor.

Mr. Bassett, aged eleven, complied with modest alacrity.

"Teacher's pet!" whispered Penrod hoarsely. He had nothing but contempt for George Bassett. The parents, guardians, aunts, uncles, cousins, governesses, housemaids, cooks, chauffeurs and coachmen, appertaining to the members of the dancing class, all dwelt in the same part of town and shared certain communal theories; and among the most firmly established was that which maintained George Bassett to be the best boy in town. Contrariwise, the unfortunate Penrod, because of some dazzling and Quixotic but disastrous attempts to control forces far beyond him, had been given a clear title as the worst boy in town. But, as the population was considerably over one hundred thousand, there must have been any number of boys wholly unknown to this circle, wide as it was; hence it is possible that neither estimate was exact.

"Miss Rennsdale will please do me the fafer to be Mr. George Bassett's partner for one moment," said Professor Bartet. "Mr. Penrod Schofield will please give his attention. Miss Rennsdale and Mister Bassett, obliche me, if you please. Others please watch. Piano, please! Now then!"

Miss Rennsdale, aged eight—the youngest lady in the class—and Mr. George Bassett one-two-three-glided with consummate technic for the better education of Penrod Schofield. It is possible that amber-curled beautiful Marjorie Jones felt that she, rather than Miss Rennsdale, might have been selected as the example of perfection—or perhaps her remark was only woman.

"Stopping everybody for that boy!" said Marjorie.

Penrod, across the circle from her, heard distinctly—nay, he was obviously intended to hear; but over a scorched heart he preserved a stoic front. Whereupon Marjorie whispered derisively in the ear of her partner, little Maurice Levy, who wore a pearl pin in his tie.

"Again, please, everybody—ladies and gentlemen!" cried Professor Bartet. "Mister Penrod Schofield, if you please, pay puttickly attention! Piano, please! Now then!"

The lesson proceeded. At the close of the hour Professor Bartet stepped to the center of the room and clapped his hands for attention.

"Ladies and gentlemen, if you please to seat yourselves quietly," he said; "I speak to you now about tomorrow. As you all know—— Mister Penrod Schofield, I am not sticking up in a tree outside that window! If you do me the fafer to examine I am here, insides of the room. Now then! Piano, pl—no, I do not wish the piano! As you all know, this is the last lesson of the season until next October. Tomorrow is our special afternoon; beginning three o'clock, we dance the cotillon. But this afternoon comes the test of manners-s. You must see if each know how to make a little formal call like a grown-up people in good societies. You have had good, perfect instruction; let us see if we know how to perform like societies ladies and gentlemen twenty-six years of age.

"Now, when you are dismissed each lady will go to her home and prepare to receive a call. The gentlemen will allow the ladies time to reach their houses and to prepare to receive callers; then each gentleman will call upon a lady and beg the pleasure to engage her for a partner in the cotillon tomorrow. You all know the correct, proper form for these calls, because didn't I work teaching you last lesson till I thought I would drop dead? Yes. Now each gentleman, if he reach a lady's house behind some other gentleman, then he must go somewhere else to a lady's house, and keep calling until he secures a partner; so, as there are the same number of both, everybody shall have a partner.

"Now please all remember that if in case—— Mister Penrod Schofield, when you make your call on a lady I beg you please remember that gentlemen in good societies do not scratch the back in societies as you appear to attempt; so please allow the hands to rest carelessly in the lap. Now please all remember that if in case—— Mister Penrod Schofield, if you please! Gentlemen in societies do not scratch the back by causing frictions between it and the back of their chairs either! Nobody else is itching here. I do not itch! I cannot talk if you must itch. In the name of Heaven, why must you always itch? What was I saying? Where—ah! the cotillon—yes! For the cotillon it is important nobody shall fail to be here tomorrow; but if any one should be so very ill he cannot possible come he must write a very polite note of regrets in the form of good societies to his engaged partner to excuse himself—and he must give the reason.

"I do not think anybody is going to be that sick tomorrow—no; and I will find out and report to parents if anybody would try it and not be. But it is important for the cotillon that we have an even number of so many couples, and if it should happen that some one comes and her partner has sent her a polite note that he has genuine reasons why he cannot come, the note must be handed at once to me, so that I arrange some other partner. Is all understood? Yes. The gentlemen will remember now to allow the ladies plenty of time to reach their houses and prepare to receive calls. Ladies and gentlemen, I thank you for your polite attention."

It was nine blocks to the house of Marjorie Jones; but Penrod did it in less than seven minutes from a flying start—such was his haste to lay himself and his hand for the cotillon at the feet of one who had so recently spoken unamiably of him in public. He had not yet learned that the only safe male rebuke to a scornful female is to stay away from her—especially if that is what she desires. However, he did not wish to rebuke her; he wished simply and ardently to dance the cotillon with her. Resentment was swallowed up in hope.

The fact that Miss Jones' feeling for him bore a striking resemblance to that of Simon Legree for Uncle Tom, deterred him not at all. Naturally he was not wholly unconscious that when he should lay his hand for the cotillon at her feet it would be her inward desire to step on it; but he believed that if he were first in the field Marjorie would have to accept. These things are governed by law.

It was his fond intention to reach Marjorie's house even in advance of herself, and it was with grave misgiving that he beheld a large automobile at rest before the sainted gate. Forthwith, a sinking feeling ensued inside him as little Maurice Levy emerged from the front door of the house.

" 'Lo, Penrod!" said Maurice airily.

"What you doin' in there?" inquired Penrod.

"In where?"

"In Marjorie's."

"Well, what shouldn't I be doin' in Marjorie's?" returned Mr. Levy indignantly. "I was inviting her for my partner in the cotillon—what you s'pose?"

"You haven't got any right to!" protested Penrod hotly. "You can't do it yet."

"I did do it yet!" said Maurice.

"You can't!" insisted Penrod. "You got to allow them time first. He said the ladies had to be allowed time to prepare."

"Well, ain't she had time to prepare?"

"When?" Penrod demanded, stepping close to his rival threateningly. "I'd like to know when——"

"When?" echoed the other with shrill triumph. "When? Why, in mamma's sixty-horsepowder limousine automobile, what Marjorie came home in with me! I guess that's when!"

An impulse in the direction of violence became visible upon the countenance of Penrod.

"I expect you need some wiping down," he began dangerously. "I'll give you sumpthing to remem——"

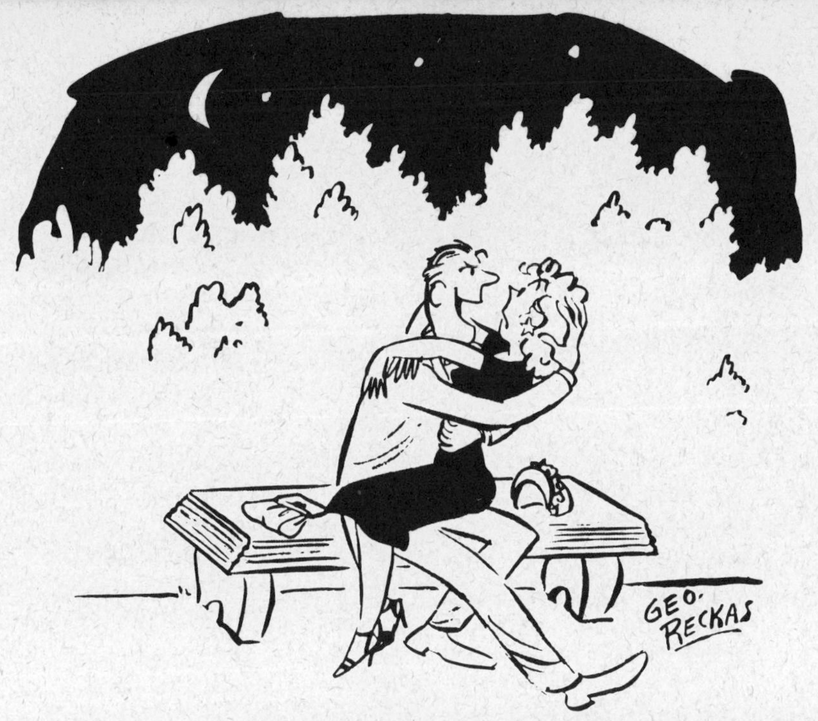

"So much for Ronald Coleman. Now I'll show you the same scene as Charles Boyer would do it."

"Two quarts of milk, a pint of cream . . . and the rest is rather personal, if you don't mind."

"Hey, *thou*!

" 'If A makes $75 and B spends $100 . . .' ask your mother to help you; this is right down her alley."

"... and that's Charlie Harris, the only unmarried man in the office."

"Why, yes—I think we can use a man in the middle west."

"And also, it was *whiter* when we were kids."

"I see we've been linked romantically."

"Oh, you will!" Maurice cried with astonishing truculence, contorting himself into what he may have considered a posture of defense.

"Let's see you try it, you—you itcher!"

For the moment defiance from such a source was dumfounding. Then, luckily, Penrod recollected something and glanced at the automobile.

Perceiving therein not only the alert chauffeur but the magnificent outlines of Mrs. Levy, his enemy's mother, he maneuvered his lifted hand so that it seemed he had but meant to scratch his ear.

"Well, I guess I better be goin'," he said casually. "See you t'morrow!"

Maurice mounted to the lap of luxury, and Penrod strolled away with an assumption of careless ease which was put to a severe strain when, from the rear window of the car, a sudden protuberance in the nature of a small, dark, curly head shrieked scornfully:

"Go on—you big stiff!"

The cotillon loomed dismally before Penrod now; but it was his duty to secure a partner and he set about it with a dreary heart. The delay occasioned by his fruitless attempt on Marjorie and the altercation with his enemy at her gate had allowed other ladies ample time to prepare for callers—and to receive them. Sadly he went from house to house, finding that he had been preceded in one after the other. Altogether his hand for the cotillon was declined eleven times that afternoon on the legitimate ground of previous engagement. This with Marjorie scored off all except five of the seventeen possible partners; and four of the five were also sealed away from him, as he learned in chance encounters with other boys upon the street.

One lady alone remained; he bowed to the inevitable and entered this lorn damsel's gate at twilight with an air of great discouragement. The lorn damsel was Miss Rennsdale, aged eight.

We are apt to forget that there are actually times of life when too much youth is a handicap. Miss Rennsdale was beautiful; she danced like a première; she had every charm but age. On that account alone had she been allowed so much time to prepare to receive callers that it was only by the most manful efforts she could keep her lip from trembling.

A decorous maid conducted the long-belated applicant to her where she sat upon a sofa beside a nursery governess. The decorous maid announced him composedly as he made his entrance.

"Mr. Penrod Schofield!"

Miss Rennsdale suddenly burst into loud sobs.

"Oh!" she wailed. "I just knew it would be him!"

The decorous maid's composure vanished at once—likewise her decorum. She clapped her hand over her mouth and fled, uttering distinctly indecorous sounds. The governess, however, set herself to comfort her heartbroken charge, and presently succeeded in restoring Miss Rennsdale to a semblance of that poise with which a lady receives callers and accepts invitations to dance cotillons. However, she continued to sob at intervals.

Feeling himself at perhaps a disadvantage Penrod made offer of his hand for the morrow with a little embarrassment. Following the form prescribed by Professor Bartet he advanced several paces toward the stricken lady and bowed formally.

"I hope," he said by rote, "you're well, and your parents are in good health. May I have the pleasure of dancing the cotillon as your partner t'morrow afternoon?"

The wet eyes of Miss Rennsdale searched his countenance without pleasure and a shivering sob wrung her small shoulders; but the governess whispered to her instructively and she made a great effort.

"I thu-thank you fu-for your polite invu-invu-invutation; and I ac——" Thus far she progressed when emotion overcame her again; she beat frantically upon the sofa with fists and heels. "Oh, I *did* want it to be George Bassett!" she lamented tearfully.

"No, no, no!" said the governess, and whispered urgently, whereupon Miss Rennsdale was able to complete her acceptance.

"And I ac-accept wu-with pu-pleasure!" she moaned, and immediately, uttering a loud yell, flung herself face downward upon the sofa, clutching her governess convulsively.

Somewhat disconcerted, Penrod bowed again.

"I thank you for your polite acceptance," he murmured hurriedly; "and I trust—I trust—— I forget. Oh, yes—I trust we shall have a most enjoyable occasion. Please present my compliments to your parents; and I must now wish you a very good afternoon."

Concluding these courtly demonstrations with another bow he withdrew in fair order, though thrown into partial confusion in the hall by a final wail from his crushed hostess:

"Why couldn't it be anybody but him!"

Next morning Penrod woke in profound depression of spirit, his Saturday ominous before him. He pictured Marjorie Jones and Maurice, graceful and light-hearted, flitting by him fairylike, loosing silvery laughter upon him as he engaged in the struggle to keep step with a partner about four years and two feet his junior. It was hard enough for Penrod to keep step with a girl of his size.

The foreboding vision remained with him, increasing in vividness, throughout the forenoon. Nevertheless he was able to take some interest in an amateur drug store in the storeroom of the empty stable, whither he bent his gloomy footsteps after breakfast. . . . It was the habit of Penrod's mother not to throw away anything whatsoever until years of storage conclusively proved there would never be a use for it; but a recent housecleaning had ejected upon the back porch a great quantity of bottles and other paraphernalia of medicine, left over from illnesses in the family, during a period of several years. The débris Della, the cook, had collected in a large market basket, adding to it some bottles of flavoring extracts that had proven unpopular in the household; also old catsup bottles, a jar or two of preserves gone bad; various rejected dental liquids—and other things. And she carried the basket out to the storeroom in the stable.

Penrod, communing silently with his wistful dog, Duke, in the storeroom, was at first unaware of what good fortune had come his way. Chin on palms, he sat upon the iron rim of a former aquarium and stared morbidly through the open door at the checkered departing back of Della. It was another who saw treasure in the basket she had left.

Mr. Samuel Williams, aged eleven, and congenial to Penrod in years, sex and disposition, appeared in the doorway, shaking into foam a black liquid within a pint bottle, stoppered by a thumb.

"Yay, Penrod!" the visitor gave greeting.

"Yay," said Penrod with slight enthusiasm. "What you got?"

"Lickrish water."

"Drinkin's!" demanded Penrod promptly. This is equivalent to the cry of "Biters" when an apple is shown, and establishes unquestionable title.

"Down to there!" stipulated Sam, removing his thumb to affix it firmly as a mark upon the side of the bottle—a check upon gormandizing that remained carefully in place while Penrod drank. This rite concluded, the visitor's eye fell upon the basket lately deposited by Della. He emitted tokens of pleasure.

"Looky! Looky! Looky there! That ain't any good pile o' stuff—oh, no!"

"What for?"

"Drug store!" shouted Sam. "We'll be partners——"

"Or else," Penrod suggested, "I'll run the drug store and you be a customer——"

"No! Partners!" insisted Sam with such conviction that his host yielded; and within ten minutes the drug store was doing a heavy business with imaginary patrons. Improvising counters with boards and boxes, and setting forth a very druggish-looking stock from the basket, each of the partners found occupation to his taste—Penrod as salesman and Sam as prescription clerk.

"Here you are, madam!" said Penrod briskly, offering a vial of Sam's mixing to an invisible matron. "This will cure your husband in a few minutes. Here's the camphor, mister. Call again! Fifty cents' worth of pills? Yes, madam. There you are! Hurry up with that dose for the nigger lady, Bill!"

"I'll tend to it soon's I get time, Jim," replied the prescription clerk. "I'm busy fixin' the smallpox medicine for the sick policeman downtown."

Penrod stopped sales to watch this operation. Sam had found an empty pint bottle and, with the pursed lips and measuring eye of a great chemist, was engaged in filling it from other bottles. First, he poured into it some of the sirup from the condemned preserves; next some extinct hair oil; next the remaining contents of a dozen small vials cryptically labeled with physicians' prescriptions; next some remnants of catsup and essence of beef; then what was left in several bottles of mouthwash; after that a quantity of rejected flavoring extract—topping off by shaking into the mouth of the bottle various powders from small pink papers, relics of Mr. Schofield's influenza of the preceding winter.

Sam examined the combination with concern, appearing unsatisfied. "We got to make that smallpox medicine good and strong!" he remarked; and, his artistic sense growing more powerful than his appetite, he poured about a quarter of the licorice water into the smallpox medicine.

"What you doin'?" protested Penrod. "What you want to waste that lickrish water for? We ought to keep it to drink when we're tired."

"I guess I've got a right to use my own lickrish water any way I want to," replied the prescription clerk. "I tell you, you can't get smallpox medicine too strong. Look at her now!" He held the bottle up admiringly. "She's as black as lickrish. I bet you she's strong all right!"

"I wonder how she tastes?" said Penrod thoughtfully.

"Don't smell so awful much!" observed Sam, sniffing the bottle—"a good deal though!"

"I wonder if it would make us sick to drink it?" said Penrod.

Sam looked at the bottle thoughtfully; then his eye wandered, fell upon Duke, placidly curled up near the door, and lighted with the advent of an idea new to him, but old, old in the world—older than Egypt!

"Let's give Duke some!" he cried.

That was the spark. They acted immediately; and a minute later Duke, released from custody with a competent potion of the smallpox medicine inside him, settled conclusively their doubts concerning its effect. The patient animal, accustomed to expect the worst at all times, walked out of the door, shaking his head with an air of considerable annoyance, and opening and closing his mouth with singular intensity—and so repeatedly that they began to count the number of times he did it. Sam thought it was sixty-nine times, but Penrod had counted seventy-one before other and more striking symptoms appeared.

All things come from Mother Earth and must return—Duke restored much at this time. Afterward he ate heartily of grass;

and then, over his shoulder, he bent upon his master one inscrutable look and departed feebly to the front yard. Perhaps he felt he would stand a better chance for convalescence there.

The two boys had watched the process with warm interest.

"I told you she was strong!" said Mr. Williams proudly.

"Yes, sir—she is!" Penrod was generous enough to admit. "I expect she's strong enough——" He paused in thought, and added: "We haven't got a horse any more."

"I bet you she'd fix him if you had!" said Sam. And it may be that this was no idle boast.

The pharmaceutical game was not resumed; the experiment upon Duke had made the drug store commonplace and stimulated the appetite for stronger meat. Lounging in the doorway, the near-vivisectionists sipped licorice water alternately and conversed.

"I bet some of our smallpox medicine would fix ole P'fessor Bartet all right!" quoth Penrod. "I wish he'd come along and ask us for some."

"We could tell him it was lickrish water," added Sam, liking the idea. "The two bottles look almost the same."

"Then we wouldn't have to go to his ole cotillon this afternoon," Penrod sighed.

"There wouldn't be any!"

"Who's your partner, Pen?"

"Who's yours?"

"Who's yours? I just ast you."

"Oh, she's all right!" And Penrod smiled boastfully.

"I bet you wanted to dance with Marjorie!" said his friend.

"Me? I wouldn't dance with that girl if she begged me to! I wouldn't dance with her to save her from drowning! I wouldn't da——"

"Oh, no—you wouldn't!" interrupted Mr. Williams skeptically.

Penrod changed his tone and became persuasive.

"Look here, Sam," he said confidentially. "I've got a mighty nice partner, but my mother don't like her mother; and so I've been thinking I better not dance with her. I'll tell you what I'll do; I've got a mighty good sling in the house, and I'll give it to you if you'll change partners."

"You want to change and you don't even know who mine is!" said Sam, and he made the simple though precocious deduction: "Yours must be a lala! Well, I invited Mabel Rorebeck, and she wouldn't let me change if I wanted to. Mabel Rorebeck'd rather dance with me," he continued serenely, "than anybody; and she said she was awful afraid you'd ast her. But I ain't goin' to dance with Mabel after all, because this morning she sent me a note about her uncle died last night—and P'fessor Bartet'll have to find me a partner after I get there. Anyway I bet you haven't got any sling—and I bet your partner's Baby Rennsdale!"

"What if she is?" said Penrod. "She's good enough for *me!*" This speech held not so much modesty in solution as intended praise of the lady. Taken literally, however, it was an understatement of the facts and wholly insincere.

"Yay!" jeered Mr. Williams, upon whom his friend's hypocrisy was quite wasted. "How can your mother not like her mother? Baby Rennsdale hasn't got any mother! You and her'll be a sight!"

That was Penrod's own conviction; and with this corroboration of it he grew so spiritless that he could offer no retort. He slid to a despondent sitting posture upon the doorsill and gazed wretchedly upon the ground, while his companion went to replenish the licorice water at the hydrant—enfeebling the potency of the liquor no doubt, but making up for that in quantity.

"Your mother goin' with you to the cotillon?" asked Sam when he returned.

"No. She's goin' to meet me there. She's goin' somewhere first."

"So's mine," said Sam. "I'll come by for you."

"All right!" Penrod sighed again.

"I better go before long. Noon whistles been blowin'."

"All right!" said Penrod dully.

Sam turned to go, but paused. The Schofields' house occupied a corner lot, and a new straw hat was peregrinating along the fence near the two boys. This hat belonged to some one passing upon the sidewalk of the cross-street; and the some one was Maurice Levy. Even as they stared he halted and regarded them over the fence with two small, dark eyes. Fate had brought about this moment and this confrontation.

"'Lo, Sam!" said Maurice cautiously. "What you doin'?"

Penrod at that instant had a singular experience—an intellectual shock like a flash of fire in the brain. Sitting in darkness, a great light flooded him with wild brilliance. He gasped!

"What you doin'?" repeated Mr. Levy.

Penrod sprang to his feet, shook the bottle with stoppering thumb, and took a long drink with histrionic unction.

"What you doin'?" asked Maurice for the third time, Sam Williams not having decided on a reply.

It was Penrod who answered.

"Drinkin' lickrish water," he said simply, and wiped his mouth with such delicious enjoyment that Sam's jaded thirst was instantly stimulated. He took the bottle eagerly from Penrod.

"A-a-h!" exclaimed Penrod, smacking his lips. "That was a good un!"

The eyes above the fence glistened.

"Ask him if he don't want some," Penrod whispered urgently. "Quit drinkin' it! It's no good any more. Ask him!"

"What for?" demanded the practical Sam.

"Go on and ask him!" whispered Penrod fiercely.

"Say, M'rice!" Sam called, waving the bottle—"Want some?"

"Bring it here!" Mr. Levy requested.

"Come on over and get some," returned Sam, being prompted.

"I can't. Penrod Schofield's after me."

"No, I'm not," said Penrod reassuringly. "I won't touch you, M'rice. I made up with you yesterday afternoon—don't you remember? You're all right with me, M'rice."

Maurice looked undecided. But Penrod had the delectable bottle again and, tilting it above his lips, affected to let the cool liquid purl enrichingly into him, while with his right hand he stroked his middle façade ineffably. Maurice's mouth watered.

"Here!" cried Sam, stirred again by the superb manifestations of his friend. "Gimme that!"

Penrod brought the bottle down, surprisingly full after so much gusto, but withheld it from Sam; and the two scuffled for its possession. Nothing in the world could have so worked upon the desire of the yearning observer beyond the fence.

"Honest, Penrod—you ain't goin' to touch me if I come in your yard?" he called. "Honest?"

"Cross my heart!" answered Penrod, holding the bottle away from Sam. "And we'll let you drink all you want."

Maurice hastily climbed the fence, and while he was thus occupied Mr. Samuel Williams received a great enlightenment. With startling rapidity Penrod, standing just outside the storeroom door, extended his arm within the room, deposited the licorice water upon the counter of the drug store, seized in its stead the bottle of smallpox medicine, and extended it cordially toward the advancing Maurice.

Genius is like that—great, simple, broad strokes!

Dazzled, Mr. Samuel Williams leaned

against the wall. He had the sensations of one who comes suddenly into the presence of a chef-d'œuvre. Perhaps his first coherent thought was that almost universal one on such huge occasions: "Why couldn't *I* have done that!"

Sam might have been even more dazzled had he guessed that he figured not altogether as a spectator in the sweeping and magnificent conception of the new Talleyrand. Sam had no partner for the cotillon. If Maurice was to be absent from that festivity—as it began to seem he might be—Penrod needed a male friend to take care of Miss Rennsdale; and he believed he saw his way to compel Mr. Williams to be that male friend. For this he relied largely upon the prospective conduct of Miss Rennsdale when he should get the matter before her—he was inclined to believe she would favor the exchange. As for Talleyrand Penrod himself, he was going to dance that cotillon with Marjorie Jones!

"You can have all you can drink at one pull, M'rice," said Penrod kindly.

"You said I could have all I want!" protested Maurice, reaching for the bottle.

"No, I didn't," returned Penrod quickly, holding it away from the eager hand.

"He did too. Didn't he, Sam?"

Sam could not reply; his eyes, fixed upon the bottle, protruded strangely.

"You heard him—didn't you, Sam?"

"Well, if I did say it I didn't mean it!" said Penrod hastily, quoting from one of the authorities. "Lookyhere, M'rice!" he continued, assuming a more placative and reasoning tone. "That wouldn't be fair to us. I guess we want some of our own lickrish water, don't we? The bottle ain't much over two-thirds full anyway. What I meant was, you can have all you can drink at one pull."

"How do you mean?"

"Why, this way: You can gulp all you want, so long as you keep swallering; but you can't take the bottle out of your mouth and commence again. Soon's you quit swallering it's Sam's turn."

"No; you can have next, Penrod," said Sam.

"Well, anyway, I mean M'rice has to give the bottle up the minute he stops swallering."

Craft appeared upon the face of Maurice, like a poster pasted on a wall.

"I can drink so long I don't stop swallering?"

"Yes; that's it."

"All right!" he cried. "Gimme the bottle!"

And Penrod placed it in his hand.

"You promise to let me drink until I quit swallering?" Maurice insisted.

"Yes!" said both boys together.

With that Maurice placed the bottle to his lips and began to drink. Penrod and Sam leaned forward in breathless excitement. They had feared Maurice might smell the contents of the bottle; but that danger was past—this was the crucial moment. Their fondest hope was that Maurice would make his first swallow a voracious one—it was impossible to imagine a second. They expected one big, gulping swallow and then an explosion, with fountain effects.

Little they knew the mettle of their man! Maurice swallowed once; he swallowed twice—and thrice—and he continued to swallow! No Adam's apple was sculptured on that juvenile throat, but the internal progress of the liquid was not a whit the less visible. His eyes gleamed with cunning and malicious triumph, sidewise, at the stunned conspirators; he was fulfilling the conditions of the draught, not once breaking the thread of that marvelous swallering.

His audience stood petrified. Already Maurice had swallowed more than they had given Duke—and still the liquor receded in the uplifted bottle! And now the clear glass gleamed above the dark contents full half the vessel's length—and Maurice went on drinking! Slowly the clear glass increased in its dimensions—slowly the dark diminished.

Sam Williams made a horrified movement to check him—but Maurice protested passionately with his disengaged arm, and made vehement vocal noises remindful of the contract; whereupon Sam desisted and watched the continuing performance in a state of grisly fascination.

Maurice drank it all! He drained the last drop, threw the bottle in the air, and uttered loud ejaculations of triumph and satisfaction.

"Hah!" he cried, blowing out his cheeks, inflating his chest, squaring his shoulders, patting his stomach, and wiping his mouth contentedly. "Hah! Ah! Aha! Waha! Waf-wah! Ha! But that was good!"

The two boys stood looking at him in a stupor.

"Well, I gotta say this," said Maurice graciously: "You stuck to your bargain all right and treated me fair."

Stricken with a sudden horrible suspicion, Penrod entered the storeroom in one stride and lifted the bottle of licorice water to his nose—then to his lips. It was weak, but good; he had made no mistake. And Maurice had really drained—to the dregs—the bottle of old hair tonics, dead catsups, sirups of undesirable preserves, condemned extracts of vanilla and lemon, decayed chocolate, ex-essence of beef, mixed dental preparations, aromatic spirits of ammonia, spirits of niter, alcohol, arnica, quinine, ipecac, sal volatile, nux vomica and licorice water—with traces of arsenic, belladonna and strychnine.

Penrod put the licorice water out of sight and turned to face the others. Maurice was seating himself on a box just outside the door and had taken a package of cigarettes from his pocket.

"Nobody can see me from here, can they?" he said, striking a match. "You fellers smoke?"

"No," said Sam, staring at him haggardly.

"No," said Penrod in a whisper.

Maurice lit his cigarette and puffed showily.

"Well, sir," he remarked, "you fellers are certainly square—I gotta say that much. Honest, Penrod, I thought you was after me! I did think so," he added sunnily; "but now I guess you like me, or else you wouldn't of stuck to it about lettin' me drink it all if I kept on swallering."

He chatted on with complete geniality, smoking his cigarette in content. And as he ran from one topic to another his hearers stared at him in a kind of torpor. Never once did they exchange a glance with each other; their eyes were frozen to Maurice. The cheerful conversationalist made it evident that he was not without gratitude.

"Well," he said as he finished his cigarette and rose to go, "you fellers have treated me nice—and some day you come over to my yard. I'd like to run with you fellers. You're the kind of fellers I like."

Penrod's jaw fell; Sam's mouth had been open all the time. Neither spoke.

"I gotta go," observed Maurice, consulting a handsome watch. "Gotta get dressed for the cotillon right after lunch. Come on, Sam. Don't you have to go too?"

Sam nodded dazedly.

"Well, goodby, Penrod," said Maurice cordially. "I'm glad you like me all right. Come on, Sam."

Penrod leaned against the doorpost and with fixed and glazing eyes watched the departure of his two visitors. Maurice was talking volubly, with much gesticulation, as they went; but Sam walked mechanically and in silence, his head sidewise, staring at his brisk companion.

They passed from sight, Maurice still conversing gayly—and Penrod slowly betook himself into the house, his head bowed upon his chest.

Some three hours later Mr. Samuel Williams, waxen clean and in sweet raiment, made his reappearance in Penrod's yard, yodeling a code-signal to summon forth his friend. He yodeled loud, long and frequently, finally securing a feeble response from the upper air.

"Where are you?" shouted Mr. Williams, his roving glance searching ambient heights. Another low-spirited yodel reaching his ear, he perceived the head and shoulders of his friend projecting above the roofridge of the stable. The rest of Penrod's body was concealed from view, reposing upon the opposite slant of the gable and precariously secured by the crooking of his elbows over the ridge.

"Yah! What you doin' up there?"

"Nothin'."

"You'd better be careful!" called Sam. "You'll slide off and fall down in the alley if you don't look out. I come pert' near it last time we was up there. Come on down! Ain't you goin' to the cotillon?"

Penrod made no reply. Sam came nearer.

"Say," he called up in a guarded voice, "I went to our telephone a while ago and asked him how he was feelin', and he said he felt fine!"

"So did I," said Penrod. "He told me he felt bully!"

Sam thrust his hands in his pockets and brooded. The opening of the kitchen door caused a diversion. It was Della.

"Mister Penrod," she bellowed forthwith, "come ahn down from up there! Y'r mamma's at the dancin' class waitin' fer ye, an' she's telephoned me they're goin' to begin—an' what's the matter with ye? Come ahn down fr'm up there!"

"Come on!" urged Sam. "We'll be late. There go Maurice and Marjorie now."

A glittering car went rapidly by, disclosing briefly a genre picture of Marjorie Jones in pink, supporting a monstrous sheaf of American Beauty roses. Maurice, sitting shining and joyous beside her, saw both boys and waved them a hearty greeting as the car turned the corner.

Penrod uttered some muffled words and then waved both arms—either in answer or as an expression of his condition of mind; it may have been a gesture of despair. How much intention there was in this act—obviously so rash, considering the position he occupied—it is impossible to say. Undeniably there must remain a suspicion of deliberate purpose.

Della screamed and Sam shouted. Penrod had disappeared from view.

The delayed dancing class was about to begin a most uneven cotillon under the direction of its slightly frenzied instructor, when Samuel Williams arrived.

Mrs. Schofield hurriedly left the ballroom; and Miss Rennsdale, flushed with sudden happiness, curtsied profoundly to Professor Bartet and obtained his attention.

"I have telled you fifty times," he informed her passionately ere she spoke, "I cannot make no such a changes. If your partner comes you have to dance with him. You are going to drive me crazy, sure! What is it? What now? What you want?"

The damsel curtsied again and handed him the following communication, addressed to herself:

"Dear Madam Please excuse me from dancing the cotillion with you this afternoon as I have fell off the barn

"Sincerly yours

"Penrod Schofield."

MASCOT

By ELLIS PARKER BUTLER

§ *If you believe something hard enough, it turns out that way. Or, put it like this: if it turns out that way, you might as well believe it.*

MAY 23, 1925

THE first time Guffy said anything to me about Katy I said to him "Yes," because what he said to me was "Gee, boy, your sister sure is a wonder!" That was the first night he came up to the house after he came back from trying his luck in the West, and in those five years Katy had grown up. She was just the age when hunting a husband is life's greatest joy game. A little later in a girl's life husband hunting may get to be a serious business, but at the age Katy was then it is all happiness and have a good time. The husband-to-be is a by-product of the merriment.

"Honest, Bill," Guffy said to me as we stood out there on the porch, "I never would have thought it. I've known you steen years, thick and thin, and if you had ever told me you had a sister that was the peach of the world I would have laughed at you. I wouldn't have thought it possible for a low-browed black-haired skinny little sawed-off gum-chewing runt like you to have a sister like Kate."

"No," I said. "I guess she takes after Noah's wife, or Eve, or one of her other far-back ancestors."

"Well, she sure is a wonder!" Guffy said.

"Anyway she thinks she is," I agreed, because you know how a fellow feels about a sister.

"And, say," Guffy said. "Listen, Bill! You won't be sore if I set out to make her mine, will you? Not that I care a hang what you have to say about it, you know. But you won't, will you? What I mean is, I'm going to win that girl, but you'll say a good word for me now and again, won't you?"

"What do you want to win her for?" I asked. "You're all right as you are, ain't you? What do you want to go and get all married up for? Here you are, back from the West, and I was counting on having some swell old times with you; and now you want to go and get married to my sister. I know how it will be—she'll tie you to her apron strings and have you locked in the house all the time, and when I ask you to come out for a little old party she'll say, 'No! Never! I know Bill—he's my brother and I know all his habits—you stay home with me!' Listen, Guffy—if you want to marry somebody go and marry somebody that ain't my sister."

"No, Bill," he said; "I'm going to marry Kate—if she'll have me. She's my mate, Bill. Say, Bill——"

"Yes?" I said sort of hopeless, for I knew he was going to get mushy.

"You don't understand how it is with me, Bill," he said. "It's not only that she's such a wonder girl, Bill. It's not only that I fell in love over my ears the minute I set my eyes on her. Bill, there's something in my soul—if that's where it is—that tells me that girl is my mascot. She's my little good-luck witch, Bill. I feel it in my bones, Bill. Ever feel that way, Bill? Ever feel, when you were near a person, that everything was all right? You know what I mean—that as long as that person was near, you couldn't lose? Mascot! You know what I mean. Say, Bill, I know a place down on Main Street where we can get a snifter of prewar. How about it? It's early yet."

"I might go down and take a piece of gum," I said.

"Oh, pshaw!" Guffy said. "You and your gum! Say, this is a time to take a real liquor. The night I met the queen of the world. Well, all right, then—come along and have a stick of tutti-frutti. I've just got to lift a glass to the star of womanhood with somebody. Bill, I love that girl! I sure do love that girl!"

Well, I said I'd go down to this Jerry's place with him, but I couldn't see anything but a mean sort of evening ahead, because he would be mushing about Kate all the while, but before I had a chance to go in for my hat the door opened and Kate came out with my hat. It was old stuff, and it made me sickish to hear her pipe up, "Oh, Mr. Guffy! I thought you had gone! Bill, you ought to have your hat on if you're going to stand out here in the cold!"

I knew what it meant—getting her chance to throw a few more hooks into Guffy and make him think she was one of these nice thoughtful ladies that don't want their dear brothers to catch cold. Swell chance that she would have brought me my hat if Guffy hadn't been there! But the minute Guffy heard her voice he turned around to face her, and that was when his heel hit the place where the end of a board in the porch is broken. He pawed in the air to catch his balance and didn't get it, and he went down the five steps backward and hit his head on the cement walk and went out. Kate screamed and went rushing down after him and gathered him in her arms as if she was doing a motion-picture act.

"Water, Bill, water!" she told me, but when I came back she was sitting on the cold cement with his head in her lap and he was back in the land of the living.

"My mascot!" he was saying. "My little good-luck mascot! My little four-leaf clover!"

Honest, he called her everything but his little horseshoe, and I guess he would have called her that if he had thought of it.

"You saved my life," he said. "If it hadn't been for you——"

I don't know what would have happened if it hadn't been for her. I suppose he would never have come to again. If it hadn't been for the soft touch of her gentle hand on his cheek I suppose he would have remained unconscious until he passed out, huh? But what can you do with a man when he gets that way?

"Oh, for cat's sake!" I said. "Tear loose! Get up, you big elephant, and come out of the clinch if you're going down to Jerry's with me. What do you think you are, a lap dog?"

"He's wounded," Kate said, pawing his hair.

"You mean the cement walk is wounded," I said. "He didn't hit it with nothing but his head."

"This is where the pain is," Guffy said, picking up her hand and putting it on the back of his head.

"Ah, your poor head!" Kate said.

"Just having your hand on it drives the pain away," Guffy said. "Rub it some more."

So I went down to this Jerry fellow's place and waited an hour or so, and then I gave it up for a bad job and went home again, and I expected to find those two mushies still sitting on that cold cement, but they had moved up to the top step.

"Does your head feel better now?" I heard Kate say.

"A little better," Guffy said. "Rub it again."

So I walked around the house to the back door and went on in and up to bed.

"And I've got to listen to that sort of stuff for six months or a year," I said to myself as I stuck my gum on the bedpost and got into bed. It was bad enough to lose a chum the first week he got back from the West, but to have to live in a house where that love stuff was being billed and cooed back and forth was a little too much. I lay awake awhile thinking it over. I saw that Guffy was as good as gone, and the only thing I saw for me to do was to hustle and help him get a job as soon as I could, so he could get married and get it over with and take his lovey-dovey stuff out of the house.

I spoke to the boss down at the garage where I work and he said he did need a man right then. The boss had got a notion that there might be money in running the ten-ton truck he took from Tom Casey for that unpaid gas and oil and repair and tire bill, and he said he would put Guffy on the truck. I didn't have to hunt Guffy up—he came in about 9:30 A.M. to tell me what a wonder girl Kate was, and I shifted him over to the boss before he was able to tell me more than ten times that Kate was the mascot of his life.

"Didn't I tell you?" he said when I told him the boss had a job for him. "I might have pounded the pavement in this man's town for a month and not have found a job, and here I meet Kate last night and there is a job waiting for me this morning. Bill, that girl is going to bring me all the luck in the world."

"I hope so," I said. "You can see the boss right now; don't let me keep you."

He went into the office and ten minutes later he was on the big truck and driving out of the garage to get a load of crushed bluestone at Herty's yard. Two minutes later, as he was driving up Main Street, he saw Kate on the sidewalk and gave her a wave of the hand, and the big ten-tonner did a skid and ran across the street, knocked down an electric-light pole and broke a gaslight post off at the base. Guffy did three turns in the air and landed with his face against the stub of the gaslight post. They had to get the pulmotor from the gas works to pump the gas out of him, and my boss was standing over him, waiting to fire him, when he opened his eyes. He opened them and looked up and saw Kate.

"My mascot!" he said: He was mighty weak, but he put a lot of feeling into it for a man as weak as he was.

"And I don't want you to put foot in my place ever again," my boss was saying to him at the same time; and the pulmotor man was saying, "You ought to go to the hospital until you're all right again."

"He'll not go to a hospital," Kate said. "Not while I have a home! Come, Mr. Guffy."

Guffy got to his feet. He staggered a little at first, but Kate got him by the arm and led him toward the other side of the street, and they were about in the middle of the street when the runabout came around the corner and got him. Luckily it was a light car and going slow, but it tossed him ten or twelve feet before it ran over his legs, only one of which was broken and, as the doc from the hospital said, as nice and clean a simple fracture as any man could want to see.

He was out of the hospital in two weeks and I will say he looked fine. He came around to the garage and I went outside to talk with him, the boss having given strict orders about Guffy.

"Kate home?" Guffy asked me.

"Not if there's anywhere to go," I said, "but she might be if all the picture houses are closed. You ain't going up there, are you?"

"Well, I thought I might," he said. "I feel as if I ought to thank her, Bill."

"Thank her? What for?" I asked him.

"Saving my life," he said. "Twice, if it comes to that. I told you she was my mascot, Bill, didn't I? Well, look how she happened to be right there when I let that truck get loose from me and ran it into that pole and all. I might have been killed, Bill. I was right in line to be killed, Bill, hitting a post like that and getting all filled full of gas, but Kate showed up just in time. Just in time to save my life, Bill. And look at that light runabout, 1918 model, that jammed into me when I was crossing the street. It might have been a ten-ton truck, Bill. It would have been if Kate hadn't had me by the arm. Look where I would be now if that had been a ten-ton truck hitting me and then running over me."

"Yes; or a steam roller; or a railroad train," I said.

"Well, not a railroad train. Not on Main Street," Guffy said. "But it might just as well have been a steam roller, like you say. Only it wasn't. It never would be, not with Kate around. I can feel that, Bill. In my bones. The luck is always going to be with me when Kate's standing by me. You think she's up at the house?"

"Well," I said, "the picture houses don't open in the forenoon and about now is when she does her facial wash, or whatever you call it, and maybe she might be at home. Only, Bill, if a storm comes up try to get out of the house. I don't want her to save you from being struck by lightning and have the house burned down. I've got a good pair of Sunday pants up in my room I don't want to lose."

"Always the bright little kidder, ain't you?" Bill said, and went his way.

When I went home to lunch it was set in the kitchen as usual, but Kate wasn't there.

"What's the matter?" I said. "Didn't Guffy come up here? How come he didn't stay to the eats?"

"The chandelier fell on him," ma said.

"What chandelier?" I asked her.

"The parlor one; what other one have we got?" ma said.

"What was he doing?" I asked. "Was he chinning himself on it or hanging by his knees?"

"He wasn't doing anything on it," ma said. "He was standing under it, looking at the snapshot album and waiting for Kate to come down, and when she came in the room it fell on him."

"What hospital did they take him to?" I asked her.

"The same one," ma said. "He wasn't injured much, but the ambulance man said they could sew up his scalp wound better there. If he had been losing much blood they would have sewed it up here. It was lucky Kate came down just when she did, because he turned when she came to the door. If he hadn't turned, the point on the bottom of the chandelier would have pierced his brain."

"Yes," I said, "Kate is his mascot."

"That's what he said," ma said.

Well, frankly, this love business is all right in a way and I'm not a man to throw a monkey wrench into any sort of machinery, and I'm not crazy to try to upset any happiness of my chum and my sister unless I see it is all for the best to do so, but I did say a few words to Guffy the second day after he got out of the chandelier affair so easy. I went up to the hospital to say them too. It seems they took the stitches in his skull cover and bandaged him up so that he looked like a Turk or something and then turned him out on the street, and he went to the first telephone he could find and called Kate up to thank her for saving his life again.

I guess he said some merry words about the bandages on his head and how they made him look, and Kate said he would look like a million dollars to her no matter how he was bandaged—or something like that. Anyway he said he was glad she felt that way because he had been planning, before the chandelier fell on him, to ask her to go to a show in the city, and now he still had the nerve to ask her if she did feel that way. So Kate said she certainly would be pleased to accept the kind invitation.

The next evening they got on the 7:15 train at Upper Westcote station and the train started, and three seconds later the train jumped the track and jammed into a freight on the siding, the first wreck on our line in fifteen years. It was as neat a sideswipe as you ever saw, and only one passenger was hurt—the end of a two-by-four on a flat car came through a window and jabbed Guffy in the shoulder, just breaking his shoulder blade neatly, and then the whole damage was done and over with. So they took Guffy back to the hospital, and I suppose when he came out of ether he was weeping because he couldn't be holding Kate's hand and telling her how lucky it was she was with him and had saved his life again.

So the next morning I went up to the hospital and had a serious talk with Guffy.

"I don't want to butt into your affairs, Guffy," I said, "but I feel it is only fair to Kate to do so on this occasion." I went at him that way because I knew that was the only way to start if I wanted him to listen to reason. "I want to ask you if you think all this is fair to Kate," I said. "Are you playing fair with the girl? Are you acting as a real man should?"

"I hope so, Bill," he said, turning white. "The only thing in the world I care a hang for is her happiness. What do you mean?"

"Well, Guffy," I said, "I'm Kate's brother and she hasn't any father and I sort of feel my duty to her is to speak out on this subject. I don't think you're giving this business the thought you ought to give it. The way you are acting you are going to ruin that girl's life."

"I'd die first," he said.

"Well, ruin it is what you're going to do," I said. "What sort of husband do you think a man would make when he is in the hospital all the time?"

"Well, not so good," Guffy admitted.

"I'll say so!" I said. "A girl who is married to a hospital hound like that would have no life at all. She wouldn't have her husband at home where he ought to be, and she'd have to work and slave to pay his hospital bills, and she'd have a miserable life—bawling her eyes out and going without the movies and everything! What I mean to say, Guffy, is that you've got Kate all wrong. You say she's your mascot, but you can see for yourself she's your jinx. She's your hoodoo. Every time you've gone near her you've got one kind of a wallop or another. Has it failed yet?"

"I've had a streak of bad luck, if that's what you mean," Guffy said, "and I've had some accidents."

"Yes," I said, "and how many did you ever have before you met Kate?"

"These things run in sets," Guffy said. "They start in on a man and they keep coming for a while, and then they stop. Unless a man has a mascot. Then they ain't ever as bad as they might be. If that two-by-four had hit me in the face, or a little lower down, where my heart is——"

"Guffy," I said, "I don't want to pester you about this, but you've got the wrong slant entirely. I tell you here and now that for you—whatever she might be for another man—Kate is a jinx. She's a born jinx for you. I knew it in the beginning. You're not cut out for each other. You're not made to be married, you and Kate. There's nothing in either of you that, joined together, would make happiness. I know you both, Guffy, and I know what I'm talking about. I've known you since you and I were babes, and I've known Kate since she was born, and you're the last man I would have picked for her, and she's the last girl I would have picked for you. Just now you're neither of you sane—you're love crazy and you can't see straight. Fo ks get that way. But they ought to listen, then, to folks that know the facts."

"Meaning you," Guffy said in a way I did not like.

"Yes," I said, sticking out my chin at him, "meaning me!"

"Bill," he said, "I'd hate to quarrel with you, but if you come between me and Kate, you can go to the devil."

"All right, if that's the way you take me, I'll go to the devil," I said, "and as for me I'm through with you. I want no more to do with any man as blind as you are. And when it comes to going to the devil, you go to the devil yourself!"

With that I went out of his room and if it hadn't been a hospital I would have slammed the door, and I thought—as I left the room—"Here's another nice thing his precious mascot has done, lost him the best friend he ever had or ever will have!"

But I thought no more along that line because just outside the door I came face to face with Kate. She had a big bunch of flowers and a bag I could see had oranges in it, and she said, "Oh, I'm so late! I've only three minutes to spend with him before visiting hours are over!"

She went into Guffy's room, and immediately I heard her scream and a big racket in the room. I turned and rushed in, of course.

Nothing had happened except that a big section of the plaster ceiling had fallen on Guffy, knocking him cold again. I caught a nurse in the corridor and she grabbed an interne somewhere and they worked over Guffy and brought him back to life, but he was mighty near the edge of things, and they put Kate out into the corridor.

On the way home I talked to her in straight plain language. I told her just what she was doing to Guffy, and I showed her case by case how she was hoodooing him every time they met.

"Have sense," I begged her. "Think it over. Every time you've met him he has got his, hasn't he? And you know it, now I've told you. I dare you to go back there and walk in on him. Something will happen as sure as fate—the hospital will fall down or a bottle of vinegar will explode and kill him or a safety pin will leap out of his bandage and stab him to death as sure as you are alive!"

"Accidents will——" she began.

"Say, listen!" I said. "I've known that lad all my life, and accidents never happened to him before. He's been the luckiest guy on earth. And now look what you're doing to him. You're his jinx. Leave him alone, Kate, for cat's sake! Keep away from him. Send him off. You know you're not built to be Guffy's wife. If you stop and think it over you'll know there's no man in the world less suited for you. You'll fight like cats and dogs as soon as you're married."

She walked along beside me for a whole block, thinking it over.

"I don't see that it's any of your business, anyway, Bill," she said then. "Who I marry is my own affair."

I saw it was no use. You can't pound sense into a girl's head when she is in love.

"All right, then," I said; "I wash my hands of it. If you want to ruin him and break all his bones and kill him, have it your own way. But don't ask me to come to your wedding; the church steeple will fall on the lot of you. You can do as you like and I can't stop you, but I did think you had some sense."

So I waited to see what would happen next. If I had been in Guffy's place I would have skipped the town the minute I got out of that hospital. I would have put a thousand miles between myself and Kate the soonest I could, and I would have steered clear of her all my life.

But the very day Guffy got out of the

hospital he came down to the garage and hunted me up.

"Well, Bill," he said, "here I am again. They can't keep a good man dead. Kate up at the house?"

"You keep away from Kate," I said.

"I couldn't do that, Bill," Guffy said. "If they chained me to the post office I'd go right ahead up to see Kate and I'd drag the post office along with me, unless the chain broke."

"You keep away from Kate," I said.

"Now, Bill, be reasonable!" Guffy said. "There's nothing in this fool idea you've got. You just let a few little accidents get your goat. Now I feel in my bones—"

"Yeh! You feel in your bones she's your mascot," I said. "And I tell you to keep away from my sister. And keep away from me. And you keep away from that house. I own that house and I tell you here and now to keep out of it and away from it, and away from me. I don't want to have anything more to do with you, and if you set foot in my house again I'll have the law on you."

"Oh, if you feel that way about it—" he said.

And he went away. When I got home I asked ma if Guffy had been to the house and she said he had not.

"I didn't know he was out of the hospital," ma said.

"Well, I've ordered him to stay away from here," I said. "Let him go his way and we'll go ours. The world is big enough for all of us if he keeps far enough away. If he don't it ain't. I'm not going to have him meeting Kate."

"You're the head of the family, Bill," ma said, "but I sort of liked Mr. Guffy."

"I'm not as big as he is," I said, "but when we were kids I licked him as often as he licked me, and I'm not afraid to try it again if he comes hanging around Kate, and you can tell him so. And you can tell her so too."

"You grow more like your father every day," ma said.

"And, at that," I said, "my father had enough sense in him to know the difference between a jinx and a mascot."

The next I heard of Guffy he had got him a job over at the Red Star Garage, and I went over and told him straight out that he was through with Kate.

"And furthermore," I said, "you may think I'm a black-browed runt and not such a much because I choose to chew gum instead of sopping up this prewar stuff that Jerry mixes in his own cellar, but I've licked you before and I can lick you again, and if you come fooling around Kate you'll get yours. You'll get it good and plenty too. My father was a little man, but in his day he could walk from one end of town to the other with a chip on his shoulder and there was not a man in town dared knock it off. That's all I've got to say to you, Guffy. If Kate's a fool I'm not, and I'm not going to have her marry a man so besotted he thinks a jinx is a mascot. I've seen a plenty of these marriages where the minute a man is married the hard fortune piles onto him twenty story thick, and it's nothing but sickness and trouble, and some poor man like me has to support the whole family for him."

Guffy said nothing. He tapped idly on a tire with a wrench and looked at the floor.

"I'm speaking for your own good," I said, "and for Kate's good and for the good of all of us."

"I think she's a mascot to me," he said.

"There you go again!" I said.

"I'll always think so," he said.

"Then think and be cursed to you!" I said. "But keep away from her! This is fair warning."

I went back to the garage. A machinist in a garage has plenty of time to think and I thought a lot about Guffy, but I knew I had done the right thing. It was not as if Guffy was the only man in the world; there had always been plenty of men about Kate and there would be plenty again, and Guffy would be none the worse for having no ceilings fall on him, as I well knew.

You only need a firm hand in these affairs. I've figured the thing out for myself pretty carefully, and at the time of life where Kate and Guffy were the person is not so important as the thing itself. Love is what folks of that age fall in love with, and if one goes another comes. All the young men are princes if they come prancing, and all the young girls are queens if they come smiling. The love-until-death business that is eternal one evening will end the next in a tiff over nothing, and the one-and-only of evening before last is forgotten for the one-and-only of the present evening, and no harm done. It was hardly a day before Kate was gadding around with this Mary Dorgan chum of hers, rushing off to the pictures, stopping the night with each other and everything the same as before Guffy showed up, back from the West. And I could not see that Guffy was weeping his eyes out either. The Red Star Garage is a good garage and a busy place, and a good man has a chance there to show how good he is. I kept a keen eye on Guffy. No more ceilings fell on him after I told him to keep away from Kate.

As a matter of fact the boss came to me one day and asked me what I had done to O'Leary's five-ton truck the last time it was in the garage for repairs.

"I did what a man could," I told him. "That truck should have been junked three years ago."

"You ought to know," he said, "for you've been doing the repair work on it all the while, but O'Leary don't know it, and that man Guffy over at the Red Star don't know it, it seems, for O'Leary took it there, and Guffy has made it like new. The whole twenty of the O'Leary fleet has gone there now, and that's one customer lost because you know about as much about a machinist's business as a cat knows about radio."

"We've got all we can handle anyway boss," I said.

"All the work, but not all the money," he said. "Have you ever heard of Wintermute Oil?"

"What is it?" I asked him. "A new heavy gravity?"

"It's a new gold mine," the boss said. "Do you remember that little red car that we put the balloon rims on? Man named Ransom? He's been selling O'Leary some stock in this Wintermute Oil Well Company, out in Texas or somewhere, but he shifted his car to the Red Star when O'Leary went there. All he did, Bill, was sell Harrity, of the Red Star, a bunch of oil stock as big as a house at a dollar a share."

"There's a new sucker born every minute," I said.

"Only," the boss said, "this time the oil stuff went up to seventeen dollars a share in one week after Harrity bought it. He put four thousand dollars in it, and four times six is twenty-four, carry the two; four times one is four, and two is six. Harrity has made sixty-four thousand dollars because you don't know a scored cylinder from a cord tire, that's all! And, if it gives you any joy, that man Guffy put four hundred dollars in the stuff himself and has made above six thousand."

"It'll not last him long," I said. "I know Guffy of old."

"Well," said the boss, "the Red Star Garage may bust, but it's not a habit it has. If it does bust, Guffy's money will be gone, for he bought an eighth interest with his six thousand dollars."

I said nothing to that.

"Harrity is going to Florida," the boss said, "and Guffy is to be manager of the garage. They tell me he's to pull down five thousand a year for that, and the garage paid thirty per cent last year."

"Oh, he was rather a problem at first, but now he just goes his way and we go ours."

"Got him!"

"Looks like Og has got himself a bad case of puppy love!"

"Gad, how I thrill to the distant baying of hounds!"

"We know what happens to bad little boys who won't eat their cereal, don't we?"

"–and now what'll it be for Aunt Mabel?"

"Where do you want it?"

"It's nice—but it isn't quite the sort of thing we had in mind."

I could figure that for myself; it would be eighteen hundred. That would mean Guffy was good for sixty-eight hundred dollars a year.

"If you knew a cotter pin from a wheel spoke I might be the man that's going to Florida," the boss said.

I said nothing to that either.

"What we need around this place," the boss said, "is a mascot"; and he went back to the office.

For a few minutes I was pretty sore. It is all right to say that a man don't dislike another man's getting ahead in the world, but when two start even, as may be, there are thoughts when one has a big wad of luck and the other hasn't.

"And but for me," I said to myself, "that man Guffy would by now be torn to shreds by a flywheel or shot to the moon in fragments by a can of gas. And that's the way it goes! One tells a man to beware a hole in the road, and he steps on the gas and shoots by you and wins out by ten miles' margin."

I wasn't so happy.

"The next thing," I said, "Guffy will be one of these self-made millionaires, and sore at me all his life because I threatened to beat him up. Oh well!"

I turned back to the job I had in hand, which was a sweet black one mussing with cracked gear case, and the wrench had just slipped, skinning my knuckles, when I heard someone say my name. I looked up and it was Guffy.

"Hello, Bill!" he said.

"All right—hello!" I said.

"How'd you like a real job?" he asked me.

"Over at the Red Star, I mean. I'm going to be boss over there and I'd like you there with me."

"Yeh!" I said. "I heard all about it. Some luck, I'll say."

"I'll say it was luck—pig-headed luck," Guffy said. "You know that talk we had about mascots and jinxes, don't you, Bill?"

"Yeh!" I said.

"You know what you said about not getting a jinx instead of a mascot, don't you, Bill?"

"Yeh!" I said.

"Well, you were right, Bill," he said. "What a man wants in this life is a mascot. And I got one, Bill."

"Yeh?" I said.

"I sure did!" Guffy said. "You know that day you came over to the Red Star and bawled me out?

"Kate and I went out and got married that night, Bill."

"Yeh?" I said.

"I told you she was my mascot," he said.

My knuckles were bleeding pretty free, so I squirted some gas on them—it's a good thing to stop any poison. Then I put the can on the floor and felt in my pocket for a piece of gum.

"All right," I said, "have it your own way. If she is she is, and if she ain't she ain't. It's nothing in my young life. But how do you account for all those accidents, hey?"

"Luck!" he said. "Bull-headed good luck, Bill. If I hadn't had Kate I wouldn't have got slammed into the hospital and I'd be working where you are. I told you she was my mascot."

"Yeh, you told me," I said. "Let it go at that. What'll you pay me over there at the Red Star, if I go over to you?"

I wasn't going to give him any satisfac-faction; you can't talk sense to a man like Guffy when he's in love and all. No use trying.

NUTS AND REASONS

By OCTAVUS ROY COHEN

§ Eddie Eller, World's Premier Juggler and Terpsichorean Artist, was goofy about Toy Williams, his partner. Goofier, in fact, after he tried to bust her one on the nose—and missed. Eddie is heartbroken because he always had it figured that he and Toy hit it off well enough to play house together for the rest of their lives.

MAY 24, 1930

THERE ain't any use beating up the bush, so I will come out straight and ask you this question: Even if me and Toy Williams did have plenty of rows, and even if I did tell her a lot of things about herself that maybe wasn't entirely true—did she have any right leaving me flat and then getting teamed up with a wrastler?

Now, mind you, I ain't claiming that maybe I didn't go too far. Of course I didn't sock her, or nothing rough like that, because she ducked—but you would think a dame would give a guy a chance to apologize for missing. But no, not Toy! First thing I know is when I waltz into my dressing room and there is a note from that cluck saying she is going to blow at the end of two weeks, and what am I going to do about it?

Well, I think this is just another lovers' quarrel, but on account our act opening the bill, I haven't got time to talk to her right then. I dance out with the Indian-club routine which I open with, and there she is, doing her job of dressing the stage, and how.

It struck me then that Toy was even easier on the opticals than I had ever suspected, and so I figure to put my pride in my pocket after the act and tell her she oughtn't to be so touchy—getting all peeved up and quitting a swell job with the world's best juggler just because he happened to lose his head for a minute and tried to sock her. It was only a love tap anyway, and I always have thought that maybe hadn't she ducked so prompt the wallop would of brought her back into my arms.

After we finish our seventeen minutes I go busting right into Toy's dressing room.

"Since when," she inquires, "did you get the idea that I am the kind of lady which lets gents come into her dressing room without knocking?"

"It's just me, Toy."

"That being the case, I'll eliminate the word 'gent.'"

"Aw, quit wisecracking. I come in for a serious talk."

"You've had it already. Now get out."

"Listen. What's all this boloney about you leaving the act in two weeks?"

"It's the truth."

"You're kidding."

"Wrap your ear around this, Eddie," she says—and I can see she is plenty hot: "When you was always rowing at me, I stood it. When you was always telling me how lucky I was to be hired by you to wear tights during your act, I stood that too. But when you took a sock at me, Eddie—then I started remembering I was a lady. And I'm blowing." I see the dame means what she is saying, or anyhow thinks she does.

"I'm sorry I took a sock at you, honey."

"Sorry because you missed?"

"No. Of course I was sorry at first that I missed, but I'm sorry now that I so far forgot I was a gent. Honest, sugarfoots, I'm goofy about you."

"Yeh! And if you was to fall any deeper in love with me you'd probly break my jaw or something. No, Eddie, being a target for a shrimp that gets an occasional yen to be a wild man is too strong for my blood. I'm through!"

"What are you going to do for a living?"

"Just what I did before I met up with your sugar-cured highness."

"You can't get a job in the profesh."

"Why not?"

"Because, honey—I got to be honest, much as it hurts me—you're a lousy actress."

"Oh, I am, am I? And I guess you're dealing a fit to Mr. Shakespeare with your juggling? I guess all the movie producers in Hollywood are chewing on United States mints to buy your act out? I guess it's all true what you been telling me about the bookers conspiring to keep you in the opening spot?"

Well, that is going too far. That girl could of took a rap at my face, or figure, or my brain, even, but when she goes to work and starts whamming my art, I gotta show a little fight.

"Lay offa that," I growls.

"Who says so?"

"Just me. And get this through that ivory crock of yours: Only for me you'd still be serving 'em sunny side up in that two-bits beanery where I found you at! You think because you've traveled twenty-two weeks with me already, and folks have said you've got a pair of good-looking gams, that you're gonna take Sarah Bernhardt's place. Well, listen to me, girl. One of these days I'm gonna come out of the stage door, and it's gonna be raining or sleeting or something, and there you will be, begging me, with tears in your eyes, won't I please take you back."

"And you'll take a sock at me, eh?"

"Don't put words in my mouth. I'll just take you in my arms and tell you that I always have loved you, even if you was awful dumb; and maybe this has been a lesson to you, and if so, maybe you can join my act again."

She gives a little laugh, and there ain't nothing of mirth in same.

"You should of been an actor, Eddie. The thing you call a brain don't work but one way, and that is around the person of Mr. Eddie Eller, World's Premier Juggler and Terpsichorean Artist."

I spoke lower, "Don't you love me, Toy?"

"Why should I?"

"There you go—always answering one question with another. I didn't ask you why should you; I asked you do you."

"Whether I do or not ain't got anything to do with this argument."

"That ain't no way to talk to the man you was almost engaged to."

"Nor it ain't no way to talk to the man I was almost socked by. You take my advice, Eddie, and get you a dame for your act which ain't got as much spirit as me, and maybe you will do better with her. But no girl with any self-respect is going to stand for always hearing about how good you are and how rotten she is. Nor neither being busted on the nose. So, for the next two weeks, Eddie, you go your way and I'll go mine, and after that it's all off between us."

"I'm heartbroken," I says, "just thinking what a mistake you are making."

But does my logic make any difference to that skirt? Not so as you could notice it. She gets ritzy around the theater, and it ain't hardly no time at all before all them other acts is noticing that something is wrong between us. And though I don't like to knock my feller artists, I got to say in honesty that nobody gives a juggling act a break. You would think that jugglers all had lepersy or some other terrible disease, the way a bunch of bum hoofers and warblers won't have nothing to do with them; and me working forty weeks a year, every year, and having played the best houses in the country, including the Palace, which is a house most of these turnips ain't ever seen excepting they paid a buck and a half for their seat, or else found a friend who had a couple comps.

Going back to Toy Williams, though, I can't get it through my dome that she's serious about doing a walkout. It ain't only the prestige that she gets out of being with my act, but it's also that I and her has sort of hit it off to play house together for the rest of our lives; only she gets fool ideas in her head like thinking that I didn't love her, just because I took a sock at her. I tried to explain that anybody's hand is libel to slip, but you can't explain nothing to no woman.

I'm really kind of cut up about this thing when I see she is serious. It ain't like I really meant to hurt her feelings. And when I think of her walking out on me I get kind of sick; only I got too much pride to tell her so right away, especially when she announces that even if I got down on my knees to her, she is through. Well, I wouldn't get down on my knees to no dame—least of all one I hoped some day to get married to—and so I tell her if that's all she thinks of my deep and unselfish love she can go to thunder and I hope she starves to death.

Well, she goes, after giving some of the boys on the bill a good play for the rest of our time together; and after I pick up a lad to work with me and do the jobs which Toy had always done, I begin to get awful hungry for her.

She's class, that kid. Good-looking, what I mean. Kind of little and blond and cuddly, and it seemed like maybe I had talked to her too much about how lucky she was just being with me. Not that it wasn't true, but then I guess even a girl like her yearns to be told once in a while that you can't live without her. And every day I wait for a letter and none comes; so finally I sit down and work for three hours writing me a note which I think is both dignified and affectionate, because I am almost entirely heartbroke over that dame leaving me flat, like she has just done, without any rimes or reasons. Says I:

My dear Toy: I suppose by this time you have found out what a terrible mistake you made in walking out on a right guy like me. Well, Toy, I also think you made a mistake and I have suffered a lot just thinking about all the nights you must of cried yourself to sleep longing for me and the old days when you was working with the World's Premier Juggler & Terpsichorean Artiste, yours truly. Now, Toy, I am nothing if not a magonomous guy and so, if you wish to return to the act, all will be forgiven and we will get married, provided you promise not always to be throwing up to me that I almost socked you on the nose. Please wire your answer. If it is yes, you can wire collect.

Affectionately, EDDIE.

You would imagine, with a sweet note like that, she would of burned up the wires. But did she? No, sir, she didn't, and for a while I thought I wasn't never going to hear from her again. But one day there comes a letter, and I don't suspect that it is from her, because it has got my agent's name in the corner, and right away I think that ungrateful bum is writing me again about that money that he says I owe him.

It's from Toy, though, and what it says is something:

Dear Mr. Eller: Your letter promptly received and contents duly noted. In reply, beg to state that I have another engagement on the stage and so cannot accept your kind offer. Said engagement is with Smack Markis, Middleweight Champion Wrestler & Physical Culture Expert in a Potpurri of Melody & Health Building, and as he is a kind and considerate man, this is a better job than with a cheap juggler who always opens the show unless there is trained animals on the bill, and then even the trained animals are sometimes spotted better than him. Referring to your offer of marriage, I also beg to state that I cannot accept that offer either, on account of having other plans.

Yours truely, Toy Williams,
Singing Comedienne.

Wouldn't that slay you? That "singing comedienne" part of it, I mean. She who never done nothing on the stage but wear tights and hand me my Indian clubs, knives, rubber balls, et cetera. And that dirty dig about where I am spotted. And the ungratefulness of her trouping with a wrastler.

I ain't even heard of this feller, and I ask some of the boys on the bill. What I hear don't cheer me up none, as they say he is a bone crusher and has probly ruint a lot of his opponents for life. Also that he has got an elegant physic, which he shows off to advantage, making himself a good attraction for vaudeville. And that ain't all.

I read something about their act in Variety, and see that it is being readied in a large way, and then I write to my agent and ask is he handling it. He writes yes and then goes on to say that the route they are to follow will be the same as mine for a lot of the distance, leaving out some few cities which cannot afford the heavy nut of the Smack Markis act, and I do not know whether to regard that as another dirty crack.

Sure enough, that agent told the truth, and you would of thought that he would of had more consideration than to get bookings for any act Toy was in, so that I and she would be playing the same bill about two weeks out of every three. I started to write him words to that effect, until suddenly I got an idea of how it happened and why Toy had stooped to go into this wrastling act.

You see, it was this way: I guess I must have hurt Toy's feelings when I took that crack at her, and she was out to make me plenty jealous, because a man can always tell when a girl is really in love with him, and I knew good and well that Toy was goofy about me—as why shouldn't she be? Anyway it was perfectly plain that she was just doing this so as to make me jealous and have me eating out of her hand. But being a man of common sense and pride, I make up my mind that such will not be the case, and I will be as upstage as a headliner, and I guess that will soon show her how much I care.

Well, it's in Cleveland that we get together for the first time—my act and hers, I mean. I'm all excited, though I don't know why, because it is plain that she is chasing me, and I am not going to take her back except on my own terms. But just the same, I happen to get to that theater early for morning rehearsal. It is a cold day and lots of snow is falling, and just as I slide into the alley which leads to the stage door a taxicab rolls up and two people get out.

The first is Toy, and I will confess that I got kind of a shock seeing her. She always was pretty, but in her little tight-fitting brown hat and a mink coat pulled around her figure, and the snow as a swell backdrop, it kind of brought a lump to my throat.

Then I lamped the gimmick that was with her. I guess Mr. Smack Markis don't look like no Dresden doll nowheres, but in a snowstorm, wearing a fur overcoat and with a little trick like Toy next to him, I'm here to remark that he appeared positively terrible.

Even in the storm, I can see that his profession has dealt kind of cruel with his face. All you could say it showed was virility, and I guess lots of better dames than Toy has fell for that. He looks like he could wrastle two oxes at one time, and when I mentioned this later to one of the lads on the bill he replies that Smack has several times give exhibitions of wrastling a wild bull. That makes me feel no better fast.

As they go past me in the snow I give a bow.

"Good morning, Toy," I says, polite and gentlemanly.

Her eyebrows go up. "Ah, Mr. Eller. I wish you good morning."

Just like that—with the "ah" and everything. At first I am crushed, but before I get inside that house I am plenty sore, and I make up my mind that Toy Williams is one dame which is going to learn that I can live just as long and twice as happy without her.

Well, she keeps on being not so cordial, and I go her one better, because I am a bird that knows how to handle women, and I realize that if you are always chasing around after them, giving them presents and letting them know they are breaking your heart, they won't have anything for you but lots of contempt, and same is what I do not want from Toy or no other woman. So I go through my rehearsal with the orchestra and never notice her at all, and even when we open that afternoon I do not pay the slightest attention to her, although I do stand in the wings and catch their act. It's a pretty nifty flash. In the first place, he's got a swell shape, with plenty of muscle, and he puts his stuff across all right for a guy that ain't an actor, but I get the hunch, from watching him, that he is kind of dumb, or even very much so. He has got one of them dead pans which some folks call "forbidding," but which I would say is just plain brainless.

He does a lot of physical culture under the spots, making his muscles jump and such, and showing how he got that way, and then he goes into a spiel about being the greatest wrastler at his weight that the world ever produced, and how he is only giving exhibitions on the stage because managers can't pay how much money he demands—which sounds like a lot of static to me.

It don't take long, either, for everybody to find out that Smack is kind of crazy about himself. He's always talking about how much money he gets and how much he's gonna get. I hear him lots of times, talking to other fellers, and it's always the same.

"There ain't nothin' cheap about me," this Markis was always saying. "I got a value and I stick to it. Any time you see me step in the ring you can bet I ain't getting a cent less than a thousand dollars; and if it's against anybody which ain't a set-up, I get at least twice that. Some of these cheap skates offer me five hundred dollars to wrastle for them, but I snap my fingers in their faces, like that. Because I don't wrastle nobody for less than a thousand berries no time. I'm good, I am, and I'm gonna see that everybody else knows it also."

Well, that wasn't no idle boast, because after two days I guess there ain't nobody within a mile of that theater which ain't heard from Smack's own lips what a wow he is, and how he never accepts less than a thousand dollars for taking a flop out of nobody—and what makes me sick is that I see Toy is lapping it up.

When Toy was in my act she didn't have nothing much to do except look pretty—which was a cinch for her—and show off her gams, which no girl constructed like her minds doing, but with Smack she has a song, and I guess that has went to her head. Also, when Smack finally wrastles with a partner of his, she walks on as referee and there is some alleged funny stuff where he tickles her ankle; and I think that sort of thing is vulgar and should be depleted, but the audience eats it up.

I make one more play for Toy, in a dignified manner, and when she does not give me no come-on sign, I climb up on a high horse of my own and begin teaching her that there are just as good fish in the sea as have ever been made chowder of. In fact, I pick out a dame on the bill named Elyse Elegant, the Latest in Fun and Fashion, and I ask her will she help me out of some trouble.

"Didn't Toy Williams used to be with you, Eddie?"

"Uh-huh."

"And you was kind of cut in the head about her, wasn't you?"

"And how!"

"Now she's showing this living walnut a good time, huh? And you want to teach her that if she don't grab you while the grabbing is good, she might not have another chance?"

"You got brain, Elyse."

"I guess you have, too—for a juggler, Eddie. One thing I'll say for your scheme—it's certainly brand-new. Nobody else ever thought of that jealousy gag before. But I don't like wrastlers anyway, and I'll help all I can. If Toy is really nuts about you it might work. If she ain't, I'll get plenty of free feeds."

That's the arrangement, and at first I see that Toy ain't so happy at the sang fried with which I sheik around with Elyse. Only it don't affect her so much that she goes home and cries her eyes out. As a matter of fact, it seems to me like everywhere me and Elyse go, there Toy is with this Smack Markis, and if Toy is having an unhappy time, she is sure a brave girl, because she is always smiling.

After Cleveland, we stick together through Detroit, and then we split for a week, with us poking into the sticks and Toy going with Smack's act into Chi. They also play Chi a second week, and I rejoin them there. Elyse has also been routed with them, and right away when we get together I ask for a report.

"Toy is working hard to make you jealous," says Elyse.

"She is succeeding," I admit.

"She is letting old battleground think that she is nuts about him."

"She is also kind of making me think same."

"But I don't believe she is. I think her heart is set on some day marrying a juggler."

My bosom gives a flutter and I ask her is she just kidding me, and she says no.

"But there's one complication, Eddie. There's only two things this radish ever talks about. One is that he never wrastles for less than a thousand dollars and the other is that no woman ain't never hooked him. Only he's soft-pedaling that last recently, because everybody in the show knows he is that way about Toy."

"And ain't I glad," says I. "Because when I take Toy away from him——"

"Yeh," she says, "when you take Toy away from him you are libel to wake up on a nice, cool, marble slab."

I give her a quick look to see if she is joking, but she ain't, and I get kind of sick; also asking her for an explanation.

"Well," she says, "from all I can find out, this Smack Markis ain't very long on brain, but he is there with the jealousy stuff. It seems that he don't get mad often, but when he does he usually tears a few ribs and a couple of shoulders out of the guy he gets mad at."

That knocks me for a ghoul. "It does seem," I says, "that Toy might have picked somebody to get jealous of me which does not drink blood every morning for breakfast."

Well, I make up my mind that I better had not fool around no more, but grab off

Toy before this Smack gets too jealous of her. So I stand in the wings during their act that afternoon, and when they come off I give Toy a sunny smile.

"Hello, kid," I says. "You looked good this afternoon."

Well, sir, she didn't give me a tumble. Just stuck that pretty little nose of hers up in the air and strutted off, and you could of knocked me down with a feather if you had had a feather, because I guess a guy knows when a girl is cuckoo about him; but nobody can't never tell about women, especially women that travel with wrastling acts.

I try again that night after the last show. I rap once on her dressing-room door and go busting in.

"Say, listen, cutie——" I start, but she clips me right off.

"If you don't get out of my dressing room," she snaps, "I will call the management and have you pitched out on your neck."

"Aw, listen——"

"I wouldn't listen to you if you had a loud-speaker. You are nothing but a bum juggler which once tried to sock me in the nose, and I am offa you for life, or longer."

"But, sweetheart——"

"I ain't your sweetheart, either; so don't go calling me out of my name."

Well, sir, I slunk out of her room, feeling like a disaster had kissed me on the dome, and the queerest thing about it is that I could almost swear I heard her crying. That was right after I closed the door. But I ask you, how can a guy figure a dame which takes him for a ride like she done me and then cries about it? Wasn't I sweet to her? Wasn't I willing to forget that I tried to sock her? Was I throwing our old quarrels up in her face?

No, I wasn't. But it begins to look like I held off my play too long, because in the weeks that follow, most of which we are together, I don't never see Toy that she ain't got that piece of tripe with her, which his name is Smack Markis.

Honest, that baby had it bad, and it looked like he was all set to cop. Can you imagine a dame passing up a regular guy like me for some feller whose idea of married life is probly to practice half nelsons and strangleholds on the lady of his choice? Besides, how does she know that pretty soon some better wrastler ain't coming along and break him up into little pieces, which I only hope I am at the ringside when it happens.

Love troubles always are tough for artists, and they even get to me. Lots of my stuff goes bad—dropping things and all, because it is very hard to keep your mind on eight different whirling knives at once when in the wings a big palooka is standing with his arms around the one and only girl—or anyway looking like his arm is around her. Some of the house managers was yelling and I was explaining that I just worked them flops into my act so it would look better when I did the trick right, but they don't seem to fall for that very hard.

Finally I cannot keep my troubles to myself no longer, so I go to Elyse, which has been a friend in need.

"For the luvva Pete," I beg, "find out what is wrong!"

That night I take her to a beanery and she tells me.

"Toy is crazy about you," she announces.

"I guess I ought to cheer. And I would if I believed you."

"It's true," she insists.

"Well, she takes an awful funny way of showing it."

"It is breaking her heart," says Miss Elegant. "But she ain't hankering to attend your funeral."

"I wasn't talking about no funeral."

"Well, I was. And so was Toy. It seemed like some kind soul went to Smack Markis several weeks ago and asked him was it true that he was sweet on Toy. He says yes, and this good friend of yours tells Smack he had better keep his eye on you, because Toy used to work in your act, and also there was rumors that you was going to get married. Well, Toy says that Smack come right to her and wanted to know was she crazy about you, and she says 'No. Why?' And he says that if his girl——"

"Where does he get that way—calling her his girl?"

"Because," explains Elyse, "Toy made a play for him to make you jealous, and the big dumb ox took it serious."

"Smart girl, that Toy. Go ahead."

"Well, anyway, Smack says that if he so much as catches his girl looking at you or talking to you, he will tear you limb from limb."

"Sweet feller!"

"So what could Toy do? She is pining for you, but if she gives you one word or a smile, Smack is promptly going to render you extinct. And if there is one thing in the world less use than a live juggler, it is a dead one."

"Lay off the wisecracks and stick to the story."

"That's all," says Elyse. "There ain't no more."

"But you ain't told me what to do."

"I would forget all about Toy," says she, "unless you got an awful yen to find out what comes hereafter."

"You don't really think he would tear me to pieces, do you?"

"I don't think it," she answers encouragingly, "I know it."

Tie that if you can. Here I am gaga about a dame which is crazy about me; and all on account she started playing another guy off against me, she has now got to remain away from me in order to save my life. But I think it is very wise of her, because every time I get another flash at that hard pan of Smack's I know that I have less and less yearning to feel him commence to operate on me. That's the way with a guy like him—no brains, but lots of emotion; and his jealousy would most likely be uncontrollable.

About the only thing which saves my life is that I know Toy hates him and wishes she had me back, which only shows a woman never appreciates a good man until he is lost to her forever. So we carry on the queerest kind of love-making. I send messages to her by Elyse and she sends 'em back by the same route. Elyse says Toy is eating out her heart for me, which shows she has got more intelligence than I thought; and finally she is crazy enough to ask can't we meet somewhere in private. In answer, I request Elyse to tell her that she can't love me very much to want to see me get killed by a punk wrastler; and she says it ain't so about her not loving me, but it seems that anything would be preferable to this. So I tell Elyse to tell her that's all right if the "anything" was going to happen to her, but please not to forget that it's me that will be on the receiving end, once this prehysteric man gets on the loose, and that I got a duty to my public, which is to keep myself completely alive and in as good health as possible for their sakes.

But just the same, the thing is telling on Toy. I can see in her face that she is grieving something terrible, and I get to wishing I had of married her in the first place and avoided all this other trouble. Also a guy which knows women had better watch his step when they begin looking at him in a hungry kind of way, because when a dame wants a man there ain't nothing going to stop her from having him. She's gonna be with him if she has to get him murdered to do it.

Just the same, it seemed to me that Toy would have more genuine affection for me than to do anything as silly as what she done. There I was, sitting in my room, all innocent and unsuspicious, and being sorry that Toy wasn't with me, and also glad that Smack Markis wasn't, when the door opens and Elyse comes screaming in.

No knock or nothing. And I know right away that lots of trouble is headed my way.

Elyse grabs my arm and says, "Beat it, quick!"

"Where to?" I inquire.

"Anywhere that's far and sudden."

"What for?"

"To save your life."

"From what?"

"Toy has gone off her nut and had an idea. She says this condition is killing her and she is going to have a show-down."

"Let her have it," says I, "provided she keeps me out of it."

"But she won't keep you out of it. She has tried to tell Markis that it is all off between them, but he won't listen, and so she is bringing him here tonight for that there show-down."

"What?" I'm on my feet then, dabbing at the cold perspiration. "Who is bringing which where when?"

"Toy is bringing Smack Markis here right now. And right before his eyes she is going to announce that she don't give a hoot for him, but is going to marry you—or whatever is left of you when Smack gets through."

"H-h-how do you know?"

"Toy told me. She's due here any minute, and if you don't lam quick, vaudeville is going to lose its premier juggler."

Well, I can take a hint as well as anybody, so I make a grab for my coat, thinking all the time how thoughtless women are when they are in love; when, whang! the door opens and Toy and Smack enter the room. Elyse takes one farewell look at me and edges out.

"Good-by, Eddie," she calls. "I won't forget you."

Toy closes the door and turns toward me. But I ain't looking at her. I got my eye on that ugly physiognomy that Smack Markis carries around with him, and believe me, it ain't no handsomer now than it always was. I realize that I am about to cut my bookings short forever, and I don't cheer about it, either.

Toy commences talking, and she stands right in front of Smack to do it, too—like she was having a lot of trouble slamming an idea through that ivory dome of his.

"I brought you up here," snaps Toy, "to make you understand that I and you are finished. You wouldn't believe it before, so I thought maybe if you met the man face to face which I am in love with and gonna marry, you would understand that I ain't going to throw myself away on no cheap wrastler."

Smack commences to fidget. The muscles are bulging under his coat, and already I can see my most important ligaments flying all over that room.

Smack is standing very close to the door, and the window of my hotel room is seven stories above the street. I ain't got a gun, either. All I have got is a hunch that I am shortly to be spoke of in the past tents.

Well, a guy's brain is supposed to work fast in a situation like that, but mine has sure gone to sleep, because I cannot think of nothing except what an untimely end I am shortly to meet. I am looking at Smack, and Smack is looking at me, and from his expression I can tell positively that he means to do me wrong. But he stands there against the wall, never saying a word. As a matter of fact, Toy is doing enough talking for the three of us.

Right away I can tell that she has had lots of unpleasant things bottled up in herself for a long time, and she takes this opportunity to explain them to Mr. Markis. If I had been Smack I would of been right embarrassed.

All this time I am staring at Smack. He ain't moved an inch, being flattened against that wall with his face kind of red, while he listens to all them things Toy is saying about him being a cheap skate and a punk grappler. I do not know how long this can go on, but so far nothing has happened except Toy's voice.

Well, the strain is getting on my nerves. Somehow this seems to be worse than anything else—just waiting for the homicide to commence. I know that something is going to break pretty soon, and most likely it will positively be me.

I look around the room, wondering ain't there some way out of this trouble, and it happens that my bureau drawer is open. Right away a wild idea hits me square in the brain.

For some time past I had been practicing a new routine with knives. Well, this practicing has been done at home, and right there in my bureau drawer are one dozen of the prettiest, sharpest, nicest knives that you ever set eyes on. I know right away that they are my only hope. I edge over to the bureau, and just then Smack Markis busts in on all the words Toy is uttering.

"I don't want to hear no more of that," he growls. "The time has come——"

I'm sunk and I know it. I guess I'm goofy and I know I'm desperate.

Before I have time to think what I am doing, I have picked up one of them new knives by the blade. I swing my arm and give that knife a whirl. It spins across the room with the sunshine gleaming on the steel, and—thrmmp!—the point of it passes through the leg of Smack's pants about six inches above the knee. It buries itself in the wall, and also attaches Mr. Markis' pants thereto.

Toy ceases talking suddenly and completely. But that ain't what catches my attention. The thing that gives me a wild hope is the look on Smack's pan.

If I ever seen a scared guy, that big egg was it. And before anybody can say anything, I grab knife number two. This one flies faster than the first. It passes through Smack's coat, very close to the epidermic, and also sticks in the wall; so that now Mr. Markis is pinned to the hotel by two knives.

With that he lets out a yell: "Stop it!" he hollers, as I reach for another knife.

The way he said "Stop it!" wasn't no threat. The thing has come so quick and unexpected that the big palooka is terrified. That gives me more courage than I ever knew I had, so when I pick up the third knife, I speak to him sternly.

"You better stand still," I says in a commanding voice. "You sure better not move even one inch."

Well, sir, I am full of enthusiasm, because I know I have got this big bozo licked. For the next three minutes the scene which occurs in that room is a wow. Nine more knives I heave at Mr. Markis, and each of them nine knives bury themselves in the wall after passing through some part of his new suit. Toy is staring at me goggle-eyed and Smack is howling that I am going to kill him, which same I do not deny.

I don't have to explain nothing to that bird; he says everything for me. He yells that he ain't aiming to come between no wild man—which is I—and his gal. He says if I will only spare his life, he will never again so much as look at Toy. And me—I don't say a word. I just plunk them knives all around him until he looks like one of these here decorated pin cushions, and is attached to the wall of that room most thoroughly.

I ain't scared of him no longer and know that I will never need to be again. So I put on my coat and walk over to him, snapping my finger in his face.

"That for you, Mr. Markis," says I—"that, and not nothing more."

I turn to Toy and bow. Also I stick my elbow out and she grabs it. We walk proudly from the room and descend downstairs in the elevator. We ramble slowly up the street, and she is gazing at me with eyes like stars.

"My great big wonderful hero!" she says.

"Huh?" I ask. "What's that?"

"I said you was my hero," she repeats. Then, in a kind of gentle voice: "Can we get married right away, Eddie?"

"Yes," I respond, "I guess so."

"You guess so? Ain't you sure?"

"I'm sure, Toy. We'll get married right now if you say so. You deserve a break."

She gives a little squeal of pleasure at being so imminently the wife of a great juggler like me, and we start towards the license bureau. But even then she don't seem entirely satisfied. She looks up at me and asks a question:

"Eddie," she whispers, "I bet you have got something on your mind."

"I sure have, Toy," I confess. "I was thinking what a knock-out the act will be when I start using that knife-throwing stunt for a finish."

Toy squeezes my arm and looks up at me with the kind of pride a wife ought to feel for her husband.

"You are marvelous, honey. But gee, I never knew you could throw knives so accurate!"

"Neither did I," says I, with a shrug. "And to tell you the truth, Toy, I never would have had the nerve to find out if I hadn't missed Smack's leg with that first knife."

Here's the Pitch

The long slow curve:

"Honey, I'm so glad you insisted that we drive over to spend this nice long Thanksgiving week-end with your mother and dad! You're right, Thanksgiving is one occasion when you really ought to be with the folks."

"My goodness, the amount of time your mother has to spend grocery shopping, not having a freezer like ours! I certainly agree with you about modern conveniences, dear; in spite of occasional minor annoyances, they do save such a lot of trouble and money in the long run."

"I was just thinking, honey, about the difference between you and your dad. Of course, he's a wonderful man, but have you noticed how sort of crabby he is, lately? I mean, he's getting along in years, and little things bother him that wouldn't bother a young man like you at all."

"Darling, isn't it amazing how fast we covered that five hundred miles driving over here? It's like you said; five hundred miles is hardly more than fifty these days—and of course, you're such a wonderful driver that I never think of getting scared, no matter how fast you go!"

And the fast break:

"It just occurred to me, dear—after I disconnected the freezer to scrub it out before we put that half a steer in, I think I remembered to connect it again, but—"

—PEG BRACKEN.

Truth Crushed to Earth Shall Rise Again

ON THE side, I run a small laboratory for disproving things. Given any kind of breaks at all, I can disprove anything. Most of my disproving I do for free, offering my findings to the world for man's greater happiness and welfare. For example, there's the job I finished only this week, in which I disproved conclusively an item I encountered in a recent magazine.

"Children like to have adults read aloud to them even when they don't understand what is being read," the article stated. "You can alternate Peter Rabbit with Plato, and they will listen to both with equal fascination."

That was enough for me. After dinner I called Jimmy and told him to bring his Peter Rabbit book. "I'm going to read to you," I said, smiling craftily. My family doesn't know about the laboratory.

"One day Peter Rabbit was skipping through the brier patch on his way home," I began. "He was in a great hurry because he was afraid of being caught by the fox. Flowing Gold looks good in the fourth at Jamaica, especially if the track is fast. Only that morning, Peter had heard that the fox—"

"The radio said that Flowing Gold was scratched," Jimmy said, interrupting the story. "Besides, she's not a bad mudder."

A lot of people would have stopped right there, but I decided to probe a little deeper. The next day I lifted Paula up on the arm of my chair.

"Once upon a time there was a little girl named Goldilocks," I said, "who one day went for a walk in the big green forest. Don't miss Captain Cutthroat, the most exciting and thrilling story ever filmed. In gorgeous technicolor. When Goldilocks reached a house in the middle of the—"

"That Captain Cutthroat is a smeller," Paula said. "I saw it at the Strand."

I left Paula and hunted up Susan. She was playing United Nations with the other kids and, since she was Russia and not attending the meeting, naturally had some time on her hands.

"Susan," I said, "your Uncle Caskie wants to tell you a story.

"This is the story," I began, "of a little boy who was so crazy that he traded his cow for a hatful of beans."

"He's crazier than me," Susan said.

"Crazier than *I*," I corrected.

"Really?" she said incredulously. "That crazy?"

Oh, well, it only takes two out of three.

—CASKIE STINNETT.

The Fittest Don't Always Survive

AS FAR as I'm concerned, they can leave the home-hints columns out of the newspapers. I'm through. Their suggestions for the safe removal of ticks, in the Your Family and Mine column of the Evening Leader, were about the rawest advice I've ever followed. Cover the tick with a coating of cold cream, the Evening Leader said, and then dab it with cotton dipped in ether. The cold cream will make it let go, the ether will deliver the knockout. It seemed simple, in a Your Family and Mine sort of way.

It just happened that the following day I returned from a walk around my mortgage, and there on my right forearm was a small tick. Coldly I set out the deadly vials. The tick gave no indication of alarm when I coated it with cold cream, nor did its expression change when I opened the can of ether. I smiled craftily. In sixty seconds, according to the directions, the tick would let go and fall.

It was late that night when I recovered consciousness and, although several of my neighbors were there, rubbing my wrists and fanning me with the Evening Leader, the tick was gone. There seems little doubt but that I let go and fell *first.*

Maybe I'm just naturally suitable for framing, editor, but you'll never catch me falling for your advice again.

—CASKIE STINNETT.

Sleepyhead

WE ARE always finding out something new about sleep. (Maybe YOU'RE not, but that's why I'M here!) For example, by the use of brain-wave tests, muscle-sugar reactions and plain common sense—a new development in science, by the way—it has been discovered that there are two kinds of people. I mean two types of sleepers: Those who wake up and those who don't.

Let me clarify that a little, if you're not going anyplace right away. There are people who wake up awake, and then there are those who wake up still asleep. See? One group, which I call Antimorpheustic or Bloody Bores, wakes up promptly, full of get-up-and-go. They bound out of bed quivering with *joie de vivre,* singing loudly and lustily, waking everyone else up and very rarely getting invited to spend the night at my house.

These people are usually half-dead about eight o'clock at night and are as likely then to trump your ace as not. They form the hard core of party spoilers who always want to go home and sleep as soon as things start getting lively.

The second group, the Promorpheustic or Good Joe bunch, is more or less the reverse. They wake up feeling as if it is extremely unlikely they'll live. They feel in the early morn as if they had been digging trenches all night, instead of sleeping. Nevertheless, this group does most of the world's important work since it really comes to life about cocktail hour, and from then on, let 'er rip, boy!

The difference, science says, is a matter of metabolism and stuff. If your body temperature zooms up beginning in the early morn you will awaken about seven A.M. fresh as a daisy and ready to wake decent people who are still sleeping, up.

If, however, your sluggish body temperature hits around absolute zero at four A.M. and then budges only slightly as the dawn comes up, you arise—if you do arise—ready to go back to bed again until noontime.

You can't change your type any more than you can change the color of your hair. (Hey! what am I talking about?) You can't change your type any more than you can change the stripes on a zebra.

Actually, though, a great deal of sleep isn't necessary. Thomas Edison only got four hours a night, and when I was living upstairs over that night club I never got any.

Experimentally, people have been kept without sleep for a hundred hours or more. It didn't harm them physically. Of course they were irritable, irrational, confused and mean-tempered. . . . But then, who isn't?

—ROBERT FONTAINE.

A CALL ON THE PRESIDENT

By DAMON RUNYON

§ *In as charming a tale as ever emerged from Runyonland, Joe and Ethel Turp of Brooklyn decide that a talk with the President of the United States is in order. Joe and Ethel are solid citizens and do not like it when the Government fires Jim the mailman. Jim, Ethel ses, is too old to do anything except carry the mail and would starve to death in no time.*

APRIL 21, 1937

WHEN I got home from work the other night my wife Ethel ses O Joe, an awful thing has happened. Jim the mailman got fired.

I ses who fired him? She ses why, the Government fired him. Somebody told the Government that they saw him take a letter out of his mail sack and burn it. The Government ses Jim, why did you do such a thing, and Jim would not tell so they fired him.

She ses Joe, you go and see some politicians and have them make the Government put Jim the mailman back to work right away because he is too old to do anything else but carry the mail and he would starve to death in no time. It is not justice to fire a man who has carried the mail for over thirty years, she ses.

I ses Ethel sweets, I do not know no politicians that have got anything to do with the Government or justice. I ses anyway we are only little people and they are big people and what is the use of talking to them? I ses they would only give me a pushing around because that is what big people always do to little people.

Well, Ethel ses, who runs the Government? I ses the President of the United States runs the Government and she ses I bet anything the President of the United States would give Jim the mailman back his job if we tell him about it. Lets us go see the President of the United States.

I ses Ethel sugar plum, the President of the United States lives in Washington and he is a busy fellow and I do not think he would have time to see us even if we went there, and she ses now there you go rooting against yourself like you always do. We will go to Washington and see the President of the United States because it is important that Jim the mailman gets his job back. Why, she ses Jim the mailman would simply lay down and die if he could not keep on carrying the mail.

So the next day I got a days layoff and then we climbed in the old bucket and drove to Washington and my wife Ethel wore her best dress and her new hat, and

I put on my gray suit and a necktie and when we arrived in Washington about noon, I ses to a cop, look cop, where do you find the President of the United States? He ses I never find him.

O, I ses, a wise guy, hay? I ses cop, I am a citizen of the United States of America and this is my wife Ethel and she is a citizen too and I asked you a question like a gentleman and you have a right to answer me like a gentleman.

Yes, my wife Ethel ses, we are from Brooklyn and we do not like to have hick cops get fresh with us. O, the cop ses, I am a hick am I, and she ses well you look like one to me. I ses pipe down Ethel honey, and let me do the talking will you, and the cop ses Buddy I have got one of those too, and I sympathize with you.

He ses you have to go to the White House to find the President of the United States. You follow this street a ways he ses, and you cannot miss. Give him my regards when you see him, the cop ses. I ses what name will I tell him. The cop ses George, and I ses George what? My wife Ethel ses drive on Joe, that hick cop is just trying to kid people.

So we followed the street like the cop ses and pretty soon we came to a big building in a yard and I ses well, Ethel, I guess that is the White House all right. Then I parked the old bucket up against the curb and we got out and walked into the yard and up to the door of this building and at the door was another cop.

He ses what do you want? I ses who wants to know? He ses I do. I ses all right, we want to see the President of the United States and he ses so does a hundred million other people. He ses what do you want to see him about anyway? My wife Ethel ses Joe, why do you waste your time talking to hick cops? I never saw so many hick cops in my life. She ses in Brooklyn people do not have to go around answering questions from cops.

Well, go back to Brooklyn the cop ses. Anyway, get away from here. I do not like to look at you he ses. Your faces make me tired. I ses cop, you are no rose geranium yourself when it comes to looks. I ses I am a citizen of the United States of America and I know my rights. I do not have to take no lip off of cops. I ses it is a good thing for you that you have got that uniform on, and that I have respect for the law or I would show you something.

He ses you and who else? I ses I do not need nobody else and my wife Ethel ses show him something anyway, Joe, and I might have showed him something all right but just then a fellow with striped pants on came out of the door and ses what is the trouble here?

I ses there is no trouble, just a fresh cop. I ses my wife Ethel and me want to see the President of the United States and this jerk here ses we cannot do so. I ses that is always the way it is with cops, when they get that uniform on they want to start pushing people around.

I ses I am a citizen of the United States of America and it is a fine note if a citizen cannot see the President of the United States when he wants to without a lot of cops horning in. I ses it is not justice for cops to treat a citizen that way. I ses what is the President of the United States for if a citizen cannot see him? My wife Ethel ses yes, we are not going to eat him, and I ses Ethel baby, you better let me handle this situation.

The fellow in the striped pants ses what do you want to see the President of the United States about? I ses look Mister, we came all the way from Brooklyn to see the President of the United States and I have got to be back to work on my job tomorrow and if I stop and tell everybody what I want to see him about I won't have no time left. I ses Mister, what is so tough about seeing the President of the United States? When he was after this job he was glad to see anybody. I ses is he like those politicians in Brooklyn now or what?

Wait a minute, the fellow in the striped pants ses, and he went back into the building and after awhile he came out again and ses the President of the United States will see you at once. What is your name? I ses my name is Joe Turp and this is my wife Ethel. He ses I am pleased to meet you and I ses the same to you. Then he took us into the building and finally into a big office, and there was the President of the United States all right. I could tell him from his pictures.

He smiled at us and the fellow in the striped pants who took us in ses this is Joe Turp of Brooklyn and his wife Ethel, and the President of the United States shook hands with us and ses I am glad to see you, and I ses likewise. He ses how are things in Brooklyn? Rotten, I ses. They always are. The Dodgers are doing better but they need more pitching, I ses. How are things in Washington? He ses not so good. He ses I guess we need more pitching here too.

He told us to set down and then he ses, what is on your mind Joe, but there was some other fellows in the office and I ses Your Honor, what my wife Ethel and me want to see you about is strictly on the q t and he laughed and motioned at the other fellows and they went out of the room laughing too and my wife Ethel ses what is so funny around here anyway? I ses nix Ethel. I ses nix now. Kindly let me handle this situation.

Then I ses to the President of the United States, Your Honor, you do not know me and I do not know you so we start even. I know you are a busy fellow and I will not waste your time any more than I have to so I better come to the point right away, I ses. My wife Ethel and me want to talk to you about Jim the mailman.

Yes, Ethel ses, he got fired from his job. I ses Ethel sugar plum, please do not butt in on this. I will tell the President of the United States all about it. Your Honor, I ses, when women start to tell something they always go about it the wrong end to, and he ses yes but they mean well. Who is Jim the mailman?

I ses Your Honor, Jim the mailman is a fellow over sixty years old and he has been carrying the mail in our neighborhood for thirty some odd years. My wife Ethel and me were little kids when Jim the mailman started carrying the mail. Your Honor, I ses, you may not believe it but my wife Ethel was a good looking little squab when she was a kid. I can well believe it, the President of the United States ses.

Well, Your Honor, I ses, you would think Jim the mailman was a grouchy old guy until you got to know him. He is a tall thin fellow with humped over shoulders from carrying that mail sack around and he has long legs like a pair of scissors and gray hair and wears specs. He is no where near as grouchy as he looks. The reason he looks grouchy is because his feet always hurt him.

Yes, my wife Ethel ses, I gave him some lard to rub on his feet one day and Jim the mailman ses he never had anything help him so much. My mother used to rub my pops feet with lard when he came home with them aching. My pops was a track walker in the subway she ses. I ses look Ethel, the President of the United States is not interested in your pops feet and she ses well that is how I thought of the lard for Jim the mailman.

I ses Your Honor, Jim the mailman was always real nice to kids. I remember one Christmas he brought me a sack of candy and a Noahs ark. Yes, my wife Ethel ses, and once he gave me a doll that ses mamma when you punched it in the stomach. I ses Ethel, honey, the President of the United States does not care where you punch it. Well, she ses you punched it in the stomach if you wanted it to say mamma.

Your Honor, I ses, old Missus Crusper

lived a couple of doors from us and she was about the same age as Jim the mailman. She was a little off her nut. My wife Ethel ses Your Honor, she was not so. She was just peculiar. You should not say such things about Missus Crusper the poor old thing Joe, she ses. You ought to be ashamed of yourself to say such things.

All right, Ethel baby, I ses. She was peculiar Your Honor. I mean Missus Crusper. She was a little old white-haired lady with a voice like a canary bird and she had not been out of her house in twenty-five years and most of the time not out of bed. Something happened to her when her son Johnny was born.

I had to stop my story a minute because I noticed Ethel at a window acting very strange and I ses Ethel, what is the idea of looking out that window and screwing up your face the way you are doing and she ses I am making snoots at that hick cop. He is right under this window and I have got him half crazy. I ses Your Honor, kindly excuse my wife Ethel, but she is getting even with a cop who tried to keep us from seeing you and the President of the United States laughed and ses well, what about Missus Crusper?

I ses well, Missus Crusper's name before she got married was Kitten O'Brien, Your Honor, and her old man ran a gin mill in our neighborhood but very respectable. She married Henry Crusper when she was eighteen and the old folks in our neighborhood ses it broke Jim the mailman's heart. He went to school with her and Henry Crusper and Jim the mailman used to follow Kitten O'Brien around like a pup but he never had no chance.

Henry Crusper was a good-looking kid, I ses, and Jim the mailman was as homely as a mule and still is. Besides he was an orphan and Henry Crusper's old man had a nice grocery store. He gave the store to Henry when he married Kitten O'Brien. But Jim the mailman did not get mad about losing Missus Crusper like people do nowadays. He ses he did not blame her and he ses he certainly did not blame Henry Crusper. He stayed good friends with them both and used to be around with them a lot but he never looked at another broad again.

The President of the United States ses another what? Another broad I ses. Another woman I ses. O, he ses, I see.

Yes, my wife Ethel ses, I bet you would not be the way Jim the mailman was, Joe Turp. I bet you would have been as sore as a goat if I had married Linky Moses but I bet you would have found somebody else in no time. I ses please, Ethel. Please now. Anyway, I ses, look how Linky Moses turned out. How did Linky Moses turn out, the President of the United States ses, and I ses he turned out a bum.

Your Honor, I ses, Missus Crusper married Henry Crusper when she was about eighteen. Henry was a good steady-going fellow and he made her a fine husband from what everybody ses and in our neighborhood if anybody does not make a fine husband it gets talked around pretty quick.

She was crazy about him but she was crazier still about her son Johnny especially after Henry died. That was when Johnny was five or six years old. Henry got down with pneumonia during a tough winter.

Yes, my wife Ethel ses, my mother ses he never would wear an overcoat no matter how cold it was. My mother ses not wearing overcoats is why lots of people get pneumonia and die. I always try to make Joe wear his overcoat and a muffler too, Ethel ses. I ses Ethel, never mind what you make me wear, and she ses well Joe, I only try to keep you healthy.

Missus Crusper must have missed Henry a lot, Your Honor, I ses. Henry used to carry her up and down stairs in his arms. He waited on her hand and foot. Of course much of this was before my time and what I tell you is what the old people in our neighborhood told me. After Henry died it was Jim the mailman who carried Missus Crusper up and down stairs in his arms until she got so she could not leave her bed at all and then Jim the mailman spent all his spare time setting there talking to her and waiting on her like she was a baby.

I ses I did not know Missus Crusper until I was about ten years old and got to running around with Johnny. He was a tough kid, Your Honor, and I had him marked stinko even then and so did all the other kids in the neighborhood. His mother could not look out after him much and he did about as he pleased. He was a natural-born con artist and he could always salve her into believing whatever he wanted her to believe.

She thought he was the smartest kid in the world and that he was going to grow up to be a big man. She was proud of Johnny and what he was going to be. Nobody in our neighborhood wanted to tell her that he was no good. I can see her now, Your Honor, a little lady with a lace cap on her head leaning out of the window by her bed and calling Johnny so loud you could hear her four blocks away because she always called him like she was singing.

My wife Ethel had quit making snoots at the cop and was sitting in a chair by the window and she jumped out of the chair and ses yes, Your Honor, Missus Crusper sing-sanged O hi, Johnny, and a hey Johnny, and a ho, Johnny, just like that.

The fellow in the striped pants stuck his head in the door but the President of the United States waggled a finger at him and he closed the door again and I ses look Ethel, when you holler like that you remind me of your mother. She ses what is the matter with my mother, and I ses nothing that being deaf and dumb will not cure. I ses Ethel, it is not dignified to holler like that in the presence of the President of the United States.

Why, Ethel ses, I was only showing how Missus Crusper used to call Johnny by sing-sanging O hi, Johnny, and a hey Johnny, and a ho, Johnny. I ses Ethel, that will do. I ses do you want to wake the dead?

Your Honor, I ses, Jim the mailman was around Missus Crusper's house a lot and he was around our neighborhood a good deal too and he knew what Johnny was doing. As Johnny got older Jim the mailman tried to talk to him and make him behave but that only made Johnny take to hating Jim the mailman. The old folks ses Jim the mailman wanted to marry Missus Crusper after she got over being so sorry about Henry but one day she told him she could never have anything to do with a man who spoke disrespectfully of her late husband and ordered him out of her house.

Afterwards Jim the mailman found out that Johnny had told her Jim had said something bad about Henry Crusper around the neighborhood and nothing would make her believe any different until long later. Your Honor, I ses, Johnny Crusper was one of the best liars in the world even when he was only a little kid.

The fellow in the striped pants came in the room about now and he bent over and said something in a whisper to the President of the United States but the President waved his hand and ses tell him I am busy with some friends from Brooklyn and the fellow went out again.

Your Honor, I ses, this Johnny Crusper got to running with some real tough guys when he was about seventeen and pretty soon he was in plenty of trouble with the cops but Jim the mailman always managed to get him out without letting his mother know. The old folks ses it used to keep Jim the mailman broke getting Johnny out of trouble.

Finally one day Johnny got in some real bad trouble that Jim the mailman could not square or nobody else and Johnny had to leave town in a big hurry. He did not stop to say good-by to his mother. The old folks ses Jim the mailman hocked his salary with a loan shark to get Johnny the dough to leave town on and some ses he sent Johnny more dough afterwards to keep going. But Jim the mailman never ses a word himself about it one way or the other so nobody but him and Johnny knew just what happened about that.

Your Honor, I ses, Johnny going away without saying good-by made Missus Crusper very sick and this was when she commenced being peculiar. Old Doc Steele ses she was worrying herself to death because she never heard from Johnny. He ses he would bet if she knew where Johnny was and if he was all right it would save her life and her mind too but nobody knew where Johnny was so there did not seem to be anything anybody could do about that.

Then one day Jim the mailman stopped at Missus Crusper's house and gave her a letter from Johnny. It was not a long letter and it was from some place like Vancouver and it ses Johnny was working and doing well and that he loved her dearly and thought of her all the time. I know it ses that, Your Honor, because Jim the mailman wrote it all out himself and read it to me and ses how does it sound?

I ses it sounded great. It looked great too because Jim the mailman had fixed up the envelope at the post office so it looked as if it had come through the mail all right and he had got hold of one of Johnny's old school books and made a good stab at imitating Johnny's handwriting. It was not a hard job to do that. Johnny never let himself get past the fourth grade and his handwriting was like a child would do.

Missus Crusper never bothered about the handwriting anyway, Your Honor. She was so glad to hear from Johnny she sent for everybody in the neighborhood and read them the letter. It must have sounded genuine because Jennie Twofer went home and told her old man that Mrs. Crusper had got a letter from Johnny and her old man told his brother Fred who was a plainclothes cop and Fred went around to see Missus Crusper and find out where Johnny was. Jim the mailman got hold of Fred first and they had a long talk and Fred went away without asking Missus Crusper anything.

Yes, my wife Ethel ses, that Jennie Twofer always was a two-faced meddlesome old thing and nobody ever had any use for her. I ses look, Ethel, kindly do not knock our neighbors in public. I ses wait until we get back home and she ses all right but Jennie Twofer is two face just the same.

Your Honor, I ses, every week for over ten years old Missus Crusper got a letter from Johnny and he was always doing well although he seemed to move around a lot. He was in Arizona California Oregon and everywhere else. Jim the mailman made him a mining engineer so he could have a good excuse for moving around. On Missus Crusper's birthdays and on Christmas she always got a little present from him. Jim the mailman took care of that.

She kept the letters in a box under her bed and she would read them to all her old friends when they called and brag about the way Johnny was doing and what a good boy he was to his mother. Your Honor, old chromos in our neighborhood whose sons were bums and who had a pretty good idea the letters were phony would set and listen to Missus Crusper read them and tell her Johnny surely was a wonderful man.

About a month ago the only legitimate letter that came to Missus Crusper since Johnny went away bobbed up in Jim the mailman's sack, I ses. It was a long thin envelope and Jim the mailman opened it and read it and then he touched a match to it and went on to Missus Crusper's house and delivered a letter to her from Johnny in Australia. This letter ses he was just closing a deal that would make him a millionaire and that he would then come home and bring her a diamond breastpin and never leave her again as long as he lived.

But Your Honor, I ses, Jim the mailman knew that it would be the last letter he would ever deliver to Missus Crusper because old Doc Steele told him the day before that she had only a few hours more to go and she died that night.

Jim the mailman was setting by her bed. He ses that at the very last she tried to lean out the window and call Johnny.

Well I ses, some louse saw Jim the mailman burn that letter and turned him in to the Government and got him fired from his job but Jim could not do anything else but burn it because it was a letter from the warden of the San Quentin prison where Johnny had been a lifer for murder all those years, telling Missus Crusper her son had been killed by the guards when he was trying to escape and saying she could have his body if she wanted it.

Your Honor, I ses, I guess we have got plenty of gall coming to you with a thing like this when you are so busy. I ses my wife Ethel wanted me to go to some politicians about it but I told her the best we would get from politicians would be a pushing around and then she ses we better see you and here we are.

But I ses it is only fair to tell you that if you do anything to help Jim the mailman we cannot do anything for you in return because we are just very little people and all we can do is say much obliged and God bless you and that is what everybody in our neighborhood would say.

Well, my wife Ethel ses, Jim the mailman has got to have his job back because I would hate to have anybody else bring me my mail. I ses Ethel baby, the only mail I ever knew you to get was a Valentine from Linky Moses four years ago and I told him he better not send you any more and she ses yes, that is the mail I mean.

The President of the United States ses Joe and Missus Turp think no more of it. You have come to the right place. I will take good care of the matter of Jim the mailman. Then he pushes a button on his desk and the man in the striped pants came in and the President ses tell them I will have two more for luncheon. The fellow ses who are they and the President ses my friends Joe and Missus Turp of Brooklyn and my wife Ethel ses it is a good job I wore my new hat.

We drove back home in the old bucket after we had something to eat and I got back to work the next day on time all right and a couple of days later I saw Jim the mailman around delivering mail so I knew he was okay too.

I never gave the trip to Washington any more thought and my wife did not say anything about it either for a couple of weeks then one night she woke me up out of a sound sleep by jabbing me in the back with her elbow and ses Joe, I have been thinking about something. I ses look Ethel, you do your thinking in the day time please and let me sleep.

But she ses no, listen Joe. She ses if ever I go back to Washington again I will give that hick cop a piece of my mind because I have just this minute figured out what he meant when he said he had one of those too and sympathized with you.

TOLL BRIDGE

By SAM HELLMAN

§ *Should you argue with your partner at bridge? Merely to point out faults and mistakes, to clear the air and resolve lurking doubts? There are two points of view about this, somewhat depending on circumstances. . . .*

APRIL 5, 1930

MY DEAR!" gasps Olivia. "Are you intimating that the Streeters cheat at bridge?"

"Of course they do," I returns, "but they don't know it. Two folks playing together as long as they have can't help cheating. To them, every hesitation, every lip movement, every flick of an eyelid's a signal painted on a white-washed fence in black letters ten feet high. Luke can tell in an instant whether Sadie's three-heart bid's a push-over, a gamble with the milk money, or a leap out on a limb for a force-up."

"Maybe they do understand each other," says the missis, "but there's no law against that, is there?"

"No," I admits. "Any set game's bound to become technically crooked after a while. That's why practically every club compels the boys and girls to pivot."

"Perhaps," suggests Olivia, "if you were to study me and my moods a bit more——"

"Wouldn't do any good," I cuts in. "The Streeters can play rings around us to begin with, and besides, have too long a start. By the time we got as intimate with our inner thoughts as they are, the sheriff'd be out on the porch auctioning off the bird's-eye-maple bedroom set."

"Well," says the frau, "we can't play against each other. There's no percentage in that."

"True," I comes back, "but where's the pretty, pretty percentage in putting the bee on the bank roll for Luke Streeter and his sister? They're not our friends any more—they're paid companions. Fifty-eight dollars last week, nearly seventy tonight, and there's no telling when they'll up and ask for a raise in salary."

"Our luck'll turn," predicts Olivia.

"Yeh," I grunts. "It's been turning for six months now—like a pneumatic drill, getting us deeper and deeper in the hole. I'm afraid we'll have to pass 'em up and pick on somebody our size."

"How do you get that—our size?" demands the missis. "I know more about contract than Sadie Streeter's forgotten—I mean——"

"Never mind what you mean," I interrupts. "That eighteen-hundred-point wallop you took on the chin's the tip-off."

"I wouldn't have been set at all," she snaps, "if you'd 've displayed as much intelligence as a gnat. The idea of you taking me out with only four spades to the queen!"

"I was trying to show you weakness," says I.

"You don't have to show me weakness, ever!" shoots over Olivia. "I can always see that just by looking at you."

"Even so," I returns, sarcastic, "you can't go to six hearts on my retreating chin and watery eyes. Anyhow, I'm through being a pay roll. If you want to play with the Streeters, get yourself another partner. I hear there's an agency in town that supplies companions for lonely women."

"I think I'll try it," says she. "Even if they send me a backward Eskimo, it'll be so much velvet. He'll know enough, at any rate, not to lead me a club when I've been discarding high diamonds for an hour."

"Probably," I agrees, "when he once fathoms your quaint device of discarding from fright or from a feeling that the Swiss tariff on Irish lace's unfair to Uruguay. I couldn't tell by your sloughs this evening whether you wanted a diamond or a pair of onyx earrings."

"Of course you couldn't, you dear," coos Olivia. "That's why you played a spade you'd reneged on and let Sadie get rid of the losing club that'd have set her."

"Oh, all right," I growls. "Have it my way, but——"

"Pardon me for intruding my aged personality at this point," remarks Uncle Joe Brice, "but how long does this go on as a rule?"

"Hours and hours. This hut's pointed out by the sight-seeing busses as The House of a Thousand Post-Mortems."

"Do you have to play bridge?" inquires Brice.

"No," I replies, "I don't have to. I do it naturally and with considerable skill, but that niece of yours is undoubtedly——"

"Undoubtedly," cuts in Uncle Joe, "but you never seem to notice it when you come home with the loot. You folks were probably taken tonight because you didn't have the tickets—or don't you have to have 'em in contract?"

"The papers and the child'll do you no harm," says I, "but it takes more than mere cards and spades to get the message to Garcia in this pastime. A pair of slickers'll make a grand slam and the rent money out of the same layout that a couple of retailers wouldn't get to first base with. You get only what you bid for in contract, and what you bid depends on the information you trade over the table."

"I should imagine," observes Brice, "that Olivia would make an excellent partner. She was never what you would call a reticent child——"

"Says you and says me!" I interjects. "There never was a chattier chit, but it doesn't help my heart make any to learn that Annabel Miffle's domestic affairs have gone tabloid. What I want's the scandal about her hand."

"Lots of good it'd do you," sniffs the little lady. "I could draw it in pictures or put it in Braille and still it'd mean no more to you than a Mozart mazurka would to a deaf-mute Digger Indian. I certainly did you a dirty trick, uncle, when I made you an in-law to this."

"That's all right," declares the big-hearted Brice. "The Seven Sutherland Sisters didn't know anything about contract, either, but they still had beautiful hair. Pete may yet work out to be an indulgent husband and a credit to the community at large."

"I wish he was at large," says Olivia. "As far as I'm concerned, he'll never be anything but a symptom of something chronic."

"Yeh," I grunts. "A chronic casualty of your misplays."

"Better pipe down, you two," suggests the elder statesman. "Remember the woman out West who shot her husband over a bridge hand?"

"Well and favorably," returns my wife. Brice picks this as a good spot for a detour.

"For my weight and age," says he, "I used to wave a pretty red flag in auction, but contract's a mystery to me——"

"You and Pete," chimes in Olivia.

"How," inquires Brice, "would you like to teach me the pastime–this greatest of American indoor spats?"

"Sure," I comes back.

"I laugh immoderately," announces the wife. "If you really want to learn the game, I'm the——"

"I laugh immoderately, doubled," says I. "You don't want to take lessons in revoking and leading out of turn, do you?"

"Suppose," offers Uncle Joe, "you both take me on. One of you can teach me the dance routine and the other the dialogue. After I get the hang of the game I'll cut in when you're playing the Streeters. That'll bust up a lot of perfect understandings, and some not so perfect, and, besides, bring a glow of peace and benevolence to the bridge table. You might even win enough from me to——"

"But," demurs Olivia, "I don't want to take money from you."

"Don't you worry," says Brice, pulling her to his lap. "Anything I lose means only so much less residue for my residuary legatee, once you've buried me with simple honors."

II

The following Tuesday we again play with the Streeters, and we're once more taken to the cleaners in a big way. Luke and his sister run shoestrings into tanneries by dovetailing their bids, while Olivia and I don't get together as often as a couple of Australian sheep herders. There's some difference of opinion as to where the fault lies, but at two in the morning the responsibility's still unfixed. That night Uncle Joe shows up for his lesson.

"Now, listen," says he. "I'm here for contract, not conflict. I've kept unmarried for a purpose. Please respect that purpose. All I want from you is the rules and regulations of the game, the simple rudiments that even you agree upon. There are some, aren't there?"

"The merest handful," I returns, "but you can count upon a peaceful and instructive evening, unaccustomed as we are to such. We are not unmindful of the fact that you're our wealthy bachelor uncle——"

"That's the spirit," interrupts Brice heartily. "Bring on the deck and let's to our learning."

"Do I understand," I opens up, "that you used to play a bouncing rubber of auction?"

"I always agreed with myself that I did," he replies, "but then I never went to the altar for a real criticism. May I also add that I've seldom been called to the phone when Lenz or Whitehead was asked for?"

"You're a very lucky lad," I tells him, "to be getting that kind of service. I'm regularly called to the phone when Annie or the Aquarium is asked for, but that's neither here nor in the operating room at St. Luke's. We're talking about contract, aren't we?"

"Are we?" inquires Uncle Joe politely.

"Contract," I explains, "is no different from auction except in the bidding——"

"And the scoring," contributes Olivia.

"My dear," says I coldly, "there are some buttons upstairs that need shirts sewed onto them. Will you kindly attend to it and leave the menfolks to their mulled wine and walnuts?"

"I'll do nothing of the sort," she flares. "It's my uncle who wants to learn auction, not yours."

"Selfish!" I scowls. "Won't even split an uncle with me."

"Keep this up," yelps Uncle Joe Brice, "and there'll be no uncle to split. He'll just disappear in a cloud of codicils. Come on. 'Livy, you tell me how the game goes."

The frau picks up where I'd left off, going into a detailed diagram of the bidding and the scoring, with side excursions into "vulnerability" and the other features that distinguish contract bridge from a bad crop year in the Yakima Valley.

"The points sure run high, loose and liberal in this pastime," remarks the old-timer. "How do you keep from confusing the count with the 1930 census figures?"

"That's easy," says I. "You put your fingers in the mouth of the census figures. If they bite you they're contract scores. How'd you like to have the game really explained to you by one in the know?"

"Shoot," invites Brice. "I'm always willing to listen to both sides of any question."

"Suit yourself," shrugs Olivia. "You might learn shark fishing from what he tells you, but you won't even get a faint clew to contract."

"That's all right," says Uncle Joe. "I've always been rather keen about shark fishing. Let's go."

I decides to do my explaining with a couple of hands dealt face up. In my mitt are the ace-king of spades and the ace of hearts. The rest of the cards are so much riffraff. Brice has a fair bunch of pushers, but nothing you could bid on even if you were playing for matches and trying to save a rubber.

"In auction, " I begins, "you'd throw this hand in the ash pit. But not so in contract. I'd say one club."

"A club!" exclaims Brice. "Why, you've only got four of 'em to the nine."

"Very true," I admits, with a trace of condescension, "but I'd bid a club even if I was blank in 'em. This is what is known to us adepts as the Vanderbilt convention. I'm merely telling you that I have three quick tricks."

"I see," says Uncle Joe. "What am I supposed to do—blush prettily and pass?"

"You can blush as prettily as you please," I returns, "but you must never pass. With your fist two courses are open. You can either go to one without or——"

"——you can call a meeting of your creditors," horns in Olivia. "Bid a no-trump on that mess and you'll sleep in the streets. Why waste your time with the Vanderbilt convention? It's as *passé* as a poke bonnet. Nowadays nobody plays it but grocers' adopted daughters and notaries whose commissions have expired."

"I rather like it," observes Brice. "In fact, I'm for anything associated with the Vanderbilts. Look what they've done with the Grand Central Station."

"A noble piece of work," I agrees, "but let's sidetrack the Central and get back to our beagle hounds. Perhaps your hand is a bit weak for a bid. In that case, you say a diamond, which indicates you haven't anything but a sunny disposition and a date with your dentist next Wednesday afternoon."

"I trust," says Uncle Joe, "I'm not left in it. After all, three square-cuts to the seven are nothing to parade the troops for."

"I wouldn't leave my worst enemy with the diamond," I assures him. "The chances are I'd go to a no-trump."

"Sure," cuts in the missis, "and if he was pressed any he'd go to seven of 'em. Ever since he heard of the Vanderbilt convention he thinks he is Vanderbilt."

"Personally," says Brice, "I think that club bid is the sliced sausage. I'll bet it gets you into jams seventy-five times out of a hundred like the double of a one no-trump. If your opponent has a good hand and you have a hot one, what can your partner have?"

"Good gosh!" I exclaims. "He's just sat down at the table and is already criticizing the food!"

I deals another sample hand, and this time I treats myself royally. I've a flock of spades with three honors, the ace-king of hearts and a peck of portraiture in the other suits. Uncle Joe has the two black aces, three other spades and a blank in diamonds.

"What would you bid with that layout?" he asks. "Three coal heavers?"

"I would in auction," I replies, "but not in contract. I'd open up with two, which is the strongest of all makes, and you'd have to keep the bidding open, going to a couple of no-trumps if you had no help. This is the way our hands'd work out: After my starter, you'd jump to three spades and I'd come back with four hearts to tip you that I had the top of the suit. You'd name five clubs, thus placing the ace for me. I'd then call five spades and you'd run to six diamonds——"

"Without a diamond?" demands Brice.

"Because you're without a diamond," says I. "You'd be telling me you had no losing tricks in the suit. Thereupon I'd bid seven spades and we'd make a grand slam without any trouble. Wouldn't we, honey?"

"I doubt it," declares the frau. "The material's there, but the chances are you'd block yourself or renege or something, and finish up with a handsome enameled set."

"She's not a wife," says I. "She's just a pal. . . . Beginning to get an idea of the game, Unk?"

"It's sitting on my lap and calling me papa," he answers, "but I've been wondering what the result'd be if you happened to be watching a dog fight at the moment and left me in that six-diamond bid."

"I wouldn't worry about that," says I. "The best hostesses are no longer featuring dog fights at bridge parties. There's enough battling going on as it is."

"I should imagine there would be," remarks Brice. "Never have I seen a game where your partner could do you so dirty. You sure got to play it in cahoots."

"Pete does," offers Olivia—"in cahoots with the opponents."

"I have to," says I. "I can't get any help from you. You wouldn't throw me a deuce if I was drowning."

"Lay off, love birds," growls Uncle Joe, "and get on with the lesson. I expect to get a diploma and a scholarship before I leave. Where do we go from where we were?"

We resume play with cold hands, Olivia kibitzing from the sidelines. The old boy's quick on the pick-up and in an hour or so he's far enough along in contract to take care of himself in the clinches. I'm about to ring the bell and dismiss the class when the missis reminds me that we haven't introduced Brice to the goulash.

"What's that?" he wants to know. "Or am I too young to be told?"

"A goulash," says I, "is to contract what spit-in-the-ocean is to a poker game—a pain in the neck, no matter who writes the nation's songs. It's got about as much business in sound bridge as a silk hat has at a clambake. It's the——"

"All right," cuts in Uncle Joe, "but let's get to the meat of the goulash. How do you do it, and when?"

"When everybody passes," I explains, "all the hands are thrown together counterclockwise and dealt without shuffling, five, five and three. Then the partners exchange cards, one, two and three. The result is a lot of cock-eyed mitts and slam bids. It's not at all unusual to gather thirteen of a suit and then have it topped a couple of times by bozos holding thirteen cards in a higher suit."

"The goulash doesn't click so heavy with me," says Brice, "but I expect I'm going to like contract. It ought to be a great game when you once know your people."

"Yeh," I grunts, "like the Streeters know each other, for example."

"Well," opines Uncle Joe, "I don't imagine it'll take me long to tumble to their stuff. I'm a fairly good journeyman when it comes to reading folks' faces."

"You can read Sadie's between the lines," suggests Olivia.

"That's just so much meow," says I. "Sadie's a looker in any league. She may not be eighteen again for quite a while, but she still puts enough of it on the ball to talk traffic cops out of tickets."

"I've met Streeter," remarks Uncle Joe Brice, "but his sister's an unknown soldier to me. How old do you think she is?"

"About thirty," I ventures.

"About that," agrees the wife, "not counting leap years and the anno dominis ending in odd numbers. Sadie's been forty so long they're thinking of using her for a parallel of latitude."

"Gosh!" exclaims Uncle Joe. "How one ages around here! I'd better beat it before I discover she's the late Miss Streeter."

III

In our next bridge we have Brice to dinner. He's been raring for a game and, it being O.K. with Luke and his sister, we invite the old singleton to pick 'em up and lay 'em down with us.

"Have you turned all your negotiables into cash?" I inquires. "We don't take slow notes around here."

"A sound policy," says Uncle Joe, "but it may interest you to know that I don't expect to lose. In fact, my agenda call for my departure along about midnight staggering under the weight of unearned increment."

"After all," I shrugs, "why not? Everybody else does. To darken my door is to lighten my bank roll."

"It may further interest you to know," he goes on, "that I've been taking postgraduate work in contract since I saw you last."

"Who from?" I asks.

"A regular teacher," returns Brice, "with a studio, an air of decayed gentility and everything."

"What," I demands, "did she show you that I didn't?"

"Not a great deal," he comes back, "outside of a picture of the old family manse at Roanoke and a plate that General Beauregard ate off of, but I've got a lot of confidence in my game now."

"That's fine," says I, "but you'd be surprised at the number of times a cowardly ace takes a confident king in this pastime. Here comes the James boy and girl now," I adds as the bell rings. "Better let me put your watch and chain in the safe."

Sadie, as usual, is dressed as if she were going to a Beaux Arts ball, instead of around the corner for a penny game in a walk-up. She's a tall, curvy blonde with eyes big enough to bathe in and a smile you could pasture bees in. Uncle Joe lets his lamps range wide and free.

"Huh!" he grunts. "I thought that dame was going to be pushed in here in a wheel chair. Where does 'Livy get that forty?"

"Snappy clothes I'm buying you these days," I remarks to Sadie, after the introductions.

"Like 'em?" she flashes. "I ordered a fur today on the strength of tonight's winnings."

"Better cancel it, girlie," I advises. "We've got new blood in the game. Haven't you ever read Brice on Contract?"

"No, I haven't," says Miss Streeter. "I know it's a book I should read, but I've barely time to keep up with the ones I shouldn't."

"Come on," barks Luke. "You're taking the bread out of my mouth with all that palaver."

"Will you take fifty and go home?" I asks.

"I will not," he declared indignantly. "That's you coupon clippers—always grinding down us wage earners. Didn't you see where Hoover's asked the country to keep the pay rolls up?"

"Yeh," says I, "but my appearance in the soup line isn't likely to spur the economic recovery to any marked extent."

Just for being greedy, Streeter's cut out of the first rubber. I draws Olivia, and Brice seems pleased to hold hands with Sadie. Luke stations himself behind her for some back-seat driving.

"Now, remember," says I to the missis. "When I lead an ace, it means I have it."

"That," she remarks, "is probably the

most valuable bit of information I'll get from you tonight."

Sadie deals and bids a couple of hearts. I've got five spades to the king-jack and the ace-king of diamonds—not such a holiday holding—but figuring to frighten Uncle Joe out of a raise, I calls two spades. Brice refuses to frighten and announces the third heart. Olivia does what the barber gets for letting the East Lynne company put billing in his window and Miss Streeter offers four hearts. The fat's in the fire.

"Pass," says I.

"Five," says Brice.

"And the sixth," declares Sadie.

"Double!" I yelps, and then, following the old Sicilian custom, I looks to see what I've doubled on.

It assays a cinch. I have a sure trick in diamonds, maybe two, one in spades, and a chance of Olivia coming through with a taking ticket.

"Redouble!" says La Belle Streeter.

"On what?" I demands.

"The thirteenth of March," she replies. "Play."

I leads the ace of diamonds and then retire entirely from the leading business. My sure trick's trumped, the ace-queen of spades lay with Uncle Joe, and Olivia's about as helpful as a rainstorm at a picnic. Seven runs, seven hits, no errors.

"Pardon me for bringing up religion," says the frau, "but what did you have for a two-spade make?"

"Sundry and divers things," I replies. "Could I tell by the shape of Uncle Joe's ears that he held the ace-queen?"

"Perhaps not," she admits. "What did that brilliant coup of Pete's cost us, Sadie?"

"Seven hundred and twenty below the line," says Miss Streeter. "Five hundred for the little slam, two hundred for the extra trick, one hundred for making the contract and a hundred and fifty for five honors. Total, sixteen hundred and seventy."

"Good grief!" wails Olivia. "And he promised to cherish me!"

"I think," observes Sadie to Brice, "that we should have gone to a grand slam."

"I guess you're right," says he. "Sorry, but we'll do better when you and I get used to each other."

"I should love it," beams the wench, meaning, of course, that she should love to do better. "As a matter of fact, it was my fault. I should have jumped to seven after the double."

"No," insists Uncle Joe. "It was my place to do it. With the ace in two suits——"

"Turn on the radio," I shouts over to Luke, "and see if you can tune in on Hearts and Flowers."

I do myself rather well on the next deal and bid three no-trump. I make it, too, but it would have been a sad story for me if Brice hadn't muffed the message behind one of Sadie's discards.

"Too bad, partner," said Uncle Joe. "I certainly threw you for a loss that time."

"You're not a bit to blame," declares Miss Streeter. "I should have thrown off a higher card. Luke would have understood my seven, but——"

"I'll understand it, too," cuts in Brice, "when I've seen more of you—of your play, I mean."

Olivia and I are twenty-five bucks in the red when the rubber comes to an end, but things perk up some after that. I'm out, and the missis, playing with Brice, manages to recover eighteen hundred points from the bills payable.

My next crack's successful, too—a particularly adroit maneuver cutting my liabilities in half.

"How do you like my game now?" I asks the wife, not without a suggestion of pride.

"I guess your game's all right," she replies, "but, personally, I prefer contract. How much are we out?"

"Only eighteen smackers," I tells her.

"That's a killing," says Olivia. "Let's declare a dividend or take a run to Europe on it or something."

We're still eighteen minus when we sits down to the last rubber—Olivia and me vs. Brice and the blonde. On a fox pass by Uncle Joe that Sadie tries hard to hang on herself, we grabs off the first frame, and the chances of us getting even look pretty good.

While the next hand's being dealt the phone rings and I goes to answer it. The call's for a gal named Laura, who's not even in our set, and I rejoins the bridgers.

"What's happened?" I asks.

"Everybody's passed but you," says Luke. "Take a look and let 'em have a goulash."

Never have I seen such cards—eleven spades with all five honors, the ace of hearts and the ace of clubs. I'm about to go slumming with a slam when I catches a quizzical look in Brice's eyes. Sometime I'm going to find out what a quizzical look is.

"Pass," says I, flipping down the hand face up. "Who do you think you're kidding?"

"Kidding!" gasps Olivia.

"Who fixed it up?" I asks. "Sadie?"

"Nobody fixed it up," comes back Miss Streeter, and I can tell from her tone that I've outsmarted myself.

"Very well," says I, reaching for the cards. "In that case I'll bid seven——"

"No, you won't," interposes Uncle Joe. "You've passed."

I'm washed up. I've neither the spirit nor the cards to carry on, and the final rubber goes against us for eight hundred points. Sadie and Luke are the evening's winners, Brice coming out even. After a bit he departs with the Streeters and I'm left alone with Nemesis.

"Well!" says she. "Do you realize what that wise wheeze of yours cost us? About thirty dollars. Instead of being a winner for the first time in months, we lost twenty-six dollars."

"Tough break," I mumbles, "but the hand seemed just too good to be honest. Not to change the subject, did it strike you that Sadie Streeter wasn't exactly an acute anathema to your Uncle Joe?"

"Uncle Joe," returns Olivia, "was just being a courteous gentleman. You must try it some day. By the way, who was it that phoned?"

"Somebody wanted a girl named Laura," I tells her.

"I'm not at all surprised," says the missis. "I can't imagine anybody wanting you."

IV

Brice goes so cuckoo over contract we have games twice a week, either at our place or over at the Streeters'. Our luck gets no better, but our losses are shaved down considerably through the cut-in process and a habit Uncle Joe has of slipping his winnings to Olivia.

About a month after the start of the five-handed game I'm passing by The Ritzmore one afternoon when I pipes Brice through a window.

He's having tea with Sadie, and there's not enough room between 'em to drive an oxcart, either. The old boy appears a bit flustered when he catches my uplifted eyebrow, but Miss Streeter smiles with calm amiability.

"So you're playing twosomes now, eh?" I remarks to him that evening.

"Purely in the interest of my bridge," he returns hastily. "You've got to know your people to put up a good game."

"Doubtless," I agrees, "but don't you see enough of her twice a week?"

"Yes," says Uncle Joe, "but always in the confusion of a card game. To the student, quiet and peaceful surroundings are essential. You've never heard of scientists renting space in boiler factories, have you?"

"I don't know," I comes back. "I'm not acquainted with many boiler factories.

When are you going to begin your study of me—at a Ritzmore tea?"

"No close study of you is necessary," he returns. "You are quite an obvious person, Sadie—Miss Streeter——"

"Call her Sadie," I suggests recklessly, "and see if I care."

"Miss Streeter, on the other hand," goes on Brice, "is a most interesting and complex character. She's not easily fathomed. There are hidden, devious depths——"

"I see," I interrupts, "and until you plumb 'em you won't know for sure whether a finesse'll go through her or not."

"Roughly speaking, yes," says he. "It's very vital in contract to know whether your fellow players are bold or overcautious. Whether they're impulsive or hardheaded, and where can one best determine that than in social intercourse when the bars of restraint are let down?"

"I hope," I remarks, "you're not letting down any bars of restraint. Sadie's an attractive woman, and even if she is around forty-five——"

"Miss Streeter," declares Uncle Joe, somewhat stiffly, "will be thirty-two on her next birthday."

"I suppose," says I, sarcastic, "you found that out in your pursuit of inside bridge. Would it make much difference in a jack lead whether the gal was twenty-five or forty-three?"

"Age might be an element to be considered," asserts Brice.

"All right," I shrugs, "but don't lead your jack to Sadie. Remember, Olivia and I've been training faithfully to become your residuary legatees."

"Don't be silly," advises the missis when I tells her about Brice. "Uncle Joe's had scores of women out to tea and elsewhere. There's no more danger of him falling for Sadie than there is of him marrying his widow. He probably is studying her for bridge purposes."

"O.K.," says I, "as long as he spells bridge with a *g*."

Whatever Brice has on foot, his brand of contract gets to be bang-up, but rather embarrassing to me. He's so darn courteous and sweet under pressure he makes me feel like a barrel-house bum every time I open my mouth in protest. Even Sadie, who used to break one off in Luke occasionally, takes the veil and lets butter melt on her tongue.

Olivia and I go away on a trip for a couple of weeks in May, and when we return, the Streeters are about ready to trek away for the summer, so we decides to call it a season with a two-cent game on the fifteenth. It's been a disastrous season for us, my books showing me to be about five hundred berries down the coal chute, most of it dropped in the pre-Brice days.

We all have dinner at our place on getaway night and gather about the cards and spades immediately thereafter. I'm all set to play 'em close to my vest for a clean-up, and at the start it looks as though I were in for a profitable session.

I get a bid of four spades, and with a little assistance from the opposition—Brice and Sadie—Olivia and I chalk up our contract and three tricks over. There's also a matter of a hundred and fifty in honors.

"I think," remarks Miss Streeter, "we'd have saved game if you'd played your queen of clubs."

"Perhaps," says Uncle Joe mildly, "but I figured you for the king. You discarded a ten——"

"That-a-boy!" I chimes in. "Tell her where she heads in." However, nothing further's said and the game goes on its amiable way. At the end of about an hour's play I'm around fifty fish to the merry and Olivia's a fair winner as well. Sadie's holding the bag.

Toward ten o'clock the frau and I again hook up with Miss Streeter and Brice. We're standing at a frame apiece when

Uncle Joe, unassisted, goes to five diamonds over my four-heart make. Olivia doubles and Brice takes it on the button for fourteen hundred points. Clouds rise in Sadie's big blues and her lips tighten.

"A foolish bid," she bites off, "when we're vulnerable."

"I did go a little strong," admits Uncle Joe, "but I wanted to save the game. They'd have made their hearts."

"Suppose they had," snaps Miss Streeter. "How childish—taking a big set to save five hundred points!"

"That's a matter of opinion," he returns, "and I regard my opinion in contract as, at least, as valuable as yours."

"Oh, you do, do you?" flares up Sadie. "Why, you poor fish, you only learned the game a couple of months ago. You haven't got out of the kindergarten yet."

"It must have burned down the day you entered," retorts Brice. "What about that revoke you made? What about——"

"Say, listen," I cuts in; "are you two, by any chance, married?"

Uncle Joe looks at me peculiarly. "Yes, we are," says he. "We had intended to keep it a secret a bit longer, but," he adds dryly, "it had to come out. It's in the cards."

"Swell game, this contract," I remarks to Olivia later. "You not only lose your money, but your prospects of money as well."

The Perfect Squelch

SOME fifty years ago, before newspapers became "big business," it was possible to start a weekly paper on a shoestring. Such a one was launched in a Southern town by the editor-publisher with only a printer and a pressman.

At first all three worked hard and lent one another a hand whenever necessary. But as the paper became a little more of a success, the publisher began to give himself airs.

He was always too deeply engaged in important matters to dirty his hands helping the printer or pressman in a pinch. He began to talk expansively of great plans to conquer new publishing worlds.

Meanwhile his printer, an overworked old-timer who could stand just so much, took to drinking. At first he confined it to off days, but one morning his boss smelled liquor on his breath and bawled him out severely. The printer announced he was quitting, then and there.

"So you'd run out on me just before deadline!" the publisher snarled. "Why, you no-good, I ought to fix it so you never get another job! I ought to sit down at that typewriter over there and write you up for what you are!"

"Go right ahead," the printer said, making for the door. "I can walk out of your circulation area in twenty minutes."

—JOHN P. MCKNIGHT.

SURE, YOU'RE A NICE GIRL . . .

By RUFUS H. JONES

§ Bachelors, this is your corner. . . . Now you can hold your head as high as other men, even after the inevitable pitying remarks flung at you by smugly married couples. The Great Experience, claims Rufus Jones, turns out to be as flat as ginger ale left five days in an open bottle.

JULY 17, 1937

THERE are ten commonly stated reasons for a young man's getting married. Half of them are for the good of somebody else, and none of the rest fool me any.

I will marry the girl who can support me in the manner to which I never really expect to become accustomed, and endow me with uninterrupted leisure to do the work I want to do, not what somebody says I've got to do. No others need apply. If she has enough money, she can even be bow-legged. That's where I stand.

I arrived at this conclusion after a lot of serious thought about marriage. I didn't want to think about marriage; I was forced into it by a whole congregation of missionaries, calling themselves my friends, who believe a man's first duty today, as in Adam's time, is to raise a family and assume the responsibilities of solid community life.

They don't come out and say it just like this, but it's what they mean.

They are married themselves, and naturally their fervor is sadistic. To them a man without a wife is the same as a native without a pair of pants is to an old-fashioned missionary. It makes me wonder a little if they don't regret the fact that once they themselves went around in a loincloth and therefore now have an unwholesome envy of the happily unencumbered. I only said I wondered.

In a society where marriage and little children are considered the goal of a man's life, and celibates are pitied—or at least patronized—the single man is on the spot. Friends snicker at him, whistle, stamp their feet, pound him on the back, and howl savagely: "Boy-o-boy! Are you going to tumble hard one of these days!" Or worse, they gush sentimentally: "Just you wait until the Right Girl comes along!" in the hope of developing in him such a fatalistic attitude toward marriage that he will eventually walk up the aisle with one of the "nice girls" they are always—so innocently!—having him meet. Again and again in noble phrases they assure him that there can be "no satisfactory single blessedness, no immortality like the clasp of a baby's hand."

Even those who, at heart, wish you well, look at you with a tear in their eye and shake their heads as they prophesy that

"Whatever you do . . . don't insult him."

TELEPHONE B

SALE

B TOBEY

"This is a list of good wrong numbers I've called at various times."

LEO GAREL

"Just let me know when it gets excruciating."

FAMOUS LAST WORDS

"Stop worrying. I can read a French menu like a native. Here comes our scrambled eggs now."

"They'll never take me. I can hardly see a thing without my glasses."

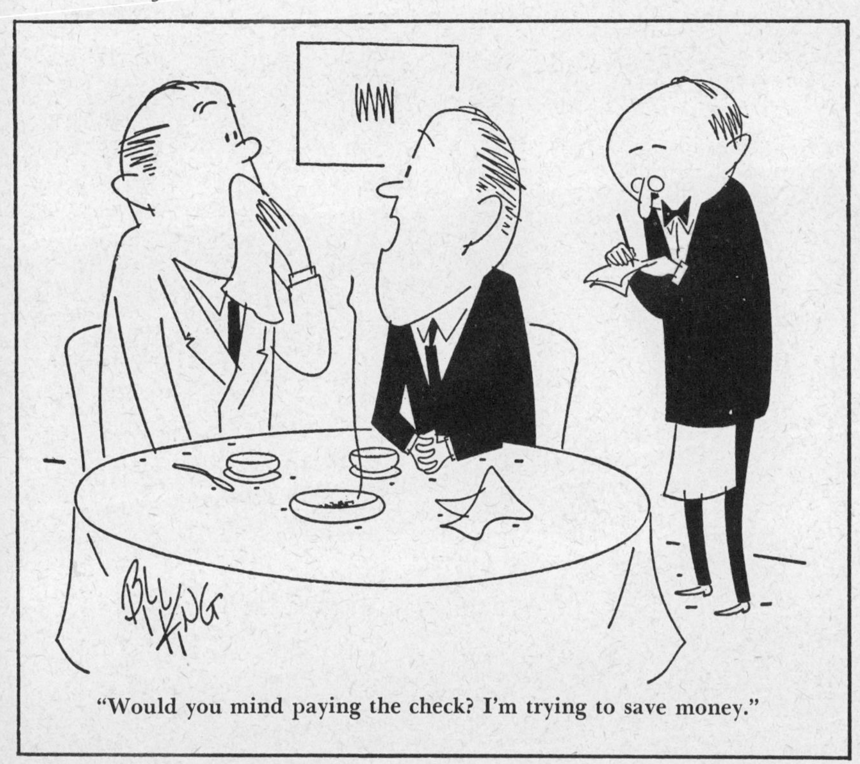

"Would you mind paying the check? I'm trying to save money."

"I met a swell girl last night, chief. She's five feet six and a quarter, weighs 117¾, has a mole on her left cheek, a small scar on her chin . . ."

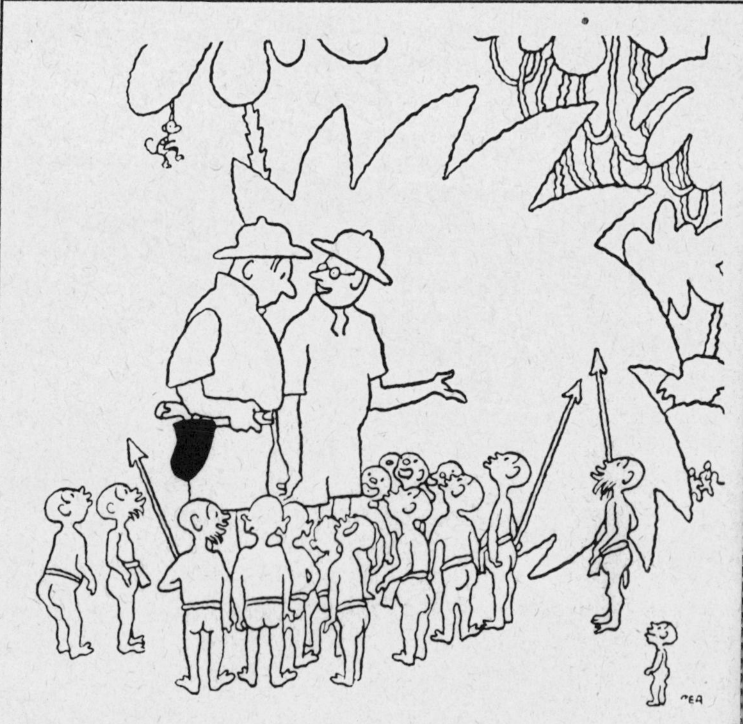

"As nearly as I can get it, they want us for their basketball team."

"you'll get married in a hurry one of these days to somebody who knocks you cold. Everybody has a Waterloo, and you aren't exempt."

Prejudice against the unencumbered extends even to business, I find. Businessmen, considering you for a job, look at you quizzically when they come to that part which says you are not married. They are inclined to assume that there must be some trait in your character which would make you undesirable for their business.

Furthermore, it is assumed that, single, you cannot be so reliable as a man with family responsibilities. They should look up the statistics on embezzlement.

Whenever I attempt to explain, defensively, why I am not married, either one of two things happens. Either my reasons are discounted categorically as timeworn or invalid, or I am accused of being frivolous.

If I say I have not married because I could never make up my mind to any one girl—"I love them all!"—or that I am perfectly satisfied as I am, or that I want to be free and untrammeled, my reasoning is tossed out as old stuff repeated many times before and therefore, by some obscure logic, unworthy of serious consideration.

Or if I say I am not married because of my face—"It's my face you know; children scream and women swoon"—I am generally, though not always, told that I am being absurd.

As a matter of fact, my face hasn't been known to scare a great many horses, although, of course, one may say that you don't meet many horses nowadays.

Beyond that I do not apologize. Few people any longer suspect that I am subnormally intelligent, now that I have learned about Dale Carnegie and let them do the talking. If I am about ten pounds overweight, still I don't look any funnier in a bathing suit than most other people.

Without wealth and within sight of my tenth college reunion, I am still the right side of thirty and may be assumed to have a "future"; if I haven't, nobody can prove it. My ancestors in this country reach back to the days when an Indian was a "varmint," and this, I suppose, makes me socially respectable. I take a bath every morning and shine my shoes as often as three times a week.

I simply mention these things to make it sound credible to you when I say that I have not been thwarted in love. I am not a misanthrope whose life has been blighted and his personality warped by an unfortunate love affair.

I do not claim to be irresistible. I'm no Gable. But not every girl is Joan Crawford, either. And some of those who have been cheated out of film stardom and Gable have managed to let it be understood—well, I've had my chances. You'll just have to take my word for it.

Saved by Ten Other Girls

But I've passed them up. I have said to myself, looking at Esther or Mary or June, "Sure, you're a nice girl, but——" There's always a "but"—a "but" born of reason and common sense, certainly not of any disinclination to fall in love. Love with me is like sinus trouble—it's constant. Just so long as she is not actually deformed or quite obviously an idiot, in the medical sense, I can look at almost any girl, a machine winds up inside me, following which the record plays I Love You.

Don't say smugly to me: "Ah, but you have never been in love!" The fact that I have been in love with many girls rather than any one affinity, destined, so the romanticists say, for me in the eternal scheme of things, is beside the point. See Exhibit A for an accurate chart of my car loadings in love.

Any honest man knows that there are inevitably any number of compatible women, each of them equally fitted to be his wife.

Every time I have been on the brink, I

have counted ten other girls I have been in love with, thought of what marriage really means for a man, and have been saved.

The average man takes more care in choosing a pair of suspenders, which few people ever see, than he does in choosing a wife, who sticks out all over a man. He meets the mystic creature, The Only Little Girl in All the World, while on vacation, at a dance, on a house party or in some similar environment where the realities are forgotten. He looks into her eyes, she looks into his eyes, they look into each other's eyes, and he thinks it's love when it is simply a reflection of his own egotism.

"Baby," he breathes, "you're beautiful!" Then he is surprised to wake up on the walk to the altar. Sometimes the waking up is deferred until a few months after marriage, when the poor guy finds that the evanescent glamour of a romantic attraction has given way to the same old dull routine of everyday life with its same irritations, exasperations, problems and petty crises. The Great Experience has turned out to be as flat as ginger ale left five days in an open bottle. The boredom and disillusionment are more acute because they are so likely to be permanent. Only one couple in six gets divorced, even in this year of 1937.

For every action except marriage, it is generally assumed that logic and reason should be employed. But when a man selects a companion for his later years who will mean as much to him as his parents in his youth, it is somehow considered unworthy of him to use his brains.

At the very time when a man has the need of a lifetime to use his head, he is told to trust his heart. Calculation on the part of a man before marriage is held to be dishonorable. Self-control may be a distinguishing feature between man and the apes, but, in marriage, impulse is praised, and self-control, pending investigation, discouraged.

Both the insistence of society on marriage as the only thing for a young man, and the encouragement given him to forsake reason in choosing a life companion, take root in the Affinity System.

From the time he or she is able to see, hear or understand, a boy or a girl is inoculated with the idea of an eventual romantic partnership with the one ideal predestined mate.

For each boy there is destined The Girl, his beautiful princess. Each girl is brought up to believe that someday she will be awakened by her soul-mate prince, Mr. Right. The theory is festooned with cupids and orange blossoms.

The man who does not accept it is a challenge to society. So society does not rest until it has forced him to marry, and thereby contribute additional statistical evidence to support the infallibility of the doctrine.

Under such pressure it is not surprising that often a man may mistake a temporary attachment for the arrival of The Affinity. Fairy stories from the works of Messrs. Grimm and Andersen, and fairy stories related by papa and mamma on anniversaries, and fairy stories from the works of Messrs. Goldwyn and Zanuck, maintain the continuity of the pressure as the boy grows older.

The more sudden the attack of love, the more romantic and delicious it is held to be. If a man can say "I was standing on a street corner when suddenly it swept over me; and when I came to, I was married," people will clasp their hands and sigh: "Oh, how romantic!"

Getting married, in the popular mind, needs no more justification than eating breakfast. Marriage, it is argued, "isn't like buying a suit of clothes"—as if this statement alone disposed of all but willful contradiction. To my mind, however, marriage

EXHIBIT A

UNLUCKY GIRLS I HAVE BEEN IN LOVE WITH, BUT DECIDED NOT TO MARRY AFTER ALL

(Partial List)

NAME	CURRENT RATING *	COLORING	EDUCATION	DISPOSITION	CHIEF INTEREST	COMMENTS
LOUISE	5 Star!	Snuggly Redhead	Mt. Holyoke	Uninhibited	Any man.	Is it hot here or is it just me? Disqualified for giggling and baby talk.
HELEN	5 Star	Cozy Brunette	Unimportant	Affectionate	Singing.	Also insisted on wiping out salad bowl with garlic.
ALICE	3½ Star	Carefully Blonde	U. S. Cal.	Acquisitive	Spending my money.	Always looking over my shoulder for the next man.
JULIE	5 Star	Cuddly Brunette	Radcliffe	Co-operative	Music—she said!	Radcliffe girls are improving; but still the seam up her stockings was always twisted.
MARIAN	2 Star	Cold Blonde	Vassar	Impersonal	Vassar girls are interested in nothing.	Ho-hum . . . my mistake!
FRANCES	3½ Star	Just Blonde	Smith	Introspective	Me—I was afraid.	Designed for home and children, but no sense of humor.
LUCILE	1½ Star	Precise Brunette	Wellesley	Managing	Russian workers' paradise.	Always planned things and you did them.
MARGIE	4 Star	Rosy and Fair	Surprising	She and Mae West both	Marriage and movie magazines.	Thought a book was something to decorate a room with.

* Key to ratings:
- 5 Star—Nice!!
- 4 Star—Nice girl!
- 3 Star—She's a nice girl
- 2 Star—Oh, yes, she's a nice girl
- 1 Star—It all depends on what you can get, I suppose

is like buying a dime-store jewel and hoping it will prove to be a diamond. It is like buying an overcoat at a fire sale and hoping it will look all right when you get it outside in daylight. Marry at haste is like looking into a gun barrel while you pull the trigger to see if it's loaded. Now and then it isn't fatal.

The Ever-Cautious Bachelor

I shall probably be burned for a witch, or at least tortured with bamboo slivers under my fingernails for daring to examine the Race Habit, marriage, and what it offers me. But every cause must have its martyrs. Exhibit B indicates some of the more commonly stated reasons why a young man should marry.

EXHIBIT B

PARTIAL LIST OF
POPULARLY ACCEPTED REASONS
WHY A YOUNG MAN SHOULD MARRY

AUTHOR'S NOTE: We accept no responsibility for these opinions.

1. Duty to contribute to the race.
2. Without a home, he will not be a responsible citizen.
3. Some woman expects him to.
4. Weddings stimulate business.
5. Marriage develops character and disciplines man's nature for the good of society.
6. Marriage, by combining two brains, helps him to get ahead faster.
7. Sympathetic companionship.
8. Care in his old age.
9. Married men live longer.
10. A man should marry.

Even a casual glance will show that 50 per cent of these reasons—Numbers 1 to 5—why a man should marry are for the benefit of somebody other than himself, either society or some woman; 10 per cent—Number 10—most popular reason of all, is only as intelligent as a woman's "just because" and may be ignored; 40 per cent—Numbers 6 to 9—are the dropped egg on the hash to make it more palatable.

It seems only logical to suspect the nature of a commodity which can only be sold under such a thick disguise. Inevitably the intelligent man—such as I—will ask himself whether the emphasis on the outward and favorable aspects of the marriage contract may not be intended to conceal outweighing disadvantages.

Whether to marry or not to marry for a man boils down to the question whether life consists in living or in functioning. My personal preference is living.

When any sociologist tears his graying hair and moans tragically, "Suppose the world were filled with marriage slackers and hermits and other practitioners of celibacy, what would happen then?" I am reminded of the argument I used to hear way back in high school: "What if everybody wanted to cut the final study period and go home?" Everybody never did. Or they weren't smart enough to think of it.

I want to be a good citizen, but I do not think that marriage would help me at all. The theory is, of course, that the discipline of married life will keep a man from getting selfish, develop the kindlier side of his nature, make him more considerate, and thereby breed a greater interest in public affairs and encourage happier social relationships. A man with a load on his back can't do much mischief, obviously. But I say he can't do much that is constructive either.

By remaining single and, therefore, objective in matters of community welfare, I shall continue to be more of an asset to society than I should by getting married, buying a house on a 20 per cent equity, worrying about the mortgage installments, and getting sore over an unexpected tax assessment for suburban sidewalks. Furthermore, anybody is ten kinds of a hazy-minded optimist who thinks a man can go on long after the wedding exhibiting his "best self, his real personality." Love cannot keep a man from being himself when he receives his wife's first-of-the-month bills in the mail on a rainy Monday morning, after a Sunday-night supper of Welsh rabbit and before he has had his coffee.

At such a time he will not listen patiently while you tell him that weddings are good because they encourage business—just look at all the new homes, the trousseaux, the electric mixers, the living-room suites, the sets of encyclopedias sold because of weddings. He will be inclined to ridicule the idea that he should have got married simply to help furniture manufacturers pay dividends, or a saleswoman in a dress shoppe to make her quota.

The fact is that marriage is slipping so badly even the girls are becoming more particular. Marriage is losing its position as a monopoly. Other careers which offer equal compensation, either in the form of service to humanity or in personal contentment, are springing up, and there are many fewer women today than, say twenty years ago, who expect some man to provide their happy ending. Girls today find lots of other things to do besides sitting around the home awaiting the appearance of the mystic prince, ordained in heaven to be her kindly master and the father of her children.

Women, Too, Are Getting Choosy

Once a lot of substandard merchandise was palmed off on unsuspecting women in the marriage market. But today girls have to be convinced of superior advantages before accepting the business of marriage instead of a career as businesswoman, doctor, decorator, lecturer, musician, lawyer, college professor or scientist.

The very increase in divorce may be a sign that women are demanding more of marriage now than when they had little to expect but marriage. Women today are raising the passing mark for husbands.

This is most intelligent of them. Married, a girl has to feed a family, bring up children, do the mending, supervise the budget, ask the right people to dinner, humor her husband when he's mad on the world and thinks life is a frame-up. As a successful wife she must be companion, educator, psychologist, purchasing agent, public-relations counsel, economist and personnel manager. All that most women get out of marriage is a lot of work with no pay. It is hard to understand why they go in for it unless it is the best work they can get.

The idea of marrying to make a woman your unpaid housekeeper has always seemed to me to be a most unworthy conception of the purpose of matrimony. We are not now pioneers, with the pioneer's practical need for a wife to help in subduing the wilderness, spinning cloth, smoking hams, raising hens, preserving garden truck and cutting up potatoes for seed. Nor do we lead the lonely life of the frontiersman, grateful for a wife's companionship. What with most women having more money in their pocketbooks than he has, any modern man can enjoy the friendly companionship of women who, financially independent because of their professions, can enter into friendship with men on an equal give-and-take basis.

He can also enjoy the particular type of companionship suited to his particular mood as well. Adelaide, for example, has brains and can discuss law, music and art. To Judie, on the other hand, Michelangelo is just another pushcart vender on Second Avenue; she likes dancing and bridge. Margot is stimulating and renews in him the ambition for success when he is getting stale. Sarah, on the contrary, has a soothing personality. She makes true the saying that not what a woman is but what she makes him think he is, is important to a man, and smooths out the kinks when he is fed up with it all.

Lots of Fun and No Overhead

The system is not unlike renting a car instead of owning it. You eliminate the overhead, but you have all the fun. And you can have an open roadster for spring evenings, a sport phaeton for touring, and a sedan for the Christmas dance at the country club. Today a man can live a normal comfortable life without being called upon to sacrifice the independence which is often requisite to achievement. Francis Bacon was the one who said long ago that: "He that hath wife and children hath given hostages to fortune; for they are impediments to great enterprise. . . ." Somebody else has said that, although Galahad may strike you as having been something of a prig, at least he got what he went after.

A married man must say "No" to any interesting experimental attitude toward life. When he has children, his freedom to move in new paths is snuffed out automatically, like a Republican revolt in Congress. His only hope is to earn enough money to pay the grocer's bill and the rent. More than that, he has signed a contract, no less strict because unwritten, to do all that he is able to insure the happiness of The Little Woman who, for reasons often obscure, has consented to live out the rest of her days with him.

He must, of course, speak thoughtfully of the way she keeps his home; he must remember to send American Beauty roses—do married men know any other flower?—on anniversaries; he must say that the biscuits made with the new recipe are delicious; he must compliment her on the new dress she knit all by herself; he must be interested in the new ruffled curtains for the guest room; he must tell her that of course she looks much younger than Fanny Pforzheimer next door; he must not forget to kiss her every morning before going to work. That is elemental—simple duty.

But he also must see to it that she enjoys all the good times of life which she deserves, goodness knows. He must put on his dress armor to go out and waste an evening playing bridge, when he hates bridge or, at best, considers it a petty problem in mathematics. He must remember that The Little Woman likes to see the new plays. He must plan little outings to break the monotony of household drudgery. If passionately devoted, or extremely dutiful, he may even go so far as to sprain his entire anatomy learning to do the rumba at the community dancing class. There are few sacrifices a married man is not called upon to make.

Can You Qualify?

He must put aside money each week for the insurance, remember to pay the taxes, budget the doctors' bills, pull weeds in a suburban lawn, hire a man to clip the bushes, pay to have the floor done over where the boiler leaked, walk around in the dark of night to soothe some temperamental brat yelling like a prima donna cast in a minor role, not be able to go anywhere without planning for it like a trip to Europe, and maybe even then be kept at home because the high-school girl who was engaged to look after the child forgot to show up.

If I must neglect either wife and home or my work, I am not sufficiently unselfish to give up progress in my profession for the sake of some woman who has chosen marriage as a career.

And I certainly won't sacrifice professional progress simply because of the theory that, although marriage may be narrowing, it at least means the thinking of two instead of one, and therefore may help me to improve my position in life. If you tell me, for example, that without a wife a man may be too ignorant of domesticity and the housewife's point of view to write good advertising copy, though advertising is his passion, I shall say that marriage simply to learn copywriting is a pretty expensive course of training. I should as soon marry because a woman is a good cook and can help me get over my indigestion.

If there is a perfect girl, she is probably already married to somebody else. But, after all, "compatibility is a process, not an accident."

As a rational being I hope that I have control over my own thinking and feeling. Show me a girl who fills my qualifications, as listed below in Exhibit C, and I promise to fall in love with her almost immediately.

EXHIBIT C

QUALIFICATIONS YOU GIRLS MUST HAVE IF YOU WANT TO MARRY ME

1. You must have lots and lots of money.
2. You must pay all the bills.
3. You must feed me rich and delicious food as often as I want it.
4. You must think I am wonderful and admire everything I do.
5. You must leave me free to do that which interests me more than you ever will.

However, if no one ever gives me a telephone number, that's all right. I can go on living. I've done fine so far, thank you.

I Love Crab Grass

I CAN understand why people do not care for some members of the plant family, such as poison ivy. But it is sad to observe the nationwide viciousness toward my good old friend, crab grass.

"Slay Crab Grass in Your Lawn!" a typical newspaper ad gloats sadistically, while everything else on the garden page is loving nature dearly and trying to think up ways to make living things live. I am willing to by-pass the moral point that it is sinful to slay any living thing except for food or sport. But let us at least look at a lawn philosophically. Crab grass is green, isn't it?

I put that question one autumn day to a neighbor who is a grassophobe—a person who goes all to pieces when crab grass is mentioned. "Green?" he said emotionally. "If you'll pardon my prying into your personal affairs, look at the dead matter on the ground around your house. Except for two or three minor oases, what color does it appear to your spectacles?"

"Brown," I said complacently. "The hue of Milton's nut-brown ale."

"And is that an admirable color for grass?"

I told him it was. I explained that in this matter of picking colors, the universe knows best. It turns everything a different color in the fall so that mankind will not go cuckoo from looking at the same thing all the time. The sky is blue, and that's enough of that. So leaves turn red and crab grass ale. "Perennial grass like yours," I explained to my neighbor, "which insists on staying grass color, is stubborn, ungrateful, irritating, and a silly sight when it finally freezes to death in a snowstorm." Unable to agree with me, he turned slightly green and stomped away in a choler.

Crab grass, or finger grass, is called by many names; one of the printable ones is *Digitaria sanguinalis*. Leaning back not too trustfully on Mr. Cicero, I make this "sanguine finger"—hence, a hopeful, confident finger that is full of pep. The fingers, or culms, sprout from the head of the plant in numbers from one to infinity. The head contains a fascinatingly intelligent brain; crab grass is as smart and trainable as a poodle. For example, the culms grow vertically until reproved by a lawn mower, then promptly turn a right angle and become recumbent in all directions, so that one plant alone will decently clothe a square foot of nude mother nature. How much will one plant of bluegrass clothe? The thought is almost indecent.

The maternal instinct of crab grass is terrific. If you sow a peck of store grass on your lawn, a hot, dry spell will immediately follow. The seeds which fell among old store grass, among their own mothers, so to speak, will die like neglected orphans in infancy, and then their stupid mothers will lie down and die on top of them. But lift up a thatch of crab grass and, underneath it, store seedlings will be adolescing lustily in the moist and shady soil, mothered there like a brood of chicks. In the fall, these foster mothers will go to heaven, leaving behind a new generation of perennial grass to which they have lovingly given their best days.

"And this is smart?" snarled a neighbor, whom I had the pleasure of enraging by demonstrating the evolution on his own lawn. "In the long run, isn't this race suicide on the part of crab grass, I fiercely hope?"

"This, if you could only read between the lines of the seed catalogue," I snapped, "is the ultimate of maternal wisdom. Crab grass says to her bluegrass babies, 'Men want you; so grow, you little dopes.' Then she drops some of her own seeds among them, whispering, 'You take over if they don't. Got to have *something* going on around here.' Crab grass hangs the rest of her seeds on the wind and on the canvas gloves of men trying to kill crab grass. The men shake these seeds all over their own lawns, and the wind spreads them all over the township. Quadrillions of tiny insurance policies to cover every blade of store grass that conks out. Do you see the beautiful, altruistic efficiency of it all?"

The grassophobe didn't. He went into a tantrum and cried that his lawn would fight my weed nursery seed for seed. He hoed up a great stretch of crab grass next to my yard, sowed the naked dirt with store grass for about fifteen bucks, raked it, wet it down into a swamp, and then the birds came gratefully to scuffle up and eat the seeds. Even the mourning doves emitted optimistic grunts.

The sower's wife nagged the birds during the daytime, and he cursed them during the long summer evenings. At length, in pity, I told him about an antibird device that he could buy—long strings of metallic streamers which even in no wind at all keep uttering, "Tinkle, tinkle!" He hung up four strings the next evening, and a wind came up, and you have never heard such an ungodly caterwauling in your life. Finally his wife stomped out and cut them all down with grass clippers, and then she and her husband had a loud spat indoors, and about three weeks later the grassophobe had a few patches of perennial fuzz in his yard, but mostly what he had was a sturdy stand of new crab grass which has served him faithfully ever since. We never discussed the matter again.

To be sure, this chap had a form of agricultural dementia. Crab grass affects most people more mildly, merely implanting in them a mental tic, a preoccupational neurosis. The victim gets relief by murdering one culm at a time. The sad part is that he is always looking, searching, yearning to find a victim. I once noticed a guest at an outdoor wedding surreptitiously murder a culm with the trowellike toe of his patent-leather pump. Then, fulfilled, he paid attention to the wedding. By that time he was too late. The bride, married, was hopelessly surrounded by the other men who wanted to kiss her.

I have another neighbor who every summer morning after breakfast steps out into his garden, intending to stick his nose into a rose. Occasionally he and a rose actually get together. More often he pauses just this side of paradise, snatches a chunk of crab grass out of his lawn and slouches dispiritedly away to the office. Evenings before dinner he makes pock marks in his lawn with a fiendish notched steel creese. He builds little stacks of his gleanings and gloats over them as if they were uranium stockpiles. One night I noticed him out on his terrace trying to drink a can of beer, but leaping up every so often to get one more culm with his can opener. Thinking to be neighborly, I strolled over, pointed to his crabgrass stacks and asked, "Going to make wine?"

"On the contrary," he replied. "I'm going to throw it all over into your yard. You're collecting it, aren't you?"

"No," I said patiently. "My mind is open to any grass that will stand on its own roots and not turn me into a nurse and my wife into a grass widow. Did you ever stop to think that the countless hours you spend on your lawn you could be spending with your wife and children?"

"What!" he cried. "And have crab grass?"

The wry philosophy of grassophobes tears at my heartstrings.

Once I had a rarely perceptive friend who sensed all the nobilities of crab grass, yet would choke sadly on this point: "Yeah, but the proof of grass is in the cutting. Just when I get going good, my lawn mower hits a wad of crab grass and the handles lam into my stomach. This goes on all summer."

"Let me tell you a parable," I said. "Once there was a man who for many years excoriated his wife for cooking meat in such a way that it came on the table tough, like a rubber heel. Finally he discovered that by having his carving knife ground, the meat cut tender. Felicity was restored to their household."

Then I examined the fellow's alleged lawn mower. "Never saw a duller one," I diagnosed. "Got saw teeth, too, from mowing butternuts and your kid's lead soldiers. The knives whack one end of the under bar and don't touch the rest of it at all. Any smart blade of grass will just lean over and crawl through without a scratch. Not store grass—it hasn't the brains." I edged the knives with a file and adjusted the bar with a screwdriver, then effortlessly mowed a strip of crab grass, pushing with only two fingers. "Do you shave with a dull razor and blame it on your beard?" I asked a little bitterly.

"I'm almost pathetically grateful," he said. "But before becoming truly your disciple, one more question—why do you use a power mower?"

Merely answering his question would have sufficed, because no really chivalrous man can go on and on allowing his wife to mow a lawn by hand. But it was only fair to tell him about the time that crab grass gave me tremors. This was during my honeymoon with the new power mower, before I saw that driving one is not really so much fun as driving an automobile. You have to walk.

One evening I went to my doctor and whimpered, "Look, is there any scientific reason why using a power lawn mower should leave me trembling for hours from the waist up like a little earthquake? If you dare call this an escape mechanism, I'll write a piece in favor of socialized medicine."

The doctor socked me on an elbow nerve with a little hammer and I automatically punched him good. "Agree on the symptoms," he said hastily. "Physically they resemble delirium tremens. Could be you're cracking up, but more likely your mower is maladjusted and is slowly vibrating you to death. Consult a mechanic. I don't practice on lawn mowers myself."

I went home and mixed a double sedative and drank it out on the lawn. It was a mystic, fairyland night, sparkling with fireflies and sweet with the drifting fragrance of linden trees. By and by, as I lay there dreamily on the chaise longue, I had the curious feeling that all my crab grass was struggling to speak to me in a thousand tiny whispers. Finally the whispering focused into a clearly audible remark: "Is it our fault, sir, if our brains make us a bit knobby and the mower goes hippety-hop over us? All you got to do is grip the handle loose instead of tight. Use your head more and your hands less, master, and stop being a human shock absorber."

My favorite grass has never spoken to me again. But often I have affectionately listened to it as it went about its own affairs. Like sweet corn on a still, warm night, it crackles as it grows.

—RALPH KNIGHT.

The number of times the average man says no to temptation is once weakly.

—SHANNON FIFE.

THE LAUGHING DEATH

By NUNNALLY JOHNSON

§ Cross-word puzzle addicts are a breed apart from their fellow men. Their speech is apt to be flavored with strange synonyms like sol, em, Ra and Yak. A unique romance results when a girl cross-word puzzler meets a swain who happens to be the Champion of New York City.

APRIL 25, 1925

THE ai, having checked up on its three toes and found them all there, made a grave study of the young man who stared at her through the fence. He was, this sloth guessed, a few months over twenty-three, unmarried, not altogether tidy, but pleasant and youngish looking, and reading law in the office of a firm in Fulton Street, probably near Broadway, where he was not regarded as particularly promising, being, as his elders said among themselves, too much of a woolgatherer.

He lived, her idle speculations continued, on Staten Island, as roomer in a private home remote enough from all transit lines to be unusually reasonable; in fact, cheap; and he wrote back to Anniston, where his mother and sister lived and boasted of their boy in New York, on an average of twice a week. Only, the ai decided, he had not been so regular with his correspondence of recent weeks; and being a mother herself, the ai wondered what had happened.

None, of course, but an exceptionally intelligent ai could have told so much about Paul Paine simply from his appearance; and not even this one, as extraordinarily brilliant as she was, was able to discover everything about him. She did not, for example, learn that——

At that moment a girl not wearing an imitation sealskin coat stepped in front of the young man, and with the suggestion of a giggle tossed a peanut through the fence.

"Take that," she said, "you two-letter word!"

An expression of deep perplexity came into the ai's face. What had this girl called her? A two-letter word? What did she mean—a two-letter word?

Reaching down for the peanut, her mind occupied with the possible significance of this new title, the ai failed to see the light of pleasure which the girl's words brought to Paul Paine's eyes. It was as though he were a stranger in some far land and had heard, for the first time, his own language spoken. He turned on her a look filled with interest.

It may have been that her coat was not imitation sealskin, or that she was pretty and blond and dainty, or that she carried a folded newspaper under her arm; but whatever it was, he spoke to her—as naturally as he would have another white man met in the jungles of Zanzibar.

"You do cross-word puzzles too."

It was a friendly statement of fact. The girl turned quickly, so quickly and ominously that he was thrown into a panic.

He had accosted a stranger, and a pretty girl at that! He was stammering, on the point of a confused apology, when the girl, reassured by the complete absence of menace in him, replied.

"Yes," she said—and no more.

Paul laughed with embarrassed relief.

"The ai," he explained nervously—"the ai, you know—why, the ai——" He seemed snagged on a two-letter word meaning a three-toed sloth, and the girl nodded encouragingly. "It's a two-letter word!" he accomplished his sentence triumphantly.

"I can't decide which you're better at," the girl commented thoughtfully, "arithmetic or spelling. How many letters are there in a bovine ruminant?"

"Three," he replied promptly. "Y-a-k."

She smiled with pleased surprise.

"That was good!" she exclaimed. "Then you are a cross-word puzzler!"

He expanded floridly with mysterious pride.

"It may savor of boastfulness," he answered hesitantly; "but—but—but"—he suddenly switched his thought—"may I introduce myself?"

"I don't mind a boast now and then," the girl said. "Who are you?"

"My name is Paul Paine."

He watched her sharply, anxiously, and was rewarded by a widening of her eyes.

"Really?" she cried. "The champion cross-word puzzler! You're not joking?"

A little uncertain which question he was to answer, he shook and nodded his head at the same time, in one bewildering movement, for he was far too filled with pride to trust himself with speech.

"What fun!" she went on. "I was just reading about the tournament you won. It must have been awfully exciting. And you are Paul Paine!"

He repeated the vague weavings of his head.

"You are not," he asked then, suddenly anxious, "irate at my accosting you?"

She glanced at him suspiciously.

"I'm not what?" she demanded.

"You aren't irate or irked at my speaking to you?"

He was so obviously in earnest, so plainly far from any spirit of levity, that she was again reassured and amused.

"Nay," she replied solemnly. "On the contrary, I am elated. You did not err."

He was relieved.

"It was the ai," he explained; "I was just thinking of its being a two-letter word when you came up." He looked around uncertainly. "Perhaps you wouldn't mind trekking around the zoo and scanning some of the other animals and feathered vertebrates?"

"E. g.," she submitted gravely, "the emu."

The ai, which had been listening to this conversation with a growing sense of astonishment, watched them saunter slowly down the walk. She saw the girl turn to the young man and heard her say, "My cognomen is Cynthia Bradley."

And that night the ai said to her husband, "Emil, I don't know what these humans are coming to! Such words as I heard today I've never heard before!" To which her husband replied curtly, "Desist and go to sleep. Your prattle roils me."

Cynthia Bradley and Paul Paine made their way to the monkey house and looked at the ape.

Then they came to the yard where were the egret, the eider, the rhea and the emu.

And presently they sauntered farther and studied together the yak and the gnu.

"It's training for me," he explained seriously. "I doubt if I'll e'er be much of a barrister, but now that I've attained a goal as a cross-word puzzler, I thought I ought to nourish my opportunity, don't you?"

"To reach the apex," she agreed, "you ought."

In point of fact, she had given as much study to him as she had to the gnu. Her first amused excitement at meeting a champion, whatever his field, had faded into a curious interest.

To her, a dilettante in puzzles, his thorough absorption in them was new and strange. She found him, though, a pleasantly comfortable person to talk with; a youth somewhat vaguely hopeless about his career in law, but keenly alive in everything else—except puzzles.

"The value of the puzzles," he declared, "lies in their aid to the vocabulary. You note words unused by you ere you were initiated."

"Some of them," she agreed again, "I haven't used in æons and æons and æons!"

"That's it!" he said. "Since my entry to puzzle work I have become avid for words. It is not bombast when I aver I must have added thousands of new words to my vocabulary."

"Aye," she answered. "And ergo, you are champion! But what of your law?"

"I am utilized," he explained, "by McGillicuddy, McGillicuddy, McGillicuddy, McGillicuddy & Mack. My aim is to try cases, torts, in court; but so far I have only been let to prepare theses. But perhaps ere long I shall be let."

They had reached the exit gate, and Cynthia turned and put out her hand.

"Unless you are going downtown," she said, "good-by. I've got to get to Staten Island."

"Why," he exclaimed, "I also live on that isle! I'll take you home."

She was in some mysterious way pleased. On the subway they studied the advertisements silently all the way to the Battery. On the ferry he pointed out to her dories, yawls, tugs, scuppers, and the orlop of a s. s.—abbr.—bound for its pier in the North River. But it was she who recalled, to his delight, that they were standing in the lee of the cabins.

As they left the boat he called her by her first name and glowed with pleasure when she did not seem to mind. He had never, he felt, met a girl of such charm, never a girl with more whole-hearted attention in her eyes. They twinkled now and then, to be sure, but her words were always gravely spoken. She, he felt, understood him.

"I hope," he said just before she entered her home, "that you did not think I was ogling you or leering at you at the zoo."

"Nay, nay!" she laughed. "Your mien was immaculate."

"And you didn't think I was an oaf or a zany?"

"Not at all, Paul. You've been very nice, very charming. I like you."

"Then," he ventured, "if you are not sated with me, I should like to come to see you sometime erelong."

"Do," she said from the door. "Come some e'en for a repast. And don't," she added, "wait an era before doing it."

II

This seemed to be one of those rare occasions when Mr. Bradley, tearing himself away from his laboratory and inventions, chose to stand staunch and immovable on his rights. In this case it was his daughter who opposed him."

"I won't have him here," he declared for the fifth or sixteenth time. "That's all—he must be kept away."

"Look, dad," Cynthia declared firmly, "you forget that Paul is still quite young. It seems to me that you are quite unreasonable about him. I like him; and if his cross-word-puzzle stuff annoys you, you needn't come into this room while he is here."

"He's a cuckoo," volunteered her brother Joe.

"He is not cuckoo!" she retorted. "And besides, I was not talking to you."

"He's cuckoo," Joe repeated, unmoved in his opinion.

"Joe," Mrs. Bradley, looking up from the

sweater which she had been knitting since shortly after the Spanish-American War, mildly reproved her son, "you mustn't say cuckoo; it isn't refined."

Mr. Bradley fixed his daughter's attention.

"Cynthia," he said, "young or old, he's got to stop confusing me with those words he uses or keep away from here. I will not be confused in my own home and at my age. What does he ask me last night? He says, 'Mr. Bradley, I'd like to lave before dinner.' That's exactly what he said! He'd like to lave!"

Joe smiled cynically.

"Go on, pop," he said; "tell the rest."

Mr. Bradley looked uncomfortable.

"There is no rest," he declared sullenly.

"No!" jeered his son. "And who brought him a razor and a shaving mug?"

Mr. Bradley flushed angrily.

"That's just what I'm trying to make plain," he declared. "He confuses me. I know what lave means as well as any man on Staten Island, but he confused me. I won't have it! Why can't Cynthia have somebody around like that young fellow Bellows who used to come to see her?"

"But, papa," Mrs. Bradley objected, "Mr. Bellows turned out to be a burglar."

"I know, I know," Mr. Bradley nodded impatiently. "But nevertheless he was a very interesting young man. Outside of being a burglar he was very nice."

"Maybe," Mrs. Bradley said, "if Cynthia had been nice to him he wouldn't have been a burglar."

"No," said Joe. "Once a burglar, always a burglar. However, I'd just as soon have a burglar around as a cuckoo."

Cynthia started to retort again, but her mother spoke first, in an effort to bring peace.

"Dad's nerves are all upset," she explained; "it's the invention—and Uncle Cedric."

Cynthia was instantly contrite. She had no faith, no sympathy whatever, in the Bradley Patent Knife, which was a table knife with a slight ridge around the edges of one side of the blade, purposed as a boon to people who were inadept at holding such spherical foodstuffs as peas on the flat of the ordinary table knife. He had labored on its perfection for a year, to the accompaniment of silence from his daughter and derisive encouragement from his son.

"It's not refined to eat with your knife of course," Mrs. Bradley helped justify her husband; "but millions of people still do it, and they ought to be protected in some way. Your father's invention will be a godsend to these unfortunates."

Cynthia had no faith in it, but her father was elderly and obsessed with the idea.

Cynthia suspected, too, that the little store on the Richmond Turnpike, which catered to a steady average of about two customers a day, was much more unsteady than he would admit.

"I'm sorry, dad," she said. "Let's don't talk about it any more. Why isn't the invention all right? I thought it was finished."

"Finished," said Mr. Bradley, "and sent out to the Little Giant Table Tools Manufacturing Company—my last chance."

"Why last?"

"It's the only one," he explained morosely, "that hasn't turned it down. They've had it two weeks now, and I ought to hear any day. If they turn it down——"

Such were the workings of kismet this day that at that very moment the postman's whistle sounded on the doorstep.

Mr. Bradley stood rooted to the spot, his face pale, his eyes bright.

"Go to the door, Joe," he said.

Joe looked at his sister.

"Go to the door, sis," he said.

Mrs. Bradley laid down her knitting and went, returning five seconds later with a long parcel. Mr. Bradley tried bravely to smile when he saw it, but he knew the earmarks of failure, and his eyes filled with tears.

"I reckon," he said, "nobody wants it." He walked, tired, suddenly very old, toward the door. He turned when he reached it and said with an effort at lightness, "Better begin packing up things, mother. We may have to get out in the street next week."

It was Joe who caught the undercurrent of tragedy.

"What do you mean?" he asked quickly.

Mr. Bradley came back. The faces of his family were suddenly alert, apprehensive.

"I thought," he said slowly, "that this time I'd be successful. I thought that maybe I'd put it over. I'd banked so on it; I'd spent so much money——"

"Papa," Mrs. Bradley interrupted frantically, "go on, tell us, what did you do?"

"Well, mother, I'm afraid I spent money that I oughtn't. I needed some tools and some pewter and some blue prints and all those things that inventors have to have and—well, I had to use some of the mortgage money; in fact, I had to use it all." He sat down heavily. "I was sure it would come out all right this time," he explained dully. "I was sure I'd get an advance royalty and be able to pay it back. But——"

He made a gesture of despair.

For a few seconds no one spoke. Stunned by the news, they sat and looked at the broken old man. Cynthia closed her eyes. It was not much that her father had spent—six hundred dollars—but she knew that it could not be raised again, not by the date on which it was due. And she knew, too, that it would be futile to look for mercy from old Silas Gallup, holder of the mortgage, who was known far and wide as the meanest man on Staten Island.

"I thought," her father began again, "that I'd be helping——"

No need to blame him. What had happened had happened. They might as well prepare themselves for it. Mrs. Bradley—now weeping softly—could go to her sister's home in the Bronx. But Mr. Bradley, old, tired, discouraged, what——

Feet pounded suddenly on the porch.

"Cynthia! Cynthia!"

An excited voice calling. She raised her head. Paul's voice, calling again, and now there was a pounding at the door. Something whispered to her that it might mean something, that in some way this boy might be bringing news, good news, hope. She ran to the door and threw it open.

Paul stood there, red of face, panting, perspiring from his long run across the lea. For a minute, while he remained the object of all attention, he gasped, unable to utter a word, and then he spoke in a spasmodic gush of sound.

"Hoy!" he said.

"Hoy?" Cynthia knitted her brows, trying to grasp the import of the news. "Hoy?"

"Hoy!" he repeated.

"Make him sit down," advised Mrs. Bradley. "Let him get his breath." She, too, sensed something important. "Take your time, Paul. Sit down now and don't worry. Get your breath."

The boy stumbled to a chair and sat for a minute, until able to speak coherently. Then he addressed Cynthia.

"That word," he said, "was 'hoy.' "

"That word?" She was annoyed in some way. "What word?"

"The one we erred on," he explained, still breathing hard. "The number sixteen horizontal meaning an English coasting vessel. It was 'hoy.' I found it today." He gazed at her proudly, triumphantly.

"It was 'hoy.' " he repeated when she failed to answer. "I thought you'd want to know, so I ran over as quickly as I could." There was still silence, an ominous silence. "It was 'hoy,' " he repeated a little uneasily.

"The word was 'hoy.' H-o-y, hoy. It was——"

He stopped. The others did not speak. Cynthia turned and leaned against the wall, her face in her arms. Mr. Bradley and Joe only looked at Paul, long and earnestly. Finally Joe broke the silence.

"Personally," he said, "I believe I'd just as soon have a burglar around the house."

Mr. Bradley nodded.

"You're right, Joe," he agreed; adding rather irrelevantly, "you know you've got a right to shoot a burglar—the law says so."

Mrs. Bradley looked thoughtful.

"Mr. Bellows," she commented, "was indeed a very, very nice young man, though a burglar."

III

It was two weeks before Paul felt that it would not be foolhardy to call again at the Bradley house. He had seen Cynthia twice in Manhattan, and had almost sobbed his regret at whatever he had done.

"I erred," he pleaded, "and I rue it. But please, dear Cynthia, do not sever our relations."

"It was just unfortunate, Paul," she smiled in spite of herself. "We were feeling so bad, so terrible, and—and—and your coming in to tell us that—that 'hoy' was a ship was just out of place. I understand, Paul; don't worry. Wait a little while."

She had been in low spirits, and his own heart ached at the thought of what she was having to go through. The payment of the money Mr. Bradley had spent on the ridged table knife was due the following week, and as yet there was no indication at all that it could be met. Neither she nor Joe earned enough to save much, and all this little had been in the sum Mr. Bradley had turned over to the pewter magnates.

Paul's first visit after the fuss brought him to the Bradley home shortly after noon on Saturday. He had just reached the gate of the little house near the edge of the woods, when through it flashed a blurred gray figure. It cut across the street and stretched out into a tremendous gallop across a stubble field.

Transfixed, Paul stared and identified it finally as Mr. Bradley. As he stood there, Joe followed, but stopped at the gate. Cupping his hands he shouted after his father.

"Step on it, pop! Don't be late!"

He turned around then and saw Paul.

"It's Uncle Cedric," he explained. "He's dying again."

He went with Joe into the house.

"Who is Uncle Cedric?" he asked Cynthia.

"He's grandfather's brother," she explained. "He's a queer old Englishman, very sweet in his odd way, but he has a down on the world." She waved vaguely toward the woods. "He has a little hut out there in those woods that he built himself. He cooks his own food and never comes out and never has anything to do with anybody."

"Ah," Paul said, "an anchoret, or recluse!"

"He scratches a good deal," Joe volunteered. "He's great on scratching."

"Acne," Paul diagnosed the trouble. "That's a postular eruption." He turned to Cynthia. "Before I took up cross-word puzzles," he said brightly, "I didn't know that at all! Acne—postular eruption." He looked around inquiringly. "Where's Mrs. Bradley?"

Cynthia answered.

"She's gone to see Silas Gallup to beg for a month's extension on the mortgage." She spoke without hope. "Perhaps something will turn up."

"And what did you mean," Paul asked, suddenly recalling Joe's curious statement, "by saying your Uncle Cedric was dying again?"

Cynthia smiled.

"Oh, Joe is unkind," she said. "Uncle Cedric is nervous about himself. Alone out there, he gets an idea every so often that he is about to die, and sends word for dad to come to him."

Joe sneered.

"It's like a fire house," he explained. "People rush in here all hours of the day and night with word that Uncle Cedric wants pop to come at once. Pop springs into his clothes, slides down the brass pole and lights out across the fields. So far," he added, "we've had nothing but false alarms."

"And does he dote on his Uncle Cedric so much?"

"Dote?"

"Yes; is he inordinately fond of him?"

The Bradley boy laughed sardonically.

"Uncle Cedric's got a lot of jack salted away out there in those woods," he said. "He's a miser. He's told us so. He's told Cynthia. And when he dies, we get it. And when he sends word that he's dying, we have to hustle. We can't afford to be late. There are a few last words we want to hear—they'll tell us where this money is."

"Joe is cruel," Cynthia declared. "We—I love Uncle Cedric, but——"

"But just now," Joe broke in, glaring for some unaccountable reason at Paul, "we need money!"

The door opened and Mrs. Bradley entered.

She said "Oh!" when she saw Paul, and then added soothingly, "Now, Paul, you just be quiet. We're all your friends. Be quiet now." And she sidled nervously around him. Joe laughed oafishly.

"I'm not the only one that thinks it," he jeered at his sister meaningly, and Cynthia flushed angrily. Paul's face bore a blank expression.

Mrs. Bradley sat down with a sigh.

"Silas Gallup is a hard man," she said sadly, shaking her head. "It's no use, children."

"You mean he would not hearken to your plea?"

Paul's voice showed his concern, but Mrs. Bradley looked at him suspiciously. Joe refused to take this news of her failure seriously.

"Keep your head up, mom," he said, with a significant jerk of his head. "We got another alarm from the woods a few minutes ago. Pop's answered it full steam ahead, dog-gone the torpedoes. The Hermit of the Yosemite Valley claims to be breathing his last again."

"Joe," Mrs. Bradley murmured, "you mustn't say dog-gone; it isn't nice."

"It's argot, or patois, Mrs. Bradley." Paul was anxious to fan any spark of camaraderie. "It is not banned by all society."

Both Joe and Mrs. Bradley showed their bewilderment, and Cynthia shot Paul a glance of warning and shook her head for him to remain a nonparticipant.

"If I have erred——" he began, when Joe, after a glance out of the window, interrupted.

"Here's pop," he announced. "He doesn't look any too frisky; Uncle Cedric must have pulled through."

Mr. Bradley entered the house. He saw Paul and ignored him.

"Uncle Cedric," he said to the others, "is very low. He had about given up hope, but he picked up a little and told me finally that he wouldn't need me, that he felt all right again." He shook his head. "I don't know," he added in a voice that may or may not have held sorrow.

"A man of his age and status," Paul commented, "has generally reached the nadir of physical resistance."

Nobody understanding, nobody replied to this. Mr. Bradley sat down and looked questioningly at his wife. She shook her head.

"Mr. Gallup is a hard, hard man, father," she said. Pain shot through Mr. Bradley's eyes. "He's coming——" She glanced toward the window as footsteps sounded on the porch. "That may be him now."

"Er—Lyons, could I see you a moment in private?"

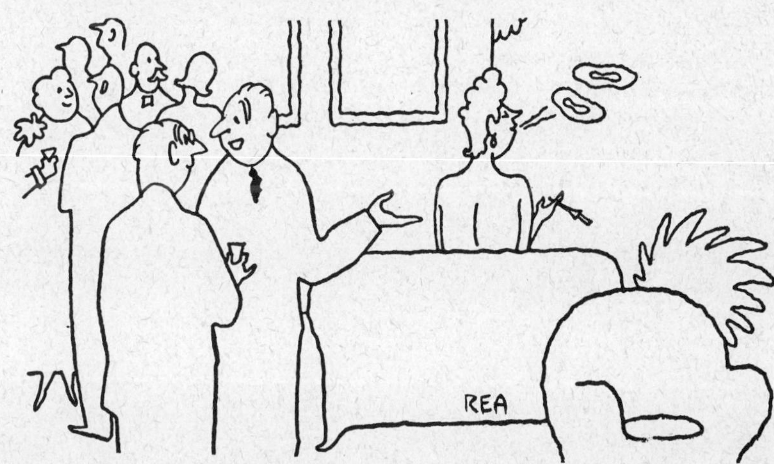

"Probably a strapless job. On the other hand, though, it *might* pay to go over and check."

"No, no! The best time to get furs is in December."

"Just tell him I invent things!"

"Suppose we find it—then what?"

"Homelike, isn't it?"

FAMOUS LAST WORDS

"If I was in a hurry I'd fly over—but on an ocean liner they've got movies, swimming pools, dances, the best cuisine . . ."

"Not *the* Angela Potter!"

"Well, what do you think of their place?"

Cynthia answered the knock and followed Silas Gallup back into the room. He stood for a minute looking around silently before he addressed the father.

"Well, Bradley," he said, "your missus called on me this afternoon with bad news. I hope it isn't—I hope it has been exaggerated. The situation in the realty field at present is such that I couldn't afford to disregard the letter of an agreement or a contract."

Paul rose uncomfortably. He did not feel that he should remain during a conversation so personal.

But Cynthia got up also and went over to him.

"Don't go now," she said. "I want you to be here with me." Her eyes pleaded; she was afraid.

"If it will allay ire," he murmured, "I will stay."

Mr. Gallup caught his words.

"Ire!" he said genially. "So you are a cross-word puzzler too!"

Paul looked self-conscious.

"If it does not seem to manifest ego," he said, "I might introduce myself. My name is Paul——"

"Mr. Bradley! Mr. Bradley!"

A child's voice rang outside the window. Something in the note, something exciting, brought them all to their feet.

"Mr. Bradley! The hermit says come! He's dying again! He says hurry!"

It was the regular bearer of the tidings. Muttering to himself, Mr. Bradley leaped across the room, snatched up his hat and darted out of the room. He reached the porch before stopping. The next second he thrust his head in the door and spoke excitedly.

"Don't go, Mr. Gallup!" he gasped. "Stay here until I get back! I—I may be able to fix this little thing up all right!"

He was off again, and a second time word came back, in a shout from the sidewalk. It was obviously a message for Joe.

"Don't let him get away! Keep him there until I get back, you hear?"

Mr. Gallup observed these hurried maneuvers with some astonishment.

"I say——" he began, and Paul sprang to his feet. Some sudden impulse to be out of so much personal matter moved him to take advantage of this opportunity to leave.

"I'll follow in Mr. Bradley's wake," he explained hurriedly. "There may be so much ado in yon woods that I'll be needed. Hope I may see you anon."

He dashed out of the room and followed the elder Bradley across the stubble field.

IV

He could not overtake Mr. Bradley. Nobody could have. The nephew of the hermit, grasping at a last straw, sprinted madly across the field and down the path through the woods. He had made up his mind suddenly to beg Uncle Cedric, provided he was still alive, to allow him to have some of the bequest at once, to stave off this calamity that lurked in Silas Gallup. He meant to insist on it.

But a hundred yards behind, Paul panted in hot pursuit, scarcely conscious of the fact that he had little or no purpose in racing thus to the possible deathbed of a hermit. But there being, on the other hand, no reason why he should turn back, he kept on.

He came at length to a clearing in the woods. Facing it was a rudely built one-room shanty, seemingly all small boards and patches and cloth stuffings, which he identified at once as the old Englishman's castle. Gathered about the door, peering in cautiously, was a group of small boys, barefooted and wide-eyed. Paul took charge.

"Disperse!" he shouted at them. "Disperse, gamins! You are harassing an ill man! Disperse!"

Baffled by his utterances, they did not move at first; but there was no mistaking his menacing gestures. They withdrew to the edge of the clearing, apparently as willing to stare at him as at a dying hermit. Paul surveyed the situation and, finding it faultless, started to enter the hut. And at that moment the door was barred—barred by the appearance of Mr. Bradley, who, with eyes staring blankly and brow knitted, stood there a full moment before speaking.

"He's dead," he said finally.

"Dead!"

"Yes, dead." Mr. Bradley's voice was almost as extinct as he added, "He died laughing—laughing!"

"But," Paul objected, "that was inane. Demises don't arouse risibilities."

"He died laughing," Mr. Bradley repeated. "He was pretty nearly gone when I got in there, but he recognized me. He tried to speak, tried to tell me something—and then he laughed."

"What was there to laugh at?" Paul insisted. "Surely you did not select such a time to narrate a comic mot."

"He died laughing," Mr. Bradley repeated monotonously. "There was no laughter in his eyes, or on his face at all; but he looked directly at me and said, 'Ha-ha!'

"Said what?"

"He laughed, 'Ha-ha,' and that was all."

Paul shook his head.

"It was inane," he repeated. "Such an antic is not apt."

Mr. Bradley recovered something of his aplomb and, at the same time, some of his antipathy to Paul. He glanced about briskly and saw the small boys.

"You stay here," he ordered Paul, "until I let Rabenold, the undertaker, know. I'll stop by his place on the way home."

He started down the path. Paul called after him.

"Tell me again, Mr. Bradley—the old man actually laughed at you?"

Mr. Bradley repeated his story.

"He just looked up at me," he said, "and laughed, 'Ha-ha,' most mirthlessly."

Then he was gone. Paul sat down on a stool at the door of the hut, very, very pensive, and then he walked over to the boys and began talking with them.

The older man went slowly down the wood path, cut across a field to the street and stopped at Rabenold's tiny office. Then he continued down the street to his home. His heart was heavy. He thought of Silas Gallup, that hard, hard man, waiting in his home, and of his wife and children. Nothing short of a miracle could save them from the fate that Silas Gallup had in store for them.

Crossing the street, he looked up and saw Silas Gallup pacing up and down impatiently on the front porch. He gave a little cry of glad surprise when he saw Mr. Bradley and leaped from the porch to meet him at the gate.

"Where's the champion?" he demanded.

"The who?"

"Mr. Paine, the cross-word-puzzle champion—where is he? Is he coming back here?"

"Oh, him!" Mr. Bradley answered sourly. "I suppose so. My Uncle Cedric died. Paul's waiting down there for the undertaker."

Mr. Gallup tapped his fingers together.

"I'll wait for him," he said. "I'd like to shake hands with him and talk to him about something."

"Each man to his taste," Mr. Bradley said, and went on into the house. His wife and children looked up anxiously as he entered. He shook his head slowly.

"What do you mean?" Joe asked. "No death or no money?"

"No money."

"What?"

Almost panic-stricken at what this meant, they were all on their feet.

"No," Mr. Bradley said. "He died laughing. He never said a word. He was almost gone. He just laughed—that was all."

"But he had some money!" Joe was angry. "He said so! Did you look?"

Mr. Gallup stepped in the door and spoke genially.

"The minute I saw that young lad," he said, "I knew he was a keen one. Just imagine, meeting the city cross-word-puzzle champion way out here in Staten Island! I'll wait until he comes back."

Joe lowered his voice for his father.

"Another one," he explained, jerking his head toward the door. "The minute Cynthia told him who her cuckoo boy friend was he began frothing at the mouth. Wants to meet Paul Paine! Wants to shake hands with him! Wants to shake hands with the champion!" He snorted with disgust.

Mr. Gallup paused at the window.

"I want to ask Mr. Paine about a five-letter word I ran against last night," he explained. "It doesn't look right, but he'll know."

He withdrew his head and resumed his nervous pacing up and down the porch.

Mr. Bradley whispered to his son.

"Has he forgot about the mortgage?" he asked. "Has he said anything about it?"

Joe shook his head.

"Not since he learned who Paul Paine was," he replied.

There was nothing more they could do. Cynthia stood at the window, looking out thoughtfully toward the woods. Poor old Uncle Cedric! She was sorry, always had been, for his eccentricities, for whatever it was that had driven him out of the society of people. A mean, crotchety, old misanthrope, and unfortunate.

Somehow she did not blame him for laughing, as unloyal as it sounded in her thoughts. They had stood around so obviously in wait for the money he was supposed to have. And yet whatever emotions her father might have had at the death, as slender as his would have been at the death of a man so remote in traits and understanding, could scarcely have maintained themselves in the confusion of these more personal calamities.

An hour passed, and then Silas Gallup came into the room again. He had his watch in his hand. His fever of cross-word-puzzle excitement apparently had worn off.

"Well, Bradley," he said, "we'd better get back to business. The champion evidently is not coming here again. I'm sorry; but business is business, Bradley. Have you the payment or not?"

"A hard, hard man," Mrs. Bradley commented, picking up her 1901-model sweater, now nearly half finished.

Mr. Bradley rose wearily.

"I haven't, Mr. Gallup. I have been unfortunate. I was——"

Mr. Gallup clucked his tongue.

"Don't go into it," he said. "Yes or no is enough. I don't want to seem mean, but business is business. The time is up today. You knew that three months ago. I can't feel responsible. A week from today I'll have to offer the place for sale."

"Mr. Gallup!" pleaded Cynthia pitifully.

Mr. Gallup raised his hand.

"I'm sorry, young lady," he said, "but business is——"

"Mr. Bradley! Mr. Bradley!"

Joe was at the window.

"It's Paine," he said; "he's running across the field." He sat down again, disappointed. "He probably wants to tell Cynthia that the three-letter word is 'sol.' "

But Cynthia was oblivious of the jape. She was gazing at the leaping, bounding cross-word-puzzle champion of New York City, as he raced across the lea, the fen and the st.—abbr.

"He's got a box under his arm!" she said suddenly. "He's got news!"

The Bradleys were crowding to the door excitedly. They met the champion in the hall. Unable to speak, he pushed the tin box he carried into Mr. Bradley's hands.

"The money!" he gasped finally. "Uncle Cedric's money!"

The old man wrenched it open. As large as a shoe box, it was stuffed with one and two dollar bills, packed in bundles, filling it to the top. For a second no one spoke, and then Joe and Mr. Bradley began a hasty count. Then they stood up.

"One thousand three hundred and fifteen dollars," Mr. Bradley exclaimed. "Enough and more!"

He counted out six hundred dollars, the amount due Silas Gallup, and handed the bundle to him. But Mr. Gallup was talking with Paul.

"I saw that puzzle you did in seven minutes sixteen and eight-seventeenth seconds, Mr. Paine," he said admiringly, "and I tried it myself. Really, you must be a genius! I couldn't make it in less than two hours and a quarter."

He felt a touch on his arm.

"The money, Mr. Gallup," Mr. Bradley was saying.

Silas Gallup, without looking up, without counting, accepted the money and thrust it unnoticed into his pocket.

"I'd like for you to come to dinner at my house sometime," Silas Gallup continued. "I'd like to show you a collection of first-edition cross-word-puzzle books that I've got."

Then, with affable farewells, he took his leave.

V

It was not until all had sat down for dinner that anyone was allowed to ask, per orders of Mrs. Bradley, how the dazzled cross-word-puzzle champion had found the money.

"No," Mrs. Bradley had said, "leave Paul alone now. Don't you people bother him. Let the boy rest, and then when we get a nice hot dinner on the table, and he is feeling all right again after his run, he can tell us. Don't any of you try to rush our Paul."

Mr. Bradley slapped him on the back and Joe called him old man. And then they sat down.

"I opine," he said finally, "lest you think it savors of gas, that I owe it all to cross-word puzzles. I. e., it was a word I learned in a cross-word puzzle that donated the clew to me. The moment that Mr. Bradley——"

"Pop," corrected Mr. Bradley. "Call me pop."

"When pop told me that the recluse had laughed during his demise, it occurred to me, as I averred to him, that it was inane. Demising people don't laugh. Also there was no comic mien to his visage. It seemed to me that he must have been essaying to tell Mr. Bradley—pop—where the moneys were cached.

"Then it flashed on me where the moneys were. I queried the gamins, and they told me of a hedge running across the lea abutting the woods. The lads and I trekked over to this hedge and found a kennel, a sort of small house, adjoining the hedge; but the lads told me that no canine had ever lived in it, that it was believed to be a possession of the anchoret.

"I pulled the refuse from its entry and groped within. Almost interred in mire, I found this box. I opened it—and there the money was."

"But how," Cynthia insisted, "did you know enough to look there?"

"That," explained Paul, "was where the cross-word puzzle helped me. Uncle Cedric was not laughing at—at pop. He was essaying to tell him that he should scan the haha."

"The what?"

"The haha. H-a-h-a, haha. It is a word of four letters meaning a hedge, seldom or never used in this country, except in puzzles, but familiar enough in England, Uncle Cedric's early home. It sounds like a manifestation of risibility, but it is actually a hedge. I——"

Joe spoke up admiringly.

"There may be something in those crossword puzzles, after all. There's no telling," he said to his father, "when a case like this will come up, is there? Can you imagine!"

"Paul's a mighty smart boy," Mr. Bradley agreed.

Cynthia looked across the table, her eyes laughing, and winked at the smart boy, an incident that so unnerved him that he tried to cover his confusion by passing his plate.

"May I have another dram of water, Mrs. Bradley?" he asked.

Mrs. Bradley looked at him fondly.

"Don't call me Mrs. Bradley, Paul," she said. "Call me mom."

The Perfect Squelch

A LEGISLATOR in a Middle-Western state, facing stiff opposition in his race for re-election, made as thorough a canvass of the voters as time would permit, but in one large township he was unable to see more than a handful of his constituents. Throughout the closing hours of the campaign he fretted and worried over whether this neglect would cost him his seat in the legislature.

Much to his amazement, he carried the township by a larger majority than almost any other, even running some votes ahead of the state candidates on his ticket. He was still groping for an explanation of this unexpected landslide several days later, when an old farmer from the township dropped in to see him.

"I was mighty proud at the fine vote your township gave me," the legislator trumpeted pompously. "But tell me, what made me so popular over there?"

"Well, it was like this," the old man said: "Your opponent, he came over there and made a speech . . . and you didn't."

—C. E. MANN.

THAT'S DIFFERENT

Taking a day off is easy; it's putting it back that's hard.

—PEGGY CAROLINE FEARS.

THE GREEK DOUBLE CROSS

Sorting Out the Smiths at Siwash

By GEORGE FITCH

§ *There wasn't a better or nobler frat on the old Siwash campus than the Eta Bitas. They were so far ahead of everything else with a Greek letter name that every freshman of taste and discrimination longed to become one of them. That year, though, the Smiths showed up. Had the Eta Bitas pledged the* right *one?*

MARCH 4, 1911

SUFFERING bear-cats! Say! excuse me while I take a long rest, Jim. I need it. I've just read a piece of information in this letter that makes me tired all over.

What is it? Oh, just another variety of competition smothered with a gentlemanly agreement—that's all; another bright-eyed little trust formed and another readjustment of affairs on a business basis. We old fellows needn't break our necks to get back to Siwash and the frat this fall, they write me. Of course they'll be delighted to see us and all that; but there's no burning need for us and we needn't jump any jobs to report in time to put the brands on the Freshmen and rescue them from the noisome Alfalfa Delts and Sigh Whoops—because there isn't going to be any rescuing this fall.

They've had an agreement at Siwash. They're going to approach the poor dumb Freshies under strict rules. No parties. No dinners at the houses. No abductions. No big, tall talk about pledging tonight or staggering through a twilight life to a frowzy-headed and unimportant old age in some bum bunch. All done away with. Everything nice and orderly. Freshman arrives. You take his name and address. Call on him, attended by referees. Maintain a general temperature of not more than sixty-five when you meet him on the campus. Buy him one ten-cent cigar during the fall and introduce him to one girl—age, complexion and hypnotic power to be carefully regulated by the rushing committee. Then you send him a little engraved invitation to amalgamate with you; and when he answers, per the self-addressed envelope inclosed, you are to love him like a brother for the next three and a half years. Gee! how that makes me ache!

Think of it! And at old Siwash too!—Siwash, where we never considered a pledge safe until we had him tied up in a back room, with our colors on him and a guard around the house! That settles me. I've always yearned to go back and cavort over the campus in the fall when college opened; but not for me no more! Why, if I went back there and got into the rushing game, first thing I knew they'd have me run up before a pan-Hellenic council, charged with giving an eligible Freshman more than two fingers when I shook hands with him; and I'd be ridden out of town on a rail for rushing in an undignified manner.

Rushing? What's rushing? Oh, yes; I forgot that you never participated in that delicious form of insanity known as a fall term in college. Rushing is a cross between proposing to a girl and abducting a coyote. Rushing a man for a frat is trying to make him believe that to belong to it is joy and inspiration, and to belong to any other means misery and an early tomb; that all the best men in college either belong to your frat or couldn't get in; that you're the best fellows on earth, and that you're crazy to have him, and that he is a coming Senator; that you can't live without him; that the other gang can't appreciate him; that you never ask men twice; that you don't care much for him anyway, and that you are just as likely as not to withdraw the spike any minute if you should happen to get tired of the cut of his trousers; that your crowd can make him class president and the other crowds can make him fine mausoleums; that you love him like real brothers and that he has already bound himself in honor to pledge—and that if he doesn't he will regret it all his life; and, besides, you will punch his head if he doesn't put on the colors. That's rushing for you.

What's my crowd? Why, the Eta Bita Pie, of course. Couldn't you tell that from my skyscraper brow? We Eta Bitas are so much better than any other frat that we break down and cry now and then when we think of the poor chaps who can't belong to us. We're bigger, grander, nobler and tighter about the chest than any other gang. We've turned out more Senators, Congressmen, Supreme Justices, near-Presidents, captains of industry, foreign ambassadors and football captains than any two of them. We own more frat houses, win more college elections, know more about neckties and girls, wear louder vests and put more cross-hatch effects on our neophytes than any three of them. We're so immeasurably ahead of everything with a Greek-letter name that every Freshman of taste and discrimination turns down everything else and waits until we crook our little finger at him. Of course, sometimes we make a mistake and ask some fellow that isn't a man of taste and discrimination; he proves it by going into some other frat; and that, of course, keeps all the men of poor judgment out of our gang and puts them in the others. Regular automatic dispensation of Providence, isn't it?

It's been a long time since I had a chance to gather with the brethren back at Siwash and agree with them how glorious we are, but this note brings it all back. My! how I'd like this minute to go back about ten years and cluster around our big grate fire, which used to make the Felta Kaps so crazy with envy. Those were the good old days when we came back to college in the fall, looked over the haycrop in the Freshman class, picked out the likeliest seed repositories, and then proceeded to carve them out from the clutches of a round dozen rival frats, each one crazy to get a spike into every new student who looked as if he might be president of the Senior class and an authority on cotillons some day. No namby-pamby, drop-three-and-carry-one crochet effects about our rushing those days! We just stood up on our hind legs and scrapped it out. For concentrated, triple-distilled, double-X excitement the first three weeks of college, with every frat breaking its collective neck to get a habeas corpus on the same six or eight men, had a suffragette tea party in the House of Parliament beaten down to a dove-coo.

There's nothing that made us love a

Freshman so hard as to have about six other frats after him. I've seen women buy hats the same way. They've got to beat some other woman to a hat before they can really appreciate it. And when we could swat half a dozen rival frats over the heart by waltzing a good-looking young chap down the walk to chapel with our colors on his coat, and could watch them turning green and purple and clawing for air—well, I guess it beat getting elected to Congress or marrying an heiress-apparent for pure, unadulterated, unspeckled joy!

Competition was getting mighty scarce in the country even then. There were understandings between railroad magnates and beef kings and biscuit makers—and even the ministers had a scale of wedding fees. But competition had a happy home on our campus. About the best we had been able to do had been to agree not to burn down each other's frat houses while we were haltering the Freshmen. I've seen nine frats, with a total of one hundred and fifty members, sitting up nights for a week at a time working out plans to despoil each other of a runty little fellow in a pancake hat, whose only accomplishment was playing the piano with his feet. One frat wanted him and that started the others. Of course we'd have got along better if we'd put the whole Freshman class in cold storage until we could have found out who the good men were and who the spoiled fruit might be. We were just as likely to fall in love with a suit of clothes as with a future class orator.

We took in one man once because he bought a pair of patent-leather tan shoes in his Junior year. We argued that, if he had the nerve to wear the things to his Y.M.C.A. meetings, there must be some originality in him after all—and we took a chance. We won. But it's a risky business. Once five frats rushed a fellow for a month because of the beautiful clothes he wore—and just after the victorious bunch had initiated him a clothing house came down on the young man and took the whole outfit. You can't always tell at first sight. But then, I don't know but that college fraternities exercise as much care and judgment in picking brothers as women do in picking husbands. Many a woman has married a fine mustache or a bunch of noble clothes and has taken the thing that wore them on spec. That's one more than we ever did. You could fool us with clothes; but the man who came to Siwash with a mustache had to flock by himself. He and his whiskers were considered to be enough company for each other.

There were plenty of frats in Siwash to make things interesting in the fall. There were the Alfalfa Delts, who had a house in the same block with us and were snobbish just because they had initiated a locomotive works, two railroads and a pickle factory. Then there were the Sigh Whoopsilons, who got to Siwash first and who regarded the rest of us with the same kindly tolerance with which the Indians must have looked at Daniel Boone. And there were the Chi Yis, who fought society hard and always had their picture taken for the college annual in dress suits. Many's the time I've loaned my dress suit to drape over some green young Chi Yi, so that the annual picture could show an unbroken row of open-faced vests. And there were the Shi Delts, who were a bold, bad bunch; and the Fli Gammas, who were good, pious boys, about as exciting as a smooth-running prayer-meeting; and the Delta Kappa Whoopsilons, who got every political office either by electing a member or initiating one; and the Delta Flushes; and the Mu Kow Moos; the Sigma Numerous; and two or three others that we didn't lie awake nights worrying about. Every one of these bunches had one burning ambition—that was to initiate the very best men in the Freshman class every fall. That made it necessary for us, in order to maintain our proud position, to disappoint each one of them every year and to make ourselves about as popular as the directors of a fresh-air and drinking-water trust.

Of course we always disappointed them. Wouldn't admit it if we didn't. But, holy mackerel! what a job it was! Herding a bunch of green and timid and nervous and contrary youngsters past all the temptations and pitfalls and confidence games and blarneyfests put up by a dozen frats, and landing the bunch in a crowd that it had never heard of two weeks before, is as bad as trying to herd a bunch of whales into a fishpond with nothing but hot air for gads. It took diplomacy, pugnacity and psychological moments, I tell you; and it took more: it took ingenuity and inventiveness and cheek and second sight and cool heads in time of trouble and long heads on the job, from daybreak to daybreak. I'd rather go out and sell battleships to farmers, so far as the toughness of the job is concerned, than to tackle the job of persuading a wise young high-school product with two chums in another frat that my bunch and he were made for each other. What did he care for our glorious history? We had to use other means of getting him. We had to hypnotize him, daze him, waft him off his feet; and if necessary we had to get the other frats to help us. How? Oh, you never know just how until you have to; and then you slip your scheme wheels into gear and do it. You just have to; that's all. It's like running away from a bear. You know you can't, but you've got to; and so you do.

Makes me smile now when I think of some of the desperate crises that used to roll up around old Eta Bita Pie like a tornado convention and threaten to engulf the bright, beautiful world and turn it into a howling desert, peopled only by Delta Kappa Whoops and other undesirables. I'm far enough away to forget the heart-bursting suspense and to see only the humor of it. Once I remember the Shi Delts, in spite of everything we could do, managed so to befog the brain of the Freshman class president that he cut a date with us and sequestered himself in the Shi Delt house in an upper back room, with the horrible intention of pledging himself the next morning. Four of the largest Shi Delts sat on the front porch that evening and the telephone got paralysis right after supper. They had told the boy that if he joined them he would probably have to leave school in his Junior year to become governor; and he didn't want to see any of us for fear we would wake him up. I chuckle yet when I think of those four big bruisers sitting on the front porch and guarding their property while I was shinning up the corner post of the back porch, leaving a part of my trousers fluttering on a nail and ordering the youngster in a blood-curdling whisper to hand down his coat, unless he wanted to lose forever his chance of being captain of the football team in his Sophomore year. He weighed the governorship against the captaincy for a minute, but the right triumphed and he handed down his coat. I sewed a big bunch of our colors on it, discoursed with him fraternally while balancing on the slanting roof, shook hands with him in a solemn, ritualistic way and bade him be firm the next morning. When the Shi Delts came in and found that Freshman pledged to another gang they had a convulsion that lasted a week; and to this day they don't know how the crime was committed.

There was another Freshman, I remember, who was led violently astray by the Chi Yis and was about to pledge to them under the belief that their gang contained every man of note in the United States. We had to get him over to the house and palm off a lot of our alumni as leading actors and authors, who had dropped in to dinner, before he was sufficiently impressed to reason with us. Of course this is not what the English would call "rully sporting, don't you know!" but in our consciences it was all classified as revenge. We got the same doses. Billings, of the Mu Kow Moos, pulled one of our spikes out in beautiful fashion once by impersonating our landlord. He rushed up the steps just as a Freshman rushee was starting down all alone and demanded the rent for six months on the spot, threatening to throw us out into the street that minute. The Freshman only hesitated long enough to get his clothes out of the house, and we didn't know for a month what had frozen his feet.

The Fli Gams weren't so slow either. They found out once that one of the men we were just about to land had a great disgust for two of our men. What did one of their alumni do but ooze craftily over our way and mention in the most casual manner the undying admiration that the boy had for those two? Of course we sandwiched him between them for a week—and of course we were pained and grieved when he tossed us into the discard; but we got even with them the next year. We picked up an eminent young pugilist, who made his headquarters in the next town, and for a little consideration and a suit of clothes that was a regular college yell we got him to hang around the campus for a week. We rushed him terrifically for a day and then managed to let the Fli Gams get him. They rushed him for a week in spite of our carefully regulated indignation and then proposed to him. When he told them that he might consider coming to school—as soon as he had gone South and had cleaned up a couple of good scraps—they let out an awful shriek and fumigated the house. They were nice young chaps, but no judge of a pugilist. They expected to be able to see his hoofs.

Well, it was this way every year all fall. Ding-dong, bing-bang, give and take, no quarter and pretty nearly everything fair. As I said, it wasn't considered exactly proper to burn a rival frat house in order to distract the attention of the occupants while they were entertaining a Freshman, but otherwise we did pretty nearly what we pleased to each other—only being careful to do it first. Of course a lot of things are fair in love and war that would not be considered strictly ethical in a game of croquet. And rushing a Freshman is as near like love as anything I know of. It isn't that we love the Freshman so much. When I think of some of the trash we fought over and lost I have to laugh. But we couldn't bear the idea of losing him. To sit by and watch another gang win the affections of a young fellow who you know is designed by Nature for your frat and the football team; to note him gradually breaking off the desperate chumminess that has grown up between you in the last forty-eight hours; to think that in another day he will have on the pledge colors of another fraternity and will be lost to you forever and ever and ever, and then some—what is losing a mere girl to some other fellow compared with that? Of course I realize now that, even if a Freshman does join another frat, you can eventually get chummy with him again after college days are over if you find him worth crossing the street to see; and I find myself lending money to Shi Delts and borrowing it from Delta Whoops just as freely as if they were Eta Bites. But somehow you don't learn these things in time to save your poor old nerves in college.

When I was in school the Alfalfa Delts, the Delta Flushes and the Chi Yis were giving us a horrible race. I'm willing to admit it now, though I'd have fought Jeffries before doing it ten years ago. Each fall was one long whirlwind. The President of the United States in an office-seekers' convention would have had a placid time compared with the Freshmen. We didn't exactly use real axes on each other and we didn't actually tear any Freshman in two pieces, but we came as near the limit as was comfortable. No frat was safe for a minute with its guests. If you tried to feed 'em there was kerosene in the ice cream. If you entertained them some frat with a better quartet worked outside the house. If you took them out to call the parlor would fill up with riffraff in no time; and if you took your eye off your victim for a minute he was gone—some other gang had got him. I sometimes think some of the crowds knew how to palm Freshmen the way magicians do, from the way they disappeared. Even the girls took a hand in it.

When I was a Sophomore I was intrusted with the task of leading a Freshman three blocks down to Browning Hall to call on one of our solid girls, and before I had gone a block two Senior girls met us. They were bare acquaintances of mine, being strong Delta Whoop allies, and they usually only managed to see me after a severe effort; but this time you'd have thought I was a whole regiment of fiancés. They literally fell on my neck. It was cruel of me, they declared, to be so unsociable. There I was, a football hero—I'd broken a rib on the scrub team—and every girl in school was dying to tell me how grand it was to suffer for one's college; and yet I wouldn't so much as hint that I wanted to come to the sorority parties—and lots more talk of the same kind. Naturally I was somewhat dazzled and I'd walked about half a block with the prettiest one before I noticed that the other one was steering Freshie the other way. I turned around and never even said "Good day" to that girl; but it was too late. About a dozen Delta Whoops appeared out of the ground and tried to look surprised as they gathered around that scared little Freshman and engulfed him. We never saw him again—that is, in his innocent condition—and the boys wouldn't trust me with the castoffs we were rushing around for bait the rest of the year. Bait? Oh, yes. Sometimes we'd pledge a man on the quiet and leave him out a week or two, so that plenty of frats could bid him—made them appreciate his worth, you know, and got every one well acquainted.

By the time I was a Senior the competition was desperate. We spent the summers scouring the country for prospects and we spent the first week of school smuggling our trophies into our houses and pledging them, without giving the other fellow a look in—that is, we tried to. We came back fairly strong in our Senior year, with a good bunch of prospects; but the one that excited us most was a telegram from Snooty Vincent in Chicago. It was brief and erratic, like Snooty himself, and read as follows:

> Freshman named Smith will register from Chicago. Son of old man Smith, multimillionaire. Kid's a comer. Get him sure! SNOOTY.

That was all. One of the half million Smiths of Chicago was coming to college—age, weight, complexion, habits and time of arrival unknown. That telegram qualified Snooty for the paresis ward. We didn't even know what Smith his millionaire father was. The world is full of Smiths who are pestered by automobile agents. All we knew was the fact that we had to find him, grab him, sequester him where no meddling Alfalfa Delt or Chi Yi could find him, and make him fall in love with us inside of forty-eight hours. Then we could lead him forth, with the colors and his *art-nouveau* clothes on, spread the glad news—and there wouldn't have to be any more rushing that fall. We'd just sit back and take our pick.

We sat back and built brains full of air-castles for about three minutes—and then got busy. It was matriculation day. There were half a dozen trains to come yet from Chicago on various roads. We had to meet them all, pick out the right man by his aura or by the way the porter looked when he tipped him, and grab him out from under the ravenous foe. The next train was due in ten minutes and the depot was a mile away. We sent Crawford down. He was trying for the distance runs anyway.

The rest of us went out to show a couple of classy boys from a big prep school how to register and find a room, and pick out textbooks; and incidentally how to tell a crowd of magnificent young student leaders from eleven wrangling bunches of miscellaneous thickheads, who wouldn't like anything better than to rope in a couple of good men to teach them the ways of the world. We were succeeding in this to the queen's taste, having accidentally dropped in on our porch with the pair, when young Crawford rushed up green with despair and took the rushing committee inside. He almost cried when he told us. He'd watched the train as carefully as he could, he said, but he couldn't be everywhere at once; and so a couple of Mu Kow Moos had got Smith. He knew it because he had heard them ask what his name was and he had told them Smith. He'd pretty nearly wrecked his brain trying to think of an excuse to butt in, but they had taken the boy away and he'd run all the way to the house to see if something couldn't be done.

Petey Simmons had listened, sitting crosslegged on the windowseat, which was a habit of his. Petey was a Senior and his deep studies in rhetoric during his four years in the frat had given him a great power of expression. He turned to the despairing Crawford and reduced him to a cinder with one look.

"So you couldn't think of any excuse to butt in!" he remarked slowly. "Say, Crawford, if you saw a young lady falling through the ice you'd write to her mother for permission to cheer her up. Which way did they go?"

"They're coming this way," said what was left of Crawford.

Petey grabbed his hat and discharged himself toward the depot. We brought in those big prep school boys and tried to give them the time of their lives, but our hearts weren't in it. We were thinking of those Mu Kow Moos—that frat of all others—blissfully towing home a prize they'd stumbled onto and didn't know anything about! We thought of those beautifully designed air-castles we were hoping to move into and we got pumpkins in our throats. Stung on the first day of school by a bunch that had to wear their pins on their neckties to keep from being mistaken for a literary society! Oh, thunder! We went in to dinner all smeared up with gloom. Then the door opened and Petey came in. He was five feet five, Petey was, but he stooped when he came under the chandelier. He had a suitcase in one hand and a stranger in the other.

"Boys," he said, "I want you to meet Mr. Smith, of Chicago."

II

At first glance you wouldn't have taken Smith for a perambulating national bank, with a wheelbarrow of spending-money every month. He was well-enough dressed and all that, but he didn't loom up in any mountainous fashion as to looks. He was runty and his hair was a kind of discouraged red. He had freckles too, and he was so bashful that his voice blushed when he used it. He didn't have a word to say until dinner, when he said "thank you" to Sam, the waiter. Altogether he was so meek that he had us worried; but then, as Allie Banks said, you can't always tell about these multimillionaires. Some of them didn't have the nerve of a mouse. He'd seen millionaires in New York, he said, who were afraid of cabdrivers.

"And besides," said Petey, when a few of us were talking it over after dinner, "I'd never have got him if he hadn't been so meek. I was determined that no Mu Kow

Moo was going to hang anything on us; and when I saw the three of them coming I waded right in. Allison and Briggs, those two dumb Juniors, were doing the steering. It was like taking candy from the baby. I just fell right into them and took about five minutes to tell those two how glad I was to see them back. I introduced myself to Smith; and—would you believe it?—he was still carrying his suitcase! I grabbed it and apologized for not having carried it all the way up from the station. You should have seen those yaps scowl. They wanted to shred me up, but I never noticed them again. I pointed out all the sights to Smith and told him his friends had written me about him. There was so little room on the sidewalk that I suggested we two walk ahead; and I shoved him right into the middle of the walk and made Allison and Briggs fall behind. I had a piece of luck just then. Old Pete and his sawed-off cab came by and I flagged him in a minute. I shoved Smith in and got in after him. Then I told the two babes that I could take care of Smith all right and that there was no need of their walking clear up to the house. After that I shut the door and we came away. If looks could kill I'd be tuning up my harp this minute. Say, if I didn't have any more nerve than those two I'd get a permit from the city to live. And all the time Smith never made a kick. I had him hypnotized. Now I'm going in and make him jump through a hoop."

We should have been very happy—and we would have been, but just then Symington came in with some astounding news. The Alfalfa Delts had a man named Smith, of Chicago, over at their house. He was on the front porch, with the whole gang around him; and from the looks of things they'd have him benevolently assimilated before twenty-four hours. Naturally this created a tremendous lot of emotion around our house. It was a serious situation. We might have the right Smith and then again we might have a Smith who would be borrowing money for carfare inside of ten minutes. We had to find out which Smith it was before we tampered with his young affections.

Did you ever snuggle up to a young captain of industry and ask him who his father was and whether he was important enough in the business world to be indicted by the Government for anything? That was the job we tackled that night. Smith was meek enough, but somehow even Petey's nerve had its limits. We approached the subject from every corner of the compass. We led up to it, we beat around it—and finally we got desperate and led the boy up to it. But he was too shy to come down with the information. Yes, he lived in Chicago. Oh, on the North Side. Yes, he guessed the stock market was stronger. Yes, the Annex was a great hotel. No, he didn't know whether they were going to put a tower on the Board of Trade or not. Yes, the Lake Shore Drive was dusty in summer.—[Good!]—He wouldn't care to live on it.—[Bah!]—Altogether he was as unsatisfactory to pump as a well full of dusty old brickbats. Just then Rawlins, who had been scouting around seeing what he could run against in the dark of the moon, arrived with the stunning information that the Chi Yis had a man named Smith, of Oak Park, at their house and that every corner of the lawn was guarded by picked men!

When we got this news most of us went upstairs and bathed our heads in cold water. Oak Park sounded even more suspicious than Chicago. It's a solid mahogany suburb and everybody there is somebody or other. You have to get initiated into the place just as if it were a secret society, it's so exclusive. That meant there were three Smiths from Chicago in school. We had only one Smith. We had a one-in-three shot.

We stuck the colors on the boys from

the big prep school just to keep our hands in and went to bed so nervous that we only slept in patches. Still, two Chicago Smiths in other frat houses were better than one. It meant that at least one frat wasn't sure of its man. Maybe neither one was. Our scouts had reported that, from what they could pick up, neither Smith had it on our Smith much in looks. That could only mean one thing: there had been a leak in the telegraph office again. What show has a guileless sixty-five-dollar-a-month operator against a bunch of crafty young diplomatists? They had read our telegram and were after the same Smith that we were.

By morning the suspense around the house could have been shoveled out with a pitchfork. If one of the other frats had the right Smith and knew it, and had pledged him during the night, there was positively no use in living any longer. Petey, who had shared his room with our Smith, reported that he was now like wax in our hands. But that didn't comfort us much. It was too confoundedly puzzling. Maybe we had the heir to a subtreasury panting to join us and maybe his freckles were his fortune. All Petey had gouged out of him during the night was the fact that his father wanted him to come to Siwash because it was a nice, quiet place. Oh, yes; it was deadly calm!

It couldn't have been more than seven o'clock when the telephone rang. Petey answered it. A relative of Smith's was at the hotel and had heard the boy was at our house. Would we please tell him to come right down? Petey said he would and then rang off. Then he grabbed the 'phone again and asked Central excitedly why she had cut him off. Central said she hadn't, but of course she rang the other line again.

"Hello!" said Petey blandly. "This is the Alfalfa Delt house?"

"No; it's the Chi Yi house," was the answer. Petey put the receiver up contentedly and we all turned handsprings over the library table. Fifty per cent safe, anyway. The Chi Yis were trying to sort out the Smiths too.

It was an hour before anything else happened. Then Matheson of the Alfalfa Delts, a ponderous personage, who wore a silk hat on Sunday and did instructing, came over and asked if we had a man named Smith with us. He was to be a pupil of his he said, and he wanted to arrange his work. Of course Matheson was hoping to get a green man at the door, but he didn't have any luck. Bangs himself let him in and let him read two or three magazines through in the library while we turned some more handsprings—in the dining room this time. The Alfalfa Delts were fishing too. It was a fair field and no favors.

After a while Bangs told Matheson that the man named Smith presented his compliments and said it was all a mistake. His tutor's name was not Matheson, but Muttonhead. That sent Matheson away as pleasant as you please.

All that day we sat around and beat off the enemy and got beaten off ourselves. Our Smith got a Faculty notice to appear at once and register—that is, it got as far as the door. We sent it back to the Chi Yi house. We sent the Alfalfa Delt Smith a telegram from Chicago, reading: "Father ill. Come at once." That only got as far as a door too. Some Alfalfa Delt got it and sent the boy back with the answer: "So careless of father!" Blanchard called up the fire department and sent it over to the Chi Yi house hoping to be able to slip over and cut out Smith in the confusion that followed; but the game was too old. The Chi Yis had played it themselves the year before and refused to bite. Meantime we had found a Chi Yi alumnus in the kitchen trying to sell a book to the cook; and in the proceedings that followed we discovered that the book had a ten-dollar bill in it. All around, it was an entertaining but profitless day. By night, there wasn't another idea left in the three camps. We sat exhausted, each clutching its Smith and glaring at the other two.

As far as our Smith was concerned we almost wished some one would steal him. He was about as interesting as a pound of baking powder. What with fishing for his Bradstreet rating, and inventing lies to keep him from going out and seeing the town, and watching the horizon for predatory Alfalfa Delts and Chi Yis, we were plumb worn out. We were so skittish that, when the bell rang about eight o'clock, we let it ring four times more before we answered it; and when the ringer claimed to be an Eta Bita Pie from Muggledorfer who had come over to attend Siwash, we made him repeat pretty nearly the whole ritual before we would consider his credentials good.

He got in at last, slightly peevish at our unbrotherly welcome, and took his place in the library circle. We were explaining the whole situation to him, when Allie Bangs gave an earnest yell and stood on his head in the corner.

"What did you say your name was?" he asked the visitor after he had been set right side up again.

"Maxwell, of Damma Yappa chapter," said the latter.

"No, it isn't," said Bangs earnestly. "You ought to know your own name!" he went on severely. "It's Smith—and you're a barb from the cornfield! You've come to Siwash to forget how to plow and tomorrow you're going to organize a Smith Club. Do you hear? Don't let me catch you forgetting your name now—and listen closely."

It was all as simple as beating a standpat Congressman. Maxwell was a stranger, of course. He was to pin his Eta Bita Pie pin on his undershirt and go forth in the morning a brand-new Smith, green and guileless. It was to occur to him just before chapel that a Smith Club ought to be formed and he was to post a notice to that effect. He would get a couple of well-known nonfraternity Smiths interested and have them visit the houses and see the Chicago Smiths. With all the Smiths in session that night, he ought to have no difficulty in finding out which was the son of old man Smith. He could be lowdown and vulgar enough to ask right out if he wished. If he found out he was to cut out that Smith and bring him to our house—if he had to bind and gag him. If he didn't he was to bring all three—if he could.

There was a quiet and most reassuring tone in Maxwell's voice as he said: "I can." They evidently had their little troubles at Muggledorfer too.

"After we get them here," said Bangs earnestly, "we'll just pledge all three from Chicago. We'll surely get the right one that way and perhaps the other two will not be so bad."

Upstairs, Petey Simmons was wearily explaining to our Smith for the ninth time that Freshmen were not allowed to appear on the campus for the first three days; and that it was considered good form to keep indoors until the Sophomore rush; and that there wasn't a room left in town anyway, and he might as well stay with us a while; and that the police were looking for college students downtown and locking them up, as they did each fall, to show their authority. Blanchard relieved him of his task and he came downstairs mopping his brow. Then we went to work and planned details until midnight. It was to be the plot of the century and every wheel had to mesh.

We spent the next day in a cold perspiration. Neither Alfalfa Delt nor Chi Yi paraded any pledged Freshmen. They were still hunting for the right Smith too—evidently. They fell for the Smith Club plan with such suspicious eagerness that it was plain each bunch had some nasty, lowlived scheme up its sleeves. We were righteously indignant. It was our game and they ought not to butt in. But Maxwell only smiled. He was a Napoleon, that boy was. He just waved us aside. "I'll run this little thing the way we do at Muggledorfer," he explained. "You fellows can play a few lines of football pretty well, but when it comes to surrounding a Freshman and making a Greek out of him, I wouldn't take lesson from old Ulysses himself." And so we left him alone and held each other's hands and smoked and cussed—and hoped and hoped and hoped.

Maxwell went after the three Smiths himself that night. He had taken a room in an out-of-the-way part of town and his plan was to take them over there after the meeting to discuss the future good of the Smith Club. Then about a dozen of us would slide gently over there—and a curtain would have to be drawn over the woe that would ensue for the other gangs. Meanwhile, all we had to do was to sit around the house and gnaw our fingers. Maxwell called for our Smith last and he had the other two in tow. Oh, no; we didn't invite them in. Two Alfalfa Delts and three Chi Yis were sitting on our porch, visiting us. Three Chi Yis and two Eta Bita Pies were sitting on the Alfalfa Delt porch. Four Eta Bites and two Alfalfa Delts were calling on the Chi Yi house. It was a critical moment and none of us was taking chances. We couldn't keep our Smiths from wandering, but we could make sure they didn't wander into the wrong place.

Maxwell led his flock of Smiths away and we all sat and talked to each other in little short bites. The Chi Yis were nervous as rabbits. They looked at their watches every five minutes. The Alfalfa Delts listened to us with one ear and swept the other around the gloom. The night was charged with plots. Innumerable things seemed trembling in the immediate future. When the visitors excused themselves a little later, and went away very hurriedly, we learned with pleasure from one of our boys, who had been wandering around to break in a new pair of shoes or something, that the Smith meeting, which had been called for the Erosophian Hall, had been attended by four nondescript and unknown Smiths and fourteen Chi Yis, who had dropped in casually. First blood for us! Maxwell had evidently succeeded in segregating his Smiths. We expected a telephone call from his room at any minute.

We kept on expecting it until midnight and then strolled down that way. The house was dark. A very mad landlady came down in response to our earnest request and informed us that the young carouser who had rented her room had not been there that evening; and that if we were his rowdy friends we could tell him that he would find his trunk in the alley. Then we went home and our brains throbbed and gummed up all night long.

We went to chapel the next morning to keep from going insane outright. The Chi Yis were there looking perfectly sour. The Alfalfa Delts on the other hand were riotous. Every one of them had a pleasant greeting for us. They slapped us on the back and asked us how we were coming on in our rushing. Matheson was particularly vicious. He came over to Bangs and put his arm around him in a friendly way. "I am going to have dinner with my pupil tonight," he said triumphantly. "He wants me to come over and get his trunk. Says he's got a good room now and he's much obliged to you fellows for your trouble. Have you heard that there's another Smith in school—son of a big Chicago man? There's some great material here this fall, don't you think?"

Bangs tripped on Matheson's pet toe and went away. Something horrible had happened. How we hated those Alfalfa Delts! They had stung us before, but this was a triple-expansion, double-back-action, high-explosive sting, with a dum dum point. We hurt all over; and the worst of it was, we hadn't been stung yet and didn't know where it was going to hit us. Did you ever wait perfectly helpless while a large, taciturn wasp with a red-hot tail was looking you over?

The Alfalfa Delts frolicked up and down college that day, Smithless but blissful. We consoled ourselves with a couple of corking chaps whom the Delta Flushes had been cultivating, and put the ribbons on them in record time. Ordinarily we would have been perfectly happy about this, but instead we were perfectly miserable. We detailed four men at a time to be gay and carefree with our pledges; and the rest of us sat around and listened to our bursting hearts. Of all the all-gone and utterly hopeless feelings, there is nothing to compare with the one you have when your frat—the pride of the nation—has just been tossed into the discard by some hollow-headed Freshman.

I took my head out of my hands just before dinner and went down the street to keep a rushing engagement. I had to pass the Alfalfa Delt house. It hurt like barbed wire, but I had to look. I was that miserable that it couldn't have bothered me much more, anyway, to see that wildly happy bunch. But I didn't see it. I saw instead a crowd of fellows on the porch who made our dejection look like disorderly conduct. There was enough gloom there to fit out a dozen funerals, and then there would have been enough left for a book of German philosophy. The crowd looked at me and I fancied I heard a slight gnashing of teeth. I didn't hesitate. I just walked right up to the porch and said: "Howdedo? Lovely evening!" says I. "How many Smiths have you pledged today?"

The gang turned a dark crimson. Then Matheson got up and came down to me. He was as safe-looking as somebody else's bull terrier.

"We don't care to hear any more from you," he said, clenching his words; "and it would be safer for you to get out of here. We're done with your whole crowd. You're lowdown skates—that's what you are. You're dishonorable and sneaky. You're cads! We'll get even. I give you warning. We'll get even if it takes a hundred years."

"Thanks!" says I. "Hope it takes twice as long." Then I went back home and let my date take care of itself.

III

We went through dinner in a daze and sat around, that night, like a bunch of vacant grins on legs. Our grins were vacant because we didn't know why we were grinning. We'd stung the Alfalfa Delts. We didn't know why or how or when. But we'd stung them! We had their word for it. Sooner or later something would turn up in the shape of particulars; only we wished it would hurry. If it didn't turn up sooner we were extremely likely to burst at the seams.

It turned up about nine o'clock. There was a commotion at the front door and Maxwell came in. He was followed by an avalanche of Smiths. There was our Smith, and a tall, lean Smith, and a Smith who waddled when he walked. They were all dirty and dusty; they all wore our pink-and-blue pledge ribbons on their coat lapels and when they got in the house they gave the Eta Bita Pie yell and sang about half of the songbook. Maxwell had not only pledged them but he had educated them.

After we had stopped carrying the bunch about on our shoulders, and had put the roof of the house back, and had righted the billiard table, and persuaded the cook to come down out of a tree in the back yard, we allowed Maxwell to tell his story.

"It was perfectly simple," he said. "Didn't expect to be kidnapped, of course; but it's all in the day's work. You've no idea what a job I had getting colors to pin on these chumps. If it hadn't been for my pink garters and a blue union suit I'd put on yesterday——"

We stopped Maxwell and backed him up to the starting pole again. But he was no story-teller. He skipped like a cheap gas engine. We had to take the story away from him piece by piece. He'd dodged his Smiths down a side street, it seems, on the plea that there weren't any more Smiths coming—and they might as well go over to his room. All would have been well if one Smith hadn't got an awful thirst. There was a corner drug store on the way to the room and while the quartet were insulting their digestions with raspberry ice-cream soda a college man with a wicked eye came by. Half an hour later, just as they were crossing the railroad viaduct near Smith's home, two closed carriages drove up and six husky villains fell upon them, shouting: "Chi Yi forever!" And after dumping them in the carriages, they sat on them while the teams went off.

"After I'd got my man's knee out of my neck," said Maxwell, "I didn't seem to care much whether I was kidnapped or not. It would bind us four closer together after we escaped; and, besides, I have never found kidnapping to pay—too much risk. Anyway, they drove us nothing less than twenty miles and bundled us into an old deserted house. The leader told us, with a whole lot of unnecessary embroidery, that we were to stay there until we pledged to Chi Yi if we rotted in our shoes. Then, of course, I saw through the whole thing: It was an Alfalfa Delt gang disguised as Chi Yis. The Alfalfa Delts would send another gang out the next day, rout the bogus Chi Yis and allow the poor Freshies to fall on their necks and pledge up. That used to be popular at Muggledorfer.

"I did the talking and let my knees knock together considerably. I told them that we'd been too badly shaken up to think, but if they would let us alone that night we'd try to learn to love them by morning. So they put us upstairs and warned us that every window was guarded; then we lay down together and I began at the first chapter and pumped those chaps full of Eta Bita Pie all night.

"It was six o'clock when they finally pledged. When the gang came up they found us adamant. 'Never!' said we. 'We'll pledge Alfalfa Delt or die martyrs to a holy cause!' Of course they didn't dare give themselves away. They couldn't even shout for joy. All they could do was to wait for the rescuing party. I spent the day teaching the boys the songs and the yell in whispers; and about three o'clock I got my grand inspiration about the colors and rigged them out. Then I dug my own pin out and put on my vest and about four o'clock the rescuing party drove up. Say, you'd have laughed to see that fight! Ham-actors in Richard the Third would have made it look tame. The Chi Yis put up a fist or two, threw a brick and then cut for the timber; and the noble Alfalfa Delts burst open the door just as I got the chorus going on that grand old song:

" '*Oh, you've got to be an Eta Bita Pie*
Or you won't get a scarehead when you die!'

"When they saw us there, with our colors on and four particularly wicked-looking chair legs in our hands, they gave one simultaneous gasp—and say, boys, I don't belief in ghosts, but I don't see yet how they disappeared so instantaneously! And anyway, for Heaven's sake, bring out the prog. We drilled eight miles to a rail-road station and my vest buttons are tickling my backbone."

Just then a telegram arrived.

"Don't look for Smith. Changed his mind and went to Jarhard!

"SNOOTY."

No wonder we couldn't blast any information out of our Smiths! Oh, they were our Smiths all right—and they weren't such a bad bunch at that. The fat one turned out to be the champion mandolin teaser in school and the lean one made the debating team; while our own particular first-edition Smith won the catch-as-catch-can chess championship of the college three years later.

Just the same I'd like to get one fair crack at that Smith who went to Jarhard. I'd get even for those three days, I'll bet a few!

The Perfect Squelch

WHEN Hollywood wanted a real baseball umpire to work with Mae West in her picture, How'm I Doing?, John E. (Beans) Reardon, of the National League, was tapped for the pleasant assignment.

The season following this uplifting experience, Reardon was back, umpiring games. The late Babe Ruth was then a National Leaguer as a member of the Boston Braves, and it fell to Beans to call a strike against the great man.

"You really mean that was a strike?" the Babe challenged.

"Sure!" snapped Beans in the arbitrary manner of umpires.

The Babe shrugged and put on his most sympathetic expression.

"Beans," he said sadly, "you're a hopeless case. If working with Mae West didn't improve your eyesight, nothing ever will."

—HAROLD WINERIP.

Children not only make the home—they subject it to constant alterations.

—HERB NELSON.

AN APARTMENT HOUSE ANTHOLOGY

By ***DOROTHY PARKER***

§ *When the pointed Parker wit selects as its target a group of New York apartment house dwellers, some highly interesting facts come to light. Don't be surprised if a few of these characters bear strong resemblance to people you know.*

AUGUST 20, 1921

The Ground Floor

MR. AND MRS. CUZZENS much prefer living on the ground floor, they often say. Sometimes, when Mrs. Cuzzens is really warmed up to it, she puts the thing even stronger, and announces to the world that she would turn down flat all offers to live on an upper floor, in this or any other apartment house in New York City, even if you were to become desperate at her firmness and present her with an apartment rent free.

In the first place Mrs. Cuzzens is never wholly at her ease in an elevator. One of her liveliest anecdotes concerns an aunt of hers on her mother's side who was once a passenger in an elevator which stopped short midway between floors, and doggedly refused to move either up or down. Fortunately it all ended happily. Cries for help eventually caught the attention of the janitor—it seemed little short of providential that he had always had quite a turn for messing around with machinery—and he succeeded in regulating the power so that Mrs. Cuzzens' aunt reached her destination practically as good as new. But the episode made a terrific impression on Mrs. Cuzzens.

Of course it is rather dark on the ground floor, but Mr. and Mrs. Cuzzens regard that as one of the big assets of their apartment. Mrs. Cuzzens had a pretty nasty example of the effects of an oversunshiny place happen right in her own family. Her sister-in-law—not, Mrs. Cuzzens is careful to specify, the wife of the brother in the insurance business, but the wife of the brother who is on the road for a big tire concern, and is doing very well at it—hung some French-blue draperies at her living-room windows. And in less than a year the sunlight turned those curtains from their original color to an unwholesome shade of greenish yellow. Why, the change was so marked that many people, seeing them in this state, almost refused to believe that they had ever been blue. Mrs. Cuzzens' sister-in-law, as is perfectly understandable, was pretty badly broken up about it. Naturally Mrs. Cuzzens would hate to have a thing like that happen in her own home.

There is another advantage to living on the ground floor. The rent there is appreciably smaller than it is on the stories above, although Mr. and Mrs. Cuzzens seldom if ever work this into the conversation. Well, it is easy to overlook it, in the press of more important reasons for occupying their apartment.

A Mean Eye for Freak News

Mrs. Cuzzens has a fund, to date inexhaustible, of clean yet stimulating anecdotes, of which the one about the elevator and the one about the curtains are representative. She specializes in the unique. Hers is probably the largest collection in the country of stories of curious experiences, most of them undergone by members of her intimate circle. She is generous almost to a fault in relating them too. About any topic that happens to come up will be virtually certain to remind her of the funny thing that once happened to her Aunt Anna or the queer experience her Cousin Beulah had that time in Springfield.

Her repertory of anecdotes undoubtedly had much to do with attracting Mr. Cuzzens to her, for Mr. Cuzzens leans heavily to the out-of-the-ordinary himself. In his after-dinner reading of the newspaper he cheats a bit on the front-page items, just murmuring the headlines over, and gathering from them a rough idea—if you could really speak of Mr. Cuzzens as harboring a rough idea—of what is going on in the way of the conventional hold-ups and graft inquiries. But he casts a mean eye over the oddities in the day's news. He never misses the little paragraph about the man in Winsted, Connecticut, who intrusts a family of orphaned eggs to the care of a motherly cat, with gratifying results to one and all; or the report of the birth on an ocean liner, to a couple prominent in steerage circles, of a daughter, named Aquitania Wczlascki in commemoration of the event.

These specialties of Mr. and Mrs. Cuzzens work in together very prettily. They provide many an evening of instructive and harmless entertainment, while so far as expense goes, the only overhead is three cents for an evening paper.

Mr. Cuzzens puts on the slippers he got last birthday, and Mrs. Cuzzens unhooks a bit here and there as the evening wears on and she can feel reasonably sure that no one will drop in. As they sit about the grained-oak table in the glow of the built-in chandelier Mr. Cuzzens will read aloud some such fascinating bit of current history as the announcement of the birth, in Zanesville, Ohio, of a calf with two heads, both doing well. Mrs. Cuzzens will cap it with the description, guaranteed authentic, of a cat her mother's cousin once possessed which had a double set of claws on each foot.

Clever Mr. Cuzzens

When the excitement of this has died down Mr. Cuzzens will find an item reporting that a famous movie star has taken a load off the public's mind by having her eyelashes insured for one hundred thousand dollars. That will naturally lead his wife to tell the one about the heavy life insurance her Uncle David carried, and the perfectly terrible red tape his bereaved family had to go through before they could collect.

After twenty minutes or so passed in their both listening attentively to Mrs. Cuzzens' recital, Mr. Cuzzens' eye, sharpened by years of training, will fall on an obscure paragraph telling how an apple tree near Providence was struck by lightning, which baked all the fruit. Mrs. Cuzzens will come right back with the story of how her little nephew once choked on a bit of the core of a baked apple, and the doctor said it might have been fatal if he had got there half an hour later.

And so it goes, back and forth, all evening long.

But the Cuzzenses have their light side too. They often make a night of it at the movies. In fact Mr. Cuzzens, who is apt to be pretty slangy at times, says that he and the little woman are regular movie fans. Mr. Cuzzens loses himself so completely in the display that he reads each subtitle aloud. If it seems to him worthy, and if the operator leaves it on long enough, he reads it through twice. Both he and his wife take deeply to heart the news pictures, showing a grain elevator destroyed by fire in Florence, Georgia; or the living head of Uncle Sam formed by a group of Los Angeles school children.

Any trick effects on the screen leave Mrs. Cuzzens bewildered. She can never figure out how, for example, they make a man seem to walk up the side of a house. However, Mr. Cuzzens is awfully clever at all that sort of thing—more than one person has told him he should have gone in for mechanical work—and he explains the process on the way home.

Occasionally Mr. and Mrs. Cuzzens patronize the drama. There is a theater near them to which come plays almost direct from their run lower down on Broadway. The casts are only slightly changed; just substitutions in five or six of the leading rôles. Both the Cuzzenses prefer comedies of the wholesome type, setting themselves on record as going to the theater to be amused. They say that they wouldn't go around the corner to see one of those unpleasant plays, for there is enough trouble in this world, anyway. And after all, who is there that can give them any argument on that one?

Now and then they devote an evening to cards, playing a little interfamily game with Mr. Cuzzens' married sister and her husband. The sport is kept absolutely clean. No money changes hands.

In the daytime, while Mr. Cuzzens is busy at his office—he is with a firm that makes bathroom scales, and it's as good as settled that they are going to do something really worth while for him the first of the year—Mrs. Cuzzens is occupied with her own activities. She often complains that the days aren't half long enough for her, but nothing really satisfactory has been done to remedy this, as yet. Much of her time is devoted to shopping, for there are always button molds to be matched, or a strip of linoleum for the washtubs to be priced, or a fresh supply of trick paper for the pantry shelves to be laid in. She is almost overconscientious about her shopping. It is no unusual thing for her to spend an entire day in a tour of the department stores, searching for a particular design of snap fastener or the exact match of a spool of silk. She reaches home at the end of one of these days of toil pretty well done up, but still game.

And then there are her social duties. She is one of the charter members of a bridge club which numbers just enough to fill two tables comfortably. The club meets every fortnight, giving the players a chance to compete for the brocade-covered candy box—the winner must supply her own candy, which is no more than fair—or the six embroidered, guest-room-size handkerchiefs, which the hostess donates in the interest of sport.

During these functions Mrs. Cuzzens takes part in a great deal of tense conversation about the way the skirt was gathered over the hips and came down longer in front. She also gives, and receives, ideas on novel fillings for sandwiches, effective patterns for home-knit sweaters, and simple yet snappy dishes for Sunday-night supper.

Neither Mr. nor Mrs. Cuzzens is a native of New York. Up to a year or so after their marriage they helped swell the population of a town in Illinois which at the last census had upward of one hundred thousand inhabitants. They celebrate Old Home Week by a visit to the folks every year, but they congratulate themselves heartily that Mr. Cuzzens' business prevents their staying more than a week. For they agree that after eight years' residence in what Mr. Cuzzens aptly calls the big city they could never bring themselves to live in a small town again.

As Mrs. Cuzzens puts it, life in New York is so much broader.

The Second Floor East

The Parmalees are always intending to move, but somehow they never get around to it. Several times Mrs. Parmalee has come out flat with the statement that the very next day she is going to look for an apartment farther downtown. But what with one thing and another coming up, she never seems to be able to make it.

Yet after all, as they argue, they might be a whole lot worse off than staying right where they are. Of course they are pretty far uptown, away from the theaters and restaurants; but everybody in their crowd, including themselves, has a car. So, to use Mr. Parmalee's very words, they should worry! It has often been remarked of Mr. Parmalee that it is not so much what he says as the way he says it.

Again, Mrs. Parmalee points out that it doesn't really matter much where they live, for they are hardly ever home, anyway. To which Mr. Parmalee retorts, just like a flash, that she has said a forkful!

And when you come right down to it, Mrs. Parmalee has seldom said a truer thing. It is indeed a cold night for the Parmalees when they have nothing to gather around but their own gas logs. The evening begins to hang heavy along around half past seven, and from then on things get no better rapidly.

The Parmalees are not ones to lose themselves in reading. Just let Mr. Parmalee see who won the first race, and give him a look at the financial page to ascertain whether Crucible Steel is plucking at the coverlet, and he is perfectly willing to call it a day as far as the pursuit of literature is concerned. As for Mrs. Parmalee, she masters the really novel murders and the better-class divorce cases, while for her heavier reading she depends on the current installment of the serial running in one of the more highly sexed magazines. That done with, she is through for the month.

Conversation could not be spoken of as a feature of the evening, either. Mr. Parmalee has been called, over and over again, a perfect scream when he is out on a party. But at home he doesn't really extend himself. A couple of half-hearted assents to his wife's comments on the shortcomings of the janitor and the unhealthful effects of such changeable weather—and that's, as someone has phrased it, that.

Life in the Parmalee Set

So you can see for yourself about the only thing left in the way of parlor entertainment is to come to the mat. The Parmalees' battles are not mere family events; they come more under the head of community affairs. The entire apartment house takes an interest, almost a pride in them. Take them when they get going really strong and you won't miss a syllable, even as far off as the top-floor apartment on the other side of the house. On a clear night with the wind in the right direction the people living three houses down have been able to enjoy every word of it.

The bouts almost invariably end in a draw. Mr. Parmalee, it is true, has a somewhat broader command of language than his wife, but she has perfected a short contemptuous laugh which is the full equivalent of a nasty crack. It leaves Mr. Parmalee practically flat, with nothing more inspired to offer than an "Is that so?" or a "Yeah, you're perfect—you are!"

But these sporting events take place only rarely. The Parmalees have little time to indulge in home pleasures. Theirs is a full and sociable life. Mr. Parmalee is in what he jocosely calls the automobile game, and most of his friends are engaged in the same pursuit. And as their wives are Mrs. Parmalee's intimates, you can just imagine how nice and clubby that makes everything.

Their social day begins around five o'clock, when the dozen or so members of their set meet at one or another's apartment, for cocktails. The Parmalee coterie has been seriously inconvenienced since prohition went into what has been called effect. It means that they can no longer meet at a hotel or a restaurant, as they used to in the old days. It is badly out of their way to gather at someone's house, for it often involves their having to go all the way downtown again for dinner. But they have to make the best of it, just like you or me.

And it is comforting to know that the gentlemen still manage, as a rule, to pick up a little something here and there before they are met by what Mr. Parmalee calls, with screaming effect, their better seven-eighths. The ladies, collectively, are usually referred to, by their husbands and by one another, as the girls—which is something of an understatement.

Up to the time of meeting, Mrs. Parmalee, like the rest of the girls, has put in a crowded afternoon at a matinée, the hairdresser's or the manicure's; a blinding polish on the finger nails is highly thought of by both the male and female members of the Parmalees' set. There is usually a great deal of trying on to be done, also, which does much toward taking up Mrs. Parmalee's time and Mr. Parmalee's money. He likes to see his wife dressed as elaborately as the wives of his friends. He is pretty fairly reasonable about the price of her clothes, just so long as they look as if they cost a lot. Neither of the Parmalees can see the point of this thing of paying high prices for unobtrusive garments. What they are after, Mr. Parmalee says, is their money's worth. As is only just.

Mrs. Parmalee and her friends dress with a soothing uniformity. They all hold the same ideas about style; really you'd seldom find a more congenial group in every way. All the girls, including Mrs. Parmalee, are fundamentally large and are increasing in weight almost daily. They are always going to start dieting next Monday.

In general style and get-up the girls resemble a group of very clever female impersonators. They run to rather larger and more densely plumed hats than the fashion absolutely insists upon, and they don't go in for any of your dull depressing colors. Always heavily jeweled, they have an adroit way of mingling an occasional imitation bracelet or necklace with the genuine articles, happily confident that the public will be fooled. In the warm weather their dresses are of transparent material about the arms and shoulders, showing provocative glimpses of very pink ribbons and of lace that you could hardly tell from the real.

There is a great deal of hearty gayety at the afternoon meetings of the crowd. You couldn't ask to see people among whom it is easier to get a laugh. Any popular line, such as "You don't know the half of it," or "You'd be surprised," is a sure-fire hit, no matter in what connection it is used. You might think that these jests would lose a little of their freshness after months of repetition, but you were never so wrong in your life. They never fail to go over big.

After a couple of hours of crackling repartee and whole-hearted drinking the Parmalees and their crowd set out for dinner. They dine at a downtown restaurant, if they plan going en masse to the theater afterwards. Otherwise they group themselves in their cars—most of the motors, like Mr. Parmalee's, are perquisites of being in the automobile game—and drive to some favorite road house, where they not only dine but get in some really constructive drinking during the evening. Mr. Parmalee is the life and soul of these parties. It is, his friends often say, as good as a show to hear him kid the waiter.

Guess-What-It-Cost-Sports

Dancing occurs sporadically after dinner, but most of the time is devoted to badinage. There is much good-natured banter, impossible to take in bad part, about the attentions paid by various of the husbands to the wives of various of the other husbands.

Often the conversation takes a serious turn among the men, as they tell about how much they had to pay for the last case of it. Stories are related of the staggering prices exacted for highballs at some restaurant where they will still listen to reason; and someone is sure to tell about the dinner he gave the night before, giving the menu in full detail, and as a climax calling upon his audience to guess what the grand total of the check was. These anecdotes are told with the pride that other sportsmen exhibit in telling about the size of the fish they caught.

The ladies spend what could be figured up to be the greater part of the evening in going out to the dressing room to keep their color schemes up to the mark.

In the warmer months the Parmalees make no radical change in their way of living. But though they do not go away for any long vacation they get a welcome glimpse of Nature by motoring to Long Beach for dinner three or four times a week with the rest of their crowd. They also manage to get a lot of wholesome country air and a refreshing eyeful of green grass down at the Belmont Park track.

What with all this talk of hard times and tight money wherever you go, it is cheering to see the Parmalees, who seem always to have it to spend. In his homy little chats with his wife Mr. Parmalee often gets quite worked up over where the money to meet their expenses is coming from; but he never lets it trouble him in his social life. Mr. Parmalee is a great advocate of being a good fellow when you have it. After all, as he has it figured out, the last places you can cut down are on theater tickets and restaurant checks and liquor.

It is also pleasant, in these days of change and restlessness, to think of the Parmalees going right along, never so much as thinking of wanting anything different. I wouldn't want to be the one to say that there is never just a dash of hard feeling between certain members of the crowd; the Parmalees never claimed to be any more than human. But such little differences as may spring up from time to time are easily dissolved in alcohol, and the crowd goes right on again, as usual.

After all, it takes Mr. Parmalee, with that wit of his, to sum up their whole existence in one clear-cut phrase. He says that it is a great life if you don't weaken.

The Second Floor West

The minute you step into her apartment you realize that Mrs. Prowse is a woman of fine sensibilities. They stick out, as you might say, all over the place. You can see traces of them in the handmade candles dripping artistically over the polychrome candlesticks; in the single perfect blossom standing upright in a roomy bowl; in the polychrome bust of Dante on the mantel—taken, by many visitors, to be a likeness of William Gibbs McAdoo; most of all in the books left all about, so that Mrs. Prowse, no matter where she is sitting, always can have one at hand, to lose herself in. They are, mainly, collections of verse, both free and under control, for Mrs. Prowse is a regular glutton for poetry. She is liable to repeat snatches of it at almost any time. There are heavier volumes, too, just as there are greater depths to Mrs. Prowse. Henry Adams, Conan Doyle in his latter manner, Blasco Ibañez, Clare Sheridan—all the boys and girls are represented.

Mrs. Prowse has not quite made up her mind as to whether it is more effective to have her books look well-thumbed or new and bright, though she rather inclines to the latter as being more decorative and less tiring. Most of the volumes are bound in red, which is, as Mrs. Prowse would put it, rather amusing with her orange curtains. If you were to pick up a book at random and go systematically through it you would find that, oddly enough, many of the pages, along after the middle, are uncut. But Mrs. Prowse's guests are not apt to go through her books, and the effect is, as I was saying only a minute ago, great.

It is not only literature that Mrs. Prowse patronizes. Beauty in any form gets a big hand from her. She can find it, too, in places where you or I would never think of looking. The delicate brown of a spoiled peach, the calm gray of a puddle on the sidewalk—such things never escape her.

Perhaps it is because she is so used to directing attention to things you might otherwise miss that Mrs. Prowse follows up the idea and coaxes you to notice those beauties which you couldn't very well avoid. She is always putting in a good word for the sunset or the sky or the moon, never letting slip an opportunity to get in a little press work for Nature.

She feels such things considerably more than most people. Sometimes, indeed, her appreciation of the beautiful stops just short of knocking her for what is academically called a goal. In the midst of a friendly conversation, or perhaps when it is her turn to bid in a bridge game, Mrs. Prowse will suddenly be rendered speechless, and lean tensely forward, gazing hungrily out the window at a lonely star or a wind-tossed cloud. She has quite a bad time in pulling herself together on these occasions. She must start perceptibly, look dazedly around the room, and press her hand against her eyes for a moment before she can return to the commonplace.

It is a blow to Mrs. Prowse and her husband that there has never been what Mrs. Prowse refers to as the patter of little feet about the house. But she manages to get a bit of comfort out of the situation. With no children to tie her down she is free to do all the worth-while things that beckon her. Look, for example, at what she accomplished during the past winter alone. She heard several lectures by visiting poets; went to two New Thought meetings; had her horoscope read and learned that her name should have been Valda; attended the annual luncheon of a club devoted to translating Browning into English; went to tea in Greenwich Village three times; took a lesson in lampshade making; heard a debate on whether or not a woman should take her husband's name, and what of it; and had her hair permanently waved.

But at that, Mrs. Prowse does not feel that her time is fully occupied. What she would really like, she admits, is to work, and work hard. And there are several jobs for which she is forced to confess that she is just as well fitted at the next one.

She would consider, for instance, giving readings from the modern poets or doing selections from Maeterlinck to a soft accompaniment on the piano. She has thought, and pretty seriously, too, of the stage, which, she can't help feeling, she could do much to raise from its present commercialism. It is really just a matter of ethics that keeps her from rushing right out and going to work at one of these positions. She doesn't feel that it would be quite fair for her to take the job away from someone who might be in real need of the money.

You wouldn't want to say right out that Mr. Prowse is not in sympathy with his wife's ideas, but then again you would scarcely be justified in saying that he cheered her on. Mr. Prowse is apt to let things take their course, and not do any worrying about them.

He is fond of his business, golf, the Yankees, meat cooked rather rare, musical comedies and his friends. Mrs. Prowse accompanies him to the theater, and often tells his friends that they must come up sometime soon. But there is about her at these times an air of gentle martyrdom. You'd almost think you could hear the roar of the waiting lions, she does it so realistically.

Mr. Prowse's policy of going about just as cheerfully as if his wife had no sensibilities whatever is a uniquely annoying one to her. Some of her most effective moods are absolutely frittered away on him. Mrs. Prowse has feelings which are almost always being severely injured; you run a chance of stepping on them if you come within ten feet of her. She is too delicately strung to come bluntly out and say what has hurt her. She seeks refuge in a brooding silence, and you must guess what it is all about.

Misunderstood but Faithful

Mr. Prowse is particularly bad at the game. He never seems to realize that anything is wrong. Sometimes she even has to call attention to her mental suffering and its cause. Even then he cannot be drawn into a really satisfactory battle. And it is, you will agree, practically impossible to work up any dramatic interest in married life when one of the principals won't take part in the big scenes.

It is little wonder that Mrs. Prowse, though never actually saying that her marriage is anything but happy, sometimes intimates that she is not always understood.

She has always been somewhat taken with the idea of having an assortment of tame young men about her—nothing really out of the way, of course, just have them come to tea, and take her to picture galleries, and send flowers, and maybe write verses, which she could drop where her husband would find them. She has even gone so far, in the privacy of her room, as to invent a rather nice little scene, in which she mapped out what she would say to some smitten young tea-hound should he become too serious. It is a credit to Mrs. Prowse to report that her answer was to the effect that she could never forget the vows she made to Mr. Prowse at the altar.

In all the books, as it is useless to tell you, it is no trouble at all for a married woman to gather a flock of attentive young men about her. But Mrs. Prowse has found it rather rough going. The young men don't seem to fall in with the idea. There was, it is true, a young man she met at a tea who was interested in interior decoration. In answer to her invitation he did call one afternoon—it was just by luck that she was wearing her beaded Georgette crêpe—and told her all about how she ought to live with purples. But when he found out that she really didn't feel they could have the living room done over for another year anyway he faded gently out of her life.

And that, as a matter of fact, was about as far as Mrs. Prowse ever got along those lines.

As is no more than you would expect, Mrs. Prowse admits but few to her circle of intimates. She is constantly being disappointed in people, finding out that they have no depths. Perhaps the sharpest blow, though one frequently experienced, is in having people whom she had accepted as kindred spirits turn out to be clever on the surface, but with no soul when you came right down to it. Mrs. Prowse often says that somehow she can never bring herself to be intimate with people who are only clever.

And that really works out awfully well, for it makes it mutual.

The Third Floor East

You couldn't find, if you were to take the thing really to heart and make a search of the city, a woman who works harder, day in and day out, than Mrs. Amy. She says so herself.

In the first place there are the two young Amys to occupy her attention. Everyone in the building is conscious of the presence of the two young Amys, but the Parmalees, in the apartment below, are most keenly aware of it.

It is in the fresh morning, when the Parmalees are striving to fulfill a normal desire for sleep, that the young Amys seem particularly near. The Amy children are early risers, and they have none of that morning languor from which office workers are so apt to suffer. Mrs. Parmalee, whose bedroom is directly beneath theirs, has often said that she would be the last one to feel any surprise if at any moment they were to come right on through.

Of course there is a resident nurse who looks after the little ones, but Mrs. Amy seems to find little or no relief in this. The nurse watches over them all day, and sleeps in the bed between their cribs at night, but, as Mrs. Amy says, she cannot worry over them as a mother would.

It is in worrying that Mrs. Amy accomplishes some of her most strenuous work. She confesses that there is scarcely a minute when her mind is at rest. Her worries even cut in on her nights, and she describes graphically how, tossing from side to side, she hears the clock strike twelve, half past twelve, one, half past one—sometimes it goes on that way up to three.

The past months have been especially trying to her, for the older Amy child has lately started school. He attends the public school around the corner, where his mother cannot help but feel that his time is devoted less to acquiring education than to running a splendid chance of contracting diseases and bringing them home, to share with his sister. During his first term Mrs. Amy has at different times detected in him symptoms of mumps, measles, chicken pox, scarlet fever, whooping cough and infantile paralysis. It is true that none of these ever developed, but that's not the point. The thing is that his mother was just as much worried as if he had had record cases of them all.

Then there are her household cares to prey upon her. Annie, a visiting maid, arrives before breakfast and stays till after dinner, but Mrs. Amy frequently sighs that she is far from satisfactory. Twice, now, her gravy has been distinctly lumpy, and just the other day she omitted to address Mrs. Amy as "ma'am" in answering her. There may be those who can throw off such things, but Mrs. Amy takes them hard. Only the fact that she worries so over the prospect of not being able to get another maid prevents her from marching right out into the kitchen and formally presenting Annie with the air.

It seems as if there were some great conspiracy to prevent things' breaking right for Mrs. Amy. Misfortunes pile up all through the day, so that by evening she has a long hard-luck story with which to greet Mr. Amy.

All through dinner she beguiles him with a recital of what she has had to endure that day—how the milkman didn't come and she was forced to send out to the grocer's; how she hurried to answer the telephone at great personal inconvenience, only to find it was someone for Annie; how the butcher had no veal cutlets; how the man didn't fix the pantry sink; how Junior refused to take his cereal; how the druggist omitted to send the soap she ordered; how—but you get the idea. There is always enough material for her to continue her story all through dinner and carry it over till bedtime with scarcely a repetition.

Mr. Amy would be glad to do what he could to lighten her burdens, but Mrs. Amy, though she all but hints in her conversation that many of her troubles may be laid at her husband's door, refuses to let him crash in on her sphere.

He has a confessed longing, for instance, to take the children out on the nurse's Sundays off. But Mrs. Amy cannot be induced to see it. Her feeling is that he would be just as apt as not to take them in a street car, or to the zoo, where they would get themselves simply covered with germs. As she says, she would worry so while they were gone that she would be virtually no good by the time they got back.

Mr. Amy often seeks to persuade his wife to join him in an evening's revelry at the movies or the theater, but she seldom consents. Her mind cannot come down to the pleasures before her when it is all taken up with what might be going on at home at that very minute. The house might burn up, the children might run temperatures, a sudden rain might come up and spoil the bedroom curtains; anything is liable to happen while she is away. So you can see how much there is on her side when she tells Mr. Amy that she feels safer at home.

Occasionally the Amys have a few friends in to dinner. Mrs. Amy obliges at these functions with one of her original monologues on the things that have gone wrong in her household during that day alone. They would entertain oftener, but what with the uncertainty of Annie's gravy and the vagaries of the tradespeople, the mental strain is too great for Mrs. Amy.

Mr. Amy often has to take a man out for dinner, in the way of business. He used to bring his business acquaintances to dine with him at home, but it got on Mrs. Amy's nerves to that degree that she had to put a stop to the practice.

She said it just bored her to death to have to sit there and listen to them talk about nothing but their business.

The Third Floor West

What is really the keynote of the Tippetts' living room is the copy of the Social Register lying temptingly open on the table. It is as if Mrs. Tippett had been absorbed in it, and had only torn herself from its fascinating pages in order to welcome you.

It is almost impossible for you to overlook the volume, but if you happen to, Mrs. Tippett will help you out by pointing to it with an apologetic little laugh. No one knows better than she, she says, that its orange-and-black binding is all out of touch with the color scheme of the room; but, you see, she uses it for a telephone book and she is simply lost without it. Just what Mrs. Tippett does when she wants to look up the telephone number of her laundress or her grocer is not explained. And few people have the strength to go into the subject unassisted.

Some day when you happen to be reading the Social Register and come to the T's, you will find that Mr. and Mrs. Tippett's names are not there. Naturally you will take this for a printer's error. But it is only too intentional. The Tippetts do not yet appear in the register, though they have every hope of eventually making the grade.

As soon as Mrs. Tippett feels that the one about using the Social Register as a telephone book has sunk in, she will begin to laugh off her apartment. She says that it is the greatest joke, their living way up here in this funny old house that has been made over into flats. You have no idea how the Tippetts' friends simply howl at the thought of their living up on the West Side.

Whimsically Mrs. Tippett adds that what with so many social leaders moving down to Greenwich Village and over by the East River, it seems to her that the smart thing to do nowadays is to live in the most out-of-the-way place you can find.

Mr. Tippett will enlarge on the thing for you, if you stay until he comes home from business. Mr. Tippett solicits advertising for one of the excessively doggy magazines. There is not much in it, but it gives him an opportunity to come in contact with some awfully nice people. He will put over some perfect corkers about living so far uptown that he goes to work by the Albany boat; or he may even refer to his place of residence as Canada for you.

He bears out his wife's statements as to

their friends' amusement at the apartment; in fact you gather from the chat that the Tippetts' chief reason for occupying the place is the good laugh it affords their friends.

The Tippetts are exceedingly well connected, as you will learn just as soon as they get a chance to tell you. Mr. Tippett's own cousin is not only included in the Social Register but has been referred to in the society weeklies—oh, not a breath of scandal, of course!—and often figures in the morning papers under the head of "among those present were." The Tippetts are deeply devoted to her. She is seldom absent from their conversation. If she is ill their calls are more regular than the doctor's. When she is away they carry her letters about and read them aloud to you at a moment's notice. Way back in midsummer they start planning her Christmas present.

The Tippetts are kept busy the year round. Sometimes Mrs. Tippett says wistfully she almost wishes they were not quite so much in demand. Almost every day she has to keep an appointment with some friend, to have tea at one of the more exclusive hotels. She keeps a sharp lookout for any smart people that may be hanging around, so that at dinner she can breathlessly tell her husband whom they were with and what they had on.

It is great fun to be out with Mrs. Tippett. She can tell you who everybody is, where they originated, whom they married, what their incomes are, and what is going the rounds about them. From a close following of the society papers she really feels that she knows intimately all those who figure in their columns. She goes right ahead with the idea, and speaks of them by the nicknames under which they appear in the society press.

Mrs. Tippett is inclined to be a trifle overpunctual; haven't you heard it called a good fault? She often arrives rather early for her tea engagements, and so, not being one to waste time, she dashes off a few notes on the hotel stationery while waiting.

Mr. Tippett—it may be from three years of close association—has got from her this admirable habit of catching up with his correspondence at odd times. For instance, when he drops in at some club, as the guest of a member, he frequently finds a few minutes to sit down at a desk and scribble off a letter on the convenient paper.

The Tippetts have many obligations to fulfill. They are so fond of Mr. Tippett's cousin that they try never to disappoint her when she invites them to anything. This means they must spend two or three week-ends at her country place, dine with her several times during the winter, and use her opera tickets once or even oftener. You'd really be amazed at the supply of subsequent conversation that the Tippetts can get out of any of these events.

Besides all this, they usually manage to attend one or two of the large charity affairs, for which tickets may be purchased at a not-so-nominal sum, and they always try to work in one session at the horse show.

This past season has been particularly crowded for Mrs. Tippett. Twice her volunteered aid has been accepted by a woman she met at Mr. Tippett's cousin's house, and she has helped arrange the counters at rummage sales. In short, things are coming along nicely with the Tippetts. They have every reason to be satisfied with their life.

Which is remarkably like Mr. Tippett's business, in that, though there is not much in it, it brings them in contact with some awfully nice people.

The Top Floor East

There was a time when Mrs. Huff kept her own carriage and lived in a three-story house with a conservatory between the dining room and the pantry. I don't feel that I am violating any confidence in telling you this, because Mrs. Huff would be the first one to say so.

All this was some time ago, when Mrs. Huff's daughter Emma was still in school—in private school, Mrs. Huff is careful to say. And one good look at Mrs. Huff's daughter Emma will convince you that her schooldays must have been indeed some time ago.

Shortly before Mr. Huff did what his widow refers to as passed on, the fortune began to meet with reverses, due mainly to Mr. Huff's conviction that he could put Wall Street in its place during his spare time. Mrs. Huff clung as long as possible to her own carriage and the three-story house with the conservatory, but she had eventually to let them go, in the order named. For a good many years, now, she has been settled in this apartment, in the midst of as much of her palmy-days furniture as could be wedged into the place.

But to Mrs. Huff those good old days are as yesterday. They are as fresh in her mind and her conversation. She can—does, even—go on for hours about how often they had to have the palms in the conservatory replaced, and how much they paid for the fountain, which represented a little girl and boy holding a pink iron umbrella over themselves—she can see it now. From there she drifts into reminiscences of all the trouble they had with drunken coachmen before they got their old Thomas, who was with them twelve years.

Mrs. Huff and her daughter live the calm and ladylike life befitting former conservatory owners. They are attended by one maid, Hannah by name, who was once Emma's nurse. She does the housework, washing, marketing and cooking; arranges Mrs. Huff's hair and corsets; remodels the ladies' clothes in the general direction of the styles; and is with difficulty persuaded to accept her wages each month—the same wages—which is rather a pretty touch of sentiment—as she was getting when she first entered Mrs. Huff's employ. As Mrs. Huff says, Hannah is really quite a help to them.

Mrs. Huff relies chiefly for her diversion on the funerals of her many acquaintances and connections. She reads the obituary column each morning in much the same spirit that other people look over the What Is Going on Today section. Occasionally if the day is fine and there is no really important funeral on hand she takes a little jaunt out to a favorite cemetery and visits various friends there.

Her minor amusements include calls on many sick and a few healthy acquaintances, and an occasional card party. Her stories of how often they had to change the palms and how much they paid for the fountain are the features of these affairs.

Miss Emma Huff suffers slightly from hallucinations; no, suffers is hardly the word. She manages to get quite a good time out of them.

She is under the impression that she is the desired of every man with whom she comes in contact. She is always arriving home fluttering from her adventure with the overzealous clerk in the shoe shop, or the bus driver who was too careful about helping her alight, or the floorwalker who almost insisted on taking her arm to direct her to the notions. Miss Huff never dares stay late at a friend's house, for fear some man may spring from the shadows and abduct her on the way home.

Between adventures Miss Huff does a good deal of embroidery. If there were ever a contest in putting cross-stitch baskets on guest towels she would be entered scratch. Also, she is a mean hand at copying magazine covers in water colors. Last year she made all her own Christmas cards, and if all goes well she plans doing it again next Christmas.

Once or twice it has been suggested by relatives or overintimate friends that it might be rather nice for Miss Huff to commercialize her talents. Or, if her feeling for art would not allow that, she might find some light and ladylike employment—just to pass the time, is always hastily added.

Mrs. Huff awards these advisers what, in anybody else, would be a dirty look. She does not waste words to reply to any suggestion that a daughter of hers should enter the business world. For Mrs. Huff can never forget that she once kept her own carriage and lived in a three-story house with a conservatory between the dining room and the pantry.

The Top Floor West

There are, of course, a Mr. and a Mrs. Plank, but they sink indistinguishably into the background. Mrs. Plank may be roughly summarized as a woman who always knows what you ought to do for that indigestion, while Mr. Plank is continually going into a new business where "none of us is going to get much money at first."

The real life of the Plank party is Arlette—Mrs. Plank let herself go, for the only time in her life, in the choosing of her daughter's name.

Arlette is, at the present writing, crowding nineteen summers, and she looks every day of it. As for her mode of living, just ask anybody in the apartment house.

Arlette stopped school three years ago by her own request. She had no difficulty in convincing her mother that she had enough education to get along with anywhere. Mrs. Plank is a firm believer in the theory that, unless she is going to teach, there is no earthly use of a girl's wasting her time in going all through high school. Men, says Mrs. Plank—and she has been married twenty-one years, so who could be a better judge—do not select as their wives these women who are all full of education. So for the past three years Arlette's intellectual decks have been cleared for matrimony.

But Arlette has not yet given a thought to settling down into marriage. There was a short season when she thought rather seriously of taking up a screen career, after someone had exclaimed over the startling likeness between her and Louise Lovely. But so far she has taken it out in doing her hair in the accepted movie-star manner, to look as if it had been arranged with an egg-beater.

Most of Arlette's time is spent in dashing about in motors driven by young men of her acquaintance. The cars were originally designed to accommodate two people, but they rarely travel without seven or eight on board. These motors, starting out from or drawing up to the apartment house, with their precious loads of human freight, are one of the big spectacles of the block.

The Skids for Eddie

It is remarkable how without the services of a secretary Arlette prevents her dates from becoming mixed. She deftly avoids any embarrassing overlapping of suitors. Her suitors would, if placed end to end, reach halfway up to the Woolworth Tower and halfway back.

They are all along much the same design—slim, not too tall, with hair shining like linoleum. They dress in suits which, though obviously new, have the appearance of being just outgrown, with half belts, and lapels visible from the back.

The average duration of Arlette's suitors is five weeks. At the end of that time she hands the favored one a spray of dewy raspberries and passes on to the next in line.

The present incumbent, Eddie to his friends, has lasted rather longer than usual. His greatest asset is the fact that he is awfully dry. He has a way of saying "absotively" and "posolutely" that nearly splits Arlette's sides. When he is introduced he says, with a perfectly straight face, "You're pleased to meet me," and Arlette can hardly contain herself. He interpolates a lot of Ed Wynn's stuff into the conversation, and

"Hawthorne here's in electric fans."

"I'm going to be frank with you; this is an old car——"

"Beg."

"'S' is here!"

"I've really been *impossible* today!"

"Well, I *do* engage in a quiet game of old maid now and then with the wife and kiddies!"

HENRY
BOLTINOFF

"Why, mother!"

"Gesundheit."

"Now we'll have to get to work on an antidote."

Arlette thinks it is just as good as the original, if not better.

Then, too, he knows a perfectly swell step. You take three to the right, then three to the left, then toddle, then turn suddenly all the way around and end with a dip; the effect is little short of professional.

But Arlette has lately met a young man who has his own car and can almost always get his father's limousine when he takes you to the theater. Also, his father owns a chain of moving-picture houses, and he can get a pass for her.

So it looks from here as if the skids were all ready to be applied to Eddie.

Mrs. Plank worries a bit over her daughter's incessant activities. She hears stories of the goings-on of these modern young people that vaguely trouble her, and she does wish that Arlette would take more rest. Naturally, though, she hesitates to bring the matter to her daughter's attention. Occasionally she goes so far as to hint that Arlette might take a little interest in watching her do the housework, so that she can pick up some inside stuff on household matters that might be useful in her married life.

For all Mrs. Plank wants, she says, is to live to see her daughter making some good man happy.

Arlette's ideas, now, seem to be more along the lines of making some good men happy.

The Perfect Squelch

MANY years ago in Ireland, after considerable bitterness, Irish tenant farmers were being permitted to buy land from the crown. In one county a titled Britisher was appointed to the ticklish task of receiving the payments begrudgingly made by the farmers. By showing considerable tact and good humor, he got along without friction until a burly son of the soil stalked up to the desk and commenced banging his money on it piece by piece. When the last halfpenny was slammed down, this man banged the desk with his big fist and roared, "There! Take yer dirty money! From this day on, I'll have no landlord but the Lord God in heaven!"

Smiling pleasantly, the Britisher replied, "I sincerely hope you get on with Him. He evicted His first tenants, you know."

—VIRGINIA S. STROEMEL.

VALOR OF A SORT

When exposed to danger, some men keep so cool that their teeth chatter.

—SHANNON FIFE.

A Child's Garden of Curses;

or, The Bitter Tea of Mr. P.

YEARS before I bought Rising Gorge, my Pennsylvania chalet, I used to run into some former friend in a railroad terminal, his arms bristling with garden tools, insecticides and poultry leaflets, and a pair of rose-colored bifocals askew on his nose. Invariably the exile would sashay into a sales talk sooner or later. "You owe it to the kiddies, old man," he would entreat, choking back a lump in his throat. "Never saw such a change in mine. Junior grew fourteen inches the first week. He's only nine, and he can split a cord of wood, milk twenty-one cows and cultivate a field of corn by sunup. Sister's not even three, but you ought to taste her preserves. They're famous for a hundred miles around."

In time the refrain began to worry me. I felt inferior on my son's third birthday that other men his age were operating combines when he could hardly shoe a horse. It humiliated me profoundly that my daughter, a strapping hulk of two, was unable to bake a pie. This process of slow erosion had its effect; one morning I awoke with a dizzy feeling and eighty acres of thistles as a proving ground for their talents.

At first, in the natural bustle of making the house unlivable, the children were forgotten. Everything had to be scraped down to the original knotty pine, good hardware replaced with rusty hinges, and wagon wheels substituted for candelabra, and the place generally made to resemble a rathskeller on the verge of bankruptcy. During this period a nurse stood guard over the brood, a sinister gargoyle with a face hewn out of Indiana limestone and the temper of a wasp. Miss Bramble had lived on some of the finest estates at Newport and had certain standards, even if she was working for poor white trash. Every afternoon she dressed her charges in Eton jackets, starched muslin and velvet ribbons, which seemed rather formal wear for the manure pile. By skillful suggestion, she built up the notion of snakes in the greenery to the point where screams rang out when a salad was placed on the table. Her martyrdom reached a climax, however, at the sight of the master carrying ashes out of the cellar. She observed tartly that her late employer at Bailey's Beach had two foreigners to do that type of work, both of whom were better groomed than myself. I stood it until the children started following me around with a chant Nanny had taught them. "Here comes that ole ash man!" they jeered. "Any rags, any bones, any bottles today?" I caught the pair of them hiding in a drain and Nanny caught the 5:15.

For a month afterward, the hardy young pioneers refused to leave the kitchen. The yard, they moaned, was full of great fur-bearing vampires with human faces on the order of Miss Bramble's. Squealing, kicking and gouging, they were flung outside each morning, only to spend the day baying through the screen door. At length I made an eloquent speech, painting the joys of a country childhood, embroidered with references to Huck Finn, barefoot boys with cheeks of tan, and fishing for bullheads. In closing, I presented the boy with a bamboo pole and a bent pin. With instinctive gallantry, the little chap promptly presented it to his sister, in the left eye. Giving him a kindly pat with a hairbrush, I changed my approach. I cited young Abe Lincoln, young Tom Edison and other movie notables distinguished for their self-reliance. I explained how a poor youth named Benjamin Franklin had arrived in a great city munching a roll and had subsequently discovered the secret of electricity.

My plea to emulate his example at once bore fruit. An hour later the porch was strewn with half-eaten rolls and someone had short-circuited the wiring by forcing a key into a floor plug.

By now, of course, their dexterity and knowledge of country lore is fabulous; they have learned to perform a thousand disagreeable chores around the house. If I need a bean bag dropped into the plumbing to tie up the water system or tacks spread in the driveway so the tires take hold, I can count on the services of two experts. No sparrow falls without finding his way to my bedroom, and there is always a freshly killed woodchuck by the breakfast plate to whet daddy's appetite. And what with the bill for hay fever, poison oak, summer colic and antitetanus, it takes a bit of whetting.

—S. J. PERELMAN.

How to Be a Baseball Expert Although Ignorant

WITH baseball a pretty lively subject these days, I think I have here some timely tips on how baseball ignoramuses can avoid being exposed. Naturally, this time of year, no social error is quite so great as admitting a lack of knowledge about league standings, data and statistics concerning all left-handed right fielders.

As an active student of the art of knowing nothing about baseball I offer these guaranteed gambits:

1. PROBLEM: En route to work on the dawn express you are awakened by a large individual who sits down and bellows into your starboard ear. "WELL! The Phillies did it again last night, huh?" You have no idea what he is bellowing about.

SOLUTION: Shout automatically: "Man, you can say that again! Say, what do you think of Milwaukee?" This establishes you as an expert—everybody has an opinion about Milwaukee. He will tell you his for the remainder of the trip.

2. PROBLEM: At a party you stumble accidentally into a group in the corner, and one member asks you candidly, "Who holds the record for runs batted in during the third inning in the American League? Settle this argument for us." All exits are blocked.

SOLUTION: Smile bitterly; declare, "I'll tell you one thing—if base running keeps getting worse, it will be lower than that." Then sneak away.

3. PROBLEM: Trapped into watching a baseball game on television, you are asked by a sweet young thing. "Which one is Yogi Berra?" Even your own wife waits trustingly for your answer. You are the only man in the world who wouldn't know Yogi if he walked through the door. You cannot feign laryngitis convincingly.

SOLUTION: Get up and rabbit-punch the television set sharply and say, "Is that clearer, folks? It must be the picture tube." If it's not your set and you risk insult to the host by doing this, simply spill your beer in your lap. All will laugh merrily and the question will be forgotten—I sincerely hope.

So bring on the Series! Merely follow these simple tactics and any baseball ignoramus can be regarded as the outstanding authority in his neighborhood. For many seasons I was held in awe at the office simply by starting arguments about the infield-fly rule, whatever that is.

—JOHN KEASLER.

THE PIG-BRISTLE SLUGGER

By LOUIS GRAVES

§ Post *editors like to tell a tale about this story. It happens to be one of the most oft-requested pieces ever published in the magazine. There is a wistfulness about it that has kept it alive in readers' minds for nearly half a century. If you haven't read it, here it is. If you have, it gets better with every reading.*

APRIL 8, 1911

FIFTY-ONE weeks in the year, every day but Sundays and holidays, Rudolph Speckeldonner officiated behind the counters of old Fritz Schneider's grocery store on Amsterdam Avenue. He was short and fat; his yellow hair stood up straight on end; and he wore a long white apron, stretching all the way from his chin to his feet, to protect him from contamination by the cheese and lard and eggs and potatoes and coffee and carrots, and countless other things that he dealt out to Schneider's customers. Seeing Rudolph in action, as he wielded the cheese knife or pushed a head of cauliflower into a paper bag, you would have said that surely he was devoid of all enthusiasm.

But there was a fifty-second week. Schneider was a kind boss and he gave his right-hand man this much time off every spring, with full pay. And if the Giants were playing at home Rudolph went to the Polo Grounds promptly at three o'clock, six days out of the six—unless there was a double-header on, in which case he was in his seat much earlier. If the Giants were away the Yankees were sure to be performing at the American League Park—and he journeyed thither. And if it rained, and there was no game, he stayed in the flat and played mournful tunes on the flute which his father had brought from Germany forty years before—played steadily, while his wife Gretchen hovered about and quarreled mildly with little Heinrich and little Minna. The flute would have been a poor substitute for baseball, even if three true notes in succession could have been lured from it; but it was manifestly the only thing left.

In the mornings of the glorious fifty-second week Rudolph would issue into the street soon after six o'clock, purchase his two favorite newspapers and return home to read the reports signed by the alleged baseball experts. Sometimes their opinions failed to agree with his own and he gurgled out uncomplimentary adjectives for the enlightenment of Gretchen and the children, who listened in silence and understood not a word of what he said.

When his vacation was over Rudolph

went back to Schneider's, donned a clean apron and once more became the visible and animated emblem of the High Cost of Living. He still read the reports of the baseball experts, but with no complaints now, because he hadn't seen the game with his own eyes and was willing to take their verdict as gospel.

After baseball—but far, far after—the thing that interested Rudolph most was Mohadji Khan. This person was lessee and sole occupant of a little shanty on one of those unimproved blocks between Broadway and Amsterdam Avenue—spaces that the Astors or other nabobs are holding for a while, until the real-estate wiseacres tell them the time is ripe for more twenty-story apartment houses. Until that day comes the nabobs sell the sides of the high board fences for advertising, to help pay taxes, and let out the aged buildings to anybody who is satisfied to dwell in them. In this particular case there was only one building and it was in the middle of the block. In the green months of the year it was almost completely hidden from the view of outsiders by the maples and elms and stunted oaks on all sides. The only approach was from the side street, a narrow path that ran between two rickety, moth-eaten fences.

Here in the shanty Mohadji Khan mended shoes and sold ropes and candles and violin strings. A sign over the gate, at the street end of the path, told the passers-by that he was there and what he would do for them if they chose to enter. Some entered and more did not; but little cared the Hindu. His rent was small, his wants were few, and he had better things to think of than the patronage of these foolish white-faced creatures who were always tearing back and forth—always going somewhere merely to come back to the same place again.

Every two days Mohadji Khan walked slowly to Schneider's to purchase his supplies. They consisted of a few cents' worth of vegetables, usually onions and carrots. Sometimes he dissipated with dried figs, but this was not often. Never was he known to spend five or ten or fifteen cents—it was always some odd sum like nine or eleven or seventeen. This was a grotesque man, with his mixture of Far-Eastern and New-Yorkish garments: shoes that the fop in a John Drew society play would not have been ashamed of, huge baggy trousers blowing about in the wind, a perfectly proper shirt—albeit with no collar—and shroudlike headgear that reeked of Kipling.

Gravely Mohadji Khan came and went, and the ordinary, every-day folks of the neighborhood eyed him with curiosity and some suspicion; for the flat-dwellers whose windows overlooked his block told of a dim light that never stopped burning, whatever the time of night—and many of them swore to hearing weird sounds, as of one engaged in the practice of magic, at hours when reputable citizens had been long in their beds.

Early one spring Rudolph Speckeldonner missed his strange customer for many days on a stretch, and presently there came to his ear the rumor that Mohadji was ill in the rear room of the shanty. The proprietor of the delicatessen shop on the corner, having carried a pair of shoes there to be resoled, had heard faint moans. The inside of the little house was so dark and desolate that the delicatessen man came away without going in, and he declared that a spell of shivers had come upon him when he looked in through the door.

Now Rudolph had long been speculating as to why such a creature as Mohadji Khan should be upon the earth at all. The utter unlikeness of the Hindu to everything right and normal was the object of his ruminations many an evening as he sat and puffed his pipe; and this is not strange when one considers that the hundreds of other human beings whom Rudolph saw every day were all of the same pattern, with variations so slight as to amount to nothing. And Rudolph was a kind-hearted man. So, when he heard the Hindu was ill, he asked leave of Schneider in the middle of the afternoon and went to call upon the mender of shoes.

There was no light in the little room that contained the workbench. Rudolph stumbled his way to the inner door leading to the room beyond and opened it. For a moment the German thought he saw a million candles, but he discovered that the effect was produced by one candle and a million mirrors, more or less. The wall was lined with them. There were round mirrors and square mirrors, mirrors whole and mirrors broken, mirrors with gilt frames, black frames, white frames and no frames at all; and every one of them seemed to shoot back at Rudolph the dim rays of the candle that stood on a tumbledown table in the middle of the floor. Except this table, the only furniture he saw at first was a chair, equally decrepit. "Vot der deffil!——" So far the visitor got in his expression of wonderment when the Hindu himself caught his eye. Mohadji Khan was lying on a cot in one corner, half covered by ragged cotton bedclothing. His breath came in little, irregular spurts, and now and then he groaned faintly. Rudolph walked to the side of the cot and put his hand on the Hindu's forehead. In less than a minute he was in the street, and in ten more minutes he was back again in the shanty with a doctor who was one of Schneider's regular patrons.

Mohadji Khan was in a bad way, but he was conscious enough to refuse to be taken to the hospital. They had to make him as comfortable as they could in the room with the mirror-walls. The doctor found time to drop in every day and Rudolph constituted himself a sort of visiting nurse. The patient was docile, swallowing whatever was given to him without a murmur; and this helped. Providence must have been extraordinarily kind, for the crude treatment was successful. The cobbler was soon free of fever and after that his return to health was rapid.

There were not many ways in which to show his gratitude to the grocery clerk, but he tried his best. He had a clever knack of making toys—scraps of wood bound together with odd pieces of rope and leather—and these he would present to Rudolph, with deep obeisances, for the children. Again and again he besought his benefactor to bring all of the Speckeldonner family's damaged shoes to him; he would feel it an honor to be allowed to make them new again. Once he brought a diamond-shaped mirror, and from his air of suppressed excitement when he offered it Rudolph knew this meant great devotion. During the Hindu's convalescence the visiting nurse had learned what a wild mania the man had for his wall decorations.

One morning—it was the second day of Rudolph's vacation—Mohadji Khan entered the grocery store and looked hurriedly around. His usually calm demeanor had departed from him and his words came quickly.

"Where is your assistant?" he asked the grocer, with the precise accent which always marked his speech.

"Rudolph? He's by home," growled Schneider, who was in a bad humor when his assistant was away. "He's loafing dis veek."

Mohadji Khan went quickly to the Speckeldonner flat, where he found the head of the family deep in the report of the baseball game of the day before.

"My friend," said the Hindu excitedly, whispering, as though he did not wish Gretchen and the children to overhear him, "I have discovered a great thing. It is the full of the moon and the great thing will happen at midnight. Will you come to my house at that time, my friend? Do not refuse me!"

Any man who had a brown skin and hung a million looking-glasses on his walls, and wore a twisted cloth around his head, was apt to do or say anything. There was no call to be excited about it. Anyhow, Rudolph wanted to get back to his paper. After demurring once or twice, chiefly on account of the late hour set for his visit, he consented.

"All right, Mister Mohajjy; I'll be dere," he said. "I don't know vot you vant; but, if you vant it so bad, vell an' goot."

A few minutes before twelve o'clock that night, Rudolph, yawning widely, passed under the cobbler's sign and proceeded along the pathway to the shanty. The sound of muffled chanting issued from the inner room—a weird sound that had its chilling effect even upon the German's prosaic soul. He saw that the connecting door was ajar, however, walked boldly to it and pushed it open. Then, at an imperious sign from Mohadji Khan, he closed it behind him. Mohadji, crouched upon the floor, was stirring a mixture in a three-legged earthen bowl. Every few moments he poured in a drop or two of some liquid from a vial, and whenever he did that the mixture spit and sparkled viciously. But for this, the only source of light was the three or four glowing coals beneath the bowl on a thick slab of stone.

The Hindu paid no attention to his guest for many minutes. Rudolph stood in the dark, looking down at the strange performance. He was about to speak when there was a great spluttering of the stuff in the bowl and a flare of vivid light. In a moment it was dark again and Mohadji Khan had risen to his knees.

"It is the golden instant now, my benefactor!" he said in a quivering voice. "Long have I hoped that I might repay you for your deeds of goodness to me. What you wish now, that you shall have; but wish it quickly."

"Vot is dat nonsense vot you say?" asked Rudolph.

"Do not trifle, my friend," returned Mohadji, breathing heavily. "What is it that you wish most in all the world?"

"Vell, I vish I get a hit ef'ry time I come to der bat," said Rudolph. And with this he let out a loud guffaw. It was a great joke.

"So be it, until I give warning of the end." The Hindu pronounced the words solemnly and then fell backward as if exhausted. Rudolph leaped forward to catch him, but Mohadji motioned him away and said: "It is nothing—I am not ill. Go—go, at once!"

So Rudolph went; and when he was outside he began to shake his head back and forth and mutter things about "niggers" and "damfoolishness." But before he reached the street he became aware that there was something queer about his muscles. Particularly did he feel a litheness in his arms that he had never known before. And of a sudden he knew that some change—he couldn't quite make out what it was—had come over his eyes. A film seemed to have been moved away from them. The outlines of things—roofs, cellar railings, trees—were clear as they had never been before. He held up his hand and looked at it. Without losing any of its size, it had taken on an entirely different appearance. The flabbiness was gone from the palm and the finger-joints moved with astonishing ease, as if they had just been freshly oiled. Rudolph had been unawed by the uncanny doings of Mohadji Khan in the gloom of the shanty; but now, walking along under the electric lights, a cold tremor ran down his back. Something—he knew it—had happened to him!

Next day—wonder of wonders!—Rudolph did not go to see the Giants play at the Polo Grounds. Instead, he boarded an excursion boat at an East Side pier and went to participate in the annual clambake of a German-American fraternal society at Glen Island. He had found out that there was to be a haphazard baseball game during the day. On the boat he looked up the young man who was managing this part of the program and transferred to him discreetly the sum of five dollars. And it turned out when the game started, soon after the midday meal, that one of the opposing nines had obtained the services of Mr. Rudolph Speckeldonner as outfielder.

Thursday the Giants were scheduled to meet the Cincinnati Reds. An hour before the game was to start one of the attendants in the clubhouse at the Polo Grounds notified John McGraw, manager, that a stranger was clamoring to speak to him. The manager was not in the best of humor, being troubled with doubts as to which of his pitchers he should send into the box this afternoon.

"Who is it?" he asked sharply; and then, without waiting for an answer: "Show him in."

Rudolph Speckeldonner entered.

"Mister McGraw," he said, "I vant to play on your team."

For a moment the manager of the Giants was dumb with astonishment at the stumpy figure before him.

"What!"

"I vant to play on your team."

"Who are you and where did you come from?"

"My name is Rudolph Speckeldonner. I vork in Schneider's grocery store on Amsterdam Affenue."

McGraw walked close to his visitor and took him gently by the elbow.

"Now, Rudolph," he said, "I guess you're a nice man and a good hand to sell Schneider's canned peaches; but think this baseball plan over for a day or two. I'm mighty busy just now."

As he was speaking the manager was deftly turning the German around and leading him toward the door, and before he knew what had happened Rudolph was on the outside and the door was closed.

Schneider's right-hand man did not get his customary joy from watching the game that day. This was not the fault of the game itself, though it might well have been. For the New York team was in the dumps—they couldn't field and they couldn't hit the ball—and Cincinnati walked away with an easy victory; but Rudolph was thinking all the time about the outcome of his interview. When the last New York batter lifted a pitiful pop fly into the shortstop's hands the grocery clerk returned to the clubhouse, slipped through the outer door and waited for his chance to see McGraw again. At last he spied the manager walking along a passageway, deep in conversation with one of the players, who seemed rather dejected at what his superior was saying to him. Rudolph walked up to them.

"Mister McGraw——"

McGraw turned and saw the same stumpy man with the bristly hair who had broken in on his thoughts two or three hours before.

"Oh, run away!" he exclaimed impatiently, and then beckoned to a burly individual who was carrying two large flesh-brushes toward the shower-bath room. "Jim!" the manager called. And when the rubber came near he whispered:

"Bughouse! Get him out of the way—quick. Don't let him in here again."

Jim was not rough. He simply laid his huge hand on the back of Rudolph's neck and impelled him, gently but surely, in the direction of Eighth Avenue. The visitor tried to expostulate, but Jim only smiled.

"Never again," he warned, as he gave his charge a final push into the open air, "or we might have to spank you next time. Goodby, sport."

Jim did not happen to be on duty next morning. It was a perfect May day, without a cloud in the sky and with a soft breeze blowing in from the river. The team had been called together for fielding practice and the players gamboled lazily in the sunshine until the boss should come and start them at real work. Soon he arrived and summoned them to him for a few pointed remarks. In a moment they were in a group around McGraw, listening to a scolding for their performances during the first half of the week.

All at once a queer-looking little man appeared at the gate near the house and ran rapidly toward them. It was Rudolph. He had eluded the sleepy day-watchman and for the third time was seeking an interview with the Giants' manager. McGraw recognized him.

"For the love of Heaven!" he cried. "Can't they keep that lunatic out o' here!"

By this time Rudolph had reached the group.

"Mister McGraw," he said, panting for breath, "vonce more I ask you—I vant to play on your team."

At first the players were too astonished to laugh and they stared at the stranger as if he had dropped out of the sky. Then they let forth a roar of merriment. The manager was amused too. At this hour of the day the minutes were not so valuable—there was time for a good joke. He looked down at Rudolph.

"Honest, now, what are you talking about?" he asked.

"I say I vant to play on your team," repeated the man from Schneider's. "I can get a hit ef'ry time I get to der bat."

This brought forth another burst of laughter, but Rudolph didn't crack a smile.

"You can, eh?" said McGraw. "And where did you learn to do that?"

"Neffer mind—I can do it! Yust gif me a chance."

"Now, look here. I thought you were drunk when you were here yesterday. Now I see you're just plain nutty. We haven't got time to talk foolishness now; so you'd better clear out. We're busy."

"I bet you fife dollar of money you hafen't got a pitcher vot can strike me out," said Rudolph.

Mathewson happened to be standing at the manager's elbow.

"Let's try him," the twirler whispered. "We won't take his money, of course. It'll be great sport to see him, though. It won't take but a minute or two."

McGraw smiled and agreed. "Oh, you babes make me tired with your nonsense," he said; "but go ahead with this jackass business and get over with it." He turned to his visitor. "What's your name, little man?"

"Rudolph Speckeldonner."

"Well, Rudolph, pick out your bat and stand up to the plate. Meyers, you get behind—and Christy, you do the pitching."

Mathewson put up a protesting hand. "I'd rather not," he said solemnly. "I haven't been knocked out of the box for a week and I don't want to lose my reputation. Let Wiltse try to strike Rudolph out."

So Meyers and Wiltse took their places with much gravity. McGraw was umpire.

"No, sir," said Rudolph stubbornly; "I don't bat if you don't put all der men in der field—first base, second base—all of 'em."

"Get in your places, men," ordered the manager sternly. When they were all ready he planted himself behind the pitcher and cried: "Play ball!"

Wiltse tossed the first one over without speed. It looked easy, but Rudolph failed to bite, as the ball passed a foot over his head.

"Ball one!" called the umpire.

"Good eye, Rudolph!" "That's the way to let 'em go by!" "He knows how to take 'em!" cheered the players.

Wiltse let loose the next one at top speed. Again Rudolph let it pass.

"Strike one!"

At this the batsman shook his head and

growled angrily, just as if he had played baseball all his life. Wiltse turned to the umpire and winked. "I'm going to give him a fast drop this time," he said. "Watch him!"

The pitcher wound up and hurled the ball with his full strength. Just before it reached the plate it "broke" and dropped five or six inches, but that fast drop was destined never to nestle in the catcher's mitt. Rudolph swung his bat; the next instant there was a resounding whack and the ball went whistling over the shortstop's head, long and low. When it fell to the ground nobody was within fifty feet of it and it kept going until it rolled against a fence.

While the centerfielder and the leftfielder raced after the ball the other seven players stood and looked at them stupidly, with mouths wide open. Then the Giants began to jeer delightedly at the pitcher, and the manager rolled over on the ground in his mirth.

"What did I tell you!" yelled Mathewson from third base. "Nobody can stand up against Rudolph!"

Of course it was an accident, but it was a capital joke on Wiltse, and the players wanted the trial to end before he could redeem himself.

"Rudolph's won his bet!" they cried. "Give him his five dollars, Wiltse. It's on you!"

McGraw was about to make that his decree when there came a stout objection from Rudolph.

"I vant to keep on," he demanded. "I bet you you can't make me strike out yet; and you can have yust so many chances as you vant."

The fielders placed themselves again and again Rudolph faced Wiltse. This time the batter met the first ball pitched and sent it singing over second base—as clean a hit as the Polo Grounds ever saw. Another shout went up. But when the thing happened a third time there was no sound from the players. They began to look at the stranger curiously, to see if they could find anything about his makeup to explain the phenomenon. Again and again he drove the ball between or over the heads of the fielders.

"Where did this Dutchman come from?" muttered McGraw under his breath.

The pitcher turned to the manager at last with a dazed look.

"Let the others try," he suggested.

And the others tried. Last of all came Mathewson. His banter had come to a stop several minutes before and he went into the box with sober thoughts. When he came out they were still soberer. His most formidable productions had been handled with ease. Drops of perspiration stood out on his brow and his hands shook nervously as he turned to the manager.

"I can't make it out," said the pitcher.

McGraw walked slowly to the plate and stopped within a yard of Rudolph Speckeldonner. The other men came up and closed in around the two. All of them stood and stared at the newcomer, unable to speak.

"Mister McGraw, I said I vant to play on your team," said Rudolph.

The manager's habitual air of confidence was not with him as he spoke.

"Where did you come from anyway? Where'd you learn it?" he asked huskily.

"Neffer mind vere I learn it yet," replied the German. "Vill I play or vill I not?"

"How do I know you can keep on doing it?" McGraw's natural suspicion was returning as he recovered from the shock which the batting exhibition had given him.

Rudolph gripped his bat. "Vell, let 'em get out dere and try it again," he challenged.

"Oh, never mind that. When do you want to start?"

"Righdt now—dis afternoon."

The manager hesitated a moment. Then

he shook himself, as if to make sure he was actually awake.

"I'll do it," he said decisively. "Turn up at two-thirty and I'll have a suit of clothes for you."

Rudolph threw down his bat.

"I'll be here," he said shortly. "But you tell first t'at feller vat you call Yim—vot said he vould spank me if I come back."

Without another word he walked across the field and disappeared through the gate. Twelve pairs of eyes, more or less, followed him until he was out of sight.

"John," said one of the older players to the manager, "did you know you didn't find out whether that Dutchman could field or not?"

"I know I didn't," said McGraw; "and I don't much care."

A good crowd turned out for the game that afternoon, for the team had but lately returned from the West for a long stay at home. There was the usual noisy chatter, the eating of peanuts, the drinking of ginger ale—the usual wise prophecies as to the outcome of the approaching conflict. Cincinnati had left town with three victories to its credit and Chicago was now on deck. A string of disasters for New York had made pessimists by the thousand and there were few on the stands who were not fearful of a fresh humiliation. The scorecard held no names that were new to the crowd.

The Giants were first at bat and went out in one-two-three order. When New York took the field the boisterous fans in the right-field bleachers were startled by the sight of a strange figure on the turf before them. It was a stumpy, awkward figure, topped by a growth of flaxen hair that stood up like bristles on a brush.

"Who is that?" asked thousands of men at the same time. And then they began to exclaim, in great excitement:

"Never saw him before!"

"Say, he's not on the card!"

"Where'd they find the runt!"

"Look at those legs!"

"Why don't he get breeches to fit!"

The first Chicago batter sent an easy grounder to short and the stands heaved a sigh of satisfaction. The second, after a ball and a strike had been called on him, lifted a high fly to right field, near the foul line. It would have been an easy proposition for the Giants' regular rightfielder. The new rightfielder saw it coming, waited a second and then started in what he seemed to think was the direction of the ball. At his first movement the crowd in the bleachers joined in one roar of laughter, for the instant forgetting its concern about the fate of the fly. To see the new fielder run was a rare sight. The operation was more like waddling than running, though the speed was fairly good. His two legs appeared to be moving in opposite directions; his stomach extended outward prominently; his head was thrown back with a sort of frightened-deer expression. When he had traveled about twenty yards he stopped suddenly, turned as if to run back and circled round and round dizzily. Then one of his feet got in the way of the other and he fell sprawling. The ball fell too—several feet away—and rolled almost to the bleachers.

The merriment of the fans had lasted only a moment—while the ball was in the air. Amusement now gave place to angry disapproval, expressed in a medley of shouts:

"Rotten!"

"Pick yerself up!"

"Where're yer eyes!"

"Go back to the farm!"

"Cut off those pig-bristles—they scared the ball away!"

"Hi, sauerkraut!"

"Put him out! Put him out! Put him out!"

Meanwhile Rudolph was scrambling after the ball. He threw it to the second baseman, who had run out to meet it, and the second baseman shot it to third to cut off the runner—too late. The Chicago man stood safe on the base, and the crowd jeered more and more. The clamor grew furious when the next batter drove a clean hit to center and brought home the man on third. The fact that the New York pitcher now achieved two strike-outs did little to appease the thousands, for one run means much in the present state of the science. And, as he walked to the bench at the end of the inning, Rudolph Speckeldonner heard applied to himself every sort of epithet under the sun. The spectators told one another, in no gentle terms, what they thought of McGraw for allowing this numskull on the field. They all agreed that the manager was either drunk or crazy. The unknown must have been put in at the last minute, for his name was not on the score-card.

A base on balls fell to the first New York batter in the second inning. And now the new rightfielder walked to the plate. There was a momentary lull in the noise as every pair of eyes fixed itself upon the stranger; but when he swung at the first ball pitched and missed it widely the jeering was renewed. Rudolph let two bad ones pass, far above his head. Then came a speedy out-curve, waist-high. He brought the bat to meet it with a full swing of the arms and a dear sound smote the ears of the fans. It was a vicious thwack. The ball sped like a bullet, some twelve feet from the ground, over the third baseman's head. It was too fast to be headed off by the leftfielder, and the Giant on first romped home easily.

Rudolph, though, was having trouble in his progress around the diamond. He made the journey to first without mishap, but on the second stage of the circuit he tripped and fell. Somehow he gained his feet again and went on to second, where he arrived just in time. A hit that should have sent him home landed him on third and a minute later he was ignominiously nailed at the plate by a throw from left field.

His timely base-hit had partially appeased the fans, but only partially. In view of his fielding and base-running they considered the two-bagger a mere accident. Whatever glory it had brought him was demolished by his failure to score on a clean hit. So, when he took his place in the field again, his friends on the bleachers were still liberal with their remarks. The wags had had time to concoct brutal witticisms at his expense and he was subjected to an unceasing volley of ridicule.

Luck was with him now, though, for the visitors sent nothing to right field in the next two or three innings. Once a fly came his way, but the second baseman was playing deep for just such an event and Rudolph judiciously stood still. Since no calamity came of it, the crowd did not give vent to any violent abuse—it merely hooted at the fielder and made facetious comments anent his shirking.

When he came to bat the second time neither team had added to its one run. New York had runners on first and third and McGraw had instructed Rudolph to let one ball pass, so that the man on first could take second. But his advice was ignored; the rightfielder struck at the ball and missed it. He reached for the next one, too, apparently trying to pick it off the ground—and missed that. The crowd yelled its disapproval. The pitcher smiled; for the job looked easy; he wound up and shot the ball far wide of the plate. It was a bait and the batter hit. Rudolph leaned over and lunged wildly. A moment later the first baseman was making a futile dive at a grounder that made dents in the turf just inside the foul line. Two Giants came home amid cheers and the new Giant roosted on first.

A buzzing, quite unlike the ordinary aimless chatter, was heard from the stands. Somebody had learned the rightfielder's name and it spread from one fan to another.

"Speckeldonner?" every man asked his neighbor. "Who is he? Where did he come from?" Nobody knew. Nobody even attempted to guess. After he had wielded his bat a third time—and a third time made a clean hit—the crowd was aghast. The wags on the bleachers kept silent and the men who had jeered at that first awkward performance began to stare at Speckeldonner with a deep awe. At quarter past five o'clock he was a famous man; his progress from the players' bench to the clubhouse was a triumph.

As he went to the showers Rudolph spied a burly figure that he had reason to recognize.

"Here, you!" he called imperiously. "Here, you—Yim! Come here and help me off mit my shoes—qvick!"

Jim had been watching the game, "Yes, sor, Mr. Speckeldonner," he replied, and came running.

Even the players themselves, who are no hero-worshipers, could not conceal their admiration. They said little to the hero himself, but they kept eying him curiously as he shed his uniform. After examining his unadorned body and finding it commonplace, they muttered things to each other and shook their heads hopelessly.

Rudolph evinced no desire to linger with them. He hastened through his bath, ascended to the elevated railroad station and went home.

"Gretchen," he announced when he reached the kitchen, "I t'ink I give up my yob at Schneider's tomorrow alretty. I'm playing baseball mit der New Yorks now—for Mister McGraw."

Gretchen took the news calmly.

"Rudolph," she said, "I t'ought you'd learn all about t'at game after vhile—you read about it so mooch. You ought to be ein goot baseball man—yes?"

"I am—fine!" he assented.

After dining he went around to call upon Schneider. On former visits to his boss he had been awed by the shining onyx wainscoting in the downstairs hall and by the aggressive glitter of the elevator boy's brass buttons; but now he walked in with the air of one whom no splendor could dazzle.

"I don't go back to vork next veek—I take a yob alretty with Mister McGraw, to play baseball mit der New Yorks," he told Schneider when they were both seated in the front room, with the pianola and the chromo of Queen Luise and the clock that produced a tune every quarter of an hour.

Schneider knew little about the national game and cared less. He had a vague idea that many deluded people spent their good money every day to see eighteen or twenty men toy with bats and balls; but somehow he had never thought of grown men's making a living out of their skill at the game. Nor did the information volunteered by his clerk make it clear to him why a man with a steady job in a grocery should quit it for any foolish sport.

"Speckeldonner," he said finally, "you are a fool!"

"Yes?" replied Rudolph. "Maybe so. But I don't come back to der shop next Monday; so you haf to get somebody else."

Early next morning he sallied forth to get his two newspapers. The same old pipe was in his mouth and he moved with no more speed than usual. Within him was a feeling of deep satisfaction—and an anticipation of satisfaction still deeper—but there was no outward sign of it. He put down two pennies, picked up his newspapers, put them under his arm and walked slowly back to the flat. When he was comfortably seated he turned to the sporting page of the American and read:

STRANGE CREATURE FROM MARS
AT THE POLO GROUNDS

By Hilliard K. Dirk

It must have come from Mars. Nobody could trace Its descent from anywhere else. Nothing like It has ever been seen on a baseball field before. It had a stumpy body and bow legs, a face without any hint of thought behind it and bristly hair that reminded you of the porcupine in the Bronx Park Zoo. It played in right field; and when a ball came that way It circled around like a top and let the ball fall fifteen feet away, while It lay kicking and pawing on the ground. When It ran bases It stumbled and fell down at each stage of the circuit.

But when It came to bat! It violated all the batting fashions. It tried to scoop 'em up off the ground and to pull 'em down out of the sky. It slammed at 'em when they were two feet wide of the plate. It ought to have struck out every time. And every time It sent the sphere sizzling between the infielders or over their heads where the outfielders couldn't even smell it—every time, ladies and gentlemen! Four times up—and four smashes! Two doubles—they might have been home runs if It could have moved faster—and two singles!

What's Its name? Speckeldonner, says Manager McGraw—Rudolph Speckeldonner. That sounds like Hoboken or a Sam Bernard musical comedy; but McGraw "ain't tellin'." He smiles wisely, as if to convey the impression that he trained up the prodigy all by himself, just to give a thrill to this jaded world. The Wise Man won't say where his discovery ever played before, or whether It is a permanent institution. Will Rudolph play today? Nobody knows. And, if It does, will It smash 'em the way It did yesterday? Nobody knows that either; but we make so bold as to prophesy that this idol's feet will turn out to contain some of that silicate known as clay.

And so on, with a detailed account of the game. It was pleasant reading. When Rudolph had read both papers he puffed silently for a minute or two. Then he smote his leg—an act of unaccustomed violence.

"By golly!" he exclaimed. "I forgot dere vas more papers yet. Here, Heinrich, run out and get all der papers each vot Ikey Stein on der corner has got."

The Giants' new rightfielder was a slow reader and it took him a good part of the morning to go through the pæans of praise. When the last one was put aside he made his way downtown to a hotel on Broadway, where he had an appointment with McGraw. By mutual consent they had postponed the discussion of finances until today. The manager led him to a table in a secluded corner of the café.

"Well, how much do you want?" asked McGraw, coming straight to business.

"Ten dollar for ef'ry hit," said Rudolph.

"That's no way to pay—who ever heard of paying a man by the hit? And do you expect to be docked for every error you make and every time you fall down running bases?"

"Sure—sure!" said Rudolph. "I gif you back fifteen cent for ef'ry error and twenty cent ef'ry time I fall down."

McGraw leaned back in his chair and looked the stolid German over in astonishment.

"Rudolph," he said, "you ought to be in Wall Street! The Polo Grounds are too confined for you."

"Vy, vot's der matter mit der bargain I say?" asked Rudolph innocently.

"Well, you know we've got to have some money left to pay the man who brushes off the plate and the man who sprinkles the grass," suggested the manager with a touch of satire.

"You t'ink ten dollar too much for a hit?" Rudolph ignored the satire.

"Very much too much. Why, I pay my best infielder but sixty dollars a week."

"Yes, and he don't get six hits in ein veek yet," said Rudolph. "He get more as ten dollar for ef'ry hit."

"Maybe so; but he can stop a ball sometimes when it comes his way. You mustn't feel bad if I say it, Rudolph, but with you in the field we might as well be there with eight men. And you're not the fastest baserunner in the league, you know."

Rudolph leaned over the table and shook his finger at the manager.

"Now, Mister McGraw, it's dis vay: A hit may not be vort' ten dollar if you can't make sure it come. It's der sureness vot count. A hit ef'ry time is vort' a lot; and I t'ink you ought to gif me ten dollars for ef'ry hit. And I tell you vot I do: Ef'ry time I come to the bat and don't make a hit alretty, I gif you ten dollar back. Vot you say?"

McGraw smiled. "Well, you seem to be getting my goat, Rudolph. Have it your own way. I hope you'll fan sometimes when there're two out and nobody on base, so I'll get some of your swag back into the treasury."

There was one other concession upon which the new Giant was still more insistent. The manager must free him from his contract on one day's notice, whenever he chose to quit. Such an agreement as this was against all traditions and McGraw objected with spirit.

"And let you jump to some other team? Not much!—I won't sign any such contract as that," he declared.

"Nutting like t'at," Rudolph assured him quickly. "I sign all der papers you vant not to play mit any one else as you. Ven I qvit, I qvit baseball altogetter."

So it was arranged. The transaction was closed then and there. When they issued into the street again the first sight that met their eyes was an afternoon newspaper being waved aloft.

"Git yer pa-aper!" the boy was shouting. "All about de pig-bristle slugger! Pa-aper!"

An ovation awaited Rudolph when he appeared on the field that afternoon. Over night the name of Speckeldonner had become known to all the world. The mystery surrounding him and the descriptions of his odd behavior had attracted thousands who cared little for the game itself; and the stands were jammed from top to bottom. The awkward figure of the newcomer was singled out at once among the squad of players as they came into view through the gate.

"There he is! There he is!" cried the crowd; and when he came nearer they called his name and sent up a mighty cheer.

In the second inning he met the first ball thrown to him and sent it straight over the shortstop's head. Next time he picked almost exactly the same spot. On his third opportunity he leaned up against the ball with such force that it went sailing over the centerfielder to the fence at the foot of the bleachers; but his fellows had been doing badly and Chicago led by one run in the ninth. There were runners on second and third when Rudolph stepped up to the plate for his last performance of the day. The pitcher set out deliberately to give him a base on balls; and the crowd, seeing this, jeered:

"Where's your nerve!"

" 'Fraid of him! 'Fraid of him!"

"Cold feet!"

"Put it over, you four-flusher!"

It is not likely that these taunts had any influence upon the southpaw from Chicago; but some strange feeling came over him—an inability to control the movement of his muscles. The catcher was standing off to one side, to receive the ball that no batter could reach, when the pitcher suddenly lost all control. The bat flew forward to meet the ball and—a roar burst from the multitude as the third baseman made a futile stab into the air! Before the ball was back in the diamond again the two runners had come home. The game was over.

Amsterdam Avenue is not in close touch with the great affairs of the world, and Rudolph's own neighbors were still treating him as an ordinary person after the news of his deeds had been flashed to every corner of the continent; but Gretchen showed a newspaper containing his photograph to the wife of the cigar man on the ground floor, and the cigar man's wife showed it to her husband—and he showed it to everybody who came in. In the afternoon everybody who had ever known Rudolph climbed up four flights of steps to remind him of what good friends they used to be. Rudolph made them all welcome. Four bucket-loads of beer were brought in before the afternoon was spent; the men smoked their pipes and the women chewed on pretzels and cheese. When night came the atmosphere had achieved a thickness that stirred every bosom to delight; but Schneider was not among the guests.

Bright and early Monday morning Jane Carew and Roy McGarrigle and half a dozen other Sunday supplement experts came to pay their respects. They drew pictures and they took photographs of Rudolph and Gretchen and Heinrich and Minna. And they asked questions—about Rudolph's ancestors, and his previous means of livelihood, and his reason for hiding his light all these years. Above all, how and where did he learn the batting end of the game? Rudolph shook his head and said nothing when they asked him this; but Gretchen was willing to tell.

"My husband neffer play—he learn it all out of reading," she informed them. "He study dis game—vot you say, baseball?—eight, six, ten years. He talk to us about it—yes—and ve do not know vot he say alretty. But all dis time he vas learning to play goot."

The story-weavers looked at her and nodded solemnly as if they believed it all. They wondered that guile could lurk behind such an innocent exterior and they wondered still more what could be the motive for such deception. The most plausible theory was that the slugger was an escaped convict, whose crime could be refastened upon him if his former baseball career were recalled.

There was little time now for him to waste in chats with reporters, though. McGraw insisted that he learn fielding. Rudolph had to go up to the Polo Grounds every fair morning at ten o'clock and stay until half-past twelve, hard at work. Brawny attendants batted flies and grounders to him, while McGraw, or some of the Giants who were dragooned into the service, stood by and sought to train the new fielder's eyes and hands and legs to work together at the proper moment.

During these lessons the spell of Rudolph's batting power was not upon his fellow players and they were moved to disgust by his awkward efforts. He would tear up under a fly at full speed—and let it pass a dozen feet or more behind him. A minute later he would retreat to where he thought the ball was bound—and it would fall far short. Often he would tumble ingloriously upon the turf, for no reason but that he tripped over his own legs. His instructors pleaded, and they gave practical demonstrations, and they cursed; and Rudolph took it all good-naturedly and kept on trying. On about the fourth day he got his hands upon a fly and clung to it like grim death. At this the two or three players who were standing by shouted with joy and clapped their hands furiously.

The queer thing about it was that the baseball public, after they once became convinced that Rudolph was hopeless in the field, took his failing as a huge joke. Perhaps they figured that by the law of compensation he had a right to murder every chance he got. Anyway, they loved him for his errors. When he started to navigate in the general direction of the ball they uttered "Ah's" of expectation; and when he committed the unpardonable sin—unpardonable in anybody else—they howled with delight. And then, a week and a day after his first appearance, he smashed the tradition he had created by a double miracle—judging a fly properly and straightway catching it. This was the most monstrous joke yet. Ten thousand men jumped to their feet, waved their hats, yelled and hurled pet names at their idol.

By some strange quirk of their collective mind, the crowd adopted a distinctive form of rooting whenever Rudolph came to the bat. Composed of a million commonplace sallies, in the aggregate it was a singsong, dirgelike production, full of bitter irony in

"NURSE!"

"Everything has been quietly arranged. At the proper moment we will step in and take charge."

"Now, doesn't this beat the Riviera?"

"Scramble two!"

"Thirsty?"

"Frankly, I'm worried."

"I shall turn to the white sales, madam, in my own good time!"

"I *thought* I heard the thunder of hoofs."

"They throw in an extra billion here, an extra billi
there . . . it all adds up."

its expression of sympathy for the visiting team. Everybody on the stands condoled with the pitcher until the crack of bat against ball—and that was the signal for a shout of exultation.

Men and women who had never seen baseball before had their interest fired by the tales of the mysterious stranger and came to worship with the old hands who had nursed the game in its cradle. And the stranger never disappointed them. Sometimes it was a modest single; sometimes a two or three bagger; occasionally—for Rudolph was learning to run—a homer. Never did one of his hits belong to the "scratch" variety. They were always solid, businesslike, decisive, uncompromising.

One of the yellow journals employed a detective of local fame to delve into Speckeldonner's past and trace his deeds and misdeeds back to the day of his birth. The sleuth started out by ransacking the rogues' gallery at police headquarters in the attempt to discover the Giant's image among the crooks' photographs. This yielding nothing, he set to work to make inquiries of the population in the neighborhood of Schneider's. There was not a missing link in the chain. Everybody seemed to know Rudolph; some of the older ones had known his parents when they lived in a little cottage, with a two-acre field around it, before the upper West Side had been evolved from the open country. There was not a period of three months in the young man's life that the detective could not lay his finger on; but if Rudolph had ever played baseball, except in the aimless, empty-lot fashion of city children, nobody had ever heard of it.

The lack of mystery in the past served only to deepen the mystery of the present. The newspaper printed the story of the rightfielder's life under the heavy-typed signature of the detective. The dates and the plentiful list of authorities—full names and addresses—nailed absolutely all wild stories of a checkered career. The most fanciful yarn could not have brought greater surprise to the public. The very commonplaceness of the record made it a sensation.

Rudolph's lineaments became as familiar to the throng as those of the ex-President of the United States. He could not appear on the street without having men point their fingers at him and call his name to one another in awed whispers. But, so far as one could tell from appearances, these attentions failed to turn his head. He went his way with a seeming mighty indifference, smoking the same vile-smelling pipe that had kept him company in days of obscurity.

McGraw continued to smile knowingly and say nothing when the reporters plied him with questions—until one of the players disobeyed orders and told the story of Rudolph's first conquest. Then the joke was on the manager. The newspapers printed a full account of the stranger's intrusion on the morning practice, dwelling cruelly upon McGraw's skepticism. Whoever told the secret did the job thoroughly, for no details were left out. The first scorn displayed by the "Polo Czar," the baiting of the unknown visitor, the discomfiture of Wiltse and finally the complete humiliation of the peerless Mathewson—all were bared to the irreverent public gaze. And the public chortled with glee.

At the beginning of the second week Rudolph began to show unmistakable improvement in the field. True, he rarely caught a fly, but he learned to judge it with a fair degree of success—to check the progress of the ball and get it started back toward the diamond. That was a considerable achievement for him. Strangely enough, grounders gave him the most trouble. He seemed unable to combat the vagaries of a bounce. If he put his legs together the ball was sure to pass to one side; if he didn't it passed between his legs. His solution of the difficulty was one that baseball followers had never seen before. He made the best guess he could as to where the ball would come in contact with the ground on one of its bounds, and then threw himself down on his side at full length. Thus he made a fence of his body. When the fence had performed its function Rudolph would get upon his feet again somehow, and make a throw to the infield.

Of course they tried to let him have as few chances as possible. By special order, the second baseman played very deep and the left and center fielders veered around toward right. If it was inevitable that Rudolph should handle a ball at least two players ran to him quickly, to make sure of a rapid recovery.

Visiting pitchers were almost driven mad by the monotony of the rightfielder's performances with the bat. They gave him drops and they gave him inshoots; they skimmed 'em just over the top of the plate and they shot 'em straight at the batter's head. They all received the same treatment. What utterly dumfounded the twirlers was that they could not present the slugger with a base on balls. They might put three balls quite out of reach, but something always happened to them when they tried the fourth. Often a pitcher came to the bench trembling from a feeling akin to terror after a futile effort to deliver a pass. The pride of Boston once broke down, blubbering, in the middle of an inning and had to be led from the box.

At the end of the first week McGraw paid Rudolph the sum of two hundred and sixty dollars. In the second week there were two rainy days and the rightfielder's check amounted to one hundred and sixty dollars. The manager was a business man first and a baseball player afterward; and he thought the arrival of the tail-end team in New York offered a good opportunity to save money. He felt sure of the Giants' ability to wallop this crew with the old makeup. So on Monday Rudolph received a curt assignment to adorn the bench and look on; but McGraw had not reckoned with public opinion. From the very moment that New York took the field in the first inning the crowd kept shouting for their favorite.

"Speckeldonner! Speckeldonner!" they yelled. "Put him in! Put him in!" And they kept on yelling, with more and more violence. Rudolph sat on the bench and didn't move a muscle. McGraw is not reckoned as sensitive to the criticism of the vulgar herd, but this demonstration was too much for him. As the din grew in fury his nerve gave way. And in the third inning Rudolph trotted out to right field.

When Lajoie and Ty Cobb had visited New York, in days past, multitudes had gone to the American League Park to worship these marvelous stick-artists. And the town had mourned that their like was not in Gotham. But now their fame had melted away—not only in the metropolis but wherever the railroad and the telegraph carried the news of the world. "Cobb!—oh, yes," the traveling salesman from the East would say condescendingly; "you mean the fellow from Detroit? Yes; we used to think he was quite clever with his bat. I believe he still stands high up in the American League."

From a bad third in the middle of May the Giants climbed steadily up the percentage ladder. The presence of an unfailing slugger stung the other men to great efforts and the team developed such a hitting streak as the Polo Grounds had rarely seen. Of course none could hope to equal Rudolph's performance, but there was a lively strife to get a few small segments from the circle of glory.

It was one evening near the end of the month that Rudolph reached the very pinnacle of fame. The Speckeldonner family were just about to begin their dinner when a brass-buttoned messenger appeared with a package and a letter. The letter was from an official of the largest retail cigar company in the country—a wing of the Tobacco Trust—begging the recipient to accept the accompanying box as a testimonial of regard. Rudolph unwrapped the package and beheld an image of himself, in many colors, in the act of batting. Underneath was the black-and-gilt legend: "The Speckeldonner Cigar—Best Five-Cent Smoke on Earth."

A little later the same evening the slugger had an opportunity to present this box for inspection to a caller—one Fritz Schneider, an Amsterdam Avenue grocer. Schneider had come on business.

"Speckeldonner," he said, "I been t'inking you and me might make ein goot bargain. Vot you say you come to my store ef'ry day and——"

"I told you I qvit my yob——" began Rudolph.

Schneider held up his hand protestingly.

"I know—I know; but I mean dis: You come ef'ry morning, von hour—tvelve to von, say it—and I gif you a goot chair and you yust sit in front of der store, vere people see you—and don't do no vork at all—yust sit dere! Vot you say?"

"Sort of puller-in you vant me for—eh?" asked Rudolph.

He was finally persuaded to accept the offer for a consideration of seven dollars a day. The hours of his morning practice were adjusted so that the new appointment could be filled.

As an advertising achievement Schneider's arrangement was a stroke of genius. He put up a sign informing the public that the greatest baseball player in the world would visit his former employer every day at noon. The first day the police reserves had to be called out to hold the throng in check; and photographs of the scene appeared in the public prints, with Schneider's name in full view. New customers came in shoals.

A team can't jump to the head of the league just because it is winning—for the teams ahead of it may be winning too. It was so at this time. Chicago and Pittsburgh were having their own way mostly with the cities lower in the list. The Giants dropped one or two games despite the hitting streak; but they crawled up—three or four points at a time. Again and again their victories could be traced directly to a timely hit by the "man who never failed." And all New York knew that he would land the Giants on top soon.

After displaying himself under Schneider's awning for an hour one warm day, Rudolph walked into the store and behind the counter. Mohadji Khan had appeared unexpectedly before him a few minutes before and, without a word, had slipped a small fragment of a sheet of writing paper into his hand. On the piece of paper two or three words had been penned in a queer foreign hand, but quite legibly.

"Mister Schneider," said Rudolph, "der team goes avay Sunday, to stay six veeks."

"Go avay vere?" asked Schneider. "Vot for it leaf town?"

Rudolph explained that each city in the league had to have its home season and that the Giants could not be the hosts all the time.

"But I get tired of dis game," he added. "I t'ink maybe I don't go." Then, after a pause, he continued casually: "A manager ask me to go on der vaudeville stage; but Gretchen she say I might start a grocery store of my own, next block down here."

In an instant Schneider saw visions of his newly acquired patrons forsaking him if his former clerk should open a rival store near by. So the older man, thinking himself very adroit, persuaded Rudolph to consent to a partnership. They arranged to sign the papers that evening.

It was a glorious fourteenth day of June—this day. The sun shone lovingly on the Polo Grounds with a gentle warmth; and a breeze, ever so slight, blew over the close-clipped grass. Pittsburgh, still at the top and leading the Giants by four points, was to appear for the first time in many weeks; and New York was thirsting for the Pirates' blood. An hour too early the crowd began to pour in—noisy, joyous, expectant.

Meantime, in the clubhouse, Rudolph Speckeldonner and John McGraw were engaged in a very private and a very heated discussion. They sat in the manager's sacred office, with the door locked. McGraw, angry at what he had heard, blustered and threatened and cajoled in turn. Rudolph mostly kept silence; and whenever he did speak it was merely to repeat something he had said before. When the team went out on the field the two were still separated from the others; and the people on the stands recognized the familiar gestures of the manager as he conversed with the rightfielder.

The Pirates led off by accumulating three runs in the first inning. This put the home team in a bad hole and it seemed in no mood to pull itself out. The Pittsburgh infield made errors, but they cost nothing; the Giants made hits, but the hits came at the wrong time. Though Speckeldonner shone as never before, he could not do it all alone. He slashed out two two-baggers and a triple the first three times up—but nobody was on base. And nobody could bring Rudolph in when he got there.

In the ninth the Pittsburgh twirler went up in the air. With two out and a man on first he delivered two free passes. There arose a mighty shout from the stands, for Rudolph Speckeldonner arose from the Giants' bench and walked to the plate. Usually he was the personification of indifference in his bearing; but now the crowd fancied they saw in him a real eagerness as he gripped his bat and swung it back on his shoulder. Whether the pitcher meant to do what he did—whether it sprang from hopelessness, defiance or a state of hypnotism—will never be known. What he did was to throw the first ball, without curve or kink, dead straight over the middle of the plate, three feet from the ground. Rudolph swung at it with all his strength. That ball, whose last triumphant flight put the Giants at the head of the league, has never been recovered. It was seen to sail over the centerfielder's head and into the fifty-cent bleachers—farther, it is said, than a ball had ever been knocked in the history of the game. As it fell in the cheap seats, it is probably treasured today as a holy relic in some section of town "where the other half lives."

The world of sports was shocked the next day by the announcement that Rudolph Speckeldonner had quit baseball. His contract, the newspapers said, permitted him to leave the team on twenty-four hours' notice—and he had given the required notice to Manager McGraw just before the first game of the Pittsburgh series. If the rightfielder had made any explanation the manager had not seen fit to divulge it; so the public was left in the dark. One of the afternoon newspapers signified its distress by putting a mourning band of ink, one inch wide, around the four sides of the sporting page.

A little after dusk that evening the Speckeldonner family issued into the street. After walking a block or two they lined up in a row on the curb of Amsterdam Avenue, backs to the roadway. There they stood, with hands joined, Rudolph at one end, Gretchen at the other, Heinrich and Minna between. Behind them, over Central Park, hung the full moon; and its soft light caressed the gilt letters of a newly painted sign. It was toward this that the four, in silence, inclined their admiring eyes—for on the sign were the words: Schneider & Speckeldonner, Fine Groceries.

Rudolph is a has-been now, but he is a has-been who retired at the height of his glory. And he is rich. For New York—

and every other place—is crowded with folks who delight to rub elbows with the famous; and these lion-hunters come in flocks to buy from the man who made Hans Wagner look like a child at the game.

The Hindu cobbler still walks gravely up Amsterdam Avenue every two or three days to buy nine or eleven or seventeen cents' worth of vegetables. Rudolph wanted to reward him handsomely with money, but he would have none of it. Only under protest from the cobbler was a carpenter brought into the wooded block and made to stop the holes in the shanty. But Rudolph knew one form of gift that Mohadji Khan could not resist—and a dozen or so new mirrors, in fantastic shapes, now adorn the walls of the dim rear room.

One Way Left to Go

A *POST* WAR ANECDOTE

EARLY in the North African campaign, when the Yanks were far from being those battle-scarred veterans who later swept across Europe, one of our combat teams was cut off from the main units and forced by great superiority of enemy numbers to retreat into the mountains. The Afrika Korps, then rich in tanks and heavy guns, was determined to capture them or wipe them out. In spite of heroic resistance, the Americans finally found themselves holding only a single mountain peak, while the swift Nazi armored divisions rapidly encircled their position.

With much of their equipment lost in the retreat, with their nerves near the breaking point and their muscles almost paralyzed with fatigue, our men appeared to be in a spot from which nothing short of a miracle could save them.

At dusk, the commanding officer addressed his men on the mountaintop. "Gentlemen," he said, "you all know our position. There are tanks in front of us. There are tanks on our right flank and on our left flank. What you may not know is that a tank column has just succeeded in getting behind us."

He paused to look them over before finishing. Then he concluded, "I know you men and what you're capable of. Tonight we will go down this mountain and rejoin our main force. All I can say is, God help those tanks!"

They rejoined the main force.

—R. J. CROT.

FORLORN HOPE

Suitors seeking perfect mates should apply to the Bureau of Missing Persons.

—SHANNON FIFE.

A WEDDING GIFT

By JOHN TAINTOR FOOTE

§ *When a confirmed fisherman is presented with one of the great opportunities of his life—even if it is on his honeymoon—shouldn't his bride make an effort to understand? Actually, thought George, she ought to be grateful. . . .*

JANUARY 13, 1923

GEORGE BALDWIN POTTER is a purist. That is to say, he either takes trout on a dry fly or he does not take them at all. He belongs to a number of fishing clubs, any member of which might acquire his neighbor's wife, beat his children or poison a dog and still cast a fly, in all serenity, upon club waters; but should he impale on a hook a lowly though succulent worm and immerse the creature in those same waters it would be better that he send in his resignation at once, sooner than face the shaken committee that would presently wait upon him.

George had become fixed in my mind as a bachelor. This, of course, was a mistake. I am continually forgetting that purists rush into marriage when approaching or having just passed the age of forty. The psychology of this is clear.

For twenty years, let us say, a purist's life is completely filled by his efforts to convert all reasonable men to his own particular method of taking trout. He thinks, for example, that a man should not concern himself with more than a dozen types of standard flies. The manner of presenting them is the main consideration. Take any one of these flies, then, and place it, by means of an eight-foot rod, a light, tapered line and a mist-colored leader of reasonable length, on fast water—if you want trout. Of course, if you want to listen to the birds and look at the scenery, fish the pools with a long line and an eight-foot leader. Why, it stands to reason that——

The years go by as he explains these vital facts patiently, again and again, to Smith and Brown and Jones. One wet, cold spring, after fighting a muddy stream all day, he re-explains for the better part of an evening and takes himself, somewhat wearily, upstairs. The damp chill of the room at whatever club he may be fishing is positively tomblike. He can hear the rain drumming on the roof and swishing against the windows. The water will be higher than ever tomorrow, he reflects, as he puts out the light and slides between the icy sheets. Steeped to the soul in cheerless dark, he recalls numbly that when he first met Smith and Brown and Jones they were fishing the pools with a long line. That was, let's see—fifteen—eighteen—twenty years ago. Then he must be forty. It isn't possible! Yes, it is a fact. It is also a fact that Smith and Brown and Jones are still fishing the pools with a long line.

In the first faint light of dawn he falls into an uneasy, muttering slumber. The dark hours between have been devoted to intense thought and a variety of wiggles which have not succeeded in keeping the bedclothes against his shoulder blades.

Some time within the next six months you will remember that you have forgotten to send him a wedding present.

George, therefore, having arrived at his fortieth birthday, announced his engagement shortly thereafter. Quite by chance I ran across his bride-to-be and himself a few days before the ceremony, and joined them at lunch. She was a blonde in the early twenties, with wide blue eyes and a typical rose-and-white complexion. A rushing, almost breathless account of herself, which she began almost the moment we were seated, was curious, I thought. It was as though she feared an interruption at any moment. I learned that she was an only child, born and reared in Greater New York; that her family had recently moved to New Rochelle; that she had been shopping madly for the past two weeks; that she was nearly dead, but that she had some adorable things.

At this point George informed me that they would spend their honeymoon at a certain fishing club in Maine. He then proceeded to describe the streams and lakes in that section at some length—during the rest of the luncheon, as a matter of fact. His fiancée, who had fallen into a wordless abstraction, only broke her silence with a vague murmur as we parted.

Owing to this meeting I did not forget to send a wedding present. I determined that my choice should please both George and his wife through the happy years to come.

If I had had George only to consider, I could have settled the business in two minutes at a sporting-goods store. Barred from these for obvious reasons, I spent a long day in a thoroughly exhausting search. Late in the afternoon I decided to abandon my hopeless task. I had made a tremendous effort and failed. I would simply buy a silver doodab and let it go at that.

As I staggered into a store with the above purpose in view, I passed a show case devoted to fine china, and halted as my eyes fell on a row of fish plates backed by artfully rumpled blue velvet. The plates proved to be hand painted. On each plate was one of the different varieties of trout, curving up through green depths to an artificial fly just dropping on the surface of the water.

In an automatic fashion I indicated the plates to a clerk, paid for them, gave him my card and the address and fled from the store. Sometime during the next twenty-four hours it came to me that George Potter was not among my nearest and dearest. Yet the unbelievable sum I had left with that clerk in exchange for those fish plates could be justified in no other way.

I thought this fact accounted for the sort of frenzy with which George flung himself upon me when next we met, some two months later. I had been week-ending in the country and encountered him in the Grand Central Station as I emerged from the lower level. For a long moment he wrung my hand in silence, gazing almost feverishly into my face. At last he spoke:

"Have you got an hour to spare?"

It occurred to me that it would take George an hour at least to describe fully his amazed delight at the splendor of my gift. The clock above Information showed that it was 12:45. I therefore suggested that we lunch together.

He, too, glanced at the clock, verified its correctness by his watch and seized me by the arm.

"All right," he agreed, and was urging me toward the well filled and somewhat noisy station café before I grasped his intention and tried to suggest that we go elsewhere. His hand only tightened on my arm.

"It's all right," he said; "good food, quick service—you'll like it."

He all but dragged me into the café and steered me to a table in the corner. I lifted my voice above an earnest clatter of gastronomical utensils and made a last effort.

"The Biltmore's just across the street."

George pressed me into my chair, shoved a menu card at me and addressed the waiter.

"Take his order." Here he jerked out his watch and consulted it again. "We have forty-eight minutes. Service for one. I shan't eat anything; or, no—bring me some coffee—large cup—black."

Having ordered mechanically, I frankly stared at George. He was dressed, I now observed, with unusual care. He wore a rather dashing gray suit. His tie, which was an exquisite shade of gray-blue, was embellished by a handsome pearl. The edging of a handkerchief, appearing above his breast pocket, was of the same delicate gray-blue shade as the tie. His face had been recently and closely shaven, also powdered; but above that smooth whiteness of jowl was a pair of curiously glittering eyes and a damp, a beaded brow. This he now mopped with his napkin.

"Good God," said I, "what is it, George?"

His reply was to extract a letter from his inside coat pocket and pass it across the table, his haunted eyes on mine. I took in its few lines at a glance:

Father has persuaded me to listen to what you call your explanation. I arrive Grand Central 2:45, daylight saving, Monday.

ISABELLE.

Poor old George, I thought; some bachelor indiscretion; and now, with his honeymoon scarcely over, blackmail, a lawsuit, heaven only knew what.

"Who," I asked, returning the letter, "is Isabelle?"

To my distress, George again resorted to his napkin. Then, "My wife," he said.

"Your wife!"

George nodded.

"Been living with her people for the last month. Wish he'd bring that coffee. You don't happen to have a flask with you?"

"Yes, I have a flask." George brightened. "But it's empty. Do you want to tell me about your trouble? Is that why you brought me here?"

"Well, yes," George admitted. "But the point is—will you stand by me? That's the main thing. She gets in"—here he consulted his watch—"in forty-five minutes, if the train's on time." A sudden panic seemed to seize him. His hand shot across the table and grasped my wrist. "You've got to stand by me, old man—until the ice is broken. That's all I ask. Just stick until the train gets in. Then act as if you knew nothing. Say you ran into me here and stayed to meet her. I'll tell you what—say I didn't seem to want you to stay. Kid me about wanting her all to myself, or something like that. Get the point? It'll give me a chance to sort of—well, you understand."

"I see what you mean, of course," I admitted. "Here's your coffee. Suppose you have some and then tell me what this is all about—if you care to, that is."

"No sugar, no cream," said George to the waiter; "just pour it. Don't stand there waving it about—pour it, pour it!" He attempted to swallow a mouthful of steaming coffee, gurgled frightfully and grabbed his water glass. "Great jumping Jehoshaphat!" he gasped, when he could speak, and glared at the waiter, who promptly moved out into the sea of diners and disappeared among the dozen of his kind.

"Steady, George," I advised as I transferred a small lump of ice from my glass to his coffee cup.

George watched the ice dissolve, murmured "Idiot" several times and presently swallowed the contents of the cup in two gulps.

"I had told her," he said suddenly, "exactly where we were going. She mentioned Narragansett several times—I'll admit that. Imagine—Narragansett! Of course, I bought her fishing things myself. I didn't buy knickers or woolens or flannel shirts—naturally. You don't go around buying a girl breeches and underwear before you're married. It wouldn't be—well, it isn't done, that's all. I got her the sweetest three-ounce rod you ever held in your hand. I'll bet I could put out sixty feet of line with it against the wind. I got her a pair of English waders that didn't weigh a pound. They cost me forty-five dollars. The rest of the outfit was just as good. Why, her fly box was a Truxton. I could have bought an American imitation for eight dollars. I know a lot of men who'll buy leaders for themselves at two dollars apiece and let their wives fish with any kind of tackle. I'll give you my word, I'd have used anything I got her myself. I sent it all out to be packed with her things. I wanted her to feel that it was her own—not mine. I know a lot of men who give their wives a high-class rod or an imported reel and then fish with it themselves. What time is it?"

"Clock right up there," I said. But George consulted his watch and used his napkin distressingly again.

"Where was I?"

"You were telling me why you sent her fishing things out to her."

"Oh, yes! That's all of that. I simply wanted to show you that from the first I did all any man could do. Ever been in the Cuddiwink district?"

I said that I had not.

"You go in from Buck's Landing. A lumber tug takes you up to the head of Lake Owonga. Club guides meet you there and put you through in one day—twenty miles by canoe and portage up the west branch of the Penobscot; then nine miles by trail to Lost Pond. The club's on Lost Pond. Separate cabins, with a main dining and loafing camp, and the best squaretail fishing on earth—both lake and stream. Of course, I don't fish the lakes. A dry fly belongs on a stream and nowhere else. Let me make it perfectly clear."

George's manner suddenly changed. He hunched himself closer to the table, dropped an elbow upon it and lifted an expository finger.

"The dry fly," he stated, with a new almost combative ring in his voice, "is designed primarily to simulate not only the appearance of the natural insect but its action as well. This action is arrived at through the flow of the current. The moment you move a fly by means of a leader you destroy the——"

I saw that an interruption was imperative.

"Yes, of course," I said; "but your wife will be here in——"

It was pitiful to observe George. His new-found assurance did not flee—flee suggests a withdrawal, however swift—it was immediately and totally annihilated. He attempted to pour himself some coffee, take out his watch, look at the clock and mop his brow with his napkin at one and the same instant.

"You were telling me how to get to Lost Pond," I suggested.

"Yes, to be sure," said George. "Naturally you go in light. The things you absolutely have to have—rods, tackle, waders, wading shoes, and so forth, are about all a guide can manage at the portages in addition to the canoe. You pack in extras yourself—change of underclothes, a couple of pairs of socks and a few toilet articles. You leave a bag or a trunk at Buck's Landing. I explained this to her. I explained it carefully. I told her either a week-end bag or one small trunk. Herb Trescott was my best man. I left everything to him. He saw us on the train and handed me tickets and reservations just before we pulled out.

I didn't notice in the excitement of getting away that he'd given me three trunk checks all stamped 'Excess.' I didn't notice it till the conductor showed up, as a matter of fact. Then I said, 'Darling, what in heaven's name have you brought three trunks for?' She said—I can remember her exact words—'Then you're not going to Narragansett?'

"I simply looked at her. I was too dumfounded to speak. At last I pulled myself together and told her that in three days we'd be whipping the best squaretail water in the world. I took her hand, I remember, and said, 'You and I together, sweetheart,' or something like that."

George sighed and lapsed into a silence which remained unbroken until his eye happened to encounter the face of the clock. He started and went on:

"We got to Buck's Landing, by way of Bangor, at six in the evening of the following day. Buck's Landing is a railroad station with grass growing between the ties, a general store and hotel combined, and a lumber wharf. The store keeps canned peas, pink-and-white candy and felt boots. The hotel part is—well, it doesn't matter except that I don't think I ever saw so many deer heads; a few stuffed trout, but mostly deer heads. After supper the proprietor and I got the three trunks up to the largest room. We just got them in and that was all. The tug left for the head of the lake at seven next morning. I explained this to Isabelle. I said we'd leave the trunks there until we came out, and offered to help her unpack the one her fishing things were in. She said, 'Please go away!' So I went. I got out a rod and went down to the wharf. No trout there, I knew; but I thought I'd limber up my wrist. I put on a Cahill Number Fourteen—or was it Sixteen——"

George knitted his brows and stared intently but unseeingly at me for some little time.

"Call it a Sixteen," I suggested.

George shook his head impatiently and remained concentrated in thought.

"I'm inclined to think it was a Fourteen," he said at last. "But let it go; it'll come to me later. At any rate, the place was alive with big chub—a foot long, some of 'em. I'll bet I took fifty—threw 'em back, of course. They kept on rising after it got dark. I'd tell myself I'd go after one more cast. Each time I'd hook a big chub, and—well, you know how the time slips away.

"When I got back to the hotel all the lights were out. I lit matches until I got upstairs and found the door to the room. I'll never forget what I saw when I opened that door—never! Do you happen to know how many of the kind of things they wear a woman can get into one trunk? Well, she had three and she'd unpacked them all. She had used the bed for the gowns alone. It was piled with them—literally piled; but that wasn't a starter. Everywhere you looked was a stack of things with ribbons in 'em. There were enough shoes and stockings for a girls' school; silk stockings, mind you, and high-heeled shoes and slippers." Here George consulted clock and watch. "I wonder if that train's on time," he wanted to know.

"You have thirty-five minutes, even if it is," I told him; "go right ahead."

"Well, I could see something was wrong from her face. I didn't know what, but I started right in to cheer her up. I told her all about the chub fishing I'd been having. At last she burst into tears. I won't go into the scene that followed. I'd ask her what was the matter and she'd say, 'Nothing,' and cry frightfully. I know a lot of men who would have lost their tempers under the circumstances, but I didn't; I give you my word. I simply said, 'There, there,' until she quieted down. And that isn't all. After a while she began to show me her gowns. Imagine—at eleven o'clock at night, at Buck's Landing! She'd hold up a dress and look over the top of it at me and ask me how I liked it, and I'd say it was all right. I know a lot of men who wouldn't have sat there two minutes.

"At last I said, 'They're all all right, darling,' and yawned. She was holding up a pink dress covered with shiny dingle-dangles, and she threw the dress on the bed and all but had hysterics. It was terrible. In trying to think of some way to quiet her it occurred to me that I'd put her rod together and let her feel the balance of it with the reel I'd bought her—a genuine Fleetwood, mind you—attached. I looked around for her fishing things and couldn't find them. I'll tell you why I couldn't find them." George paused for an impressive instant to give his next words the full significance due them. "They weren't there!"

"No?" I murmured weakly.

"No," said George. "And what do you suppose she said when I questioned her? I can give you her exact words—I'll never forget them. She said, 'There wasn't any room for them.' Again George paused. "I ask you," he inquired at last, "I ask you as man to man, what do you think of that?"

I found no adequate reply to this question, and George, now thoroughly warmed up, rushed on.

"You'd swear I lost my temper then, wouldn't you? Well, I didn't. I did say something to her later, but I'll let you be the judge when we come to that. I'll ask you to consider the circumstances. I'll ask you to get Old Faithful in your mind's eye."

"Old Faithful?" I repeated. "Then you went to the Yellowstone later?"

"Yellowstone! Of course not! Haven't I told you we were already at the best trout water in America? Old Faithful was a squaretail. He'd been in the pool below Horseshoe Falls for twenty years, as a matter of record. We'll come to that presently. How are we off for time?"

"Thirty-one minutes," I told him. "I'm watching the clock—go ahead."

"Well, there she was, on a fishing trip with nothing to fish with. There was only one answer to that—she couldn't fish. But I went over everything she'd brought in three trunks and I'll give you my word she didn't have a garment of any sort you couldn't see through.

"Something had to be done and done quick, that was sure. I fitted her out from my own things with a sweater, a flannel shirt and a pair of knickerbockers. Then I got the proprietor up and explained the situation. He got me some heavy underwear and two pairs of woolen stockings that belonged to his wife. When it came to shoes it looked hopeless, but the proprietor's wife, who had got up, too, by this time, thought of a pair of boy's moccasins that were in the store and they turned out to be about the right size. I made arrangements to rent the room we had until we came out again to keep her stuff in, and took another room for the night—what was left of it after she'd repacked what could stay in the trunks and arranged what couldn't so it wouldn't be wrinkled.

"I got up early, dressed and took my duffel down to the landing. I wakened her when I left the room. When breakfast was ready I went to see why she hadn't come down. She was all dressed, sitting on the edge of the bed. I said, 'Breakfast is ready, darling,' but I saw by her face that something was wrong again. It turned out to be my knickers. They fitted her perfectly—a little tight in spots—except in the waist. They would simply have fallen off if she hadn't held them up.

"Well, I was going in so light that I only had one belt. The proprietor didn't have any—he used suspenders. Neither did his wife. She used—well, whatever they use. He got me a piece of clothesline and I knotted it at each end and ran it through the what-you-may-call-'ems of the knickers and tied it in front. The knickers sort of puckered all the way round, but they couldn't come down—that was the main thing. I said, 'There you are darling.' She walked over and tilted the mirror of the bureau so that she could see herself from head to foot. She said, 'Who are going to be at this place where we are going?' I said, 'Some of the very best dry-fly men in the country.' She said, 'I don't mean them; I mean the women. Will there be any women there?"

"I told her, certainly there would be women. I asked her if she thought I would take her into a camp with nothing but men. I named some of the women: Mrs. Fred Beal and Mrs. Brooks Carter and Talcott Ranning's sister and several more.

"She turned around slowly in front of the mirror, staring into it for a minute. Then she said, 'Please go out and close the door.' I said, 'All right, darling; but come right down. The tug will be here in fifteen minutes.'

"I went downstairs and waited ten minutes, then I heard the tug whistle for the landing and ran upstairs again. I knocked at the door. When she didn't answer I went in. Where do you suppose she was?"

I gave it up.

"In bed!" said George in an awe-struck voice. "In bed, with her face turned to the wall; and listen, I didn't lose my temper, as God is my judge. I rushed down to the wharf and told the tug captain I'd give him twenty-five dollars extra if he'd hold the boat till we came. He said all right and I went back to the room.

"The breeches had done it. She simply wouldn't wear them. I told her that at a fishing camp in Maine clothes were never thought of. I said, 'No one thinks of anything but trout, darling.' She said, 'I wouldn't let a fish see me looking like that.'" George's brow beaded suddenly. His hands dived searchingly into various pockets. "Got a cigarette? I left my case in my other suit."

He took a cigarette from me, lighted it with shaking fingers and inhaled deeply.

"It went on like that for thirty minutes. She was crying all the time, of course. I had started down to tell the tug captain it was all off, and I saw a woman's raincoat hanging in the hall. It belonged to someone up in one of the camps, the proprietor told me. I gave him seventy-five dollars to give to whoever owned it when they came out, and took it upstairs. In about ten minutes I persuaded her to wear it over the rest of her outfit until we got to camp. I told her one of the women would be able to fix her up all right when we got there. I didn't believe it, of course. The women at camp were all old-timers; they'd gone in as light as the men; but I had to say something.

"We had quite a trip going in. The guides were at the head of the lake all right—Indian Joe and a new man I'd never seen, called Charlie. I told Joe to take Isabelle—he's one of the best canoemen I ever saw. I was going to paddle bow for my man, but I'd have bet a cooky Indian Joe could stay with us on any kind of water. We had to beat it right through to make camp by night. It's a good stiff trip, but it can be done. I looked back at the other canoe now and then until we struck about a mile of white water that took all I had. When we were through the other canoe wasn't in sight. The river made a bend there, and I thought it was just behind and would show up any minute.

"Well, it didn't show up and I began to wonder. We hit out first portage about ten o'clock and landed. I watched downstream for twenty minutes, expecting to sight the other canoe every instant. Then Charlie, who hadn't opened his head, said 'Better go back,' and put the canoe in again. We paddled downstream for all that was in it. I was stiff with fright. We saw 'em coming about three miles lower down and back-paddled till they came up. Isabelle was more cheerful-looking than she'd been since we left New York, but Joe had that stony face an Indian gets when he's sore.

"I said, 'Anything wrong?' Joe just grunted and drove the canoe past us. Then I saw it was filled with wild flowers. Isabelle said she'd been picking them right off the banks all the way along. She said she'd only had to get out of the boat once, for the blue ones. Now, you can't beat that—not in a thousand years. I leave it to you if you can. Twenty miles of stiff current, with five portages ahead of us and a nine-mile hike at the end of that. I gave that Indian the devil for letting her do such a thing, and tipped the flowers into the Penobscot when we unloaded for the first portage. She didn't speak to me on the portage, and she got into her canoe without a word.

"Nothing more happened going in, except this flower business had lost two hours, and it was so dark when we struck the swamp at Loon Lake that we couldn't follow the trail well and kept stumbling over down timber and stepping into bog holes. She was about fagged out by then, and the mosquitoes were pretty thick through there. Without any warning she sat down in the trail. She did it so suddenly I nearly fell over her. I asked her what was the matter and she said, 'This is the end'—just like that—'this is the end!' I said, 'The end of what, darling?' She said, 'Of everything!' I told her if she sat there all wet and muddy she'd catch her death. She said she hoped so. I said, "It's only two miles more, darling. Just think, tomorrow we'll be on the best trout water in the world!' With that she said, 'I want my mother, my darling mother,' and bowed her head in her hands. Think it over, please; and remember, I didn't lose my temper. You're sure there's nothing left in your flask?"

"Not a drop, George," I assured him. "Go ahead; we've only twenty-five minutes."

George looked wildly at the clock, then at his watch.

"A man never has it when he wants it most. Have you noticed that? Where was I?"

"You were in the swamp."

"Oh, yes! Well, she didn't speak after that, and nothing I could say would budge her. The mosquitoes had got wind of us when we stopped and were coming in swarms. We'd be eaten alive in another ten minutes. So I told Joe to give his pack to Charlie and help me pick her up and carry her. Joe said, 'No, by damn!' and folded his arms. When an Indian gets sore he stays sore, and when he's sore he's stubborn. The mosquitoes were working on him good and plenty, though, and at last he said, 'Me carry packs. Charlie help carry—that.' He flipped his hand over in the direction of Isabelle and took the pack from Charlie.

"It was black as your hat by now, and the trail through there was only about a foot wide, with swamp on each side. It was going to be some job getting her out of there. I thought Charlie and I would make a chair of our arms and stumble along with her some way; but when I started to lift her up she said, 'Don't touch me!' and got up and went on. A blessing if there ever was one. We got to camp at ten that night.

"She was stiff and sore next morning—you expect it after a trip like that—besides, she'd caught a little cold. I asked her how she felt, and she said she was going to die and asked me to send for a doctor and her mother. The nearest doctor was at Bangor and her mother was in New Rochelle. I carried her breakfast over from the dining camp to our cabin. She said she couldn't eat any breakfast, but she did drink a cup of coffee, telling me between sips how awful it was to die alone in a place like that.

"After she'd had the coffee she seemed to feel better. I went to the camp library and got The Dry Fly on American Waters, by Charles Darty. I consider him the soundest man in the country. He's better than Pell or Fawcett. My chief criticism of him is that in his chapter on Streams East of the Alleghanies—east of the Alleghanies, mind you—he recommends the Royal Coachman. I consider the Lead-Wing Coachman a serviceable fly on clear, hard-fished water; but the Royal—never! I wouldn't give it a shade over the Professor or the Montreal. Just consider the body alone of the Royal Coachman—never mind the wings and hackle—the body of the Royal is——"

"Yes, I know, George," I said; "but——"

I glanced significantly at the clock. George started, sighed, and resumed his narrative.

"I went back to the cabin and said, 'Darling, here is one of the most intensely interesting books ever written. I'm going to read it aloud to you. I think I can finish it today. Would you like to sit up in bed while I read?' She said she hadn't strength enough to sit up in bed, so I sat down beside her and started reading. I had read about an hour, I suppose, when she did sit up in bed quite suddenly. I saw she was staring at me in a queer, wild way that was really startling. I said, 'What is it, darling?' She said, 'I'm going to get up. I'm going to get up this instant.'

"Well, I was delighted, naturally. I thought the book would get her by the time I'd read it through. But there she was, as keen as mustard before I'd got well into it. I'll tell you what I made up my mind to do, right there. I made up my mind to let her use my rod that day. Yes, sir—my three-ounce Spinoza, and what's more, I did it."

George looked at me triumphantly, then lapsed into reflection for a moment.

"If ever a man did everything possible to—well, let it go. The main thing is, I have nothing to reproach myself with—nothing. Except—but we'll come to that presently. Of course, she wasn't ready for dry flies yet. I borrowed some wet flies from the club steward, got some cushions for the canoe and put my rod together. She had no waders, so a stream was out of the question. The lake was better, anyway, that first day; she'd have all the room she wanted for her back cast.

"I stood on the landing with her before we got into the canoe and showed her just how to put out a fly and recover it. Then she tried it." A sort of horror came into George's face. "You wouldn't believe anyone could handle a rod like that," he said huskily. "You couldn't believe it unless you'd seen it. Gimme a cigarette.

"I worked with her a half hour or so and saw no improvement—none whatever. At last she said, 'The string is too long. I can't do anything with such a long string on the pole.' I told her gently—gently, mind you—that the string was an eighteen-dollar double-tapered Hurdman line, attached to a Gebhardt reel on a three-ounce Spinoza rod. I said, 'We'll go out on the lake now. If you can manage to get a rise, perhaps it will come to you instinctively.'

"I paddled her out on the lake and she went at it. She'd spat the flies down and yank them up and spat them down again. She hooked me several times with her back cast and got tangled up in the line herself again and again. All this time I was speaking quietly to her, telling her what to do. I give you my word I never raised my voice —not once—and I thought she'd break the tip every moment.

"Finally she said her arm was tired and lowered the rod. She'd got everything messed up with her last cast and the flies were trailing just over the side of the canoe. I said, 'Recover your cast and reel in, darling.' Instead of using her rod, she took hold of the leader close to the flies and started to pull them into the canoe. At that instant a little trout—couldn't have been over six inches—took the tail fly. I don't know exactly what happened, it was all over so quickly. I think she just screamed and let go of everything. At any rate, I saw my Spinoza bounce off the gunwale of the canoe and disappear. There was fifty feet of water just there. And now listen carefully: Not one word did I utter—not one. I simply turned the canoe and paddled to the landing in absolute silence. No reproaches of any sort. Think that over!"

I did. My thoughts left me speechless. George proceeded:

"I took out a guide and tried dragging for the rod with a gang hook and heavy sinker all the rest of the day. But the gangs would only foul on the bottom. I gave up at dusk and paddled in. I said to the guide—it was Charlie—I said, 'Well, it's all over, Charlie.' Charlie said, 'I brought Mr. Carter in and he had an extra rod. Maybe you could borrow it. It's a four-ounce Meecham.' I smiled. I actually smiled. I turned and looked at the lake. 'Charlie,' I said, 'somewhere out there in that dark water, where the eye of man will never behold it again, is a three-ounce Spinoza—and you speak of a Meecham.' Charlie said, 'Well, I just thought I'd tell you.' I said, 'That's all right, Charlie. That's all right.' I went to the main camp, saw Jean, the head guide and made arrangements to leave the next day. Then I went to our cabin and sat down before the fire. I heard Isabelle say something about being sorry. I said, 'I'd rather not talk about it, darling. If you don't mind, we'll never mention it again.' We sat there in silence, then, until dinner.

"As we got up from dinner, Nate Griswold and his wife asked us to play bridge with them that evening. I'd told no one what had happened, and Nate didn't know, of course. I simply thanked him and said we were a little tired, and we went back to our cabin. I sat down before the fire again. Isabelle seemed restless. At last she said, 'George.' I said, 'What is it, darling?' She said, 'Would you like to read to me from that book?' I said, 'I'm sorry, darling; if you don't mind I'll just sit here quietly before the fire.'

"Somebody knocked at the door after a while. I said, 'Come in.' It was Charlie. I said, 'What is it, Charlie?' Then he told me that Bob Frazer had been called back to New York and was going out next morning. I said, 'Well, what of it?' Charlie said, 'I just thought you could maybe borrow his rod.' I said, 'I thought you understood about that, Charlie.' Charlie said, 'Well, that's it. Mr. Frazer's rod is a three-ounce Spinoza.'

"I got up and shook hands with Charlie and gave him five dollars. But when he'd gone I began to realize what was before me. I'd brought in a pint flask of prewar Scotch. Prewar—get that! I put this in my pocket and went over to Bob's cabin. Just as I was going to knock I lost my nerve. I sneaked away from the door and went down to the lake and sat on the steps of the canoe landing. I sat there for quite a while and took several nips. At last I thought I'd just go and tell Bob of my loss and see what he said. I went back to his cabin and this time I knocked. Bob was putting a few odds and ends in a shoulder pack. His rod was in its case, standing against the wall.

"I said, 'I heard you're going out in the morning.' He said, 'Yes, curse it, my wife's mother has to have some sort of a damned operation or other.' I said, 'How would a little drink strike you, Bob?' He said, 'Strike me! Wait a minute! What kind of a drink?' I took out the flask and handed it to him. He unscrewed the cap and held the flask to his nose. He said, 'Great heavens above, it smells like——' I said, 'It is.' He said, 'It can't be!' I said, 'Yes, it is.' He said, 'There's a trick in it somewhere.' I said, 'No, there isn't—I give you my word.' He tasted what was in the flask carefully. Then he said, 'I call this white of you, George,' and took a good stiff snort. When he was handing back the flask he said, 'I'll do as much for you some day, if I ever get the chance.' I took a snifter myself.

"Then I said, 'Bob, something awful has happened to me. I came here to tell you about it.' He said, 'Is that so? Sit down.' I sat down and told him. He said, 'What kind of a rod was it?' I said, 'A three-ounce Spinoza.' He came over and gripped my hand without a word. I said, 'Of course, I can't use anything else.' He nodded, and I saw his eyes flicker toward the corner of the room where his own rod was standing. I said, 'Have another drink, Bob.' But he just sat down and stared at me. I took a good stiff drink myself. Then I said, 'Under ordinary circumstances, nothing on earth could hire me to ask a man to——' I stopped right there.

"Bob got up suddenly and began to walk up and down the room. I said, 'Bob, I'm not considering myself—not for a minute. If it was last season, I'd simply have gone back tomorrow without a word. But I'm not alone any more. I've got the little girl to consider. She's never seen a trout taken in her life—think of it, Bob! And here she is, on her honeymoon, at the best water I know of. On her honeymoon, Bob!' I waited for him to say something, but he went to the window and stared out, with his back to me. I got up and said good night and started for the door. Just as I reached it he turned from the window and rushed over and picked up his rod. He said, 'Here, take it,' and put the rod case in my hands. I started to try to thank him, but he said, 'Just go ahead with it,' and pushed me out the door."

The waiter was suddenly hovering above us with his eyes on the dishes.

"Now what do you want?" said George.

"Never mind clearing here," I said. "Just bring me the check. Go ahead, George."

"Well, of course, I can't any more than skim what happened finally, but you'll understand. It turned out that Ernie Payton's wife had an extra pair of knickers and she loaned them to Isabelle. I was waiting outside the cabin while she dressed next morning, and she called out to me, 'Oh, George, they fit!' Then I heard her begin to sing. She was a different girl when she came out to go to breakfast. She was almost smiling. She'd done nothing but slink about the day before. Isn't it extraordinary what will seem important to a woman? Gimme a cigarette."

"Fifteen minutes, George," I said as I supplied him.

"Yes, yes, I know. I fished the Cuddiwink that day. Grand stream, grand. I used a Pink Lady—first day on a stream with Isabelle—little touch of sentiment—and it's a darn good fly. I fished it steadily all day. Or did I try a Seth Green about noon? It seems to me I did, now that I recall it. It seems to me that where the Katahdin brook comes in I——"

"It doesn't really matter, does it, George?" I ventured.

"Of course, it matters!" said George decisively. "A man wants to be exact about such things. The precise details of what happens in a day's work on a stream are of real value to yourself and others. Except in the case of a record fish, it isn't important that you took a trout; it's exactly how you took him that's important."

"But the time, George," I protested.

He glanced at the clock, swore softly, mopped his brow—this time with the blue-bordered handkerchief—and proceeded.

"Isabelle couldn't get into the stream without waders, so I told her to work along the bank a little behind me. It was pretty thick along there, second growth and vines mostly; but I was putting that Pink Lady on every foot of good water and she kept up with me easily enough. She didn't see me take many trout, though. I'd look for her, after landing one, to see what she thought of the way I'd handled the fish, and almost invariably she was picking ferns or blueberries, or getting herself untangled from something. Curious things, women. Like children, when you stop to think of it."

George stared at me unseeingly for a moment.

"And you never heard of Old Faithful?" he asked suddenly. "Evidently not, from what you said a while ago. Well, a lot of people have, believe me. Men have gone to the Cuddiwink district just to see him. As I've already told you, he lay beside a ledge in the pool below Horseshoe Falls. Almost nothing else in the pool. He kept it cleaned out. Worst sort of cannibal, of course—all big trout are. That was the trouble—he wanted something that would stick to his ribs. No flies for him. Did his feeding at night.

"You could see him dimly if you crawled out on a rock that jutted above the pool and looked over. He lay in about ten feet of water, right by his ledge. If he saw you he'd back under the ledge, slowly, like a submarine going into dock. Think of the biggest thing you've ever seen, and that's the way Old Faithful looked, just lying there as still as the ledge. He never seemed to move anything, not even his gills. When he backed in out of sight he seemed to be drawn under the ledge by some invisible force.

"Ridgway—R. Campbell Ridgway—you may have read his stuff, Brethren of the Wild, that sort of thing—claimed to have seen him move. He told me about it one night. He said he was lying with just his eyes over the edge of the rock, watching the trout. Said he'd been there an hour, when down over the falls came a young red squirrel. It had fallen in above and been carried over. The squirrel was half drowned, but struck out feebly for shore. Well, so Ridgway said—Old Faithful came up and took Mister Squirrel into camp. No hurry; just came drifting up, sort of inhaled the squirrel and sank down to the ledge again. Never made a ripple, Ridgway said; just business.

"I'm telling you all this because it's necessary that you get an idea of that trout in your mind. You'll see why in a minute. No one ever had hold of him. But it was customary, if you fished the Cuddiwink, to drop a few casts over him before you left the stream. Not that you ever expected him to rise. It was just a sort of gesture. Everybody did it.

"Knowing that Isabelle had never seen trout taken before, I made a day of it—naturally. The trail to camp leaves the stream just at the falls. It was pretty late when we got to it. Isabelle had her arms full of—heaven knows what—flowers and grass and ferns and fir branches and colored leaves. She'd lugged the stuff for hours. I remember once that day I was fighting a fourteen-inch fish in swift water and she came to the bank and wanted me to look at a ripe blackberry—I think it was—she'd found. How does that strike you? And listen! I said, 'It's a beauty, darling.' That's what I said—or something like that. . . . Here, don't you pay that check! Bring it here, waiter!"

"Go on, George," I said. "We haven't time to argue about the check. You'd come to the trail for camp at the falls."

"I told Isabelle to wait at the trail for a few minutes, while I went below the falls and did the customary thing for the edification of Old Faithful. I only intended to make three or four casts with the Number Twelve Fly and the hair-fine leader I had on, but in getting down to the pool I hooked the fly in a bush. In trying to loosen it I stumbled over something and fell. I snapped the leader like a thread, and since I had to put on another, I tied on a fairly heavy one as a matter of form.

"I had reached for my box for a regulation fly of some sort when I remembered a fool thing that Billy Roach had given me up on the Beaver Kill the season before. It was fully two inches long; I forgot what he called it. He said you fished it dry for bass or large trout. He said you worked the tip of your rod and made it wiggle like a dying minnow. I didn't want the contraption, but he'd borrowed some fly oil from me and insisted on my taking it. I'd stuck it in the breast pocket of my fishing jacket and forgotten it until then.

"Well, I felt in the pocket and there it was. I tied it on and went down to the pool. Now let me show you the exact situation." George seized a fork. "This is the pool." The fork traced an oblong figure on the tablecloth. "Here is Old Faithful's ledge." The fork deeply marked this impressive spot. "Here is the falls, with white water running to here. You can only wade to this point here, and then you have an abrupt six-foot depth. 'But you can put a fly from here to here with a long line,' you say. No, you can't. You've forgotten to allow for your back cast. Notice this bend here? That tells the story. You're not more than twenty feet from a lot of birch and what not, when you can no longer wade. 'Well then, it's impossible to put a decent fly on the water above the sunken ledge,' you say. It looks like it, but this is how it's done: Right here is a narrow point running to here, where it dwindles off to a single flat rock. If you work out on the point you can jump across to this rock—situated right here—and there you are, with about a thirty-foot cast to the sunken ledge. Deep water all around you, of course, and the rock is slippery; but—there you are. Now notice this small cove, right here. The water from the falls rushes past it in a froth, but in the cove it forms a deep eddy, with the current moving round and round, like this." George made a slow circular motion with the fork. "You know what I mean?"

I nodded.

"I got out on the point and jumped to the rock: got myself balanced, worked out the right amount of line and cast the dingaree Bill had forced on me, just above the sunken ledge. It didn't take the water lightly and I cast again, but I couldn't put it down decently. It would just flop in—too much weight and too many feathers. I suppose I cast it a dozen times, trying to make it settle like a fly. I wasn't thinking of trout—there would be nothing in there except Old Faithful—I was just monkeying with this doodle-bug thing, now that I had it on.

"I gave up at last and let it lie out where I had cast it. I was standing there looking at the falls roaring down, not thinking about anything in particular, when I remembered Isabelle, waiting up on the trail. I raised my rod preparatory to reeling in and the what-you-may-call-'em made a kind of a dive and wiggle out there on the surface. I reached for my reel handle. Then I realized that the thingamajig wasn't on the water. I didn't see it disappear, exactly; I was just looking at it, and then it wasn't there. 'That's funny,' I thought, and struck instinctively. Well, I was fast—so it seemed—and no snags in there. I gave it the butt three or four times, but the rod only bowed and nothing budged. I tried to figure it out. I thought perhaps a waterlogged timber had come diving over the falls and upended right there. Then I noticed the rod take more of a bend and the line began to move through the water. It moved out slowly, very slowly, into the middle of the pool. It was exactly as though I was hooked onto a freight train just getting under way.

"I knew what I had hold of then, and yet I didn't believe it. I couldn't believe it. I kept thinking it was a dream, I remember. Of course, he could have gone away with everything I had any minute if he'd wanted to, but he didn't. He just kept moving slowly, round and round the pool. I gave him what pressure the tackle would stand, but he never noticed a little thing like that; just kept moving around the pool for hours, it seemed to me. I'd forgotten Isabelle; I admit that. I'd forgotten everything on earth. There didn't seem to be anything else on earth, as a matter of fact, except the falls and the pool and Old Faithful and me. At last Isabelle showed up on the bank above me, still lugging her ferns and what not. She called down to me above the noise of the falls. She asked me how long I expected her to wait alone in the woods, with night coming on.

"I hadn't had the faintest idea how I was going to try to land the fish until then. The water was boiling past the rock I was standing on, and I couldn't jump back to the point without giving him slack and perhaps falling in. I began to look around and figure. Isabelle said, 'What on earth are you doing?' I took off my landing net and tossed it to the bank. I yelled, 'Drop that junk quick and pick up that net!' She said, 'What for, George?' I said, 'Do as I tell you and don't ask questions!' She laid down what she had and picked up the net and I told her to go to the cove and stand ready.

"She said, 'Ready for what?' I said, 'You'll see what presently. Just stand there.' I'll admit I wasn't talking quietly. There was the noise of the falls to begin with, and—well, naturally I wasn't.

"I went to work on the fish again. I began to educate him to lead. I thought if I could lead him into the cove he would swing right past Isabelle and she could net him. It was slow work—a three-ounce rod—imagine! Isabelle called, 'Do you know what time it is?' I told her to keep still and stand where she was. She didn't say anything more after that.

"At last the fish began to come. He wasn't tired; he'd never done any fighting, as a matter of fact. But he'd take a suggestion as to where to go from the rod. I kept swinging him nearer and nearer the cove each time he came around. When I saw he was about ready to come I yelled to Isabelle. I said, 'I'm going to bring him right past you, close to the top. All you have to do is to net him.'

"When the fish came round again I steered him into the cove. Just as he was swinging past Isabelle the stuff she'd been lugging began to roll down the bank. She dropped the landing net on top of the fish and made a dive for those leaves and grasses and things. Fortunately the net handle lodged against the bank, and after she'd put her stuff in a nice safe place she came back and picked up the net again. I never uttered a syllable. I deserve no credit for that. The trout had made a surge and shot out into the pool and I was too busy just then to give her any idea of what I thought.

"I had a harder job getting him to swing in again. He was a little leery of the cove, but at last he came. I steered him toward Isabelle and lifted him all I dared. He came up nicely, clear to the top. I yelled, 'Here he comes! For God's sake, don't miss him!' I put everything on the tackle it would stand and managed to check the fish for an instant right in front of Isabelle.

"And this is what she did: It doesn't seem credible—it doesn't seem humanly possible; but it's a fact that you'll have to take my word for. She lifted the landing net above her head with both hands and brought it down on top of the fish with all her might!"

George ceased speaking. Despite its coating of talcum powder, I was able to detect an additional pallor in his countenance.

"Will I ever forget it as long as I live?" he inquired at last.

"No, George," I said; "but we've just exactly eleven minutes left."

George made a noticeable effort and went on:

"By some miracle the fish stayed on the hook; but I got a faint idea of what would have happened if he'd taken a notion really to fight. He went around that pool so fast it must have made him dizzy. I heard Isabelle say, 'I didn't miss him, George';

and then—well, I didn't lose my temper; you wouldn't call it that exactly. I hardly knew what I said. I'll admit I shouldn't have said it. But I did say it; no doubt of that; no doubt of that whatever."

"What was it you said?" I asked.

George looked at me uneasily.

"Oh, the sort of thing a man would say impulsively—under the circumstances."

"Was it something disparaging about her?" I inquired.

"Oh, no," said George, "nothing about her. I simply intimated—in a somewhat brutal way, I suppose—that she'd better get away from the pool—er—not bother me any more is what I meant to imply."

For the first time since George had chosen me for a confidant I felt a lack of frankness on his part.

"Just what did you say, George?" I insisted.

"Well, it wasn't altogether my words," he evaded. "It was the tone I used, as much as anything. Of course, the circumstances would excuse—still, I regret it. I admit that. I've told you so plainly."

There was no time in which to press him further.

"Well, what happened then?" I asked.

"Isabelle just disappeared. She went up the bank, of course, but I didn't see her go. Old Faithful was still nervous and I had to keep my eye on the line. He quieted down in a little while and continued to promenade slowly around the pool. I suppose this kept up for half an hour more. Then I made up my mind that something had to be done. I turned very carefully on the rock, lowered the tip until it was on a line with the fish, turned the rod under my arm until it was pointing behind me and jumped.

"Of course, I had to give him slack; but I kept my balance on the point by the skin of my teeth, and when I raised the rod he was still on. I worked to the bank, giving out line, and crawled under some bushes and things and got around to the cove at last. Then I started to work again to swing him into the cove, but absolutely nothing doing. I could lead him anywhere except into the cove. He'd had enough of that; I didn't blame him, either.

"To make a long story short, I stayed with him for two hours. For a while it was pretty dark; but there was a good-sized moon that night, and when it rose it shone right down on the pool through a gap in the trees fortunately. My wrist was gone completely, but I managed to keep some pressure on him all the time, and at last he forgot about what had happened to him in the cove. I swung him in and the current brought him past me. He was on his side by now. I don't think he was tired even then—just discouraged. I let him drift over the net, heaved him out on the bank and sank down beside him, absolutely all in. I couldn't have got to my feet on a bet. I just sat there in a sort of daze and looked at Old Faithful, gleaming in the moonlight.

"After a half hour's rest I was able to get up and go to camp. I planned what I was going to do on the way. There was always a crowd in the main camp living room after dinner. I simply walked into the living room without a word and laid Old Faithful on the center table.

"Well, you can imagine faintly what happened. I never got any dinner—couldn't have eaten any, as a matter of fact. I didn't even get a chance to take off my waders. By the time I'd told just how I'd done it to one crowd, more would come in and look at Old Faithful; and then stand and look at me for a while; and then make me tell it all over again. At last everybody began to dig up anything they had with a kick in it. Almost everyone had a bottle he'd been hoarding. There was Scotch and gin and brandy and rye and a lot of experimental stuff. Art Bascom got a tin dish pan from the kitchen and put it on the table beside Old Faithful. He said 'Pour your contributions right in here, men.' So each man dumped whatever he had into the dish pan and everybody helped themselves.

"It was great, of course. The biggest night of my life, but I hope I'll never be so dog-tired again. I felt as though I'd taken a beating. After they'd weighed Old Faithful—nine pounds five and a half ounces; and he'd been out of the water two hours—I said I had to go to bed, and went.

"Isabelle wasn't in the cabin. I thought, in a hazy way, that she was with some of the women, somewhere. Don't get the idea I was stewed. But I hadn't had anything to eat, and the mixture in that dish pan was plain TNT.

"I fell asleep as soon as I hit the bed; slept like a log till daylight. Then I half woke up, feeling that something terrific had happened. For a minute I didn't know what; then I remembered what it was. I had landed Old Faithful on a three-ounce rod!

"I lay there and went over the whole thing from the beginning, until I came to Isabelle with the landing net. That made me look at where her head should have been on the pillow. It wasn't there. She wasn't in the cabin. I thought perhaps she'd got up early and gone out to look at the lake or the sunrise or something. But I got up in a hurry and dressed.

"Well, I could see no signs of Isabelle about camp. I ran into Jean just coming from the head guide's cabin and he said, 'Too bad about your wife's mother.' I said, 'What's that?' He repeated what he'd said, and added, 'She must be an awful sick woman.' Well, I got out of him finally that Isabelle had come straight up from the stream the evening before, taken two guides and started for Buck's Landing. Jean had urged her to wait until morning, naturally; but she'd told him she must get to her mother at once, and took on so, as Jean put it, that he had to let her go.

"I said, 'Let me have Indian Joe, stern, and a good man, bow. Have 'em ready in ten minutes.' I rushed to the kitchen, drank two cups of coffee and started for Buck's Landing. We made the trip down in seven hours, but Isabelle had left with her trunks on the 10:40 train.

"I haven't seen her since. Went to her home once. She wouldn't see me; neither would her mother. Her father advised not forcing things—just waiting. He said he'd do what he could. Well, he's done it—you read the letter. Now you know the whole business. You'll stick, of course, and see me through just the first of it, old man. Of course, you'll do that, won't you? We'd better get down to the train now. Track Nineteen."

George rose from the table. I followed him from the café, across the blue-domed rotunda to a restraining rope stretched before the gloomy entrance to Track Nineteen.

"George," I said, "one thing more: Just what did you say to her when she——"

"Oh, I don't know," George began vaguely.

"George," I interrupted, "no more beating about the bush. What did you say?"

I saw his face grow even more haggard, if possible. Then it mottled into a shade resembling the brick on an old colonial mansion.

"I told her——" he began in a low voice.

"Yes?" I encouraged.

"I told her to get the hell out of there."

And now a vision was presented to my mind's eye; a vision of twelve fish plates, each depicting a trout curving up through green waters to an artificial fly. The vision extended on through the years. I saw Mrs. George Baldwin Potter ever gazing upon those rising trout and recalling the name on the card which had accompanied them to her door.

I turned and made rapidly for the main

entrance of the Grand Central Station. In doing so I passed the clock above Information and saw that I still had two minutes in which to be conveyed by a taxicab far, far from the entrance to Track Nineteen.

I remember hearing the word "quitter" hurled after me by a hoarse, despairing voice.

The Perfect Squelch

WHEN Calvin Coolidge was about to leave his home for the White House, his New England neighbors arranged to present him with a handmade rake in remembrance of his devotion to the old farm. They got up quite a ceremony, and during the course of it the amateur orator who was to make the presentation devoted some time to discussing the qualities of the hickory wood from which he said the rake was made. "Hickory," he concluded with a flourish, "is like our President: sturdy, strong, resilient, unbroken."

Then he handed the rake to Mr. Coolidge, and the audience leaned forward in anticipation of a graceful speech of acknowledgment. For a long moment Coolidge examined the rake. He seemed to be reaching for just the right words of gratitude. Finally he looked up.

"Ash," he said.

—ROGER M. WOOD.

It Had to Upcome

I AM worried about this word, "upcoming," that I have been encountering in print for several years now. Just the other day, for example, I read in a newspaper that someone's "autobiography is upcoming shortly in book form."

I don't like the word. Furthermore, one rotten apple can spoil the whole barrel, so I expect the worst any day now, as follows:

As I enter an elevator in some big glossy office building, along come two brisk young men with the crew cuts and bow ties of today's empire builders.

Says one to the operator, "Are you upgoing, miss?"

"Yes, sir. Instep, please, and frontface in the car."

They instep and uppick their conversation where they offleft.

"Is George aroundhanging town this trip?"

"No, just throughpassing. He thought there were a couple of things here that might bear intolooking, but they didn't outpan."

"Well, I'm glad. I'm about upfed with George."

At this point—I'm daydreaming now—one of these boys happens to overbend, and before I know it my foot is upswinging.

—SCOTT CORBETT.

MY OWN TRUE LOVE STORY

By HORATIO WINSLOW

§ Try as he would, Myron could not resist the Grand Passion which had entered his life in the person of Opal T——, the new girl in town. This presented complications, for Myron was already engaged to Lucy V——.

APRIL 23, 1927

WHILE glancing through your valued paper of even date, noted prize reward sum of twenty-five dollars ($25.00) offered for best account of experiences under subject My Own True Love Story, and with purpose of winning above reward am submitting following personal facts for valued approval. Will add everything stated here is truth and nothing but same, and if necessary can prove by eyewitnesses. Will also add reason for using initials instead of names is because do not wish to embarrass anybody by account which please find below.

Was born year 19–, in city of R——, state of W——, but at age of ten parents moved to capital city of said state entitled M——, where have lived ever since and where scene of Own True Love Story is located.

For many months had been secretly engaged to Lucy V—— of 16– T—— St., also living in city of M——. In fact, we had known each other and been on friendly terms ever since my family had moved to Madison welve years before. But as the moment to announce our engagement drew near I was surprised to find myself getting daily grouchier and grouchier, and knew not why.

And every time I would see a large pendulum swinging in a clock or boys playing marbles with large blue alleys, or anything at all that was round or painted blue or both, I would feel a bitter regret the same as if I was doing something I ought not to be doing. And once at a railroad crossing I pretty near got hit by a train because of watching two big, round, moving signals that made me want to burst into tears, I knew not why. Sometimes I thought I was going crazy.

But every day I would fight against all this and try to take myself in hand saying, "Now, Myron, what is the matter with you anyhow? Why are you acting so foolish? You are going to marry Lucy Vail, so make the best of it, as it is a suitable match and she is a swell girl from a fine family."

That is what I would repeat to myself during the day; but when the hours of evening fell and I started on my way to 16— T—— St., then I would find my disposition as stated above, and likely as not I would come to myself standing in front of a certain optician's office, I knew not why, and looking sadly up at his illuminated sign.

Often I would argue with myself saying, "Myron, what more could you wish? Lucy is not only a sweet girl but she is the best possible match, because she is practical and not always doing things for no reason at all. How happy you ought to be to know you have won the heart of a girl whose every action is sensible." But the more I argued, the grouchier I got, until one spring evening, when like a flash from a clear sky the secret came out.

Walking down M—— St., I was about to pass the hall where the Protective and Mutual Order of Traveling S—— were holding their annual benefit dance, when I observed something that made me stop short and shiver the same as if a piece of ice had been dropped down the back of my neck.

And as I looked this girl in the eyes and remembered I had seen her at another dance a month before, I understood all that had been happening to me.

There was no use trying to continue where duty called. And though I could not help wishing that the earth would open and swallow me up before I had time to telephone Lucy about feeling sick, and before I had time to buy a ticket for the P. and M. O. dance–nothing like that happened. Hence a few minutes later I made part of the merry throng of revelers, and on the other side of the hall was the pair of blue eyes responsible for my action.

"Remember, Myron," I said to myself with a last impulse of decency, "that you are an engaged man, and there is yet time to turn back and live up to the sacred promise you have given."

But even before I had finished this remark, the girl had turned her head slightly and had begun to roll those mysterious eyes in my direction.

I can only describe the effect by saying it made me feel the same as if I was walking on a tight rope and somebody had cut it at one end. Before I could control myself my feet had taken me across the room, and in a sincere voice I was uttering the following falsehood: "Excuse me, but I am sure you remember me. We were introduced at the Jolly Five Dance a month ago."

What she said to this or what happened immediately after I do not know. The next thing I remember is calling her Opal and being called Myron, and hearing her say to her escort, "Kindly go back and sit down, Harold. Can't you see I am in the middle of an interesting conversation? Please go on, Myron. Perhaps it is because I can never explain to myself anything I do that it is such a pleasure to me to listen to a thinking man of the world like yourself who has reasoned everything out."

I must have acted strange the next night when I called on Lucy V——, and during the week that followed she must have been surprised more than once by the regular way I kept falling sick, thereby having to break dates. But though I despised myself for thus acting, whenever I thought of Opal T—— and her eyes I did not seem to be able to do any different.

It was on Friday evening, a week after the dance above mentioned, that, arriving at the Vail residence, I was ushered into the parlor and found Lucy waiting for me, a smile on her face that seemed changed from her ordinary pleasant look, though I could not tell how. "Myron," she said in her usual voice, though even this was not exactly as usual—"Myron, I think it would be best for both of us tonight not to try to take that Spanish lesson over the radio."

I felt uncomfortable, I knew not why, as I responded, "All right, Lucy; only you always said Spanish would be a practical language for us to learn."

"My opinion on the subject has not changed, Myron. I still believe you ought to follow that hunch you spoke of some time ago and start out for yourself. I am sure you could export quantities of that patent article to the various Spanish-American countries, which would make a knowledge of the Spanish language useful as well as ornamental. But I think this evening we will omit our radio lesson in favor of a little frank and confidential chat."

"All right, Lucy," was my comment, "what shall we talk about?" Though not noticeable from my remarks, I had begun to feel distinctly uneasy.

"We will talk about you, Myron, because that is probably the most interesting topic in our repertoire. Myron, during the last four weeks, and especially during the past few days, you have changed in an alarming manner. Before you never noticed the moon; now you cannot look at it without a respiratory disturbance. Ten days ago flowers meant nothing to you; now I never see you without a decorated buttonhole."

She stopped, but I did not say anything.

"Two evenings ago I offered you a piece of chocolate cake with walnuts in the frosting, and you declined. It is the first time in recorded history, Myron, that you ever declined anything to eat. And lastly, when in the dear dead past beyond recall I have tried to interest you in poetry, you have assumed a facial expression that would have made your fortune in the movies. Yet yesterday Myrtle Middlestone told me that during the past week you have spent all your noonings in the library, reading Famous Love Poems and sighing and snuffling over them to such an extent that she has had to ask you to control your emotions, because complaints were being made at the desk."

I sat there wishing I was somewhere else.

"Myron, I am a practical woman, and the fact that we have been contemplating matrimony makes it necessary for me to continue being practical. Myron, you are in love."

"Yes, Lucy," was my manly reply, thought up on the spur of the moment, "I am in love with you."

"The sentiment does you credit, Myron, but it is not true. According to the most reliable reports, you are in love with a new girl in town named Opal Tregennis."

I tried to insist it was all a mistake, but she would not listen.

"I know you, Myron, and I know myself. I am not one of those superb and mysterious personages like Opal T——, capable of inspiring a man with the grand passion. I am just a simple girl, with nothing mysterious or inexplicable about her; and rather than see you ruin your life to keep a foolish promise, I prefer to set you free. Myron, our engagement is at an end."

"No, no," I cried wildly, finding my voice. "You do not know what you are saying, Lucy. You will break my heart."

"I know exactly what I am saying, Myron. I cannot fight against the grand passion and I have no intention of trying. In your present mood I would not be a helpmeet in the great struggle for existence—I would merely cramp your style. I love you dearly, but it is better that we part. Good luck, Myron. Here is your ring. And remember I am always your friend, and in the future if ever you wish to know how a practical woman looks at some problem that puzzles you—ask me, Myron, ask me. Good night, Myron, and mind your step." The door closed. I stood on the front porch of the Vail residence, my right hand across my fevered forehead and feeling that my heart was going to break.

II

Though I had been quite honest in thinking that my heart would break, at the same time I was not displeased when, after walking a couple of blocks, I found it had not done anything of the kind. In fact, before reaching home I twice caught myself breaking into a merry whistle, and later I went to sleep smiling as I thought of the new idol of my heart.

Such was the end of my secret engagement to Lucy and the beginning of my open courtship of a pair of blue eyes. (By this last I mean Opal Tregennis.)

I shall not try to describe all my emotions during the period that followed; I had so many it would use up your entire paper. Let me state that every time Opal rolled her eyes in my direction I had the same sensation as being knocked over by a big wave. I would wake at night covered with sweat and saying, "If Opal does not return my affection, then I had better crawl into some deserted cellar and there breathe my last; but if Opal loves me, the world is mine." And during the day, when not with Opal, I would find myself sighing, I knew not why, or writing poetry on a blotter, or smelling of a flower, or listening to a bird on the roof. And the hours passed like a dream.

But my affection, I saw, was returned; and when Opal would place her two hands on my cheeks and say, "I may be very impractical, Myron, and do many things on impulse and for no reason, but you know that my love for you is steadfast, don't you, Myron?" then all my doubts would be at an end.

Though it might be supposed that from now on I was perfectly happy, such was not altogether the case.

Often, as she stated, Opal's actions were inexplicable.

After a game of bridge with her parents she would say, "Myron, you are simply wonderful. You remind me of Napoleon B——."

"Why do I remind you of Napoleon B——?"

"Because he was so lucky at cards," would be the reply.

But the next day, instead of giving me any more compliments, she would remark, "Myron, for heaven's sake stop looking at me. Say something or I will scream."

In the matter of dates she was more than ordinarily inexplicable. I would come over at eight o'clock only to be met by her mother, who would say:

"I am, indeed, sorry, Myron, but Opal wants me to tell you that she forgot all about having a previous engagement. She regrets it extremely."

Or I would be preparing to go somewhere else when the telephone would ring and a familiar voice would say:

"I am going to a dance, Myron, but if you haven't time to take me, I can get someone else."

And in all these cases her first escort, Harold H——, was invariably mixed up.

"Opal," I said finally, "this has got to stop. Either you are interested in this silly-faced high-school boy or you are interested in me. Either say the words that will make you mine—all mine—or let me go quietly away to Africa and enlist in the Foreigners' Legion."

Such was the process by which Opal and myself became openly engaged, while Harold H—— dropped out of the picture for good. But though I had thus won Opal, and hoped soon to lead her to the altar a blushing bride, in certain other ways everything was not so good.

One afternoon when returning from work I ran into my Uncle Mark. "Yesterday, Myron," he said, "at the M—— Club I was talking with your esteemed employer, and he told me that you seemed unable to tell time."

"Unable to tell time," I repeated, not believing my ears.

"He said you were daily mistaking 9:30 A.M. for nine o'clock."

"What did you say?"

"I took the liberty of telling him that you were just passing through a phase and that a little later you would doubtless plunge with renewed vigor into the early-to-bed-and-early-to-rise stuff."

"What did he say?"

"Aplenty, Myron, aplenty. But, boiled

down, it came to this: Outside the office, in his opinion, you were spending more than you earned and inside you weren't doing your job. If I were you, Myron, I should stop tearing around with this matrimonially inclined beauty."

"Are you insinuating anything against Miss Tregennis?" I said, clenching my fists.

"I am just stating a philosophical fact, Myron. A lad who becomes infatuated with a woman in that state of mind is running a terrible risk."

"Do you mean it would be a risk for me to marry Miss Tregennis?"

"Not the kind of a risk you mean, Myron. Although Miss Tregennis is a marrying woman, and although she wants to get married, I'm sure she hasn't any intention of getting married to you. Think that over."

Giving my Uncle Mark a look full of quiet contempt, I walked on down the street.

But it was impossible to rid my mind of all that he had said. As a matter of fact, I had been coming late to the office, and my nightly excursions with Opal had reduced my bank balance to practically nothing.

Moreover, I had abandoned all efforts to invent a certain article I had in mind, because since going with Opal I had been kept absorbed about entirely different matters. And I knew I would never be able to settle down again to any kind of work until our future was definitely arranged.

"Opal," I said that night, "we are now engaged to be married."

"Yes, Myron."

"How happy I would be, Opal, if you would only name the day."

Her eyes rolled in my direction, and I felt as if I had been struck by lightning.

"You are wonderful, Myron—so wonderful that before I answer your question I am going to ask a favor of you."

"What is it, Opal? You have only to name what you want me to do, and I will do it."

"There is a terrible man in town, Myron. Only this afternoon he looked at me so insultingly that I am still all upset."

"Tell me his name, Opal, and I will go around and paste him in the map."

"Oh, no, Myron! I would not have you create a scandal for worlds, and besides I don't know his name. That is why I am calling on you. I want you to find out who he is so that in the future I can avoid him and his insulting looks. He is staying at the P—— Hotel, I hear. And he is fat and his hair is red and he looks as though he lived in some large city and was well off. Find out who he is, Myron, so that I can keep away from him."

Using the information given I started out, and though having had little or no detective training, I experienced no difficulty in locating the party mentioned. His name was Mr. Herman F—— and he was a real-estate agent from the city of C——, in the state of I——. Though not among Chicago's wealthiest citizens, he was nevertheless well off and had come to Madison for a rest and a vacation, as the doctor had said he was too nervous. On seeing Mr. Fellaker I wanted to go up and paste him in the map as hitherto stated, but remembering what I had promised Opal, I restrained myself in a suitable manner.

"You are simply wonderful, Myron," said Opal when I had given her this information, and her large blue eyes spoke more eloquently than words. "Simply wonderful with a capital S."

"Well," I suggested, thinking this was a good opportunity, "when are we going to get married?"

"Kiss me, Myron," she said, looking at me and rolling her eyes, and I was halfway home before I remembered she had forgot to answer my question.

The next afternoon at the office one of the boys said, "Hey, My, come and look out of the window. Something here that ought to interest you."

"What is it?" I asked, feeling strangely

uneasy, I knew not why. "An automobile accident?"

"I'll say it's an automobile accident, and there is no insurance that will cover that."

I looked where he pointed. A magnificent green de-luxe sport roadster which had been held up at the corner was now sweeping on down the street, and within, side by side, were seated Mr. Fellaker, the red-haired real-estate man and Opal Tregennis.

As they passed she rolled her eyes at him and his face got an expression on it that made you think of a dying calf, and at the same time he stepped on the gas so hard that he pretty near cut the legs off of a Spanish-American War veteran.

III

I have never seen myself in such a state as I was in the rest of the afternoon. I could not get my mind on my work, and every time I looked out of the window and saw a bird or a flower or anything like that I could feel my teeth grit together.

Instead of going home for dinner I walked immediately to the Tregennis residence on C— St., and, walking up to the front door, rang the bell and asked for Opal. "She is not here," said Mrs. T—, "but I expect her home any minute. Won't you come in, Myron, and wait?"

"No," I replied between my teeth, "I will wait out here on the porch."

And this I did in spite of her utmost protestations. From time to time she would stick her head out the front door and say, "Don't you want me to bring you a cup of tea, Myron? You will catch your death of cold waiting out there this weather."

"No," I answered between my teeth; "I am very much obliged, Mrs. Tregennis, but I do not wish any tea. I have something else that keeps me warm." And I was not referring to any pocket flask either.

It was 5:20 when I reached the Tregennis residence and it was 11:34 when the green sport roadster drew up in front of the house and Mr. Fellaker climbed out, followed by Opal.

I stood there in the shadows with my watch in my hand, timing them while for fifteen minutes Mr. F— held on to Opal and talked to her in a low persuasive voice. More than once I was on the point of going down and demanding what he thought he was doing, and then I decided I had better not make a scandal.

At 11:49, when Opal backed up the front steps waving her hand to Mr. F— while the latter disappeared around the corner, I stepped out from behind the porch pillar and said, "Opal, what does this mean?"

She gave a little scream. "Myron, to think of finding you here! You are simply wonderful. All evening I have been longing to be by your side, and here you are. Don't speak, Myron; don't spoil this heavenly minute by speaking. Just hold me tight."

I waited about thirty seconds, and then stated in a sarcastic voice, "Well, Opal, I have just one observation to make. If you really wanted to keep out of the way of Mr. Fellaker, all you had to do was not to get into his car. There is no law in the state of Wisconsin which forces a girl to get into a man's automobile unless she wants to."

"Hush, Myron! Don't say anything to spoil this wonderful minute when we are so near together—so close to one another. I accepted Mr. Fellaker's invitation just to have the opportunity to put him in his place, and I think I did, Myron; I think I did. He knows now how I despise him. I would not even condescend so far as to wipe my feet on him. He has passed out of my life forever. Do not say another word, but look up at that wonderful moon that seems to be shining down on just us two. Kiss me, Myron. Oh, how happy we are going to be together!"

The next night when I was calling, there came a ring at the bell, and Mrs. Tregennis came into the kitchen where we were making fudge. "These flowers are for you, Opal. Mr. Fellaker just left them. He says he will be back in a few minutes."

"Oh, he will, will he?" said Opal in a significant voice. "Well, I will have a little surprise for him when he does come. Seena, take this bouquet of flowers and dump it on top of the garbage can, and roll the can over to the left a little so that when he gets out of his car he will have to look at it. And if that doesn't stop him, kindly tell him, mother, that I am not at home to him either tonight or any other night."

Opal's mother gasped. Meanwhile Opal explained to me: "He richly deserves it, Myron. And it is only a small payment on account for those insulting leers with which he greeted me when he passed me on the street."

This little incident did much to soothe my outraged feelings of the night before. Two days later I was also pleased to hear a friend of mine say, "Well, Myron, you are certainly showing up this city slicker from Chicago."

"What do you mean?" I asked, though having a pretty good idea of what he meant.

"Don't be modest, Myron. This bird Fellaker who came here for two weeks is getting thin and nervous, and the reason is that your girl friend has him running in circles. He is sure getting the razz from his friends for losing out in a small town. Keep up the good work, Myron, and show him that we can produce our own sheiks."

At first I had thought I was being kidded, but a glance at Mr. F— a day later showed that he had, indeed, changed. Not only did he look strained and nervous but when we passed and Opal cut him dead, in spite of his brick complexion he turned pale and I could notice him close his eyes and swallow with a great effort.

Indeed, a day later another friend came up to me and said, "Listen, My, I don't want to spread any bad tidings, but if I were you I would not go out on any lonely roads without packing that gun of yours. Your girl friend has got this Chicago bird upside down and walking on his hands, and he thinks it is all your fault. Keep your eyes open."

Not being hard-hearted by nature I would have felt sorry for Mr. Fellaker if an unexpected event had not turned my sympathies in another and more personal direction.

I had reached the office at the usual hour and was trying to draw Opal the way she looked from the side and was just putting in the eye when I felt a hand on my right shoulder.

"Myron," said the boss, with an unpleasant smile on his face, "I am sorry to interfere with your artistic pursuits, but I thought I might as well tell you that beginning this morning you are no longer on our distinguished pay roll. So you are now at liberty to cultivate your love for the beautiful twenty-four hours a day."

This petty cheeseparing attitude filled me full of silent contempt. For a minute I sat there to pull myself together, and then rising in a dignified manner, I walked to the cashier's desk.

It was still early in the morning—that is, about quarter to ten. Turning my new problem over and over in my head, I walked down first one street and then another, and it was with a shock of surprise that I found myself standing, I knew not why, across the road from the Vails' residence. As I looked I saw Lucy hurry out of the house and begin sweeping off the front porch.

"Why, Myron," was her response to my greeting, "what have you been doing with yourself? I hope you aren't sick."

"No," I said, "not sick."

"From the way you are standing over there, I thought that perhaps you were enjoying a stroke of paralysis in the legs. But maybe the board of aldermen has just passed some new traffic regulation about not crossing a street at ten in the morning."

I laughed, and before I knew it was seated at the Vails' dining-room table, reluctantly accepting some strong coffee and about eighteen buckwheat cakes, together with some genuine maple sirup which the Vails received every year from their Uncle Henry V— of Vermont. After the third cup of coffee and a few more cakes, I decided to place my problem before Lucy.

"You have done well to tell me this," she said when I had finished. "A woman's viewpoint is always worth something, particularly where another woman is concerned. Speaking to you as a friend, full of interest in your welfare, I can assure you, Myron, that you need not worry over your sentimental life—at least for the present. The fact that you have almost exhausted your bank account and that you have lost your position will make little or no difference to Miss Tregennis in her immediate decisions."

"Do you think so?" I said, much encouraged.

"I am sure of it, Myron."

"But as much as I love her, Lucy, I do not want to take advantage of an impulsive girl, one who often does things on the spur of the moment that she admits herself are inexplicable."

"You are not going to take advantage of anyone, Myron. All you have to do is to state the facts fully, and your conscience will be clear. And believe me, she will not give you the air—on the contrary. And now, Myron, I am going to presume on our friendship by slipping you a sealed envelope which I want you to place in your pocket and carry with you wherever you go."

"What is inside?" I asked when she came back from the other room, envelope in hand.

"Emergencies, Myron, come into the lives of all of us. I do not wish to frighten you, but you are about to marry a young lady who often does things which, as you say, she admits herself are inexplicable. If you ever find yourself, Myron, in an emergency as the result of some inexplicable action on the part of Miss Tregennis, open this envelope. If you do not understand the contents, call me up."

That evening I told Opal all about my changed circumstances and added that if she wished I would pass out of her life forever and go to Africa and enlist in the Foreigners' Legion.

"Myron," she sobbed, her head on my breast, "money means nothing to me. What do I care whether you are a millionaire or a beggar? You have asked me many times to name the day. Very well, let it be Thursday evening at seven. And let us not be practical and do the sensible and reasoned thing. You have enough money left to buy some sort of a secondhand car, haven't you, Myron? Then let us run away in that. No one will understand why we do it—not even ourselves—but what care we? And we will get married in Rockford and then pass our honeymoon like two gypsies. And the birds will sing for us, Myron, and we will gather wildflowers by the way; and after the sun has sunk in a sea of gold, we will sit hand in hand and let the moon flood us with silver. And take along your revolver, Myron, because I am afraid of Mr. Fellaker."

"Opal," I remarked, "Opal," my emotion forbidding me to say more.

Will now particularly beg esteemed favor of valued attention for what immediately follows, and will add that these personal experiences have been written not so much for prize reward sum of twenty-five dollars ($25.00) as to point out to public moral lesson which please find inclosed in Part Four.

IV

Thursday night came, though for a long time I thought it never would. In the afternoon I passed Mr. F— on the street and can only say he looked thin and desperate. Even his red hair seemed to be sort of depressed. As I passed, I noticed him take a quick peek at me and double up his fists. In a way I felt sorry for him.

There had been enough left in the old bank roll to buy a car for a hundred and fifty dollars, and by selling some things, including a Liberty Bond, I had raised pretty nearly as much more for expenses. It seemed to me that this would last us maybe a month, and then I would sell the car if necessary and get a job.

Full of excitement Opal was waiting for me at the Tregennis residence. "Wait, Myron," she said; "wait a minute. I am feeling a little faint, and it will take me a minute to recover myself. It is so wonderful to think of running away to the ends of the earth with you."

"That is all right," I said; "take all the time you want."

She hurried into the kitchen and said something in a low voice. Some other person, apparently a little boy, responded, saying, "Yes, I understand. I will take it to him right off."

"Come, Myron," Opal said, as she hurried through the swinging door. "Hurry! There is not a minute to spare."

"I thought you were feeling faint," I suggested, as she practically shoved me into the car and climbed behind the wheel herself.

"I was, Myron, I was," she replied, as the car started off, while she waved her hand to her mother, who seemed to think it was just an ordinary occasion. "But that was because of being so worried about the First Church Social tomorrow night. I said I would give palmistry readings and, of course, now that is impossible, and I felt faint because I wasn't sure that the note would reach the right party in time for him to get somebody else and yet after we were well on our way."

This explanation seemed a little peculiar, but Opal was always doing inexplicable things, so I said nothing except, "That is some moon tonight, Opal. It makes me feel very close to you. If we could only ride on in this moonlight forever it would be my idea of heaven."

"You said it, Myron," she responded, at the same time letting the car out till it sounded like a tin-pan factory in an earthquake. "By the way, I asked you to carry your revolver on this trip. Have you got it?"

"Yes," I said, "it is in my back pocket. Opal, I am so happy I hardly know what I am doing. I smell the scent of flowers borne on the night air."

"Is it loaded?"

"Loaded with the odor of honeysuckles, Opal, and with the perfume of your hair."

"I am talking about the revolver, Myron. For goodness' sake, wake up!"

"Yes, the revolver is loaded. . . . Listen, Opal, don't you hear that saxophone sobbing in the distance?"

"I hear something. Is there a safety catch on it?"

"I don't know, Opal; I have never played it myself. I can play the banjo a little, but not good enough to be in an orchestra. There is no safety catch on a banjo."

"The revolver—the revolver!" she said in an impatient voice.

"No, you just pull the trigger." There was a pause, and then I added, "Opal, I would give a good deal to know just what you are thinking about at this moment."

"Myron," she answered, "I am thinking about you and about how simply wonderful you are—how simply wonderful."

We are about seven miles outside the city of M——, and on the road south, when she turned the car to one side of the road and stalled the engine.

"What is the matter?" I asked.

"Myron, you know I am a creature of inexplicable moods and impulses. I have just had a feeling that it would be bad luck for me if we did not stop here a minute. So if you will oil up those front springs, I will take your revolver and defend us from any prowlers who happen to be round about."

In my opinion there were no prowlers in the vicinity, but just to oblige her I did as she said. I had begun oiling the front springs, when suddenly from the rear of the car—Bang! Bang! Bang!—three shots rang out on the still night air.

For a minute my heart stood still as the result of thinking that perhaps some terrible accident had happened and that it was my fault to have trusted an impractical young girl with a deadly weapon. And I made up my mind that if such was actually the case I would atone for my folly by turning the revolver against my own breast and stilling my throbbing heart forever so that it would no longer throb.

But I had hardly taken one jump when I heard her voice: "Myron, something terrible has happened."

"What is it? Where are you hurt?"

"Nowhere, Myron. But I thought I saw somebody moving around there in the bushes and I thought it might be some prowler getting ready to harm you, and before I really knew what I was doing I had fired your revolver at the bushes three times, and I'm afraid one of the shots grazed a tire."

I looked and whistled. Each one of the three shots had picked out a tire, with results that do not have to be described.

"Well," I said, "I have no tire-patching apparatus along with me, and I don't think it would do much good anyhow. Those holes are too big. It is bad luck. I'd better look for the nearest telephone and call up a garage and buy some spare tires."

"No, Myron, wait a minute first. I have an intuition that someone will come along and help us. It seems to me I hear an auto now."

There was a horn hollering, and pretty soon two big rays of light poked up over the hill.

It drove down toward us and was maybe a hundred yards away when to my surprise, Opal, jumping out into the middle of the road, began to run toward the car, yelling, "Save me! Save me, Herman!"

The green sport roadster stopped the same as if it had smacked into a brick wall, and Herman F——, of the city of C——, in the state of I——, jumped out.

"Oh," he said to me, "so that is your game, is it?—kidnaping innocent young girls! Well, I will show you there are still decent people in the world, even though you may not think so."

Then while I stood there stunned, he looked down at Opal, who was now in his arms, and said, "You see, honey, I didn't lose any time."

"I knew you wouldn't, Herman; you are so wonderful." And though I could only see the back of her head, I knew she was rolling her eyes at him.

For a minute he stood there looking at her, and then, straightening up, shook himself and roared like a bull. "And I am not going to lose any time now either!" he yelled. "Has the brute got a gun?"

"Not now, Herman; I got it away from him after he tried to shoot me just now. Here it is."

Breaking the revolver open he threw the cartridges in one direction and the gun in another.

"If he ever tries anything like that after we are married, I will have him sent over the road for life. Come on now, you low bully, and put up your hands and I will show you what happens to an insulter of womanhood when he runs up against a man from Chicago."

And while I stood there stunned as the result of all this treachery, and unable to speak, he walked up and pasted me in the map, and that is the last thing I remember. I don't know how long it was before I sat up. When I did, I was sore. I do not mean I was sore simply in a mental sense, but also in a physical sense. And the worse the latter got, the worse the former got.

The first thing I decided between gritted teeth was to get another revolver in case I could not find the first, and pursue Opal T—— and Herman F—— to the end of the earth if necessary, and then shoot them both full of bullets. Having thus decided I said with a scornful laugh, "Well, that reminds me of Lucy's envelope. She told me to open it in case I was in an emergency as the result of one of Opal's inexplicable actions. Ha-ha, let us see what the poor simple little thing has to say."

With this I pulled the envelope out of my pocket, and opening it, held the inclosed sheet of paper to the light. There was nothing on either side. The paper not only was absolutely blank but showed no signs of ever having been written on.

Something about this made me even sorer than I was before. I stood there trembling as I thought of how two different girls had kidded me and how each one had got away with it. Then I decided that before leaving the vicinity of the city of M——, I would at least call up Lucy and tell her in plain language what I thought about her action.

A few minutes later, from a neighboring farmhouse, I was relieving my mind.

"Wait a minute, Myron," Lucy said. "I told you to open that envelope in case Miss Tregennis did something inexplicable. Now talk slowly, Myron—what did she do that was inexplicable?"

"Well," I said, "she quit me and ran off to marry that fellow from Chicago. And she thought the world of me."

"You mean she used you the way she used Harold before you, and the way she may or may not use Mr. Fellaker after you. Now just a minute, Myron, and control your temper. How much are you worth in money?" I told her. "And how much is the Chicago gentleman worth?"

"They say he has got a half million."

"Well, then, Myron, just what did she do that was so inexplicable?"

I tried to say something, but the words would not come.

"Listen, Myron, here is a little thought gem to write down in your pocket memorandum. All girls, Myron, by nature and by training are extremely practical—particularly those who claim they aren't. Everything a girl does has a reason, and generally a good one. Personally I know of only one instance where a girl of my acquaintance has even considered doing a thing which might be called inexplicable."

"What instance is that?" I asked, not because I was interested but merely to say something.

"Well, Myron, I am the girl myself. And the totally inexplicable thing I am going to do is to tell you a couple of secrets. Myron, I have sent for a pamphlet entitled How to Patent Your Invention, and a new radio Spanish course is starting at 7:30 tomorrow night."

And she hung up the receiver.

And that is My Own True Love Story, and in conclusion will state that I consider a man is foolish to fall into power of any woman whatever and be at her beck and call, and since having been cured have gone into business independently with a patented article, exporting same largely to Spanish-American countries, and if proof of these true personal facts is desired, can refer you to my wife (formerly Lucy V——) but now of same name and number as myself, residing in the city of M——, state of W——.

OFFICER MULVANEY AND THE HOT BUTTERED PIG

By ***WIN BROOKS***

§ *Here's an amusing story of a faithless leprechaun, a rabbit that squealed, and a buxom widow whose cooking would make most any man turn aside from the path of duty.*

MAY 25, 1946

OFFICER Mulvaney was in the black mood, he was. Wee birdies sang their love songs and the leafy bowers along the country lanes of his new beat were noisy with discussion of postwar nesting materials recently unfrozen. The first dandelions were in the fields. The sun shone, benevolent and bright and warm. All along the new beat of Officer Mulvaney were romance and spring and rejoicing, except in the heart and soul of Officer Mulvaney. Transferred to the sticks, he was, and sent caretaker to a pig!

The staggering injustice of the world in general occupied the attention of Officer Mulvaney to the exclusion of the birds and the flowers. He was not having any of them. He was having, instead, the bitterness of a frustrated career and a galling ache of the feet, the latter resulting from the stones of what passed for a sidewalk. He was thus occupied with the bruising of spirit and flesh when his hearing was arrested by a sound he had been missing the week past. This was a small shrill voice which came piping now from a burdock leaf by the roadside.

"Hear me, Mulvaney!" it called.

"Aha!" said Mulvaney. "The harm is done, so you decide to come back. Be off with you!"

"Hear me, Mulvaney!" piped the small voice. "A word of caution to ye!"

"Be gone!" said Mulvaney. He stopped, nevertheless. He scrooched as best he might and peered under the burdock leaf, seeing nothing as usual. "Where were you a week gone when the bad thing happened?"

"Business I had in the old country," piped Mulvaney's leprechaun, for this it was, no less. "Sorry I was to lave ye that cannot look after himself, but there was a meeting of the little people at my granther's castle at Cloghboy, Loughros Beg Bay, in Ardara. Ye mind it, no doubt?"

"I mind the boulders at Malin Beg," said Mulvaney with disparagement. "And I mind what happened when you deserted me. Me that is twenty years on the force, with the promise of sergeant. Made laughingstock of the department and sent to patrol the hinterlands. Transferred," said Mulvaney, "to the sticks!"

His own words quickened his anger over

the faithlessness of his unseen guardian. He stooped suddenly over his magnificent bay and made a quick snatch under the burdock. The leprechaun eluded him and made an angry chittering in the grass.

"A warning to ye, Mulvaney!" piped the whisky tenor.

"Go back," said Mulvaney. "Go home to Donegal and make the little boots for your fairies, and leave me alone that is a lifetime with the police and sent this day to arrest a pig!"

He was moving swiftly away when a series of loud coughs exploded behind him. They had the sound of a freight locomotive getting under way, "Ahuff . . . ahuff . . . ahuff . . . huff,huff,huff,huff!" Series One ended and Series Two began, and Mulvaney wheeled to confront his tormentor, a huge and hatless bald-domed man with mustaches flapping like raven's wings, and shoulders like the beams of a barn, rocked now by the earthquake of a vast amusement. "Ahuff," roared the belittler. "Ahuff . . . ahuff . . . huff,huff,huff,huff,huff!" Tears streamed from small, squinted eyes.

In a lifetime of communion with all the wee people and with his own personal leprechaun in particular, Mulvaney never had suffered the indignity of a witness, let alone a scoffer. His brow darkened and his voice was that cold Irish voice of anger, "And what's funny, now?"

The other did not answer. Laughter beyond speech shook him. He let go his aching sides and stooped over a paunch as glorious as Mulvaney's own. He made a quick sweep in pantomime under the burdock leaf. This he had witnessed. Its result he had not foreseen. The laughter died. An expression of pain and surprise replaced the lusty mirth. He withdrew his hand quickly and held it before him in unbelief. Blood welled from a tiny hole in his forefinger.

"So!" said Mulvaney; and on the quick urge of inspiration, "A great joke it is to be bit by a rattlesnake."

"Rootlesnake?" whispered the other. "A rootler?"

"No less," said Mulvaney. "They rattle for the warning of death. I was trying to catch him in the line of my duty at the risk of my life. Be still now and I'll go for the priest. You'll be having insurance for the funeral expense?"

"A rootlesnake! Do something! I can feel the spread of the poison in me!"

"So they say you can," said Mulvaney with exasperating calm. "It spreads quick and works fast. The victim has fits and barks like a dog. No, 'tis not the way I said. That would be the rabies. Let me see, now. The snakebite was in my training a long time back. Wait! I have it! You run!"

The victim of the rootler made a despairing motion with a bloody hand.

"You run," said Mulvaney. "Run maybe a mile or two. Then quick to your bed and take a pint of the salts with the white of an egg. Call the doctor. If you survive, be sure to sleep the first night with your feet in a tub of mustard water."

But the other was off like the scratch man in a handicap sprint. Mulvaney last saw him taking the corner by the River Road on two wheels and throwing smoke.

"Ye was too hasty with me, Mulvaney," piped the voice of his leprechaun. "Bit him, I did, for mocking you."

" 'Twas a nettle did it," said Mulvaney. "You'll not be claiming the credit to my ear. There's a black mark on the blotter you cannot erase."

The small voice made no answer, no answer at all. There was a sound like a tiny sob, but it could have been a cricket sounding out a string gone rusty with the winter.

Mulvaney was tempted to reconsider. He thrust temptation aside and moved along with heavy heart and step, thinking of the pig. He turned down the River Road, which, at this juncture, was one boundary of his new beat. Beyond a few scattered homes, wide green slopes led to the river, and beyond a meadow and dump acreage he came to the long sheds and brick administration building of Wyde Park Mfg. Co., Inc. Some distance beyond the factory gates he arrived at a square white colonial house with a garden of new tulips along a picket fence. Below the garden he glimpsed a small pen, and on the breeze, as colorful as the tulips in its own peculiar fashion, he caught the aroma of pig on hoof. This would be the place. Mulvaney turned in at the gate.

He took notice of a red cart in the gravel way—a popcorn wagon. It would be property of one of the widow's boarders, no doubt. He climbed a step fashioned from a millstone and confronted a brass knocker on the door. He rapped it once. The sound was loud and hard. He rapped it twice more. Its response was like the protest of his own soul. He set upon it with enthusiasm and vigor, and found an outlet for his black mood. He was belaboring it with all the delicacy of a building wrecker knocking out a heavy joist when the door flew open and he fell into the arms of a woman.

"If you've finished beating the house down, you might be trying the barn next," she said. She was tall and full of shoulder and generous of beam. She had a bright blue eye and black hair and a skin like the sunset sky behind the hills of Donegal.

"You've red ears," she said. "Do you have a tongue in your head?"

"I do," gulped Mulvaney. "I'll have it handy in a minute. You'll be the Widow Malone. I'm sent about the pig."

"Pig?" said she. "What pig is that?"

"The pig," said Mulvaney. "I've a complaint."

"Complaint?" said she. "If you've a complaint, take it to the police."

"To the police?" gulped Mulvaney. "I'm the police!"

"Oh, dear, oh, dear!" said she. Her blue glance went down and up his uniform like a window shade lowered and raised. "The Boy Scouts are forever stopping by for the popcorn since Mr. McNelis came. A mistake is easy made."

Not taken in was Mulvaney. Scout uniforms are khaki.

"The little house below the garden," he said. "There would be a pig in it."

"So you say."

"I could have a look."

"Trespass and illegal search," said she. She smiled suddenly. Mulvaney's bruised bachelor heart went flippity, floppity, flip, like a child's somersaulting toy. "Come in," she invited, "and I will return the good for evil with coffee fresh made. Then you can go along hunting the pig elsewhere."

Mulvaney for some time since had been conscious of the fragrance of the coffee. It was stronger than the fragrance of the pig.

"It's kind you are," he accepted, and stepped into a spick-and-span hall and followed her through a dining room of white linen and old pewter to a kitchen of wide pine boards and burnished brass.

The coffee cup was extra large, the coffee extra strong, with tiny iridescent spots from the heavy cream the widow poured. Doughnuts were crumbly crisp and flavorsome. A wedge of cherry pie was a melting paradise of flake and fruit and sirup, its richness balanced by a slab of good cheese with a bite to it.

A lonely man was Mulvaney, and heartsick; forsaken by his leprechaun and ill-treated by his superiors; victim of a dire injustice, and hungry. It would have been strange indeed if that which was in his heart and the black mood of him did not come pouring out.

"This very week I was to have been promoted," said Mulvaney under the influence of his fourth doughnut. "It was the safe robberies ruined the chance and all but ruined me. You read of them in the papers?"

She nodded in close sympathy and filled his cup. "Poor man," she said. "Your wife will be disappointed."

"Never a wife," said Mulvaney, "never al these years."

"Is that so?" she said. Her eyes glistened. "A fine handsome man like yourself! I mistrust there's holes in your socks. No, you don't have to explain. Mr. Malone never wore a holey sock in his life, peace be with him. And your stomach! Eating the slop in those lunchrooms!"

"A man must suffer," Mulvaney admitted. "I have a room in a lodging house on my old beat and I eat where I can. That's a long car ride from here all the way in town." He eyed the doughnut crock. "Your house will be full up, I suppose."

"One good room I have left," said the Widow Malone, dropping her eyes. "On the east side it is, and cool for summer, and you have your own bath, except sharing it with Mr. McNelis, the popcorn man. I do all the cooking myself. Three roasts a week we have. And fish for Friday."

"I'll take it," said Mulvaney. He neither knew nor cared its cost or appointments or convenience. He felt with a sudden eager joy, that this was the most important decision of his life, that this was the turning point of his life. He let his eye wander over the fine figure of the Widow Malone and he thought how nice it would be, with the other boarders gone for the day, sitting with her over a cup in the kitchen, with the doughnut crock on the table and fresh pies in the oven. As his glance returned suggestively to the doughnut crock, the back door opened and a small gray man with the beak and eye of an eagle came noiselessly into the kitchen. He eyed the widow with suspicion and Mulvaney with a somber peevishness. He said nothing.

"My father, Mr. Finucane," said the Widow Malone. . . . "This is Officer Mulvaney, papa. He's new on the beat."

"Small protection he'll be giving us," said the old man. He went to a chair in the corner and fumbled with a clay pipe. "Mulvaney, did you say? Little the Mulvaneys ever did for the old country or this country ayther. You'll be well along in years for a new man on the force."

"New man!" bridled Mulvaney. "For twenty years——"

"And still a patrolman!" cackled The Finucane. "Sent out to the country you were!"

"Shush!" said the widow. "He's taking the spare room."

"God save us all," said the old man.

It occurred to Mulvaney that despite the excellence of the food and the widow, in that order, he might have been a bit hasty about the room. He was engaged in turning this thought over in his mind when there was a commotion through the front door and dining room, and the late victim of the rattlesnake staggered into the kitchen clutching at the door frame.

"Why, it's Mr. McNelis!" said the widow. "Whatever is the matter?"

"Matter?" echoed McNelis. His squint eyes lit on Mulvaney. " 'Tis him," he whispered, and made a lunge.

In his corner The Finucane dropped his pipe and sprang to his feet. "Up, Finucanes!" he cried, squaring off like a banty cock.

"Wait, now," cautioned Mulvaney, the table between him and McNelis.

"Rootlesnake!" said McNelis. "A rootler, says he! Run, says he, for your life! Keep running!"

He made another lunge and Mulvaney did a quick sidestep. Not moving from his corner, The Finucane unloosed another cry of the hills, shuffled his small feet and feinted with his right.

"Wait now," said Mulvaney. McNelis, he saw, was a tired man.

"I ran," said McNelis. "I ran four miles to the hospital. For what?" He held up a finger the length and shape of a railroad-tie spike. There was a small smear of iodine on it. "A thorn prick, the doctor said!"

He sank exhausted into a chair, breathing heavily.

An unease crept over Officer Mulvaney. He thought of the leprechaun. He thought of his curt dismissal of that small voice which had been a friendly guide since his childhood. "A warning," the leprechaun had said. Then the Widow Malone smiled and took the cover from the doughnut crock. Not till he went off duty did Mulvaney remember the pig.

The subject of the pig was raised by the desk sergeant after roll call next morning. The telephone had brought another complaint. The pig must go. Mulvaney said he would see to the matter.

He had given notice at his in-town lodging house. He would stop by at the widow's house now and tell her he would be moving in and, with diplomacy of course, raise again the problem of the pig and its fate.

He was approaching the River Road when he heard the small, familiar piping again, "Hist, Mulvaney! A word of caution!" The voice came from a lilac bush, and Mulvaney paused. "Hear me now," came the voice. "Many the years I wasted as guardian for ye, and only once did I leave. Trouble came to ye then through no fault of mine, and sore-treated I've been since. Will ye be having the friendship again? One word and all is well."

Sore tempted was Mulvaney, for he had treated his leprechaun ill. This he knew. But there was a new complication which boded ill for their relationship. What would the widow think? She'd not want a leprechaun about the house. It would be a sort of triangle, he thought.

"Ye be wavering," piped the small voice in triumph. "I'll not be going yet."

"I am not," denied Mulvaney. "Go back. Go back to your granther's castle at Loughros Beg Bay and leave me alone."

No answer came.

Mulvaney kept to his march, his back as straight as an arrow, his front the curve of the bow. 'Twixt widow and leprechaun he had made his choice.

At the Wyde Park Mfg. Co., Inc., he saw the red popcorn cart set up outside the gates, and the giant McNelis was between the shafts.

"A grand business you have there," observed Mulvaney. "Your own boss too."

"Ha!" said McNelis, a sound like the safety exhaust on a full head of steam.

"You'll be rare gifted," said Mulvaney, "making the little seeds go pop like that. I never cared for it meself," he added, reaching in for a handful. He said, "Mind you wash out the tub after you take your bath . . . if you take a bath."

He moved quickly out of range of a voice which came suddenly to life, and he felt good about this snapper, and when he came to the Widow Malone's he moved in at the gate with the air and swagger of the proprietor himself. He saw the widow's sweet self below the garden. Over her dress she wore a long white apron, the ends of which she held in her hands to make a pocket for a mound of yellowed popcorn.

"The morning to you," called Mulvaney. "Let me help you there."

"Oh," she said, "it's Officer Mulvaney. I'll be right up."

"I'll be moving in Saturday." Mulvaney continued his approach.

"Your room is ready," said the widow. She was not quite wide enough to screen the front of the pen. "I'm feeding the rabbit," she said.

"A new breed," Mulvaney observed.

"I call him a rabbit," said the widow. "Look at him, the darling pet. How he loves the popcorn of Mr. McNelis."

She lifted a corner of the hutch roof and shook out the contents of her apron. The rabbit with the corkscrew tail snuffed and sniffed and wallowed and guzzled. Mulvaney stood by in indecision, torn by his sense of duty and his desire for the widow's favor.

The widow whispered a secret, "A rabbit fattened on popcorn makes a ham that slices like tenderloin. And heavy bacon, streaked lean and fat and rich."

The saliva started in Mulvaney's mouth.

"Step into the kitchen," invited the widow. "The coffee is made."

"The complaint—" faltered Mulvaney. "The pig—" He followed and said no more.

For the hand of the widow and the delicacies of her table, Mulvaney, the patrolman, and McNelis, the popcorn man, became open rivals in the days that followed. Each suffered in silence a number of indignities traceable to the other. These began with the matter of the mysteriously clogged bathroom bowl which suddenly overflowed, to the embarrassment of Officer Mulvaney. A few days later, two nicks appeared in the blade of his favorite razor, and the badger of his shaving brush suddenly began to molt. Mulvaney called it all even with a large bottle of Subtle Ravishment Perfume which he sprinkled liberally on the other's bathrobe and slippers. For a few days the aroma of the pig and the stifling fumes of The Finucane's pipe were not discernible in McNelis' presence.

Each brought little gifts for the widow's pleasure—flowers and candy, a runner for the table—and each watched with jealous eye the distribution of choice cuts and dainty morsels from the widow's kitchen. Two other boarders, an elderly spinster and a young bookkeeper, came and ate and slept and departed without disturbing the quiet routine, and were not involved in the division of the delectables. One day it was Mulvaney who was served the thick browned outside cut of roast beef, and the next day it was McNelis who received the lean and tender section of the hot smoked shoulder. The kidney chops were theirs in turn, and they always had the same number of breakfast eggs; if McNelis made a request for four, Mulvaney was served four, though normally he ate but three.

In the matter of the pig, the complaints abruptly ceased, and the desk sergeant, having noted Mulvaney's new address, said no more. Even as Mulvaney and McNelis, the pig grew stouter. Its fare, for the most part, was unsold popcorn that McNelis brought home daily from his stand at the Wyde Park plant gates, and Mulvaney came to hate the pig on this account, looking upon it as a protégé of McNelis and a bond between McNelis and the widow. A situation of girths and gastronomy was building up.

One night when he was early home, Mulvaney heard The Finucane's voice raised in querulous plaint about the prospects of a new son-in-law. It drifted from the kitchen with pipe smoke like fumes from a burning tar barrel.

"Little the good to ayther," the old man said. "The one with the cart of the popcorn, and him a grown giant of a man, and the other a lifetime on the police and still a patrolman. Between the two they'll eat me out of house and home."

Mulvaney cocked his ear to catch the widow's reply. "Mr. McNelis is a fine man," she said, "and he has an independent income. The popcorn business is only to keep his mind occupied, so he told me. But Mr. Mulvaney is a fine man, too, and a bit the handsomer. If it's another husband I'm having—"

Her voice was drowned out in a crackling sputter of The Finucane's pipe, but Mulvaney, his heart singing, did not doubt her choice. He looked ahead to the days when McNelis would be but a memory, and himself, retired on pension, would be established head of the house, a master of gracious living and without need, except on special occasions, for collar and shoes. He went tiptoe to his room.

The storm broke a week later, when the captain had him on the carpet.

"When they transferred you, I was told you couldn't catch a burglar. Now it appears you can't even catch a pig."

"A pig," echoed Mulvaney. He had forgotten the complaints about the pig.

"I learn from the sergeant you were detailed several times to rid the premises of one Widow Malone of a pig about which there have been complaints."

" 'Tis true," said Mulvaney in sorrow.

"But the pig is still there. The complainant called me personally to tell me. It seems the pig is not only there but you're there too."

" 'Tis true," Mulvaney admitted. "I've been a bit lax, sir."

"I would hate," said the captain, "to have to break a man over the small matter of a pig—especially a man who has so much time in for his pension."

"The pig will go this night," Mulvaney promised fervently.

"The pig goes or you go," said the captain with finality.

Mulvaney turned, with heavy heart, to leave. It wasn't just the pig; he would take delight in sticking the pig himself—the pig fattened on the popcorn of McNelis. It was the disfavor the widow would be bound to show, the affront she would feel. With this thought a small suspicion was born in Mulvaney's mind.

"Who complained about the pig, sir? Was it a husky voice with a strange kind of brogue—a man by the name of McNelis?"

"No," said the captain. "A small squeaky voice he had, like an old man."

"A squeak," whispered Mulvaney. "Me leprechaun. Oh, the traitor, the black, black, double-crossing traitor."

That night he was early home, and let himself quietly into the house. He had procured a crocus sack, an old potato burlap, from the grocery, for the business of the night. He was tiptoeing to the stairs when he heard the widow's warm laughter in the kitchen, and the deep voice of McNelis. Mulvaney went softly through the dining room and pushed the swing door to the kitchen a wee crack. McNelis sat at table over the thickest, juiciest steak Mulvaney ever had envied, and standing by McNelis was the Widow Malone, her hand upon his shoulder.

McNelis did not appear for supper. "He had a small bite and went off to the pictures," said the widow. "You'll have a cup of tea in the kitchen after?"

"I'll not," said Mulvaney, remembering the "small bite" and where her hand had rested.

"And some of the strawberry tarts and my company?" the widow invited.

"I'll be early to bed," said Mulvaney. "I'm a bit upset."

He went to his room and sat in the dark by his window, which overlooked the abode of the pig. That he was a bit upset was an understatement. He felt completely betrayed—by the widow, by his leprechaun, by all mankind. He sat in the darkness and the bitterness for a long time, vaguely aware of the sounds of the household retiring. He heard The Finucane go grumbling to his room. He heard the spinster close and lock her door and set a chair against it. Heard the bookkeeper's voice calling good night from the stairs. And finally he heard the widow herself climbing the stairs, which creaked. She went heavily down the hall and another door was closed.

He waited nearly an hour, then went softly down the stairs with his crocus sack and let himself out the back door into the dark of the yard. He approached the hutch stealthily. He lifted the top and put one foot inside. The pig snored, then sniffed.

"Be easy, my beauty," Mulvaney whispered.

He spread the mouth of the sack, and as the pig stood to its front feet he whipped the sack over its head. The pig was greasy with the butter of countless bags of popcorn, and it felt unhealthily warm.

"It's the hot buttered pig, you are," whispered Mulvaney.

The pig protested with a pair of stifled "Woinks!" and gobbled like a turkey as Mulvaney closed the sack. It was heavier and livelier than Mulvaney had expected. It squirmed in the sack and kicked, and its hoofs rapped Mulvaney's back as he shouldered the burden. He ran heavily through the garden and a distance down the street to be out of hearing of the household. He crossed to the river side of the street away from the street lamps and found it necessary to shift his burden, carrying it in both arms. There was a wharf down behind the Wyde Park plant where the river ran fast and deep, and a pig in a sack, with stones to weigh it, would never again endanger the pension of a policeman. He turned off the River Road near the Wyde Park gates; there was an old path there.

Thus he was hurrying toward the completion of his duty, puffing no little and perspiring freely in the warm night, when he became aware of a small squirming with the big squirming in the sack.

He felt it and squeezed, and heard the small piping, "Hist, Mulvaney! Leave be! Ye hurt!"

"Aha!" said Mulvaney. "So that's where you went. Living with a pig. The shame of it!"

"To be near ye, Mulvaney. To watch out for ye."

"Living with a pig and betraying me to the captain!" said Mulvaney. "The shame of it. I'll be drownding you with the pig, and good riddance."

"You'll not, Mulvaney!" piped the leprechaun. "You've the cold heart, but ye would not drownd me that's befriended ye all the years!"

Mulvaney knew it was so. He couldn't do it. He rested the sack at his feet and reached in for the leprechaun. The sack wiggled and jumped and heaved as the pig came alive.

"Tickling him, I am!" called the leprechaun. "Leave us out, Mulvaney! Leave us both out! This is the place!"

The sack flew open and the pig shot from its mouth, knocking Mulvaney to his knees. In the ill light of the distant street lamp, unless his eyes deceived him, Mulvaney saw his leprechaun for the first time—a wee old man with a long white whisker, clad in scarlet dobby cap, brown weskit and green leggings, and balanced astride the fat of the pig's back above the loins, lashing madly with a tiny staff. Pig and leprechaun vanished through a hole under the fence.

Mulvaney said a bad word and thought of his pension, and in a wink he had recovered the sack and was up and after, and over the fence on the third try. It was darker beyond the fence and he could no longer see his quarry, but the grunts of the pig under the flogging of its small rider served to guide him. He was conscious of an open door and a commotion inside. A faint pencil of light winked and went out. He heard the heavy breathing of the pig and the cry of the leprechaun and the sound of a chair overturned. Then there was a red flash and the slam of a gun fired close.

Mulvaney dropped to the floor and rolled sideways. Amazement and black anger gave him the sixth sense that comes sometimes with an emergency. He rolled over again and was on his knees when the gun fired a second time. He leaped with his sack in the direction of the flash, and suddenly had that in it which was bigger than a pig and twice as lively. He dug his fingernails into a hairy wrist and felt the gun drop on his foot. He yanked the sack hard down on its contents and secured two wrists in handcuffs. Then he struck a match and located a wall switch.

Light flooding the office of the Wyde Park Mfg. Co., Inc., revealed a watchman trussed and gagged on the floor in one corner. In another stood a heavy safe whose outside door hung wide on broken hinges. A small tank, an acetylene torch and pry bars stood in neat array at the feet of the sacked and handcuffed burglar.

Mulvaney snatched the sack from the head and shoulders of his prisoner. There stood McNelis, squinting his eyes and blowing his mustaches.

"Ten cents a bag!" crowed Mulvaney. "With butter!"

Of leprechaun and pig there was no sign.

"You'll be staying on, I hope," said The Finucane slyly from his corner.

"I can't say," said Mulvaney over a rasher and eggs, with a small steak on the side.

"I never trusted that man," sighed the widow.

"I was grieved the long weeks watching him deceive you both," said Mulvaney. "And him a Turk—a Turk posing as an Irishman."

"I mistrusted him," said the old man. "Myself thought you were here to catch him."

"A Turk," repeated Mulvaney, "with a phony name and a brogue that deceived you both. The beguiling way he had, and you both fell for him." He savored a juicy cut of the rump and wiped his mouth. "I tracked him here weeks ago. That's why I came. He carried the tools of his trade in the bottom of that popcorn cart and he used the popcorn business as a blind to keep watch on the plants and learn when the pay-roll money arrived and where it was hidden."

"I never liked his eye," said The Finucane. "I knew you would get the better of him."

"And he pulling the wool over your eyes all the time," pursued Mulvaney for the satisfaction of his soul. "A burglar with a long record and a term in Auburn! I feared he would be marrying into the family before I had a chance to catch him with the goods. Now he's made a full confession to the other jobs, and most of the loot has been recovered. Not all," said Mulvaney. "Some, I hear, was spent for flowers and candy and the like of that."

The Widow Malone sniffled a small sob. She said, "Your pictures in the papers did you small justice."

"I'm not the vain man," said Mulvaney, "nor one easy taken in."

"As a sergeant, now," said The Finucane, "you could be staying on here despite your transfer to headquarters as detective. The patrol car could be riding you back and forth."

"I hate to think of you going back to the slop they serve in the restaurants," said the widow. "And no one to care about looking after you. I'm planning a stuffed shoulder for tomorrow and a turkey for Sunday. You'd have the bath all to yourself."

Fair lost was Mulvaney. It was true, as the old man suggested, he might stay on here in comfort and depend upon a department car for his transportation. A fine woman was the widow, and a cook unsurpassed. Mulvaney thought of the lonely nights in a lodging-house room and the one-arm breakfasts of lukewarm oatmeal and coffee brewed from retreads. He thought of the widow's steaks and chops and roasts and the hot biscuits and the pies. He thought of the rich coffee with cream. He mopped a half biscuit in the juice of his steak and he glanced at the Widow Malone. Her blue eyes, downcast, were misty.

"Well, now," said Mulvaney. "Maybe, after all . . ."

He stopped. Under the table, a small kick had been delivered against his ankle.

"Hist, Mulvaney," he heard the whisper. "A word of caution to ye."

Mulvaney laid his biscuit aside.

"You were saying?" prompted The Finucane.

"Just that I'll be going up to pack my trunk," said Mulvaney.

WANNA BUY A DUCK?

By JOE PENNER

§ *A famous phrase, and how it started.*

NOVEMBER 10, 1934

ONE hot day in Birmingham, Alabama, in 1931 B.C.—Before Cooling systems—I was standing in the wings of a Publix Theater, watching a perspiring master of ceremonies trying vainly to hold the attention of an apathetic audience. It was so hot in Birmingham that day that the audience was ice cold. In show business the expression "ice cold" has nothing to do with degrees Fahrenheit. A "cold" audience is one that just sits out there with an expression on its collective face that says to those on the other side of the footlights: "Well, go ahead and make me laugh. Let's see you do it!" Stokowski playing the Tiger Rag wouldn't have made that Birmingham audience sit up and take notice. The master of ceremonies was having a tough time. A rather pleasant fellow, with a warm personality, he was giving them everything he had, in a futile effort to interest them. He was receiving as much attention in return as one more blonde in Hollywood. Suddenly, before I knew what I was doing, I found myself walking out on the stage. I don't know why. My feet just moved, and I followed them. I reached the side of the harassed master of ceremonies, and almost mechanically my mouth opened and out came four words: "Wanna buy a duck?"

I might have said: "Wanna lease a buffalo?" or "Wanna climb a rainspout?" But it so happened that "Wanna buy a duck?" was the first nonsensical thing that popped into my mind. It had no point whatever, and I had no idea what was to come next—or if anything was to come next.

A faint, barely discernible titter floated back over the footlights. The grateful master of ceremonies rose to the occasion. He turned to me, scowling furiously, while the audience sat up, wondering what it was all about, and what was coming next.

The master of ceremonies and I were also wondering what was coming next. He solved the problem.

"Oh, go away from here," he retorted. "Can't you see I'm busy?" Then, seizing the advantage of the audience's aroused interest, he went on with his lines. Again, for no reason at all, I butted in:

"Well, does your brother wanna buy a duck?"

If you will study theater audiences, you will know why those Roman lions played to standing room when they ate up Christians. You will understand why a busy, hurrying crowd will stop to laugh at a man chasing his hat down a windy street. The psychological quirk in human nature that causes those things is responsible for the existence of the stooge. But the stooge is another story, and just now we're only telling this one. So, to return to the master of ceremonies in Birmingham.

"Will you please go away from here and let me alone?" he rasped, and this time he scowled so hard his eyebrows tickled his nose. In a voice loud enough for the audience to hear, he said: "I haven't any brother. Now go on, get out of here."

He started to speak to the cash customers once more, but this time it was their laughter that interrupted him. I tugged at his coat sleeve apologetically.

"Well, if you had a brother, do you think he might consider it?" I wheedled. And so the thing went on, until it was time for me to go into my act. By that time the house was wide awake, willing to laugh at anything. The nonsense about the duck had caught their fancy.

At this point a good writer might give you a soliloquy about how thus a radio program was born. But I do not claim to be a good writer. I do not claim even to be sure about the way you spell "soliloquy." So let's get back to the duck. I can spell that.

I kept thinking about that silly, meaningless line: "Wanna buy a duck?" I couldn't see anything especially funny about it, but then I don't like spinach, although they tell me a lot of discriminating people ask for second helpings. Plainly, the audience had liked "Wanna buy a duck?" The answer was simple. The audience was composed of customers, and the customer was always right. They had liked "Wanna buy a duck?" so "Wanna buy a duck?" was funny. Accidental as it had been, there were the facts.

That night I worked over the line. I tried accenting each word. I studied the inflection I thought would be best to sell it. I got it down pat, and it has never gone back on me. It has been a real pal for years, and has rarely failed to draw a laugh. And laughs are a comedian's stock in trade; they're his bread and butter, or, if he can get enough of them, may even be his champagne and caviar. Experience teaches a comedian just when and where to use a gag line. He understands the tempo of comedy as a composer understands music, and though comedy and music seem two dissimilar arts, in the final analysis they are kindred.

I don't know myself exactly how much money I've made or will make with each one of those four short words: "Wanna buy a duck?" Optimists have set the figure as high as $250,000 a word, but, between you and me, it probably won't be nearly that much. I've got ten or twelve dollars in the bank—if the bank is still there—but even if I didn't have a penny in the world, I'd still be happy as long as I could make people laugh.

But here I seem to be getting technical, talking shop. If you are getting bored, just skip the two paragraphs immediately following, and go on from there. My feelings won't be hurt.

Occasionally I have worried for fear audiences would tire of the constant repetition of "Wanna buy a duck?" and I've changed it to "Wanna buy an ash can?" or "Wanna buy a rhinosommonous?" but none ever received a reaction like the old reliable, so I've always gone back to "Wanna buy a duck?" It makes them laugh, but don't ask me why.

Other lines I have used on the stage and over the air have been born in pretty much the same way, lines such as "Y-e-e-ow nathty man!" or "Wo-o-oe is me!" or "Don't ne-e-ver do-o-o tha-a-at!" They all just popped into my mind as I stood before a microphone or on a stage, and I tried them. Some clicked. Some didn't. There being no reason why any such meaningless phrases should draw laughs, it is impossible to tell beforehand which ones will and which will not. So, when one flops, I forget it and try another. That is the business of being a comic. And take it from me, it is no joke.

SCHEELE MEMORIAL LIBRARY
3 6655 00023428 6
PS536 .S16
Carnival of humor. Edited by R

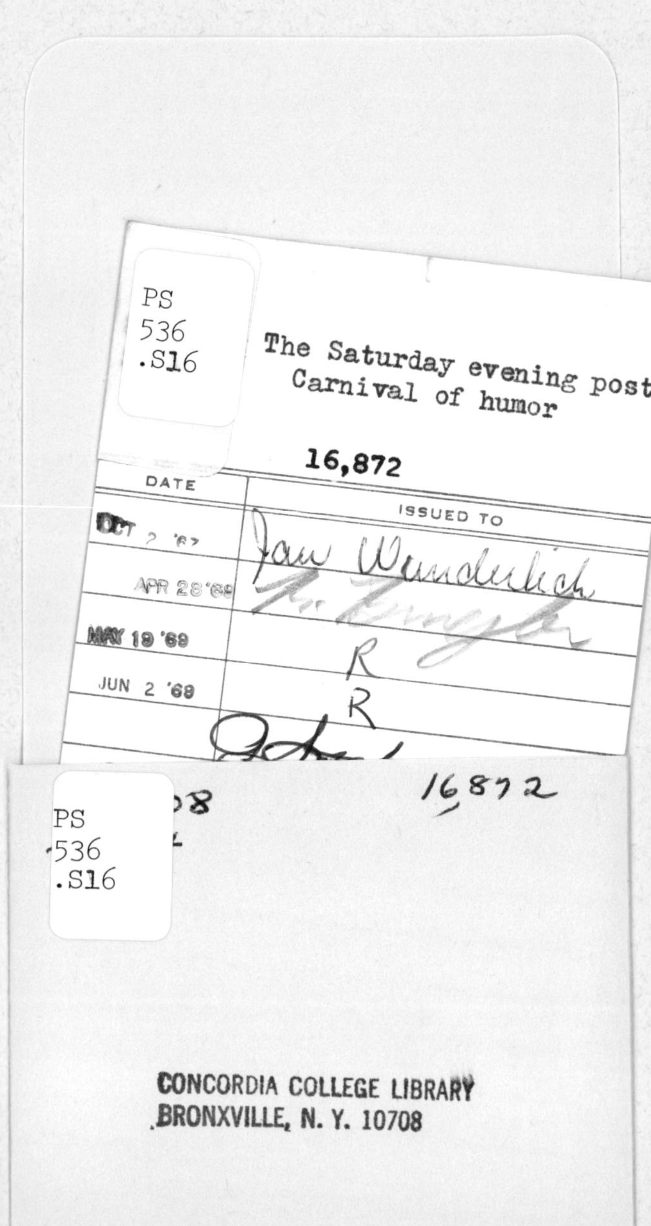
PS
536
.S16
The Saturday evening post
Carnival of humor
16,872
DATE
ISSUED TO
APR 28 '69
MAY 19 '69
JUN 2 '69
R
R
PS
536
.S16
16,872
CONCORDIA COLLEGE LIBRARY
BRONXVILLE, N. Y. 10708

THE SATURDAY EVENING POST
An Illustrated Weekly Magazine
Founded Aº Dº 1728 by Benj. Franklin
JANUARY 13, 1906
FIVE CENTS THE COPY
THE CURTIS PUBLISHING COM
THE SATURDAY EVENING POST
OCTOBER 4, 1919
5c THE COPY
THE SATURDAY EVENING POST
5cts THE COPY
THE SATURDAY EVENING POST
An Illustrated Weekly Magazine
Founded Aº Dº 1728 by Benj. Franklin
MAR. 19, 1910
5c THE COPY
a Half Circulation Weekly
THE SATURDAY EVENING POST
Weekly
Benj. Franklin
JUNE 14, 1919
THE SATURDAY POST
JAN 23 1926
THE PARASITE
THE SATURDAY POST
AUG. 18 1928
George Weston—Will Payne
Leonard H. Nason
THE SATURDAY EVENING POST
An Illustrated Weekly
JUNE 12, 1915
In This Number: Former Governor George H. Hodges
Peter B. Kyne—Edwin Lefèvre—Mary Roberts Rinehart
Will Payne—Constance Skinner—Edward Mott Woolley
THE SATURDAY POST
Stewart Edward White—George Wharton Pepper—Guglielmo Ferrero
Leonard H. Nason—Sam Hellman—Brenda Ueland—Guy Gilpatric